Second Grade

Everyday Mathematics®

Teacher's Lesson Guide
Volume 2

**The University of Chicago
School Mathematics Project**

EVERYDAY
LEARNING

Chicago, Illinois

UCSMP Elementary Materials Component

Max Bell, Director

Authors

Max Bell
Jean Bell
John Bretzlauf*
Amy Dillard*
Robert Hartfield
Andy Isaacs*
James McBride, Director
Kathleen Pitvorec*
Peter Saecker

Technical Art

Diana Barrie*

Second Edition only

Everyday Learning Development Staff

Editorial: Anna Belluomini, Mary Cooney, Julie Crawford, Christine Fraser,
Elizabeth Glosniak, Bernadette Lopez, Michael Murphy
Design: Fran Brown, Jess Schaal
Production: Annette Davis, Tina Dunlap, Elizabeth Gabbard, Silvana Valenzuela

Additional Credits

Donna Antkowiak, Elizabeth Allen, Nancy Baty, Kathy Burke, Lindaanne Donohoe,
Susan Halko, Herman Adler Design Group, Scott LaPierre, Made in Chicago Design,
Yoshi Miyake, Point West, Inc., Precision Graphics, Randi Robin Design, Adam Sugarman,
Katie Telser, Regina Thoeming, Cathy Wacaser

Photo Credits

Phil Martin/Photography
Jack Demuth/Photography
Cover: Bill Burlingham/Photography
Photo Collage: Herman Adler Design Group

Contributors

Librada Acosta, Carol Arkin, Robert Balfanz, Sharlean Brooks, Jean Callahan,
Anne Coglianese, Ellen Dairyko, Tresea Felder, James Flanders, Dorothy Freedman,
Rita Gronbach, Deborah Arron Leslie, William D. Pattison, LaDonna Pitts,
Danette Riehle, Marie Schilling, Robert Strang, Sadako Tengan, Therese Wasik,
Leeann Wille, Michael Wilson

Permissions

page 438, Project 5: Snow Crystals, 2453 Illustrations,
    W. A. Bentley and W. J. Humphreys, Dover Publications, Inc.
page 447, Myrleen Ferguson Cate/PhotoEdit
page 894, http://vraptor.jpl.nasa.gov/voyager/gold.gif
page 899, Myrleen Ferguson Cate/PhotoEdit

ISBN 1-57039-829-1

Everyday Learning Corporation
P.O. Box 812960
Chicago, IL 60681
www.everydaylearning.com

2 3 4 5 6 7 8 9 QW 05 04 03 02 01

Contents

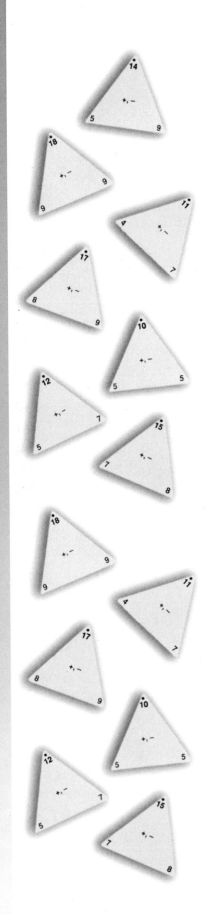

Volume 2

Unit 7
Patterns and Rules

overview

Unit 7 concentrates on three themes: number patterns, computation, and data analysis. Number patterns are explored to reinforce numeration skills and develop readiness for multiplication and division; computational skills are extended to addition of several 1- and 2-digit numbers and subtraction of 2-digit numbers from multiples of 10; and applications of mathematics involving the collection, representation, and interpretation of real-life data are investigated.

contents

learning goals
in perspective

learning goals	links to the past	links to the future
7a **Developing Goal** Find missing addends for any multiple of 10. **(Lesson 7.3)**	Children worked with complements of 10 in first grade. *(Related Grade 2 lessons: 6.1, 6.4, 6.5)*	Children will continue to practice finding addends for multiples of 10 using mental math strategies throughout the grades. *(Related Grade 2 lessons: 11.1, 11.2)*
7b **Developing Goal** Find the median (middle value) of a data set. **(Lesson 7.8)**	In first grade, children were introduced to the concept of the middle value of a data set. *(Related Grade 2 lessons: 3.5, 6.3)*	Students will continue to work with medians and frequency distributions in third grade. *(Related Grade 2 lessons: 11.9, 12.6)*
7c **Developing Goal** Add three 2-digit numbers mentally. **(Lesson 7.4)**	In Kindergarten and first grade, children found ways to add smaller numbers. In second grade, children worked with 2-digit addition in Units 4 and 6. *(Related Grade 2 lessons: 1.4, 1.13, 2.1–2.5, 2.10, 4.6, 4.8, 4.9, 6.1)*	In third grade, children will add larger numbers and will use three addends in problem-solving situations. *(Related Grade 2 lesson: 11.1)*
7d **Developing/Secure Goal** Measure to the nearest inch. **(Lesson 7.7)**	In Kindergarten and first grade, children used both nonstandard (e.g., arm span) and standard units to measure length. *(Related Grade 2 lesson: 4.7)*	In subsequent grades, measurement activities will be extended to acquaint children with equivalent units and to show how decimals and fractions are used in measurement. In Unit 9, children will use fractional units of an inch. *(Related Grade 2 lessons: 9.1–9.6)*
7e **Developing/Secure Goal** Measure to the nearest centimeter. **(Lesson 7.7)**	In Kindergarten and first grade, children used both nonstandard (e.g., cubit) and standard units to measure length. *(Related Grade 2 lesson: 4.7)*	In subsequent grades, measurement activities will be extended to acquaint children with equivalent units and to show how decimals and fractions are used in measurement. In Unit 9, children will use meters, decimeters, and fractions of centimeters. *(Related Grade 2 lessons: 9.1–9.6)*
7f **Secure Goal** Know complements of 10. **(Lesson 7.3)**	Children began working with complements of 10 on a number grid. They also modeled problems with counters or base-10 blocks, drew pictures, and eventually, calculated mentally. *(Related Grade 2 lessons: 1.7, 3.4, 4.3, 6.1, 6.4, 6.5)*	Children will continue to practice mental math strategies throughout the grades. *(Related Grade 2 lessons: 11.1, 11.2)*
7g **Secure Goal** Count by 2s, 5s, and 10s and describe the patterns. **(Lesson 7.1)**	In Kindergarten and first grade, children worked with various patterns, including skip counting. *(Related Grade 2 lessons: 1.1, 1.8, 2.3–2.5, 2.10)*	Proficiency with skip counting helps children to count money, tell time using analog clocks, and learn multiplication facts. *(Related Grade 2 lessons: 10.5, 11.3, 11.5–11.8, 12.2, 12.4)*
7h **Secure Goal** Find missing addends for the next multiple of 10. **(Lesson 7.2)**	Children worked with complements of 10 in first grade. *(Related Grade 2 lessons: 6.1, 6.4, 6.5)*	Children will continue to practice finding missing addends for the next multiple of 10 using mental math strategies throughout the grades. *(Related Grade 2 lessons: 11.1, 11.2)*
7i **Secure Goal** Solve number-grid puzzles. **(Lesson 7.2)**	Number grids were introduced in first grade. *(Related Grade 2 lesson: 1.9)*	Children will move on from number-grid patterns to the more abstract arrow-path puzzles. Number-grid patterns will be extended to include 3- and 4-digit numbers in third grade. *(Related Grade 2 lessons: 10.6, 11.2)*
7j **Secure Goal** Plot data on a bar graph. **(Lesson 7.9)**	Children have been doing graphing activities since Kindergarten. *(Related Grade 2 lessons: 3.5, 6.3)*	Children will continue to graph and analyze data in a variety of situations in third grade. *(Related Grade 2 lessons: 11.9, 12.6)*

☑ Informal Assessment

Math Boxes These *Math Journal* pages provide opportunities for cumulative review or assessment of concepts and skills.

Ongoing Assessment: Kid Watching Use the Ongoing Assessment suggestions in the following lessons to make quick, on-the-spot observations about children's understanding of:
* Operations and Computation **(Lessons 7.1 and 7.3–7.6)**
* Measurement and Reference Frames **(Lessons 7.2 and 7.8)**

Portfolio Ideas Samples of children's work may be obtained from the following assignments:
* Making Patterns by Coloring Grids **(Lesson 7.1)**
* Making Up Arrow-Path Puzzles **(Lesson 7.2)**
* Making Up and Solving Number Stories **(Lesson 7.7)**
* Write a Doubles or Halves Story **(Lesson 7.10)**

☑ Unit 7 Review and Assessment

Oral and Slate Assessments Use oral or slate assessments during Lesson 7.10 to assess children's progress toward the following learning goals: Goals 7a, 7b, 7c, 7f, 7g, and 7h

Written Assessment Use a written review during Lesson 7.10 to assess children's progress toward the following learning goals: Goals 7a, 7b, 7c, 7d, 7e, 7h, and 7i

Performance/Group Assessment Use the small-group activity in Lesson 7.10 to assess children's progress toward the following learning goals: Goals 7a, 7c, and 7h

assessment handbook

For more information on how to use different types of assessment in Unit 7, see the Assessment Overview on pages 59–62 in the *Assessment Handbook*. The following Assessment Masters can be found in the *Math Masters* book:

* Unit 7 Checking Progress, pp. 429 and 430
* Unit 7 Class Checklist, p. 460
* Unit 7 Individual Profile of Progress, p. 461
* Class Progress Indicator, p. 488
* Math Logs, pp. 493–495
* Self-Assessment Forms, pp. 496 and 497
* Interest Inventories, pp. 491 and 492

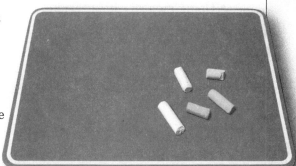

problem**solving**

A process of modeling everyday situations using tools from mathematics

Encourage children to use a variety of strategies when attacking a given problem—and to explain those strategies. *Strategies children might use in this unit:*

- Identifying and using patterns
- Using mental computation
- Making a data display
- Making a table
- Using information from a story
- Acting out the problem

Four Problem-Solving REPRESENTATIONS

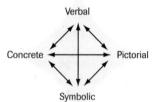

Lessons that teach *through* problem solving, not just *about* problem solving

Lesson	Activity	Lesson	Activity
7.1	Finding number patterns on a grid	7.5	Finding how many Wubbles are in your room
7.2	Solving arrow-path puzzles	7.6	Sharing $5.00 equally among 4 children
7.3, 7.4	Playing *Hit the Target* and *Basketball Addition*	7.9	Finding the median length of standing jumps and arm spans of children in the class

For more information about problem solving in *Everyday Mathematics,* see the *Teacher's Reference Manual,* pp. 197–208.

cross-curricular**links**

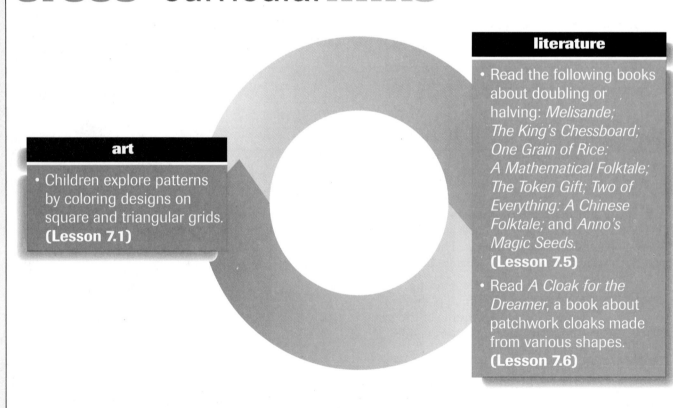

art

- Children explore patterns by coloring designs on square and triangular grids. **(Lesson 7.1)**

literature

- Read the following books about doubling or halving: *Melisande; The King's Chessboard; One Grain of Rice: A Mathematical Folktale; The Token Gift; Two of Everything: A Chinese Folktale;* and *Anno's Magic Seeds.* **(Lesson 7.5)**

- Read *A Cloak for the Dreamer,* a book about patchwork cloaks made from various shapes. **(Lesson 7.6)**

meeting INDIVIDUAL needs

◆ RETEACHING

The following features provide additional instructional support:

Adjusting the Activity

- **Lesson 7.1, Parts 1, 2**
- **Lesson 7.2, Part 1**
- **Lesson 7.3, Part 1**
- **Lesson 7.4, Part 1**
- **Lesson 7.5, Part 1**

Options for Individualizing

- **Lesson 7.1** Counting by 2s, 5s, and 10s
- **Lesson 7.3** Reviewing Strategies for Extended Addition Facts
- **Lesson 7.4** Using Base-10 Blocks to Add
- **Lesson 7.4** Playing *Three Addends*

◆ ENRICHMENT

The following features suggest enrichment and extension activities:

Adjusting the Activity

- **Lesson 7.1, Part 1**
- **Lesson 7.2, Part 1**
- **Lesson 7.6, Part 1**
- **Lesson 7.7, Part 1**

Options for Individualizing

- **Lesson 7.1** Making Patterns by Coloring Grids
- **Lesson 7.2** Making Up Arrow-Path Puzzles
- **Lesson 7.2** Playing the *Attribute Train Game*
- **Lesson 7.3** Playing *Hit the Target*
- **Lesson 7.5** Doubling and Halving Situations Found in Literature
- **Lesson 7.7** Making Up and Solving Number Stories

◆ LANGUAGE DIVERSITY

The following features suggest ways to support children who are acquiring proficiency in English:

Adjusting the Activity

- **Lesson 7.5, Part 1**
- **Lesson 7.6, Part 1**

Options for Individualizing

- **Lesson 7.5** Visual Images for Doubles and Halves
- **Lesson 7.7** Discussing Meanings of the Word *Span*
- **Lesson 7.8** Discussing Meanings of the Word *Median*

◆ MULTIAGE CLASSROOM

The following chart lists related lessons from Grades 1 and 3 that can help you meet your instructional needs:

Grade 1	3.2–3.5	2.1 3.3 9.1	2.3 9.2	9.4		3.4 8.6 8.8	3.13 4.6	6.12	3.13 6.12
Grade 2	7.1	7.2	7.3	7.4	7.5	7.6	7.7	7.8	7.9
Grade 3	1.11	1.2	2.2	2.9	1.11 7.1	4.3 10.4	3.1–3.3	10.7	10.10

materials

lesson	math masters pages	manipulative kit items	other items
7.1	Home Link Master, p. 330 Teaching Masters, pp. 122–124; and pp. 125 and 126 (optional) transparency of Teaching Master, p. 122 (optional) **See Advance Preparation, p. 510**		calculator half-sheets of paper
7.2	Home Link Master, p. 331 Teaching Master, p. 127	Class Number Grid Poster attribute blocks	ruler
7.3	Home Link Master, p. 332 Teaching Master, p. 128 (optional)	Class Number Grid Poster	calculator
7.4	Home Link Master, p. 333 Teaching Masters, pp. 101 and 102; and p. 130 (optional) transparency of Teaching Master, p. 129 (optional) **See Advance Preparation, p. 528**	1 twenty-sided polyhedral die or 3 regular dice per group base-10 blocks number cards 0–20	
7.5	Home Link Masters, pp. 334 and 335 Teaching Masters, p. 25; and p. 128 (optional)		calculator various literature selections **See Advance Preparation, p. 533**
7.6	Home Link Master, p. 336 Teaching Masters, p. 128 (optional); and pp. 131–133 Teaching Aid Assessment Master, p. 498	Pattern-Block Template pattern blocks	bath scale(s) set of books over 15 lbs 5-lb bag of flour (optional) bills and coins per group calculator *A Cloak for the Dreamer* by Aileen Friedman (optional) **See Advance Preparation, p. 539**
7.7	Home Link Masters, pp. 337 and 338 Teaching Masters, pp. 22, 117–119, and 134	tape measure 2 six-sided dice, 1 twelve-sided die, or an egg-carton number generator per small group 1 twenty-sided polyhedral die or number cards	masking tape chalk or penny ruler **See Advance Preparation, p. 545**
7.8	Home Link Masters, pp. 339 and 340 Teaching Aid Assessment Master, p. 498 (optional)		masking tape ruler half-sheets of paper **See Advance Preparation, p. 550**
7.9	Home Link Master, p. 341 Teaching Masters, p. 130; and p. 135 (optional) transparencies of Teaching Masters, pp. 136 and 137 (optional) **See Advance Preparation, p. 556**	1 twenty-sided polyhedral die or 3 regular dice per small group	Class Data Pad (optional) stick-on notes construction paper; ribbon pinch-style clothespins overhead markers stapler, tape or glue
7.10	Home Link Masters, pp. 342–345 Teaching Masters, pp. 22, 128, 130, and 138 Assessment Masters, pp. 429 and 430	slate 1 twenty-sided polyhedral die or 3 regular dice per small group	object weighing about 10 lbs calculator ruler counters bath scale

planningtips

Pacing

Pacing depends on a number of factors, such as children's individual needs and how long your school has been using *Everyday Mathematics*. At the beginning of Unit 7, review your Content by Strand Poster to help you set a monthly pace.

	← MOST CLASSROOMS →	
JANUARY	FEBRUARY	MARCH

Using the Projects

Choose any of Projects 1, 3, 6, or 7 during Unit 7. In Project 1, your class will name fractional parts and use paper-folding techniques to make paper boxes. Project 3 is an introduction to the 12-year cycle of the Chinese calendar. For Project 6, your class will create a time capsule and make predictions about life four years from now. You may prefer to use Project 6 at the end of the year. Children describe a collection in terms of number, size, age, and other attributes in Project 7.

Home Communication

Share Home Links 7.1–7.9 with families to help them understand the content and procedures in this unit. At the end of the unit, use Home Link 7.10 to introduce Unit 8. Supplemental information can be found in the *Home Connection Handbook*.

NCTM Standards

Standard	1	2	3	4	5	6	7	8	9	10
Unit 7 Lessons	1–6	1–3, 5, 6	6	6, 7	7–9	1–9	7–9	1–9	1–9	1–9

Content Standards
1 Number and Operation
2 Patterns, Functions, and Algebra
3 Geometry and Spatial Sense
4 Measurement
5 Data Analysis, Statistics, and Probability

Process Standards
6 Problem Solving
7 Reasoning and Proof
8 Communication
9 Connections
10 Representations

PRACTICE *through* Games

Everyday Mathematics uses games to help children develop good fact power and other math skills.

- Identify blocks that differ by one attribute in the *Attribute Train Game* **(Lesson 7.2)**
- Practice counting up mentally and using a calculator with *Hit the Target* **(Lessons 7.3, 7.5, 7.6, and 7.10)**
- Add three or more 1-digit and 2-digit numbers by playing *Basketball Addition* **(Lessons 7.4, 7.9, and 7.10)**
- Practice adding three or more numbers in *Three Addends* **(Lesson 7.4)**
- Match numbers with the total number of dots in an array in *Array Bingo* **(Lesson 7.7)**

The notes below highlight the major content ideas presented in Unit 7. These notes may help you establish instructional priorities.

Number Patterns (Lesson 7.1 and following)

Number-pattern activities are used throughout *Everyday Mathematics* to introduce children to the mathematics of rule-based number sequences, functions, and relations. Children discover number patterns and make predictions based on such patterns.

Lesson 7.1 reviews counting activities that have been part of *Everyday Mathematics* since Kindergarten. Prior to Grade 2, these activities advanced from oral group counting to symbol-oriented patterns on number lines and number grids.

In Lesson 1.11 of *Second Grade Everyday Mathematics,* children used calculators to count forward and backward from any number and looked for patterns in the ones digits of their counts.

For the counting activities on the calculator, you should be aware that certain functions on some new models of calculators work a bit differently from those on commonly used, inexpensive calculators described in *Everyday Mathematics.*

▷ On some calculators, the "repeat" function (for calculator counts) is activated by pressing ⊕ or ⊖ twice instead of pressing ⊕ or ⊖ once and then pressing ⊜ repeatedly.

▷ Some calculators have a "constant" key that allows calculator counts to be done in a different way from those done on older calculators.

Lesson 7.2 emphasizes the fact that our numeration system is a base-10 system by reviewing patterns on number grids and on pieces of number grids. The pieces of a number grid form the basis for arrow-path puzzles in which grid cells are replaced by arrows: Horizontal arrows represent increases or decreases by 1, vertical arrows by 10, and diagonal arrows by combinations of 1 and 10. Arrow-path puzzles are somewhat more abstract than number-grid puzzles; they present an interesting approach to reviewing and reinforcing the structure of our numeration system. Because of the format, you can easily create puzzles to provide more practice for children.

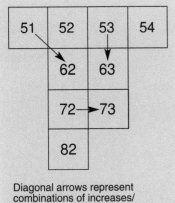

Diagonal arrows represent combinations of increases/decreases by 10 and 1.

Vertical arrows represent increases/decreases by 10.

Horizontal arrows represent increases/decreases by 1.

"What's My Rule?" and Frames-and-Arrows routines, introduced in Kindergarten and first grade, are revisited with regularity through review exercises in Math Boxes. These exercises use increasingly complex patterns and relationships.

Computational Skills (Lessons 7.3–7.5)

In Lesson 7.3, children find complements of tens; that is, they answer such questions as: "What must I add to 6 to get 10? What must I add to 32 to get 40? To get 70?" Such problems can be extended to complements of hundreds and, later, thousands: "How many tens are needed to get from 320 to 400? How many tens and then how many hundreds are needed to get from 320 to 800?" Finding complements is an important prerequisite for understanding and performing multidigit subtraction.

In Lesson 7.4, children practice addition of three or more 1-digit and 2-digit numbers by playing an imaginary basketball game. This game can be played by the entire class.

The story about the Wubbles in Lesson 7.5 introduces exponential growth, a topic that will be developed further in subsequent grades. It is surprising to most people how quickly a number grows through repeated doubling or how quickly a large number shrinks by repeatedly dividing it in half. In future grades, children encounter real-life examples of exponential growth, such as compound interest on money saved and population growth in bacteria cultures.

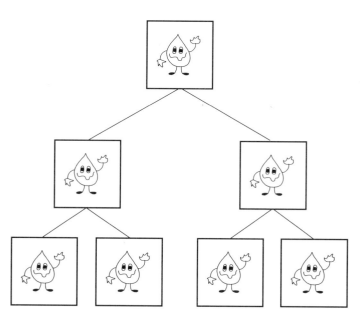

Doubling Wubbles introduces exponential growth.

Explorations: Weights and Scales, Equal Sharing, and Block Patterns (Lesson 7.6)

In Exploration A, children use a bath scale to gain experience in reading a scale. After making stacks of books of certain weights, children lift the books to develop a sense for the feel of the weights.

Children revisit the equal sharing use of division in Exploration B. They solve the problem of equally sharing a whole number of dollars among different numbers of people and interpreting remainders.

In Exploration C, children continue to experience aspects of the concept of area. They utilize the idea of covering a surface with no gaps or spaces while creating a pattern-block design.

Applications of Mathematics (Lessons 7.7–7.9)

In Lessons 7.7–7.9, children collect data, find the median of sets of data, make frequency tables, draw line plots and bar graphs, and analyze data. They have done such activities before in first grade and in the early part of second grade; these activities will be repeated over and over in this and future grades.

In Lesson 7.7, children collect data by measuring their arm spans and the lengths of their standing long jumps. In Lesson 7.8, they find the median jump length for the class. In Lesson 7.9, they organize the class data on arm span length in a frequency table and represent the data in a line plot and bar graph. They use the line plot to find the median of the data set.

NOTE: In *First Grade Everyday Mathematics,* children had experience finding a middle value for a set of data. In Lesson 3.5, children found middle values for numbers of pockets.

The routine for finding the median is quite simple: List all of the data, arrange them in ascending or descending order, and then count from either end to the number in the middle. If the data set consists of an even number of data, there are two middle values, and the median is a number halfway between those two middle values. At this stage, any number in the range of these two middle values is acceptable.

One way data are analyzed is by comparing pairs of figures. In this unit, such comparisons are done by asking, "How much more (or less)?" Bar graphs provide a visual impression of such comparisons. At a later time, comparisons will also be made by asking, "About how many times as much? What fraction of?"

Set of Data

12

13

18 ← Median is the number halfway between the two middle values.

20

21

25

The median in an even number of data

For additional information on the following topics, see the *Teacher's Reference Manual:*

- counting: plain and fancy
- data collection, organization, and analysis
- grids, scrolls, and lines
- mental arithmetic
- numeration and place value

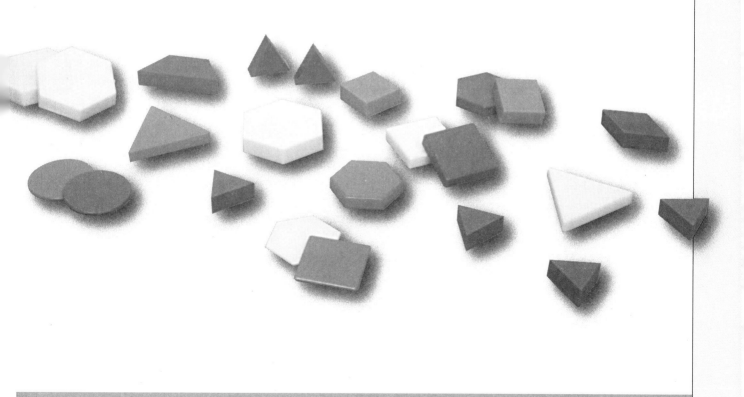

7.1

Patterns in Counting

OBJECTIVES To review counting by 2s, 5s, and 10s; and to describe patterns that result from counting.

1-26-06

Lesson 7.1 (N.ME.02.04)
Do Part 3, **Reteaching:** "Counting by 2s, 5s, & 10s"; include counting by 3s & 4s.

summaries / materials

1 Teaching the Lesson

Children count by *n* from an arbitrary starting number, orally and with a calculator. [Numeration; Patterns, Functions, and Algebra]

Children make and describe counting patterns on a number grid. [Numeration; Patterns, Functions, and Algebra]

- ☐ *Math Journal 2*, p. 165
- ☐ Teaching Master (*Math Masters,* p. 122)
- ☐ Teaching Master transparency (*Math Masters,* p. 122; optional)
- ☐ calculator
- ☐ half-sheets of paper

See Advance Preparation

2 Ongoing Learning & Practice

Children complete a timed-facts inventory of addition and subtraction facts. [Operations and Computation]

Children practice and maintain skills through Math Boxes and Home Link activities.

- ☐ *Math Journal 2*, p. 166
- ☐ Teaching Master (*Math Masters,* p. 123)
- ☐ Home Link Master (*Math Masters,* p. 330)

See Advance Preparation

3 Options for Individualizing

Reteaching Children correlate rhythmic counting by 2s, 5s, and 10s to different movements. [Numeration]

Enrichment Children make patterns by coloring square and triangular grids. [Patterns, Functions, and Algebra]

Extra Practice Children count by 2s, 5s, and 10s. [Numeration; Patterns, Functions, and Algebra]

- ☐ Teaching Masters (*Math Masters,* p. 124; and pp. 125 and 126, optional)
- ☐ *Minute Math*®, pp. 5, 7, 29, and 31

Additional Information

Advance Preparation Before beginning the *Marking a Number Grid with Counts by n* activity in Part 1, make extra copies of *Math Masters,* page 122 for children who make errors and need to start over or for children who finish quickly and want to make other number patterns. You may also want to make an overhead transparency of this page.

Before beginning the first activity in Part 2, you might want to cut *Math Masters,* page 123 into four separate tests. See the Adjusting the Activity at the bottom of page 513.

Getting Started

Math Message
Start from 20 and count by 2s.

Count as far as you want to go.

Write your counts on a half-sheet of paper.

1 Teaching the Lesson

✦ Math Message Follow-Up

WHOLE-CLASS ACTIVITY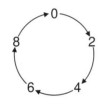

Have small groups or the whole class count by 2s from several 2-digit even numbers. Extend to counts from 3-digit numbers if children do well. Keep oral counting brisk and rhythmic. Ask volunteers to describe the pattern in counts by 2s. All counts are even numbers; the pattern of the ones digits repeats over and over: 0, 2, 4, 6, 8, 0, 2, ….

When counting by 2s, the pattern of the ones digits—
0, 2, 4, 6, 8, 0, 2, …—repeats over and over again.

Repeat with counts by 5s and 10s. For counts by 5s, begin with numbers that end in 0 or 5. For counts by 10s, begin with numbers that end in 0. Encourage children to describe the patterns in these counts. Counts by 5s from numbers ending in 0 or 5 end in 0 and 5. Counts by 10s from numbers ending in 0 end in 0.

✦ Using a Calculator to Display Counts

WHOLE-CLASS ACTIVITY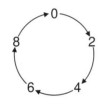

Review counting by n from a given number on the calculator. For example, to count from 20 by 2s, press 20 ⊕ 2 ⊜ ⊜ ⊜ …. The display will show 22, 24, 26, and so on once you start pressing the ⊜ key.

 Adjusting the Activity To extend the activity, ask children to count backward, as well as forward. In addition, have children discuss the pattern of counts by 10s starting from any number. As you count from one number to the next, the ones digit remains the same and the tens digit is increased by 1: 3**0**3, 3**1**3, 3**2**3, 3**3**3, …. If the tens digit is 9, then the tens digit becomes 0 and the hundreds digit is increased by 1: 3**9**3, 4**0**3, ….

NOTE: On most calculators, to count by n from a starting number s, you need to press s ⊕ n ⊜ ⊜ ⊜ …. If this keying sequence does not work on your calculators, press s ⊕ n ⊜ ⊕ n ⊜ ⊕ n ⊜ …. The display will show the counts by n each time you press the ⊜ key.

Adjusting the Activity If children have difficulty using a calculator to display counts, write the following on the board. Tell the calculator:

1. to clear.

2. to start with a certain number.

3. to count up (+) or down (−).

4. to count up or down by a certain number.

5. to count by pressing ⊜ repeatedly.

Try group counts with numbers other than 2, 5, and 10. Use such numbers as 3, 4, and 9. Children press the appropriate keys on their calculators as they count in unison. *Suggestions:*

▷ Count from 22 by 3s. Press 22 ⊕ 3 ⊜ ⊜ ⊜ ....

▷ Count from 22 by 4s. Press 22 ⊕ 4 ⊜ ⊜ ⊜ ....

▷ Count from 80 by 6s. Press 80 ⊕ 6 ⊜ ⊜ ⊜ ....

▷ Count from 180 by 9s. Press 180 ⊕ 9 ⊜ ⊜ ⊜ ....

Extend the range of numbers to challenge children's capabilities.

Have volunteers record some of the counts on the board so that the class can observe the patterns in the ones digits. You might find it helpful to circle the ones digits.

✦ Marking a Number Grid with Counts by *n*
(*Math Journal 2,* p. 165; *Math Masters,* p. 122)

PARTNER ACTIVITY 👥

Solve Problem 1 on the journal page as a class so that children will understand how to complete the remainder of the page. Children count by 5s from the starting number 102. Press 102 ⊕ 5 ⊜ ⊜ ⊜ .... Display shows 102, 107, 112, 117, 122, ... As children count, they color the numbers on their number grids (see the journal page in the margin; for readability, children's colored answers are indicated with circles). You can mark the number pattern on an overhead transparency of *Math Masters,* page 122. Observe and discuss the patterns for the numbers children have colored. All numbers fall in two columns of the grid. The ones digit alternates between 2 and 7.

Assign Problem 2 on the journal page as independent work for partners. Partners must first decide on a starting number and then a number to count by. *Suggestions:*

▷ Children can select any *starting number,* but it should be a number less than 320.

▷ Children can select any *number to count by,* but encourage them to count by some number other than 2, 5, and 10.

▷ Some children may count without using a calculator. That is fine, but ask them to use a calculator to check their results.

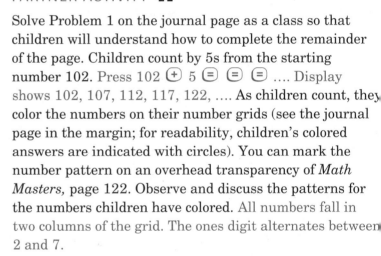

Number Patterns

1. Count by 5s starting with the number 102. Color in the numbers on the grid with a crayon. Can you find a pattern?

									100
101	(102)	103	104	105	106	(107)	108	109	110
111	(112)	113	114	115	116	(117)	118	119	120
121	(122)	123	124	125	126	(127)	128	129	130

2. Pick a number to start with. Pick a number to count by. Mark your counts using a crayon. Sample answers:

									300
301	302	303	(304)	305	306	307	308	309	(310)
311	312	313	314	315	(316)	317	318	319	320
321	(322)	323	324	325	326	327	(328)	329	330
331	332	333	(334)	335	336	337	338	339	(340)
341	342	343	344	345	(346)	347	348	349	350
351	(352)	353	354	355	356	357	(358)	359	360
361	362	363	(364)	365	366	367	368	369	(370)

I counted by __6s__ starting with the number __304__.

I used a __green__ crayon to mark the counts.
(color)

Here is the pattern I found: Sample answer: Numbers are shaded every other column. The ones digits are always even numbers.

✦ *Math Journal 2,* p. 165

STUDENT PAGE

Example: Beth and Sara decide to start at 304 and count by 6s. They fill in their journal page as follows:

I counted by __6s__ starting with the number __304__.

I used a _____green_____ crayon to mark the counts.
(color)

Here is the pattern I found: Sample answer: Numbers are shaded in every other column. The ones digits are always even numbers.

Use with Lesson 7.1.   (one hundred sixty-five) **165**

They will color the squares numbered 304, 310, 316, 322, ….

Partners write in their journals about any number patterns they observe for their count. When the majority of children has completed the journal page, bring the class together to share and discuss their statements and observations.

 Adjusting the Activity Make extra copies of *Math Masters,* page 122 for children who finish early and want to repeat Problem 2 using different numbers. Extra copies are also useful for children who make an error and need to start again.

Addition and Subtraction Facts

1. 3 + 4 = __7__	**2.** 1 + 6 = __7__	**3.** 8 + 2 = __10__
4. 0 + 1 = __1__	**5.** 8 + 0 = __8__	**6.** 3 + 1 = __4__
7. 2 + 7 = __9__	**8.** 2 + 4 = __6__	**9.** 5 + 4 = __9__
10. 8 − 3 = __5__	**11.** 6 − 3 = __3__	**12.** 8 − 6 = __2__
13. 5 − 1 = __4__	**14.** 7 − 2 = __5__	**15.** 9 − 0 = __9__
16. 10 − 7 = __3__	**17.** 10 − 4 = __6__	**18.** 8 − 1 = __7__
19. 9 + 9 = __18__	**20.** 4 + 8 = __12__	**21.** 5 + 7 = __12__
22. 5 + 8 = __13__	**23.** 9 + 3 = __12__	**24.** 8 + 3 = __11__
25. 7 + 6 = __13__	**26.** 8 + 8 = __16__	**27.** 2 + 9 = __11__
28. 15 − 8 = __7__	**29.** 14 − 9 = __5__	**30.** 14 − 7 = __7__
31. 14 − 6 = __8__	**32.** 16 − 7 = __9__	**33.** 11 − 6 = __5__
34. 11 − 4 = __7__	**35.** 17 − 8 = __9__	**36.** 13 − 9 = __4__

◇ *Math Masters,* p. 123

 Ongoing Learning & Practice

◆ Taking a Timed Inventory of Addition and Subtraction Facts (*Math Masters,* p. 123)

INDEPENDENT ACTIVITY

It is expected that the majority of children has mastered the addition and subtraction facts. Use *Math Masters,* page 123 to assess children's progress.

Allow children 5 minutes (about 8 seconds per problem) to complete the test. Adjust the amount of time as you see fit. However, it is important to remember that children should not be given enough time to *figure out* the answers. The point is to know the answers "by heart."

 Adjusting the Activity If children are having difficulty mastering facts, do not administer the entire test at one sitting. Cut *Math Masters,* page 123 apart into 4 separate tests. Give each test on a different day and allow children about 90 seconds per test.

ONGOING ASSESSMENT
The test is organized in the following clusters of similar problems:

▷ Problems 1–9: "easy" addition facts,

▷ Problems 10–18: "easy" subtraction facts,

▷ Problems 19–27: "more difficult" addition facts,

▷ Problems 28–36: "more difficult" subtraction facts.

You can use these clusters as you assess children's work to quickly see which facts they need to practice further.

Math Boxes 7.1

1. Write a number model for a ballpark estimate. Then subtract.

$$81 - 22$$

Answer
59

Ballpark estimate:

__80 − 20 = 60__

2. Share 1 dozen cookies equally among 5 children. Draw a picture. Sample answer:

Each child gets __2__ cookies.

There are __2__ cookies left over.

3. 8 books per shelf. 4 shelves. Fill in the multiplication diagram and solve.

shelves	books per shelf	books in all
4	8	?

There are __32__ books.

4. Measure the line segment.

_____

about __3__ in.

about __8__ cm

5. 15 dogs.
13 cats.
12 birds.

How many animals?

__40__ animals

6.

1 hour earlier is __8__ : __35__.

1 hour later is __10__ : __35__.

◆ Math Journal 2, p. 166

Count by 2s, 5s, and 10s

Home Link 7.1

Family Note

In this lesson, your child has been counting by 2s, 5s, and 10s. After your child has completed these problems, help him or her look for patterns in the ones digits of the answers. In the example, the ones digits repeat: 0, 2, 4, 6, 8, 0, 2, 4, and so on. If your child is successful with these problems, ask him or her to count backward by 2s, 5s, or 10s. Start from a number that is a multiple of 10, such as 200.

Please return this Home Link to school tomorrow.

Example

Count by 2s. Begin at 100. Write down your first 10 counts.

_100_, _102_, _104_, _106_, _108_, _110_, _112_, _114_, _116_, _118_

1. Count by 2s. Begin at 200. Write down your first 10 counts.

_200_, _202_, _204_, _206_, _208_, _210_, _212_, _214_, _216_, _218_

2. Count by 5s. Begin at 500. Write down your first 10 counts.

_500_, _505_, _510_, _515_, _520_, _525_, _530_, _535_, _540_, _545_

3. Count by 10s. Begin at 550. Write down your first 10 counts.

_550_, _560_, _570_, _580_, _590_, _600_, _610_, _620_, _630_, _640_

Look at your counts. Tell someone at home about any patterns that you find in the counts.

Sample answers:
In Problem 1, the ones digits repeat: 0, 2, 4, 6, 8, 0, 2, 4, ...
In Problem 2, the ones digits repeat: 0, 5, 0, 5, ...
In Problem 3, the ones digits are all 0.

⌄ Math Masters, p. 330

◆ Math Boxes 7.1 (*Math Journal 2*, p. 166)

INDEPENDENT ACTIVITY

Mixed Review This journal page provides opportunities for cumulative review or assessment of concepts and skills.

◆ Home Link 7.1 (*Math Masters*, p. 330)

Home Connection Children count forward from 3-digit numbers. They record some of their counts and look for patterns in their answers.

3 Options for Individualizing

◆ RETEACHING Counting by 2s, 5s, and 10s

SMALL-GROUP ACTIVITY 5–15 min

For children who still have difficulty counting by 2s, 5s, and 10s, try correlating rhythmic counting with some form of movement. *For example:*

▷ 1, 2 (clap), 3, 4, (clap), …

▷ 1, 2, 3, 4, 5 (touch toes), 6, 7, 8, 9, 10 (touch toes), …

▷ 1, 2, 3, 4, 5, 6, 7, 8, 9, 10 (jumping jack), …

◆ ENRICHMENT Making Patterns by Coloring Grids (*Math Masters,* pp. 124–126)

INDEPENDENT ACTIVITY 15–30 min

Art Link Using at least two colors, children color a design on the square grid on *Math Masters,* page 124. They color a second design on the triangular grid. Those who enjoy this activity can color additional designs on copies of *Math Masters,* pages 125 and 126.

This activity is open-ended. Do not require that children's designs have any repeating or organized pattern. Eventually some children will make regular designs and patterns.

This kind of open-ended patterning activity should be repeated as often as possible. Display the designs children make in a class booklet or on a bulletin board.

Portfolio Ideas

✦ EXTRA PRACTICE Minute Math

SMALL-GROUP ACTIVITY 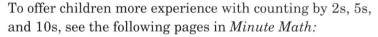 **5–15 min**

To offer children more experience with counting by 2s, 5s, and 10s, see the following pages in *Minute Math:*

Basic Routines: pp. 5 and 7

Counting: pp. 29 and 31

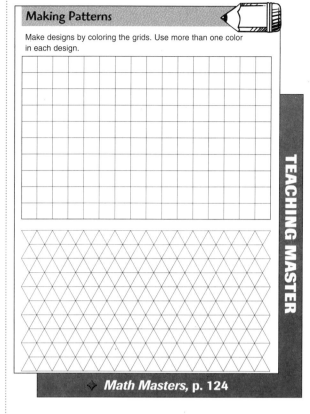

Making Patterns

Make designs by coloring the grids. Use more than one color in each design.

Math Masters, p. 124

TEACHING MASTER

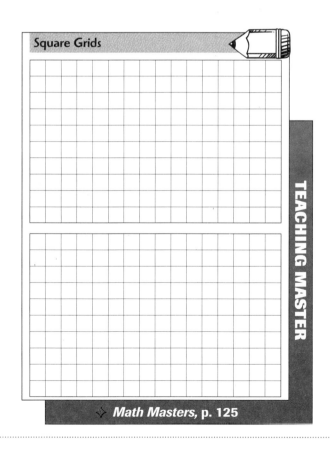

Square Grids

Math Masters, p. 125

TEACHING MASTER

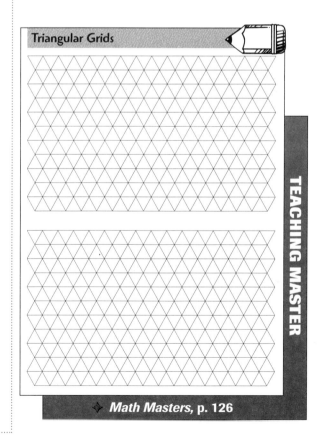

Triangular Grids

Math Masters, p. 126

TEACHING MASTER

7.2 Number-Grid Patterns and Arrow Paths

OBJECTIVES To review ones and tens patterns on number grids; and to develop place-value awareness by solving number-grid and arrow-path puzzles.

Lesson 7.2 (N.FL.02.06, N.MR.02.08)
Part 1, Extend: Wherever arrow path ends, have students tell how much more they need to get to the next 100 & demonstrate how they solved the problem on the # grid.

Lesson 7.2 (N.FL.02.06, N.MR.02.08) - continued
Do Part 3, Enrichment: "Making up Arrow Path Puzzles." **Extend:** As partner solves puzzle, he/she writes a # model/# sentence to show how each answer was found.

materials

1 Teaching the Lesson

Children review the structure and patterns of the number grid and use place value to complete number-grid puzzles. Children then use place value to track arrow paths through pieces of the number grid and to solve arrow-path puzzles.
[Numeration; Patterns, Functions, and Algebra]

- ☐ *Math Journal 2,* p. 167
- ☐ Home Link 7.1
- ☐ Class Number Grid Poster

2 Ongoing Learning & Practice

Children use a ruler to measure the lengths of various objects to the nearest inch and the nearest centimeter. [Measurement]

Children practice and maintain skills through Math Boxes and Home Link activities.

- ☐ *Math Journal 2,* pp. 168 and 169
- ☐ Home Link Master (*Math Masters,* p. 331)
- ☐ ruler

3 Options for Individualizing

Enrichment Children make up arrow-path puzzles; children solve each other's puzzles. [Numeration; Patterns, Functions, and Algebra]

Enrichment Children play the *Attribute Train Game* in which they identify blocks that differ by one attribute—size, color, or shape. [Patterns, Functions, and Algebra]

- ☐ Teaching Master (*Math Masters,* p. 127)
- ☐ set of attribute blocks

Additional Information
Vocabulary • **number-grid puzzle** • **arrow path** • **arrow-path puzzle**

Getting Started

Mental Math and Reflexes
Write the problems shown below on the board in both horizontal and vertical formats.
Ask children to subtract by counting up mentally.

70 − 55 = ? 15   40 − 8 = ? 32   80 − 29 = ? 51   50 − 12 = ? 38   90 − 67 = ? 23

Math Message

Fill in the missing numbers on the number grid.

25	26	
35	36	37
45		

1 Teaching the Lesson

✦ Math Message Follow-Up

WHOLE-CLASS DISCUSSION

Expect that many children will realize that the empty squares are in the 30s row of the number grid and will correctly fill in the numbers 35, 36, and 37.

Use the Class Number Grid Poster to review patterns. Remind children that:

• The digits 0 through 9 are used for writing all numbers.

• The ones digit changes by 1 as you move from one cell to another across a row.

Examples: Left to right: 1<u>1</u>, 1<u>2</u>, 1<u>3</u>, …
      Right to left: 3<u>9</u>, 3<u>8</u>, 3<u>7</u>, …

• The tens digit changes by 1 (and the number itself changes by 10) as you move from one cell to another, up or down a column.

Examples: Down a column: <u>1</u>1, <u>2</u>1, <u>3</u>1, …
      Up a column: <u>9</u>8, <u>8</u>8, <u>7</u>8, …

✦ Drawing Horizontal and Vertical Patterns on the Number Grid Using Arrow Paths

WHOLE-CLASS ACTIVITY

Draw a **number-grid puzzle** on the board and write 25 in the cell as shown in the margin.

1. Draw an arrow from 25 pointing down to the cell under it. Which number goes in this cell? 35 Enter the number.

2. Draw another arrow from 35 pointing to the next cell to the right. Which number goes in this cell? 36 Enter the number.

3. Draw another arrow from 36 to the next cell to the right. Which number goes in this cell? 37 Enter the number.

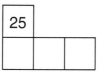

Number-grid puzzle

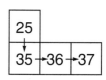

Filled-in puzzle with arrow path

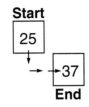

Start
25
→ 37
End

Arrow path without grid

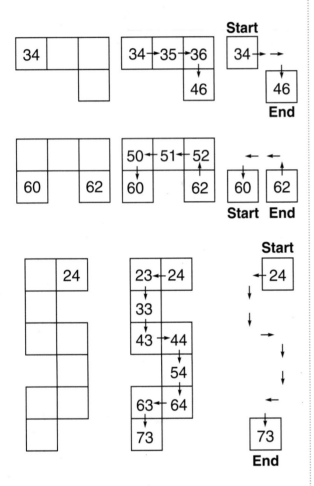

Creating arrow-path puzzles

Draw the same **arrow path,** this time without the grid. Discuss how this arrow path is like the number grid: Each arrow shows a path to the next cell in a vertical or horizontal direction. Which number goes in the End box? 37

Repeat the same routine a few more times until children have the idea. Use grid puzzles that combine horizontal and vertical combinations of cells. Have children help you draw the arrow path without the grid. Three suggestions are given in the margin.

◆ **Drawing Diagonal Patterns on the Number Grid Using Arrow Paths**

WHOLE-CLASS ACTIVITY

Next, challenge the class with a more difficult grid puzzle. Draw the puzzle shown below.

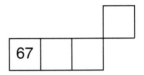

1. Draw an arrow from 67 pointing to the next cell to the right. Which number goes in this cell? 68 Enter the number.

2. Draw another arrow from 68 to the next cell to the right. Which number goes in this cell? 69 Enter the number.

3. Draw a diagonal arrow from 69 to the cell to the right and up. Which number goes in this cell? 60 Enter the number. Ask children to describe the strategy that they used to determine the number.

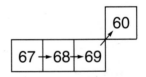

There are two strategies that children may use to determine the result of the diagonal move. The first of these strategies starts with a move to the right (add 1), followed by a move up (subtract 10). So the end cell must be 69 + 1 − 10, or 60. The second strategy starts with a move up (subtract 10), followed by a move to the right (add 1). So the end cell must be 69 − 10 + 1, or 60. Either strategy is fine and will solve the puzzle.

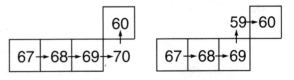

Two strategies for solving this number-grid puzzle

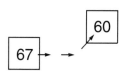

Draw the same arrow path, this time without the grid. (See the margin.) Discuss how this arrow path is like the number grid: Each arrow shows a path to the next cell in a vertical, horizontal, or diagonal direction. Which number goes in the End box? 60

Repeat the same routine a few more times until children have the idea. Use grid pieces that combine horizontal, vertical, and diagonal combinations of cells. *Suggestion:*

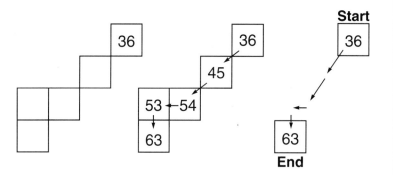

◆ Solving Arrow-Path Puzzles

WHOLE-CLASS ACTIVITY

Draw an **arrow-path puzzle** like the one at the right. Explain to children that to solve the puzzle, they need to find the number at the end of the arrow path. Solve the puzzle together. Use the number grid to check the solution. 76

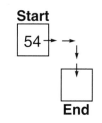

Now draw an arrow-path puzzle that uses diagonal arrows like the one at the right. Solve the puzzle together. Use the number grid (ignoring the hundreds) to check the solution. 276

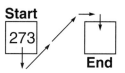

◆ Solving Number-Grid and Arrow-Path Puzzles
(*Math Journal 2,* p. 167)

INDEPENDENT ACTIVITY

The purpose of solving number-grid puzzles is to develop place-value awareness that will aid children in improving their addition and subtraction skills. Arrow-path puzzles are a more abstract form of number-grid puzzles.

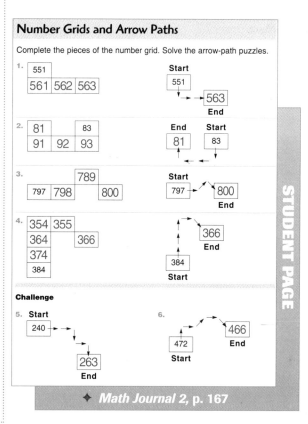

◆ *Math Journal 2, p. 167*

STUDENT PAGE

Measuring Lengths with a Ruler

Use your ruler to measure the length of each object to the nearest inch and the nearest centimeter.

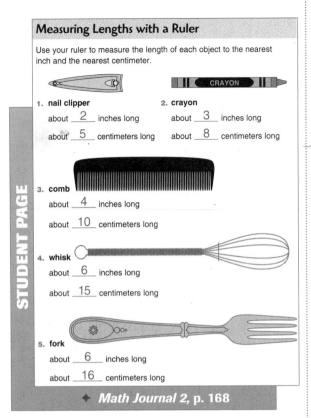

1. **nail clipper**

   about __2__ inches long

   about __5__ centimeters long

2. **crayon**

   about __3__ inches long

   about __8__ centimeters long

3. **comb**

   about __4__ inches long

   about __10__ centimeters long

4. **whisk**

   about __6__ inches long

   about __15__ centimeters long

5. **fork**

   about __6__ inches long

   about __16__ centimeters long

   ✦ *Math Journal 2,* p. 168

STUDENT PAGE

Math Boxes 7.2

1. Continue.

   312, 314, 316, __318__, __320__,

   __322__, __324__, __326__, __328__

2. Draw 5 nests with 3 eggs in each.

   How many eggs in all?

   __15__ eggs

3. Solve.

	Unit
	children

   70 − 20 = __50__

   __130__ = 90 + 40

   __40__ = 120 − 80

   150 − 60 = __90__

4. Fill in the missing numbers.

196	197	
	207	208
216	217	218

5. Use your calculator. Start at 92. Count by 5s.

   92, 97, __102__, __107__, __112__,

   __117__, __122__, __127__, __132__

6. Use the partial-sums algorithm to add. Show your work.

   ```
      35
    + 79
     100
    +  14
     114
   ```

   ✦ *Math Journal 2,* p. 169

Arrow-path puzzles give children a mental image of moves on a number grid.

 Adjusting the Activity Do not be concerned if some children find arrow-path puzzles difficult. Do not dwell on this type of puzzle. Instead, focus on the number-grid puzzles in Problems 1–4 and skip Problems 5 and 6. If children are having difficulty with 3-digit numbers, encourage them to ignore the hundreds digit and focus on the tens and the ones digits. Children's answers may then be checked on the number grid.

If the number-grid puzzles are too easy for some children, challenge them by changing the 3-digit numbers to 4-digit numbers.

2 Ongoing Learning & Practice

✦ Measuring Lengths with a Ruler
(*Math Journal 2,* p. 168)

INDEPENDENT ACTIVITY

Children use a ruler to measure the lengths of various objects represented by full-scale drawings. Children measure each object to the nearest inch and to the nearest centimeter.

> ### ONGOING ASSESSMENT
> In Lesson 7.7, children measure long jumps to the nearest centimeter and arm spans to the nearest inch. The measurements are then used in various data activities. It is expected that children will be able make these measurements. Use journal page 168 to assess children's skill level. If necessary, you may wish to have children do several brief measurement exercises prior to Lesson 7.7 so that they will be prepared for that lesson's activities.

✦ Math Boxes 7.2 (*Math Journal 2,* p. 169)

INDEPENDENT ACTIVITY

 Mixed Review This journal page provides opportunities for cumulative review or assessment of concepts and skills.

◆ Home Link 7.2 (*Math Masters*, p. 331)

Home Connection Children solve a number-grid puzzle to develop place-value awareness that will help them with addition and subtraction skills.

3 Options for Individualizing

◆ ENRICHMENT Making up Arrow-Path Puzzles

INDEPENDENT ACTIVITY   15–30 min

Children make up arrow-path puzzles for each other to solve. Consider combining the puzzles into a book. Children may look through the book in their spare time and try to solve the puzzles. Encourage the author of each puzzle to include the answer on the back of the page.

Portfolio Ideas

◆ ENRICHMENT Playing the *Attribute Train Game* (*Math Masters*, p. 127)

SMALL-GROUP ACTIVITY   15–30 min

Solving number-grid and arrow-path puzzles involves determining, according to the positions of cells, which number comes next. When playing the *Attribute Train Game*, children choose a block that differs from the previous block in the train in only one way: by color, size, or shape.

Once children become comfortable with the rules of the game, the attribute blocks are randomly shared among group members for Game 2. Children follow the same rules as before. Any player who does not have a block that meets the requirements loses a turn. Children continue until no blocks can be played. The object of the game is to end up with the fewest number of blocks.

Number-Grid Puzzle   Home Link 7.2

Family Note In this lesson, your child solved a special type of puzzle called a *number-grid puzzle*. Solving number-grid puzzles promotes place-value awareness that will help your child develop addition and subtraction skills. In the number grid shown below, the numbering starts at 100, and then the numbers increase by 1 as you move from left to right in each row. The shaded cells of the number grid should not be filled in. However, if your child is having difficulty, you might fill in a few of the shaded cells to provide some additional clues.

Please return this Home Link to school tomorrow.

Fill in the blank (unshaded) cells of the number grid.

									100
101	102	103	104	105	106	107	108	109	110
	112								120
	122								130
	132	133	134	135					140
	142			145					150
	152			155					160
	162			165				169	170
	172			175	176	177	178	179	180
	182			185					190
	192			195					200
	202	203	204	205					210

→ *Math Masters*, p. 331

HOME LINK MASTER

Attribute Train Game

Work in a small group.

Materials ☐ set of attribute blocks

Game 1

1. Place the blocks in the center of the table.

2. The first player takes a block and puts it down to start a train.

3. The next player chooses a block that is different from the first block. The second block should be different in *only one* way—in shape, size, or color. The second player adds that block to the train.

4. Players continue taking turns until no more blocks can be played.

small red circle	small red **triangle**	small **yellow** triangle	**large** yellow triangle	large **blue** triangle

Game 2

1. Share the blocks equally among all of the players in the group.

2. The first player begins the train by laying down a block.

3. The next player adds a block that is different in only one way.

4. Players take turns.

5. Any player who does not have a block that is different in only one way loses that turn.

6. Continue until no more blocks can be played.

7. The player with the fewest number of blocks left wins.

→ *Math Masters*, p. 127

TEACHING MASTER

Lesson 7.2   **521**

7.3

Extending Complements of 10

Lesson 7.3 (N.FL.02.06)
Part 1: Include using 100 as one of the #s, eg. "Enter 45, change to 100. Did you add or subtract? Which # ?" "Enter 100, change to 71. Did you add or subtract? Which #?"

OBJECTIVES To find complements of 10; and to find differences between 2-digit numbers and higher multiples of 10.

summaries	materials
1 Teaching the Lesson	
Children review complements of 10 and multiples of 10. [Operations and Computation; Patterns, Functions, and Algebra] Children practice finding differences between 2-digit numbers and higher multiples of ten by playing *Hit the Target.* [Operations and Computation]	☐ *Math Journal 2,* p. 170 ☐ Home Link 7.2 ☐ Teaching Master (*Math Masters,* p. 128; optional) ☐ Class Number Grid Poster ☐ calculator
2 Ongoing Learning & Practice	
Children estimate differences and subtract 2-digit numbers by using the trade-first subtraction algorithm. [Operations and Computation] Children practice and maintain skills through Math Boxes and Home Link activities.	☐ *Math Journal 2,* pp. 171 and 172 ☐ Home Link Master (*Math Masters,* p. 332)
3 Options for Individualizing	
Enrichment Children practice finding differences between 3-digit numbers and higher multiples of 100 by playing *Hit the Target.* [Operations and Computation] **Reteaching** Children review strategies for solving extended addition facts. [Operations and Computation; Patterns, Functions, and Algebra] **Extra Practice** Children find complements of 10 and multiples of 10. [Operations and Computation; Patterns, Functions, and Algebra]	☐ Teaching Master (*Math Masters,* p. 128; optional) ☐ calculator ☐ *Minute Math*®, p. 9

Getting Started

Mental Math and Reflexes

Children practice counting by 2s, 5s, 10s, and 25s in the context of coins.

7 nickels = 35 cents	90 cents = 9 dimes	2 quarters = 50 cents
30 cents = 6 nickels	70 cents = 7 dimes	2 dimes = 20 cents

How many dimes in a dollar? 10 dimes   How many nickels in a dollar? 20 nickels

If some children are having difficulty finding equivalent amounts, encourage them to use coins to count. For example, place a nickel on the table and say, "5 cents." Place another nickel on the table and say, "10 cents," and so on.

1 Teaching the Lesson

◆ Math Message Follow-Up

WHOLE-CLASS DISCUSSION  M^2

Volunteers share how they found the missing amounts. Most children will know the addition and subtraction facts, but some may have counted up in various ways.

Extend this activity to finding the distance (difference) between a given 2-digit number and the next-higher multiple of 10. Illustrate with problems, such as the following:

▷ 25 + ___ = 30 5   ▷ 50 − ___ = 44 6

▷ 70 = 63 + ___ 7   ▷ 70 − ___ = 61 9

◆ Making 10s Using a Calculator

INDEPENDENT ACTIVITY

Have children try a few of the following problems. As you discuss each problem, ask children to use the Class Number Grid Poster to "prove" their answers.

• Enter 45 into your calculator. Change it to 50. Did you add or subtract? add Which number? 5

• Enter 33. Change to 40. Add or subtract? add Which number? 7

• Enter 60. Change to 52. Add or subtract? subtract Which number? 8

• Enter 80. Change to 71. Add or subtract? subtract Which number? 9

NOTE: The ability to extend skills with single-digit numbers to skills with larger numbers is a powerful tool that children will develop over time.

 Adjusting the Activity Demonstrate on the Class Number Grid Poster that the distance from 25 to 30 is the same as the distance from 5 to 10.

						0
4	5	6	7	8	9	10
14	15	16	17	18	19	20
24	25	26	27	28	29	30
34	35	36	37	38	39	40

Making 10s

Record three rounds of *Hit the Target*.

Example Round

Target Number: __40__

Starting Number	Change ⤷	Result	Change ⤷	Result	Change ⤷	Result
12	+38	50	–10	40		

Round 1

Target Number: _____

Starting Number	Change ⤷	Result	Change ⤷	Result	Change ⤷	Result

Round 2

Target Number: _____

Starting Number	Change ⤷	Result	Change ⤷	Result	Change ⤷	Result

Round 3

Target Number: _____

Starting Number	Change ⤷	Result	Change ⤷	Result	Change ⤷	Result

STUDENT PAGE

✦ *Math Journal 2*, p. 170

NOTE: *Math Masters,* page 128 is a record sheet for *Hit the Target* similar to the journal page. Some children will always need this record sheet, no matter how many times they play the game. But most will not need a record sheet after today's introduction. Make additional copies of the master as necessary.

Adjusting the Activity It may be helpful to remind children of the possible target numbers by listing them on the board: 20, 30, 40, 50, 60, 70, 80, 90.

Extend this skill to problems in which the differences are 10 or greater. For each problem, discuss the strategies that children used to find the answer.

- Enter 32. Change to 50. Add or subtract? add Which number? 18

  A child might reason as follows:

  "Which number, added to 2, will give me 10? It's 8, so 32 + 8 = 40.

  Which number, added to 40, will give me 50?

  40 + 10 = 50

  Finally, 8 + 10 = 18."

- Enter 80. Change to 46. Add or subtract? subtract Which number? 34

  A child might reason as follows:

  "Which number, added to 6, will give me 10? It's 4, so 46 + 4 = 50.

  Which number, added to 50, will give me 80?

  50 + 30 = 80

  Finally, 4 + 30 = 34."

◆ **Introducing *Hit the Target***
(*Math Journal 2,* p. 170; *Math Masters,* p. 128)

PARTNER ACTIVITY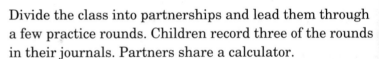

Divide the class into partnerships and lead them through a few practice rounds. Children record three of the rounds in their journals. Partners share a calculator.

Directions

1. Players choose a 2-digit multiple of 10 as a *target number.*

2. Player A selects a *starting number* less than the target number. The target number and starting number are recorded in Player B's journal.

3. Player B enters the starting number into the calculator and tries to change the starting number to the target number by adding a number to it on the calculator. Players check the calculator display to see if the target number is shown. If not, Player B continues by adding or subtracting other numbers, until the target number is shown.

4. Player A acts as the record keeper and records information in Player B's journal. Whenever Player B adds or subtracts a number, Player A records that number and a + or − sign in a Change column. After Player B pushes the ⊜ key to display the result, Player A records the number displayed in a Result column.

5. To complete the round, players select a new *target number*. Player B selects a *starting number* less than the target number. Player A now tries to change the starting number to the target number, while Player B acts as the record keeper.

6. The player who needed fewer tries to hit the target number wins the round. In the case of a tie, players play another round.

Target Number: __40__

Starting Number	Change	Result	Change	Result	Change	Result
12	+38	50	−10	40		

Players choose 40 as their target number.
Player A selects 12 as the starting number.
The diagram shows the order of the moves made by Player B.

 Adjusting the Activity If children are having difficulty hitting the target number, suggest that they begin by changing the starting number to the next-higher multiple of 10. Changing that result to the target number should then be easy. For the Example Round on journal page 170, first change the starting number 12 to 20 (by adding 8); then change 20 to the target number 40 (by adding 20).

 ONGOING ASSESSMENT
Use the record sheet for *Hit the Target* to assess children's ability to find the difference between 2-digit numbers and any higher multiple of 10. Identify those children who can find the difference in one step and those who begin by finding the next-higher multiple of 10.

2 Ongoing Learning & Practice

◆ Using Estimation and the Trade-First Subtraction Algorithm (*Math Journal 2*, p. 171)

INDEPENDENT ACTIVITY

Review the instructions for this journal page. (A similar page appeared in Lessons 6.10 and 6.11.) Children begin by making a ballpark estimate for each difference.

▷ If their estimated difference is 50 or less, they should subtract one number from another to find an exact answer.

▷ If their estimated difference is more than 50, they should not subtract one number from another to find an exact answer.

NOTE: In Lesson 7.4, children return to this journal page and solve the problems for which the estimated differences are more than 50.

Trade-First Subtraction Practice

For each problem, do the following:

• Before subtracting, write a number model for your ballpark estimate.

• If your estimate is 50 or less, subtract the numbers. Write your answer in the answer box.

• If your estimate is more than 50, you do not have to find an exact answer. Leave the answer box empty.

1. 7 4 − 3 1	Answer 43	2. 5 7 − 2 8	Answer 29	3. 8 4 − 1 7	Answer

Ballpark estimate: Ballpark estimate: Ballpark estimate:
70 − 30 = 40   60 − 30 = 30   80 − 20 = 60

4. 5 6 − 1 8	Answer 38	5. 8 7 − 2 5	Answer	6. 9 3 − 7 5	Answer 18

Ballpark estimate: Ballpark estimate: Ballpark estimate:
60 − 20 = 40   90 − 30 = 60   90 − 80 = 10

7. 8 4 − 2 7	Answer 57	8. 7 6 − 1 7	Answer	9. 5 3 − 2 9	Answer 24

Ballpark estimate: Ballpark estimate: Ballpark estimate:
80 − 30 = 50   80 − 20 = 60   50 − 30 = 20

◆ *Math Journal 2, p. 171*

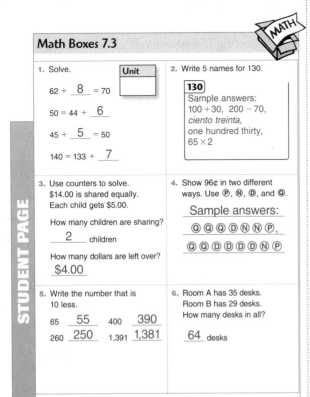

Math Boxes 7.3

1. Solve.

Unit

$62 + \underline{8} = 70$

$50 = 44 + \underline{6}$

$45 + \underline{5} = 50$

$140 = 133 + \underline{7}$

2. Write 5 names for 130.

130

Sample answers:
$100 + 30$, $200 - 70$,
ciento treinta,
one hundred thirty,
65×2

3. Use counters to solve.
$14.00 is shared equally.
Each child gets $5.00.

How many children are sharing?

$\underline{2}$ children

How many dollars are left over?

$\underline{\$4.00}$

4. Show 96¢ in two different ways. Use Ⓟ, Ⓝ, Ⓓ, and Ⓠ.

Sample answers:

Ⓠ Ⓠ Ⓓ Ⓝ Ⓝ Ⓟ,

Ⓠ Ⓠ Ⓓ Ⓓ Ⓓ Ⓝ Ⓟ

5. Write the number that is 10 less.

65 $\underline{55}$ 400 $\underline{390}$

260 $\underline{250}$ 1,391 $\underline{1,381}$

6. Room A has 35 desks.
Room B has 29 desks.
How many desks in all?

$\underline{64}$ desks

 STUDENT PAGE

◆ **Math Boxes 7.3** (*Math Journal 2,* p. 172)

INDEPENDENT ACTIVITY

Mixed Review This journal page provides opportunities for cumulative review or assessment of concepts and skills.

◆ **Home Link 7.3** (*Math Masters,* p. 332)

Home Connection Children practice finding differences between 2-digit numbers and the next-higher multiples of 10. Children also find the differences between various numbers and 70.

3 Options for Individualizing

◆ **ENRICHMENT** **Playing** *Hit the Target* (*Math Masters,* p. 128)

PARTNER ACTIVITY   **15–30 min**

This game can be made more challenging by placing certain restrictions on the target and starting numbers. For example, the target number must be a 3-digit number, and the difference between the target number and the starting number must be greater than 100.

◆ **RETEACHING** **Reviewing Strategies for Extended Addition Facts**

INDEPENDENT ACTIVITY   **5–15 min**

In order to solve problems that involve finding differences between 2-digit numbers and next-higher multiples of 10 or any higher multiples of 10, some children may benefit from reviewing strategies for solving extended addition facts.

Consider the problem $90 - 30 = ?$ If children know $9 - 3 = 6$, they can use this fact to solve $90 - 30 = ?$ They can think of 90 as 9 tens and 30 as 3 tens.

▷ **9** [ones] − **3** [ones] = **6** [ones]

▷ **9** [tens] − **3** [tens] = **6** [tens]

Missing Addends

Home Link 7.3

Family Note

In this lesson, your child found the difference between a number and a multiple of 10. In Problems 1 and 2, your child will find the difference between a number and the next-higher multiple of 10. For example, your child will determine which number added to 62 equals 70 (8). In Problem 3, your child will find different combinations of numbers that add to 70. If your child has difficulty with this problem, suggest changing the first number in each combination to the next-higher multiple of 10. For example, add 2 to 48 to make 50 and then add 20 to 50 to make 70. $2 + 20 = 22$, so $48 + 22 = 70$.

Please return this Home Link to school tomorrow.

1. $4 + \underline{6} = 10$

$10 = 3 + \underline{7}$

$\underline{5} + 5 = 10$

$10 = \underline{9} + 1$

$8 + \underline{2} = 10$

2. $54 + \underline{6} = 60$

$90 = 83 + \underline{7}$

$75 + \underline{5} = 80$

$40 = 31 + \underline{9}$

$\underline{8} + 62 = 70$

3. Make 70s. Show someone at home how you did it.

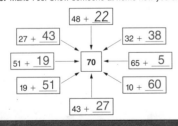

$48 + 22$

$27 + 43$ $32 + 38$

$51 + 19$ → 70 ← $65 + 5$

$19 + 51$ $10 + 60$

$43 + 27$

HOME LINK MASTER

Consider the problem ? = 70 + 90. If children know 16 = 7 + 9, they can use this fact to solve ? = 70 + 90. They can think of 70 as 7 tens and 90 as 9 tens.

▷ **16** [ones] = **7** [ones] + **9** [ones]

▷ **16** [tens] = **7** [tens] + **9** [tens]

✦ EXTRA PRACTICE Minute Math

SMALL-GROUP ACTIVITY   5–15 min

To offer children more experience with finding complements of 10 and multiples of 10, see the following page in *Minute Math:*

Basic Routines: p. 9

PLANNING AHEAD

Before beginning optional Part 3 of Lesson 7.5, obtain the following books:

▷ *Melisande* by E. Nesbit (Candlewick Press, 1989)

▷ *The King's Chessboard* by David Birch (Dial Books for Young Readers, 1988)

▷ *One Grain of Rice: A Mathematical Folktale* by Demi (Scholastic Press, 1997)

▷ *The Token Gift* by Hugh William McKibbon (Annick Press, 1996)

▷ *Two of Everything: A Chinese Folktale* by Lily Toy Hong (Albert Whitman & Co., 1993)

▷ *Anno's Magic Seeds* by Mitsumasa Anno (Philomel Books, 1994)

Hit the Target

Round 1

Target Number: _____

Starting Number	Change	Result	Change	Result	Change	Result

Round 2

Target Number: _____

Starting Number	Change	Result	Change	Result	Change	Result

Round 3

Target Number: _____

Starting Number	Change	Result	Change	Result	Change	Result

Round 4

Target Number: _____

Starting Number	Change	Result	Change	Result	Change	Result

Math Masters, p. 128

7.4

Mental Arithmetic: A Basketball Game

OBJECTIVE To build mental arithmetic skills for adding three or more 1-digit and 2-digit numbers.

summaries	materials
1 Teaching the Lesson	
Children add three or more 1-digit and 2-digit numbers (from 1 through 20) by playing *Basketball Addition*. [Operations and Computation]	☐ *Math Journal 2*, p. 173 ☐ Home Link 7.3 ☐ Teaching Master transparency (*Math Masters*, p. 129; optional) ☐ Teaching Master (*Math Masters*, p. 130; optional) ☐ 1 twenty-sided polyhedral die or 3 regular dice per group of 3–5 children ***See* Advance Preparation**
2 Ongoing Learning & Practice	
Children estimate differences and subtract 2-digit numbers by using the trade-first subtraction algorithm. [Operations and Computation] Children practice and maintain skills through Math Boxes and Home Link activities.	☐ *Math Journal 2*, pp. 171 and 174 ☐ Home Link Master (*Math Masters*, p. 333)
3 Options for Individualizing	
Reteaching Children use base-10 blocks (tens and ones) to practice adding three or more numbers in the most convenient order. [Operations and Computation] **Reteaching** Children practice adding three or more numbers by playing *Three Addends*. [Operations and Computation]	☐ *Math Journal 1*, p. 133 ☐ Teaching Masters (*Math Masters*, pp. 101 and 102) ☐ base-10 blocks: 27 cubes and 4 longs ☐ number cards 0–20 (from the Everything Math Deck, if available)

Additional Information

Advance Preparation Before playing *Basketball Addition* in Part 1, draw the class scoreboard shown on journal page 173 on the board or make an overhead transparency of *Math Masters*, page 129.

Getting Started

Mental Math and Reflexes

Pose addition and subtraction problems involving multiples of 10. *Suggestions:*

27 + __ = 80 53	80 − 23 = __ 57	__ = 70 − 36 34	24 + __ = 90 66
50 = __ + 22 28	__ + 34 = 60 26	40 − 18 = __ 22	50 − 34 = __ 16

Math Message

12 + 17 + 8 = ___ 37

___ = 4 + 9 + 16 + 11 40

Unit
points

Home Link 7.3 Follow-Up

Review answers as necessary. To assess children's progress, ask them to explain the strategy that they used to solve 27 + ___ = 70. Ask them to write their answers on the back of Home Link 7.3.

1 Teaching the Lesson

✦ Math Message Follow-Up

WHOLE-CLASS DISCUSSION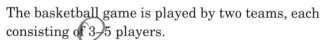

Have children share solution strategies. In what order did they find it easiest to add the numbers?

▷ For 12 + 17 + 8, which would you add first, 12 and 17, 12 and 8, or 17 and 8? Why? *12 + 8 = 20; 20 + 17 = 37 is then an easy sum to find.*

▷ For 4 + 9 + 16 + 11, why is it easier to start by adding 4 and 16 and then 9 and 11? *Both sums are 20; 20 + 20 = 40.*

✦ Demonstrating *Basketball Addition*
(*Math Journal 2,* p. 173; *Math Masters,* p. 129)

WHOLE-CLASS ACTIVITY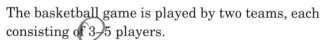

The basketball game is played by two teams, each consisting of 3–5 players.

The number of points scored by each player in each half is determined by rolling 1 twenty-sided polyhedral die or by rolling 3 regular dice and using their sum. The team that scores the greater number of points wins the game.

To demonstrate how to play the game, divide the class into two groups. Use the class scoreboard on the board (or on an overhead transparency of *Math Masters,* page 129) to record information.

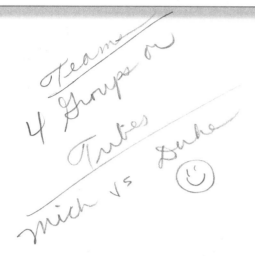

Basketball Addition

	Points Scored			
	Team 1		Team 2	
	1st Half	2nd Half	1st Half	2nd Half
Player 1				
Player 2				
Player 3				
Player 4				
Player 5				
Team Score				

Point Totals	1st Half	2nd Half	Final
Team 1	___	___	___
Team 2	___	___	___

1. Which team won the first half? _____
   By how much? _____ points
2. Which team won the second half? _____
   By how much? _____ points
3. Which team won the game? _____
   By how much? _____ points

STUDENT PAGE

✦ *Math Journal 2,* p. 173

```
  10s  1s
   1   3
       7
   1   5
 + 1   2
 ─────────
   3   0
 + 1   7
 ─────────
   4   7
```

One child used the partial-sums addition algorithm.

$$20 + 20 + 7 = 47$$

Another child combined numbers that were
easier to add.

NOTE: *Math Masters,* page 130 provides an
additional basketball scoreboard for groups
that need one.

ONGOING ASSESSMENT

Circulate and take notes about the
strategies that children use to
simplify the problems. For example,
do children add all of the tens first,
or do they look for combinations of
numbers that are easier to add?

Use the following procedure for the first half of the game:

1. Choose teams made up of 3–5 children from each
   group, depending on the number of players you list on
   the scoreboard. Players take turns rolling the
   polyhedral die (or 3 regular dice).

2. Select a volunteer from each group to record each
   player's roll on the scoreboard. After each roll of the die
   by two opposing players, ask which team is ahead.

3. After all players have taken a turn, ask the children in
   each group to find the total number of points scored by
   the members of their team. Give them plenty of time to
   solve the problem. Remind those who finish early to
   check their work and to try to find another way to solve
   the problem.

4. Encourage children to share different ways that team
   members' points can be added. Ask them to look for
   ways to simplify the problem. For example, add all of
   the tens first, or look for combinations of numbers that
   are easier to add.

5. Which team is ahead at halftime? By how many points?
   Allow plenty of time for solving the problem and for
   sharing strategies.

Follow the same routine to find both teams' scores in the
second half of the game. For greater student participation,
choose different children to roll the die and record the
scores.

After children have figured out the second-half scores, ask
them to find out which team won the game. By how many
points?

Adjusting the Activity As the teams play, watch for
children who are having difficulty. You may need to
rearrange some of the groups so that more skilled
children can help others; or you may need to provide
additional whole-group interactions over a period of
time before this game becomes one that children can
handle easily as an independent group activity.

◆ Playing *Basketball Addition*
(*Math Journal 2,* p. 173; *Math Masters,* p. 130)

SMALL-GROUP ACTIVITY

Divide the class into groups—each group having two
teams of 3–5 players each. Each group keeps score on the
scoreboard on only one player's journal page. That way,
children may play the game several times, using a
different player's journal for each new game.

Ongoing Learning & Practice

◆ Using Estimation and the Trade-First Algorithm (*Math Journal 2*, p. 171)

INDEX ACTIVITY

Children complete the journal page by calculating the differences whose estimates were more than 50. The answers to Problems 3, 5, and 8 are 67, 62, and 59, respectively. For children who did not have time to work on this page in Lesson 7.3, let them do so now.

◆ Math Boxes 7.4 (*Math Journal 2*, p. 174)

INDEPENDENT ACTIVITY

Mixed Review This journal page provides opportunities for cumulative review or assessment of concepts and skills.

◆ Home Link 7.4 (*Math Masters*, p. 333)

Home Connection Children add 3 or more 1-digit and 2-digit numbers. They should be encouraged to add the numbers in several different ways.

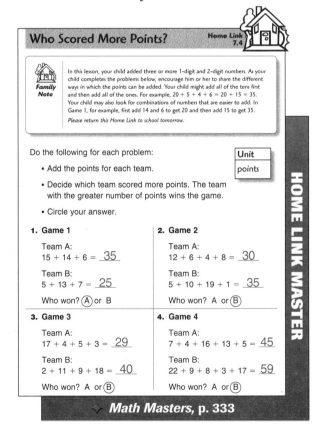

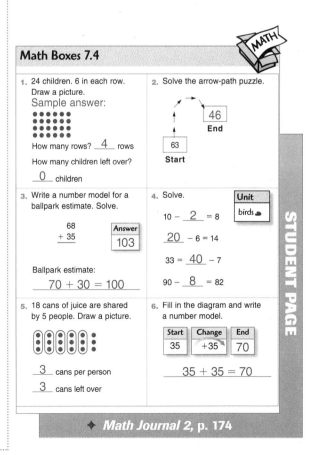

Materials □ number cards 0–20

Players 2

Directions

- Shuffle the cards. Place the deck number-side down.
- Turn over the top 3 cards. Each partner writes the 3 numbers.
- Add the numbers. Write a number model to show the order in which you added.
- Compare your answers with your partner's.

Example Numbers and number models vary in Problems 1–6.

The cards 6, 5, and 14 are turned over. Gillian records the numbers. She adds 14 and 6 first and then adds 5. She records her number model and compares her answer with her partner's.

Numbers: _6_, _5_, _14_ Number model: _14_ + _6_ + _5_ = 25

1. Numbers: ___, ___, ___
   Number model:

   ___ + ___ + ___ = ___

2. Numbers: ___, ___, ___
   Number model:

   ___ + ___ + ___ = ___

3. Numbers: ___, ___, ___
   Number model:

   ___ = ___ + ___ + ___

4. Numbers: ___, ___, ___
   Number model:

   ___ = ___ + ___ + ___

5. Numbers: ___, ___, ___
   Number model:

   ___ + ___ + ___ = ___

6. Numbers: ___, ___, ___
   Number model:

   ___ + ___ + ___ = ___

STUDENT PAGE

✦ *Math Journal 1*, p. 133

Three Addends Record Sheet

For each turn:

- Write the 3 numbers.
- Add the numbers.

Numbers and number models vary.

- Write a number model to show the order in which you added.

1. Numbers: ___, ___, ___
   Number model:

   ___ + ___ + ___ = ___

2. Numbers: ___, ___, ___
   Number model:

   ___ + ___ + ___ = ___

3. Numbers: ___, ___, ___
   Number model:

   ___ = ___ + ___ + ___

4. Numbers: ___, ___, ___
   Number model:

   ___ = ___ + ___ + ___

5. Numbers: ___, ___, ___
   Number model:

   ___ + ___ + ___ = ___

6. Numbers: ___, ___, ___
   Number model:

   ___ + ___ + ___ = ___

7. Numbers: ___, ___, ___
   Number model:

   ___ + ___ + ___ = ___

8. Numbers: ___, ___, ___
   Number model:

   ___ + ___ + ___ = ___

9. Numbers: ___, ___, ___
   Number model:

   ___ = ___ + ___ + ___

10. Numbers: ___, ___, ___
    Number model:

    ___ = ___ + ___ + ___

TEACHING MASTER

✦ *Math Masters*, p. 101

---

3 Options for Individualizing

◆ **RETEACHING** **Using Base-10 Blocks to Add**
(*Math Masters*, p. 102)

INDEPENDENT ACTIVITY   **15–30 min**

Have children represent each addend with the least number of base-10 blocks—longs and cubes—possible. Consider the problem 12 + 17 + 8 = __. Children display the following on *Math Masters*, page 102:

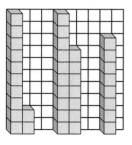

12 + 17 + 8 = ?

Encourage children to look for a combination that will result in trading ones for tens or making tens. *For example:*

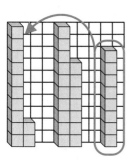

12 + 8 + 17 = ?
20 + 17 = 37

◆ **RETEACHING** **Playing *Three Addends***
(*Math Journal 1*, p. 133; *Math Masters*, p. 101)

PARTNER ACTIVITY   **15–30 min**

Three Addends provides practice with adding three 1-digit numbers. Some children may benefit from playing this game several times before playing *Basketball Addition*. Directions for the game can be found on the journal page. An additional record sheet is provided on *Math Masters*, page 101.

7.5 Patterns in Doubles and Halves

OBJECTIVE To practice repeated doubling and halving.

summaries	materials

1 Teaching the Lesson

Read a story that illustrates how quickly numbers increase through doubling and how quickly they decrease through halving. [Operations and Computation; Patterns, Functions, and Algebra]

- ☐ *Math Journal 2*, p. 175
- ☐ Home Link 7.4
- ☐ calculator

2 Ongoing Learning & Practice

Children practice finding differences between 2-digit numbers and higher multiples of ten by playing *Hit the Target*. [Operations and Computation]

Children practice and maintain skills through Math Boxes and Home Link activities.

- ☐ *Math Journal 2*, p. 176
- ☐ Teaching Master (*Math Masters*, p. 128; optional)
- ☐ Home Link Masters (*Math Masters*, pp. 334 and 335)
- ☐ calculator

3 Options for Individualizing

Enrichment Children read various literature selections that illustrate doubling and finding halves of numbers; children identify similarities and differences among some of the stories. [Operations and Computation; Patterns, Functions, and Algebra]

Language Diversity Children use visual images to double numbers and find halves of numbers. [Operations and Computation; Patterns, Functions, and Algebra]

- ☐ children's literature selections
- ☐ Teaching Master (*Math Masters*, p. 25)

See **Advance Preparation**

Additional Information

Advance Preparation Before beginning the optional Enrichment activity in Part 3, obtain the following books: *Melisande* by E. Nesbit (Candlewick Press, 1989), *The King's Chessboard* by David Birch (Dial Books for Young Readers, 1988), *One Grain of Rice: A Mathematical Folktale* by Demi (Scholastic Press, 1997), *The Token Gift* by Hugh William McKibbon (Annick Press, 1996), *Two of Everything: A Chinese Folktale* by Lily Toy Hong (Albert Whitman & Co., 1993), and *Anno's Magic Seeds* by Mitsumasa Anno (Philomel Books, 1994).

Vocabulary • half • double

Getting Started

Mental Math and Reflexes

Write the following problems on the board:

? = 9 + 3 + 11 + 17 40
? = 12 + 13 + 17 + 8 50
25 + 4 + 16 + 15 = ? 60
33 + 25 + 25 + 17 = ? 100

Math Message

Rule	in	out
double	5	10
	4	8
	7	14
	6	12

Home Link 7.4 Follow-Up

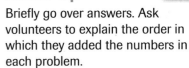

Briefly go over answers. Ask volunteers to explain the order in which they added the numbers in each problem.

---

1 Teaching the Lesson

◆ Math Message Follow-Up

WHOLE-CLASS ACTIVITY

Talk about the relationship between doubling an amount and finding half of it. For example, **half** of 12 can be thought of as "What do you **double** to get 12?"

◆ Doubling and Halving Numbers
(*Math Journal 2*, p. 175)

WHOLE-CLASS ACTIVITY

Read "The Wubbles" to the class as part of an activity that involves doubling and halving.

The Wubbles

Wubbles are very well-behaved and they brush their teeth regularly. You would like to play with one—for a short time. The trouble with Wubbles is that they double. When Wubbles go to sleep, they double and wake up twins.

Suppose your mother let you invite a friend to spend spring vacation at your house. You invite your friend, who is a Wubble. After school on Friday, you and the Wubble go home, play, eat dinner, play some more, and go to bed.

Sometime during the night, while you are sleeping, there is a slight POP! and the Wubble splits into two Wubbles.

On Friday there was 1 Wubble.

STUDENT PAGE

The Wubbles

1. On each line, write the number of Wubbles after doubling. Use your calculator to help you.

   You started on Friday with __1__ Wubble.

   On Saturday, there were __2__ Wubbles.

   On Sunday, there were __4__ Wubbles.

   On Monday, there will be __8__ Wubbles.

   On Tuesday, there will be __16__ Wubbles.

   On Wednesday, there will be __32__ Wubbles.

   On Thursday, there will be __64__ Wubbles.

   On Friday, there will be __128__ Wubbles.

   A Wubble

2. On each line, write the number of Wubbles after halving. Use your calculator to help you. Remember that "$\frac{1}{2}$ of " means "divide by 2."

   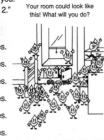
   Your room could look like this! What will you do?

   There were __128__ Wubbles.

   After Wink 1, there were __64__ Wubbles.

   After Wink 2, there were __32__ Wubbles.

   After Wink 3, there were __16__ Wubbles.

   After Wink 4, there were __8__ Wubbles.

   After Wink 5, there were __4__ Wubbles.

   After Wink 6, there were __2__ Wubbles.

   After Wink 7, there was __1__ Wubble.

   Adapted with permission from *Calculator Mathematics Book 2* by Sheila Sconiers, pp. 10 and 11 (Everyday Learning Corporation. © 1990 by the University of Chicago).

◆ *Math Journal 2*, p. 175

Saturday morning, there were 2 Wubbles. You're a little worried because your mother said you could have only one friend for the week. So the Wubbles take turns playing with you while one hides in your room.

That night both Wubbles go to sleep. You are very curious, so you stay awake and, sure enough, just before sunrise early Sunday morning, you hear one POP! Then you hear another POP! Now there are 4 Wubbles in your room!

What to do? What to do? You decide to hide the Wubbles and again have them take turns coming out to play. You are very worried, though. If things keep going like this, you will have a lot of Wubbles to hide by the end of vacation week. You decide not to panic but to figure out how many Wubbles there could be by next Friday morning.

At this point in the story, stop reading. Children complete the first half of journal page 175. Ask what happens to the Wubbles every night. They double in number. It may be helpful for you or a child to draw on the board the Wubbles that will be in the room on Sunday 4 and on Monday 8.

Partners may use calculators to figure out how many Wubbles there are each morning. Ask children to share their strategies for doubling.

After everyone has finished doubling the Wubbles, briefly discuss the question to the right of Problem 2 on the journal page, "What will you do?" Tell children that there is more to the story and continue reading.

There you are with your room full of Wubbles. So far, your mother hasn't seen them all, and you have to find a way to get them out of the house before she discovers them. One of the Wubbles asks you why you look so worried. You explain that you're supposed to have only one friend visiting.

The Wubble laughs and tells you that there is an easy solution. It says, "If you blink with half of your eyes, half of us will disappear." This sounds like a riddle. What does it mean to "blink with half of your eyes"? (Pause) You think awhile and then you wink. Sure enough, a whole lot of Wubbles disappear.

Adapted with permission from *Calculator Mathematics Book 2* by Sheila Sconiers, pp. 10 and 11 (Everyday Learning Corporation, © 1990 by the University of Chicago).

Adjusting the Activity Demonstrate how to use a calculator to show the doubling of Wubbles. Press 2 ⊗ ⊜ ⊜ ⊜ .... The calculator display will show 2, 4, 8, 16, ... Children will be amazed at how fast the numbers grow. (The keying sequence just given may not work for all calculators; however, the sequence 2 ⊗ 2 ⊜ ⊗ 2 ⊜ ⊗ 2 ⊜ ... will always work.)

Ask children what happens to the Wubbles when you wink. Half of them disappear.

Share strategies for halving the numbers of Wubbles. Remind children that to find half of a number, you can divide it by 2 (make 2 equal parts), or ask what number to double to get that number. You had 128 Wubbles in your room. After Wink 1, there were half that number. How many Wubbles are left? 64

Keep winking! Partners complete the second half of their journal pages by halving the numbers of Wubbles.

After everyone has finished (and you are back to 1 Wubble), ask what would happen if you winked again. There would be $\frac{1}{2}$ of a Wubble left.

Draw a Wubble on the board. Erase half of it. What if you winked once more? $\frac{1}{2}$ of $\frac{1}{2}$ of a Wubble Erase $\frac{1}{2}$ of the half-Wubble. Continue dividing the last Wubble by erasing half of the remaining picture each time.

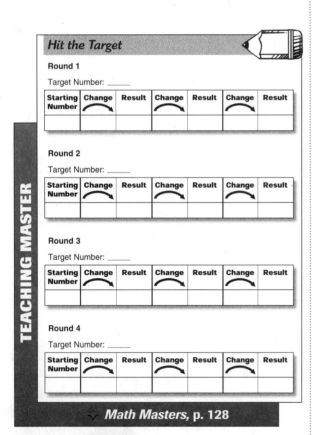

Adjusting the Activity If children have difficulty imagining $\frac{1}{2}$ of $\frac{1}{2}$ of a Wubble, suggest these more familiar examples:

- What is half of a dollar? 50 cents And what is half of 50 cents (half of half of a dollar)? 25 cents, or a quarter

- (Draw a pizza, divided into quarters.) If you eat half of the pizza, how much is left? 2 pieces, or a half-pizza If you eat half of what is left, how much is left then? 1 piece, or a quarter-pizza

 Ongoing Learning & Practice

◆ **Playing *Hit the Target***
(*Math Masters,* p. 128)

PARTNER ACTIVITY

This game was introduced in Lesson 7.3 and gives children practice in finding the difference between 2-digit numbers and higher multiples of 10. As children continue to play the game, their responses should become essentially automatic. Some children may need a copy of *Math Masters,* page 128 to keep a record of their play.

✓ **ONGOING ASSESSMENT**
Use the record sheet for *Hit the Target* to assess children's ability to find the difference between 2-digit numbers and any higher multiple of 10. Identify children who can find the difference in one step and those who begin by finding the next-higher multiple of 10.

◆ Math Boxes 7.5 (*Math Journal 2*, p. 176)

INDEPENDENT ACTIVITY

Mixed Review This journal page provides opportunities for cumulative review or assessment of concepts and skills.

◆ Home Link 7.5 (*Math Masters*, pp. 334 and 335)

Home Connection Children solve doubling and halving problems. They fill in a rule box and a "What's My Rule?" table, complete Frames-and-Arrows diagrams, and solve a number story.

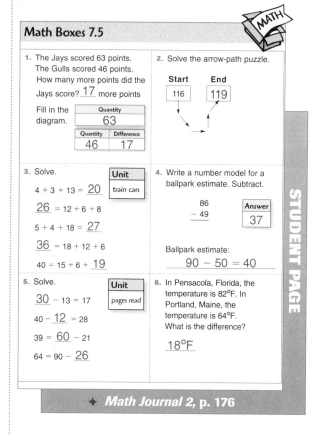

Math Boxes 7.5

1. The Jays scored 63 points. The Gulls scored 46 points. How many more points did the Jays score? __17__ more points

   Fill in the diagram.

Quantity
63

Quantity	Difference
46	17

2. Solve the arrow-path puzzle.

   Start 116   **End** 119

3. Solve.   **Unit** train cars

   $4 + 3 + 13 = \underline{20}$

   $\underline{26} = 12 + 6 + 8$

   $5 + 4 + 18 = \underline{27}$

   $\underline{36} = 18 + 12 + 6$

   $40 = 15 + 6 + \underline{19}$

4. Write a number model for a ballpark estimate. Subtract.

   $\begin{array}{r} 86 \\ -\ 49 \\ \end{array}$ **Answer** 37

   Ballpark estimate:

   $90 - 50 = 40$

5. Solve.   **Unit** pages read

   $\underline{30} - 13 = 17$

   $40 - \underline{12} = 28$

   $39 = \underline{60} - 21$

   $64 = 90 - \underline{26}$

6. In Pensacola, Florida, the temperature is 82°F. In Portland, Maine, the temperature is 64°F. What is the difference?

   18°F

Math Journal 2, p. 176

STUDENT PAGE

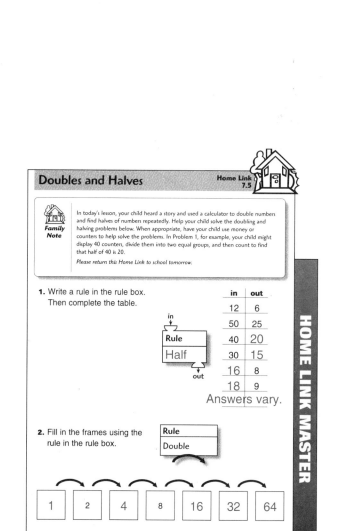

Doubles and Halves   Home Link 7.5

Family Note In today's lesson, your child heard a story and used a calculator to double numbers and find halves of numbers repeatedly. Help your child solve the doubling and halving problems below. When appropriate, have your child use money or counters to help solve the problems. In Problem 1, for example, your child might display 40 counters, divide them into two equal groups, and then count to find that half of 40 is 20.

Please return this Home Link to school tomorrow.

1. Write a rule in the rule box. Then complete the table.

   Rule Half

in	out
12	6
50	25
40	20
30	15
16	8
18	9

   Answers vary.

2. Fill in the frames using the rule in the rule box.

   Rule Double

   1 → 2 → 4 → 8 → 16 → 32 → 64

Math Masters, p. 334

HOME LINK MASTER

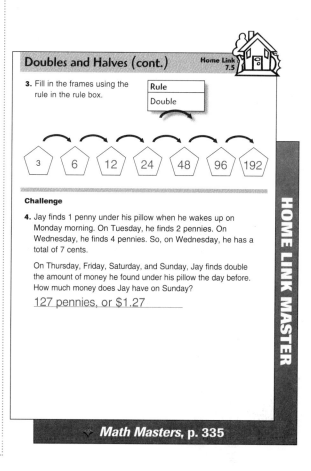

Doubles and Halves (cont.)   Home Link 7.5

3. Fill in the frames using the rule in the rule box.

   Rule Double

   3 → 6 → 12 → 24 → 48 → 96 → 192

Challenge

4. Jay finds 1 penny under his pillow when he wakes up on Monday morning. On Tuesday, he finds 2 pennies. On Wednesday, he finds 4 pennies. So, on Wednesday, he has a total of 7 cents.

   On Thursday, Friday, Saturday, and Sunday, Jay finds double the amount of money he found under his pillow the day before. How much money does Jay have on Sunday?

   127 pennies, or $1.27

Math Masters, p. 335

HOME LINK MASTER

Options for Individualizing

◆ **ENRICHMENT** Doubling and Halving
Situations Found in Literature

WHOLE-CLASS ACTIVITY 15–30 min

Literature Link Read the following books to
children, or have them read the books themselves.

Melisande

Summary: Cursed by an evil fairy at her christening,
Princess Melisande grows up bald. She wishes for, and is
granted, golden hair a yard long that grows an inch every
day. Her hair grows twice as fast every time it is cut.

Two of Everything: A Chinese Folktale

Summary: This is a simple story of a curious brass pot
that doubles whatever is put into it.

Anno's Magic Seeds

Summary: This challenging book on number patterns is
based on a magic seed and the number of seeds it
produces when planted.

The King's Chessboard;
One Grain of Rice: A Mathematical Folktale;
The Token Gift

Summary: Each of these stories is a version of a classic
folktale that explores the power of doubling. The common
theme is grains of rice that are doubled each day. For
example, on the first day, there is 1 grain of rice; on the
second day, 2 grains of rice; on the third day, 4 grains of
rice; and so on.

◆ **LANGUAGE DIVERSITY** Visual Images for
Doubles and Halves (*Math Masters,* p. 25)

SMALL-GROUP ACTIVITY 5–15 min

Math Masters, page 25 was offered in Lesson 2.3 to help
children visualize doubles facts. It may be a useful way to
reinforce the idea of doubling and halving with simple
numbers. For example, show the picture of two hands.
Ask, *What is half of 10 fingers?* Cover up one of the hands.
5 fingers With one of the hands still covered, ask, *What is
double 5 fingers?* Show both of the hands. 10 fingers

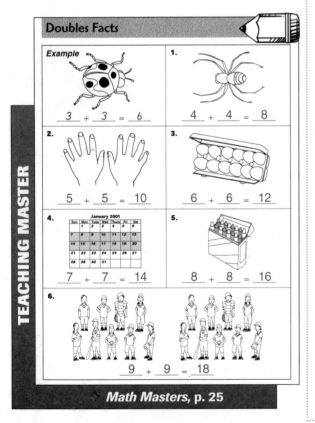

TEACHING MASTER

Doubles Facts

Example

$3 + 3 = 6$

1.

$4 + 4 = 8$

2.

$5 + 5 = 10$

3.

$6 + 6 = 12$

4.

January 2001

$7 + 7 = 14$

5.

$8 + 8 = 16$

6.

$9 + 9 = 18$

Math Masters, p. 25

7.6

EXPLORATIONS

Exploring Weights and Scales, Equal Sharing, and Block Patterns

OBJECTIVES To read weights in pounds on a bath scale; to develop readiness for division; and to explore area and patterns.

summaries

materials

1 Teaching the Lesson

Exploration A: Children practice reading a bath scale; children estimate weights and then weigh objects on a bath scale. [Measurement and Reference Frames]

Exploration B: Children solve a problem involving the equal sharing of money. [Operations and Computation; Measurement and Reference Frames]

Exploration C: Children use two pattern-block shapes to create a continuous pattern—a pattern that leaves no spaces between blocks. [Geometry]

☐ Home Link 7.5

Exploration A: Per group:
☐ Teaching Master (*Math Masters,* p. 131)
☐ bath scale(s); half-sheets of paper
☐ set of books weighing more than a total of 15 pounds
☐ 5-pound bag of flour (optional)

Exploration B: Per group:
☐ Teaching Master (*Math Masters,* p. 132)
☐ Teaching Aid Assessment Master (*Math Masters,* p. 498)
☐ money per group: one $5 bill, five $1 bills, 4 quarters, 10 dimes, 20 nickels, and 100 pennies
☐ half-sheet of paper

Exploration C: Per partnership:
☐ Teaching Master (*Math Masters,* p. 133)
☐ Pattern-Block Template; pattern blocks
☐ *A Cloak for the Dreamer* (optional)
***See* Advance Preparation**

2 Ongoing Learning & Practice

Children practice finding differences between 2-digit numbers and higher multiples of 10 by playing *Hit the Target.* [Operations and Computation]

Children practice and maintain skills through Math Boxes and Home Link activities.

☐ *Math Journal 2,* p. 177
☐ Teaching Master (*Math Masters,* p. 128; optional)
☐ Home Link Master (*Math Masters,* p. 336)
☐ calculator

3 Options for Individualizing

Extra Practice Children practice identifying different shapes. [Geometry]

☐ *Minute Math®,* pp. 17 and 18

Additional Information

Advance Preparation For the Math Message, select one book that weighs about 1 pound and another that weighs about 3 pounds. Place these near the problem.

For Exploration A, obtain a bath scale (more than one, if available) with an analog display. A scale with a digital display is optional. Gather together a set of books whose total weight exceeds 15 pounds. Include several heavy books that weigh at least 5 pounds each. For Exploration C, you may want to obtain *A Cloak for the Dreamer* by Aileen Friedman (A Marilyn Burns Brainy Day Book. Scholastic, 1994).

Getting Started

Mental Math and Reflexes

Pose doubling and halving number stories.
Suggestions:

- Marta's allowance was $2.00 per week. Her parents decided to double it. What is her new allowance? $4.00
- Grace's allowance was $1.50 per week. Her parents decided to double it. What is her new allowance? $3.00
- Quentin's new allowance is $5.00. What was his allowance before his parents decided to double it? $2.50

Math Message

Lift each book and hold it. Estimate how many pounds each book weighs. Write down your estimates.

Home Link 7.5 Follow-Up

Ask children to share the strategies that they used to solve the Challenge problem.

This illustration shows the proper way to lift a heavy object so that injuries are avoided.

Measuring Weight with a Bath Scale

1. Place books on a bath scale. Try to make a stack of books that weighs about 5 pounds. Lift the stack of books and feel the weight of that stack.

2. Start again. Make a stack of books that weighs about 10 pounds. Then lift the stack and feel the weight.

3. Start again. Make a stack of books that weighs about 15 pounds. Then lift the stack and feel the weight.

Make a 5-pound stack of books.

Make a 10-pound stack of books.

Make a 15-pound stack of books.

4. Make a stack of books on the floor. Estimate how much your stack weighs. Weigh the stack and see how close your estimate was.

5. Repeat with other stacks of books that are different sizes.

Are you getting better at estimating weight?

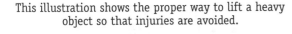

Math Masters, p. 131

---

1 Teaching the Lesson

✦ Math Message Follow-Up

WHOLE-CLASS DISCUSSION

Discuss children's estimates. Expect that many children will have a very poor perception of weight, and be prepared for exaggerated guesses that may be as high as 20 pounds for the heavier book.

✦ Exploration A: Weighing with a Bath Scale
(*Math Masters*, p. 131)

SMALL-GROUP ACTIVITY

This bath scale exploration has two objectives. The first is to have children gain experience in reading the scale. The second is to improve children's perception of weight so that they can make more realistic estimates of weights.

NOTE: Learning a new skill is often difficult. If children are having difficulty reading the bath scale, don't resort to using a scale with a digital display. Consider allowing children to use a scale with a digital display only to check their work.

Before beginning the Exploration, remind children how to lift heavy objects properly to avoid injury. (See the margin.) They should be sure to use their leg muscles as they lift, *not* their back muscles.

Work through Problems 1–3 on *Math Masters,* page 131 with the group, even if you have more than one bath scale available. Help children to understand the scale divisions that are marked on the scale you are using. Some scales have marks at 1-pound intervals, others at 2-pound intervals, and others only at 5-pound intervals.

Pause several times during the building of each stack of books and ask children to report the current weight. When the stack approaches the target weight, it may be necessary to trade some of the books already stacked for others.

Each time a stack of books matches one of the target weights, make sure that every child has the opportunity to lift and feel the weight of that stack.

NOTE: A useful personal reference for weight is a 5-pound bag of flour. Consider having one available for children to see and hold.

Children should complete Problem 4 with minimal guidance.

ONGOING ASSESSMENT

Ask children to divide a half-sheet of paper into 3 columns and to label the columns Estimate, Weight, and Difference. For Problems 4 and 5, have children record their estimates and the actual weights of the stacks they make. Then they calculate the difference. Collect and assess to see if children's skills at estimating weight are improving with practice.

◆ Exploration B: Sharing Money
(*Math Masters,* pp. 132 and 498)

SMALL-GROUP ACTIVITY

Each group is presented with the following problem:

At school, 4 children found an envelope. Inside was a $5 bill. They took the envelope to the principal. A week went by and nobody claimed the money. The principal returned it to the children and said that it now belonged to them.

How would you divide $5 so that each of the children gets the same amount of money?

Adjusting the Activity To extend the activity, one child steps on the scale and reports his weight to the group. The child then stands on the scale while books are handed to him. The weight of the books is calculated by subtracting the weight of the child from the weight of the child holding the books. For example, Theo weighs 63 pounds. While holding 1 book, he weighs 68 pounds. How much does the book weigh? 5 pounds Note that this activity should be done only if weight is not a sensitive issue for any child in your class.

TEACHING MASTER

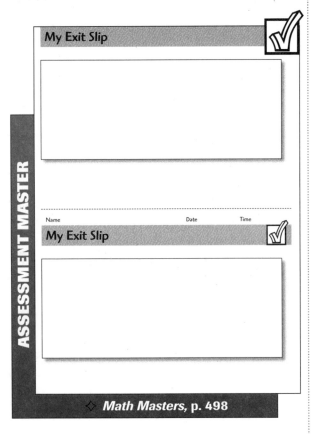

My Exit Slip

Name   Date   Time

My Exit Slip

Math Masters, p. 498

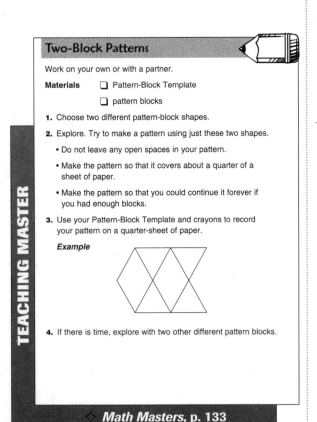

Two-Block Patterns

Work on your own or with a partner.

Materials ❏ Pattern-Block Template
❏ pattern blocks

1. Choose two different pattern-block shapes.

2. Explore. Try to make a pattern using just these two shapes.

   • Do not leave any open spaces in your pattern.

   • Make the pattern so that it covers about a quarter of a sheet of paper.

   • Make the pattern so that you could continue it forever if you had enough blocks.

3. Use your Pattern-Block Template and crayons to record your pattern on a quarter-sheet of paper.

   Example

4. If there is time, explore with two other different pattern blocks.

Math Masters, p. 133

Together each group works out solutions and uses whichever methods group members wish: acting the problem out with bills and coins, mental arithmetic, or paper-and-pencil procedures.

After children have satisfactorily solved the problem, they make up other problems for dividing amounts of money equally among 4 or 5 children.

 Adjusting the Activity For children who are having difficulty making up their own problems, provide several suggestions:

▷ $8.00 shared equally among 5 people $1.60 each

▷ $9.00 shared equally among 10 people $0.90 each

▷ $5.00 shared equally among 3 children $1.66 each, with 2 cents left over

▷ $5.00 shared equally among 8 children $0.62 each, with 4 cents left over

ONGOING ASSESSMENT

Sometimes it is beneficial for children to focus on how they work in a small group. At the conclusion of this activity, you may want to have children answer questions such as the following on an Exit Slip:

· What worked well in your group today?

· What could you have done to help your group work better?

· What do you like or dislike about working in a group?

◆ Exploration C: Creating Two-Block Patterns
(*Math Masters*, p. 133)

PARTNER ACTIVITY

Individuals or partners choose two different pattern-block shapes and create a continuous pattern that will cover an area of about a quarter-sheet of paper.

Children record their patterns, using their Pattern-Block Templates and crayons. They may create more than one pattern. Consider making a bulletin board display or a class book of the patterns.

Adjusting the Activity If children are unclear about what it means to create a pattern without any open spaces, demonstrate with single pattern blocks. Each of the pattern blocks can be used to create a pattern without any open spaces.

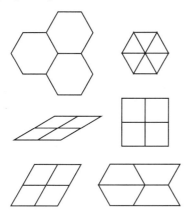

Literature Link *A Cloak for the Dreamer* by Aileen Friedman (A Marilyn Burns Brainy Day Book. Scholastic, 1994) tells the story of tailors designing patchwork cloaks. One is made from rectangles, another from triangles, and a third from squares. The fourth is unacceptable because it is made from circles and is full of open spaces. The tailor thinks of a unique way to fix the cloak.

2 Ongoing Learning & Practice

◆ Playing *Hit the Target* (*Math Masters*, p. 128)

PARTNER ACTIVITY

This game provides children with practice in finding differences between 2-digit numbers and higher multiples of 10. This game was introduced in Lesson 7.3 and played again in Lesson 7.5.

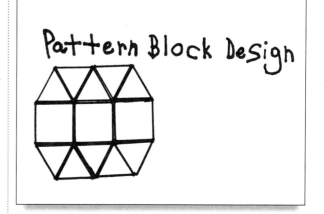

Children explore the concept of area by creating continuous patterns.

Hit the Target

Round 1

Target Number: _____

Starting Number	Change	Result	Change	Result	Change	Result

Round 2

Target Number: _____

Starting Number	Change	Result	Change	Result	Change	Result

Round 3

Target Number: _____

Starting Number	Change	Result	Change	Result	Change	Result

Round 4

Target Number: _____

Starting Number	Change	Result	Change	Result	Change	Result

◆ *Math Masters, p. 128*

TEACHING MASTER

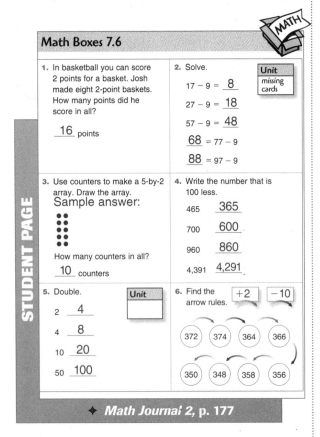

Math Boxes 7.6

1. In basketball you can score 2 points for a basket. Josh made eight 2-point baskets. How many points did he score in all?

___16___ points

2. Solve.

Unit
missing
cards

$17 - 9 =$ __8__

$27 - 9 =$ __18__

$57 - 9 =$ __48__

__68__ $= 77 - 9$

__88__ $= 97 - 9$

3. Use counters to make a 5-by-2 array. Draw the array.
Sample answer:

How many counters in all?

___10___ counters

4. Write the number that is 100 less.

465 ___365___

700 ___600___

960 ___860___

4,391 ___4,291___

5. Double.

Unit

2 ___4___

4 ___8___

10 ___20___

50 ___100___

6. Find the arrow rules. $+2$ -10

372 374 364 366

350 348 358 356

STUDENT PAGE

◆ **Math Boxes 7.6** (*Math Journal 2*, p. 177)

INDEPENDENT ACTIVITY 👤

Mixed Review This journal page provides opportunities for cumulative review or assessment of concepts and skills.

◆ **Home Link 7.6** (*Math Masters*, p. 336)

Home Connection Children determine the best estimate of weight for a variety of items.

3 Options for Individualizing

◆ **EXTRA PRACTICE** Minute Math

SMALL-GROUP ACTIVITY 👥👥 5–15 min

To offer children more experience with identifying shapes, see the following pages in *Minute Math:*

Basic Routines: pp. 17 and 18

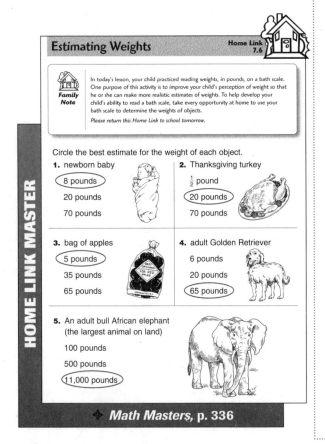

Estimating Weights

Home Link 7.6

Family Note

In today's lesson, your child practiced reading weights, in pounds, on a bath scale. One purpose of this activity is to improve your child's perception of weight so that he or she can make more realistic estimates of weights. To help develop your child's ability to read a bath scale, take every opportunity at home to use your bath scale to determine the weights of objects.

Please return this Home Link to school tomorrow.

Circle the best estimate for the weight of each object.

1. newborn baby

⬭ 8 pounds

20 pounds

70 pounds

2. Thanksgiving turkey

$\frac{1}{2}$ pound

⬭ 20 pounds

70 pounds

3. bag of apples

⬭ 5 pounds

35 pounds

65 pounds

4. adult Golden Retriever

6 pounds

20 pounds

⬭ 65 pounds

5. An adult bull African elephant (the largest animal on land)

100 pounds

500 pounds

⬭ 11,000 pounds

HOME LINK MASTER

7.7 Data Day: Standing Jumps and Arm Spans

OBJECTIVE To measure length to the nearest centimeter and to the nearest inch.

summaries	materials
1 Teaching the Lesson	
Children measure the length of a standing long jump in centimeters and the length of an arm span in inches. [Measurement and Reference Frames]	☐ *Math Journal 2*, pp. 178 and 179 ☐ Home Link 7.6 ☐ tape measure ☐ masking tape for starting lines ☐ chalk or penny to use as a marker ***See* Advance Preparation**
2 Ongoing Learning & Practice	
Children practice finding the total number of items in an array by playing *Array Bingo*. [Operations and Computation; Numeration] Children practice and maintain skills through Math Boxes and Home Link activities.	☐ *Math Journal 2*, p. 180 ☐ Home Link Masters (*Math Masters*, pp. 337 and 338) ☐ 2 six-sided dice, 1 twelve-sided die, or an egg-carton number generator per group ☐ 9 cards labeled "A" cut from *Math Masters*, p. 117 ☐ 7 cards not labeled "A" cut from *Math Masters*, p. 117 (optional) ☐ Teaching Masters (*Math Masters*, pp. 118 and 119) ☐ 1 twenty-sided die or number cards with one card for each of the numbers 1–20 per partnership or group (from the Everything Math Deck, optional) ☐ ruler
3 Options for Individualizing	
Enrichment Children make up and solve number stories about the greatest leaps of different animals. [Operations and Computation; Measurement and Reference Frames] **Language Diversity** Children discuss the various meanings of the word *span*. [Measurement and Reference Frames]	☐ Teaching Masters (*Math Masters*, pp. 22 and 134)

Additional Information

Advance Preparation Be sure to include the simple stick figure on the next page when you write the Math Message problem on the board.

For the standing long jump activity in Part 1, use masking tape to make lines on the floor in various spots in the classroom. Children will use these lines as starting lines.

Vocabulary • arm span

Getting Started

Mental Math and Reflexes

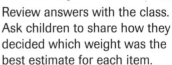

Pose addition and subtraction problems involving multiples of 10.

48 + __ = 90   42

60 = __ + 34   26

50 − 15 = __   35

__ + 23 = 70   47

__ = 80 − 31   49

60 − 17 = __   43

Math Message

A friend measures your arm span in inches.

Another friend measures your arm span in centimeters.

Who do you think will report the larger number?

Draw the simple figure in the margin below on the board.

Home Link 7.6 Follow-Up

Review answers with the class. Ask children to share how they decided which weight was the best estimate for each item.

NOTE: Remind children of the "2-inch, no zap" rule from Unit 4: Do not "zap" the tape measure until no more than 2 inches are showing. Following this rule will extend the life of the tape measures.

---

1 Teaching the Lesson

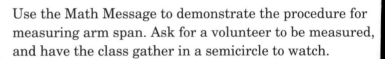

✦ Math Message Follow-Up

WHOLE-CLASS ACTIVITY

Use the Math Message to demonstrate the procedure for measuring arm span. Ask for a volunteer to be measured, and have the class gather in a semicircle to watch.

The volunteer stands with arms fully extended. **Arm span** is the distance from fingertip to fingertip across outstretched arms. Have one student helper hold the end of the tape measure at the tip of the volunteer's right middle finger. Pull the tape tight across the child's chest. Have a second helper hold the tape at the tip of the volunteer's left middle finger and read the tape to the nearest inch. Turn the tape over, repeat the procedure, and read the tape to the nearest centimeter.

Do you get a larger number when you measure in inches or in centimeters? centimeters Why? Centimeters are smaller units of length than inches. You can fit more centimeters than inches in the arm span.

Repeat this routine several times, using different volunteers and student helpers. Check that the measurements reported are correct to the nearest inch and the nearest centimeter.

✦ Collecting and Recording Standing Long Jump Data (*Math Journal 2,* p. 178)

SMALL-GROUP ACTIVITY

Divide the class into groups of four. Children will remain in these groups for both data activities. Each activity wil focus on a single unit of length. For standing long jumps, all measurements will be in centimeters. For arm spans, all measurements will be in inches.

Children are to make two jumps and record the length of each jump on the journal page. Discuss how the data for the jumps will be gathered. One teacher reported success using the following procedure:

1. Assign a job to each group member.

   ▷ The "Jumper" jumps.

   ▷ The "Line Judge" sees that the Jumper's toes don't cross the line.

   ▷ The "Marker" marks where the Jumper lands.

   ▷ The "Measurer" measures the length of the jump with the Jumper's help.

   ▷ When the Jumper has finished jumping, group members rotate jobs so that each child eventually performs all of the different jobs. (See the margin.)

2. Show how to place a chalk dot, penny, or other marker where the Jumper's back heel lands and how to measure from the starting line to the marker. The jumps are measured to the nearest centimeter.

3. Demonstrate a practice jump. The toes of both feet should be just touching the starting line. There is no running start. No step back may be taken.

4. Let each child take several practice jumps before measuring a jump.

5. Each Jumper makes two jumps that are measured. They record their own jumps in their journals. They also record which jump is longer. All measurements should be in centimeters.

NOTE: The standing long jump data recorded on the journal page will be used in the following lesson. A middle value (median) length of the jumps will be found at that time.

♦ **Collecting and Recording Arm Span Data**
(*Math Journal 2*, p. 179)

SMALL-GROUP ACTIVITY

Children follow the routine for collecting arm span data that was demonstrated in the Math Message Follow-Up. As you circulate, ensure that all children are taking a turn reading the tape measure. Assist children who have difficulty reading measures between the inch marks. If a measure falls exactly on the half-inch mark, tell children to report the next higher inch.

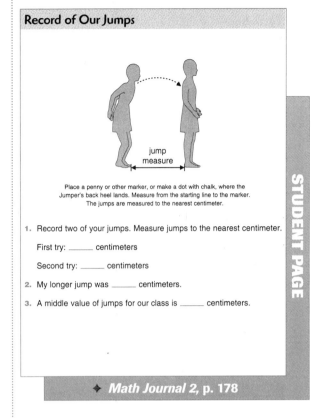

Record of Our Jumps

Place a penny or other marker, or make a dot with chalk, where the Jumper's back heel lands. Measure from the starting line to the marker. The jumps are measured to the nearest centimeter.

1. Record two of your jumps. Measure jumps to the nearest centimeter.

   First try: _____ centimeters

   Second try: _____ centimeters

2. My longer jump was _____ centimeters.

3. A middle value of jumps for our class is _____ centimeters.

♦ *Math Journal 2*, p. 178

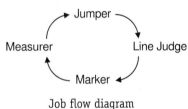

Job flow diagram

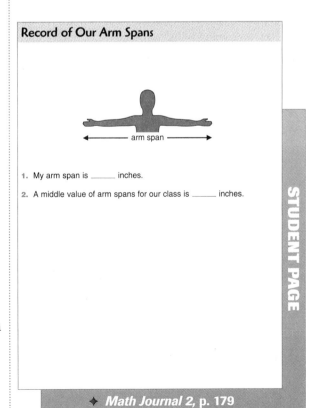

Record of Our Arm Spans

1. My arm span is _____ inches.

2. A middle value of arm spans for our class is _____ inches.

♦ *Math Journal 2*, p. 179

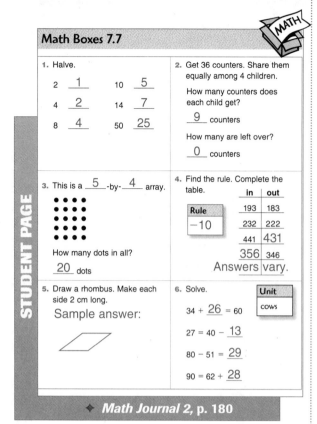

Math Boxes 7.7

1. Halve.

2 __1__   10 __5__

4 __2__   14 __7__

8 __4__   50 __25__

2. Get 36 counters. Share them equally among 4 children.

How many counters does each child get?

__9__ counters

How many are left over?

__0__ counters

3. This is a __5__ -by- __4__ array.

How many dots in all?

__20__ dots

4. Find the rule. Complete the table.

Rule	in	out
−10	193	183
	232	222
	441	431
	356	346

Answers vary.

5. Draw a rhombus. Make each side 2 cm long.

Sample answer:

6. Solve.

Unit
cows

34 + __26__ = 60

27 = 40 − __13__

80 − 51 = __29__

90 = 62 + __28__

◆ *Math Journal 2, p. 180*

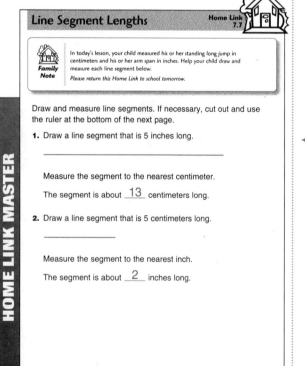

Line Segment Lengths

Home Link
7.7

Family Note

In today's lesson, your child measured his or her standing long jump in centimeters and his or her arm span in inches. Help your child draw and measure each line segment below.

Please return this Home Link to school tomorrow.

Draw and measure line segments. If necessary, cut out and use the ruler at the bottom of the next page.

1. Draw a line segment that is 5 inches long.

_____

Measure the segment to the nearest centimeter.

The segment is about __13__ centimeters long.

2. Draw a line segment that is 5 centimeters long.

_____

Measure the segment to the nearest inch.

The segment is about __2__ inches long.

◆ *Math Masters, p. 337*

Children record their own arm spans in their journals. All arm span measurements should be to the nearest inch.

NOTE: The arm span data recorded on the journal page will be used in Lesson 7.9. A middle value (median) length of the arm spans will be found at that time.

 Adjusting the Activity To extend the activity, groups that finish early may also want to measure and record their members' arm spans to the nearest centimeter.

❷ Ongoing Learning & Practice

◆ **Playing *Array Bingo*** (*Math Masters*, pp. 117–119)

SMALL-GROUP ACTIVITY

This game gives children practice in identifying arrays with a certain number of dots. Directions for *Array Bingo* were given on *Math Masters*, pages 118 and 119. The *Array Bingo* cards are found on *Math Masters*, page 117. This game was introduced in Lesson 6.10.

◆ **Math Boxes 7.7** (*Math Journal 2*, p. 180)

INDEPENDENT ACTIVITY

MATH **Mixed Review** This journal page provides opportunities for cumulative review or assessment of concepts and skills.

◆ **Home Link 7.7** (*Math Masters*, pp. 337 and 338)

Home Connection Children draw line segments using one unit of length; they then measure those segments using a different unit of length.

3 Options for Individualizing

◆ ENRICHMENT Making up and Solving Number Stories (*Math Masters*, pp. 22 and 134)

INDEPENDENT ACTIVITY   15–30 min

Portfolio Ideas

After completing the standing long jump activity, some children may be interested in learning about the jumping capabilities of adults, as well as other animals.

Children use the data from the Amazing Leaps master to make up stories for the class to solve. Point out that the jump lengths are for the *greatest* distances jumped. Encourage number stories involving multiplication, as well as comparison number stories. *Examples:*

▷ If a Goliath frog makes 5 leaps, about what distance will it cover? About 45 feet

▷ How much farther can a tree frog jump than a flea? 23 inches; or 1 foot, 11 inches; or about 2 feet

◆ LANGUAGE DIVERSITY Discussing Meanings of the Word *Span*

SMALL-GROUP ACTIVITY   5–15 min

The word *span* is used in several related ways. Ask children to share any meanings of the word that they are familiar with.

▷ Children may know that for a bridge, *span* means either the distance from one end to the other or the distance between major supports.

▷ The *span* of a bird or an airplane is the distance from wing tip to wing tip.

▷ A *span* of time is the length of time between one event and another.

▷ A life *span* is the length of time that an organism is alive.

Line Segment Lengths (cont.)   Home Link 7.7

3. Draw a line segment that is 8 centimeters long.

_____

Measure the segment to the nearest inch.

The segment is about __3__ inches long.

4. Draw a line segment that is $6\frac{1}{2}$ inches long.

_____

Measure the segment to the nearest centimeter.

The segment is about __17__ centimeters long.

5. Draw a line segment that is $3\frac{1}{2}$ inches long.

_____

Measure the segment to the nearest centimeter.

The segment is about __9__ centimeters long.

◆ *Math Masters*, p. 338

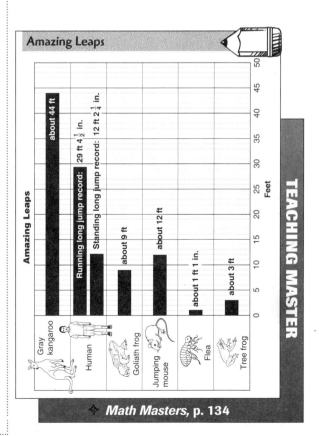

◆ *Math Masters*, p. 134

7.8 Middle Value (Median) of a Set of Data

OBJECTIVES To sort numerical data and arrange data in ascending or descending order; and to find the middle value (median) for a set of numerical data.

summaries	**materials**
1 Teaching the Lesson	
Children sort their class standing long jump data by arranging the data in ascending order. Children find the median jump length for the class. [Data and Chance]	☐ *Math Journal 2*, p. 178 ☐ Home Link 7.7 ☐ masking tape (about 20 feet) ☐ half-sheets of paper ***See* Advance Preparation**
2 Ongoing Learning & Practice	
Children measure pictured objects to the nearest inch and the nearest centimeter. [Measurement and Reference Frames] Children practice and maintain skills through Math Boxes and Home Link activities.	☐ *Math Journal 2*, pp. 181–183 ☐ Teaching Master (*Math Masters*, p. 498; optional) ☐ Home Link Masters (*Math Masters*, pp. 339 and 340) ☐ ruler
3 Options for Individualizing	
Language Diversity Children discuss various meanings for the word *median*. [Data and Chance]	

Additional Information

Advance Preparation For the Math Message, place a stack of half-sheets of paper next to the problem.

Before beginning the *Sorting the Standing Jump Data* activity in Part 1, tape a 20-foot baseline along the floor in a large, open space.

Vocabulary • sort (the data) • median • middle value

Getting Started

Mental Math and Reflexes

Write problems like the following on the board:

$21 + 4 + 6 + 19 = ?$ 50
$? = 25 + 3 + 17 + 35$ 80
$? = 15 + 18 + 12 + 5$ 50
$50 + 50 + 29 + 11 = ?$ 140

Math Message

Turn to journal page 178. Write your longer jump length on a half-sheet of paper.

86 cm

Example

Teaching the Lesson

◆ Math Message Follow-Up

WHOLE-CLASS DISCUSSION

Use a brief series of questions and answers to determine which child had the shortest jump length. Similarly, determine which child had the longest jump length. Write the shortest and longest jump lengths on the board. (See sample in the margin.)

Working together, calculate the difference between the longest and shortest jumps. Draw a comparison diagram on the board. Fill in the known quantities—the longest and the shortest jump lengths. The difference is what you want to find, so write ? in the difference box. Some children may use the trade-first subtraction algorithm to find the difference. Others may subtract by counting up.

◆ Sorting the Standing Jump Data

WHOLE-CLASS ACTIVITY

One of the most common first steps in analyzing numerical data is to **sort the data**—that is, to arrange it in ascending or descending order. This sorting is typically done with paper and pencil or a computer. The original set of data is frequently listed in haphazard order. It is then sorted and relisted in ascending or descending order.

Class Results
Shortest jump is 39 cm.
Longest jump is 94 cm.

Quantity
94 longest

Quantity	Difference
39 shortest	?

94 − 39 = 55
The difference is 55 cm.

Children will sort the standing jump data by arranging themselves in a single line—from shortest jump length at one end of the line to longest jump length at the other end. Use the following routine:

1. Select a large, open space and tape a 20-foot baseline along the floor.

2. Have children stand away from the line until they are called. Children should carry their half-sheets of paper (showing their jump lengths) with them.

3. Ask the children who made the shortest and the longest jumps to step forward and stand on the line— shortest at one end and longest at the other end.

4. One-by-one, ask the remaining children to step forward and find their correct position on the line. They do this by comparing the length of their jump to the lengths of the other children's jumps, as shown on their half-sheets of paper. (You should pause several times during the routine to make sure that the children standing on the line are evenly distributed along it. Even distribution will allow for spaces for the remaining children to fit themselves into the line.)

5. Several children may have the same jump length. If this is the case, they should all be together on the line, but it does not matter which order these children are in.

Once all children have found their places on the line, make an oral check that they are sorted by the lengths of their jumps. Begin at the end with the shortest length. Move down the line, in order, asking each child to say his or her jump length. If any child says a length that is smaller than a length already named, that child is not in the correct position.

Children find their correct positions on the line.

◆ Finding the Median Length of the Standing Long Jumps (*Math Journal 2*, p. 178)

WHOLE-CLASS ACTIVITY

The term **median** is another widely used name for **middle value.** If you have not already done so, you might want to introduce the term *median* at this time.

The routine for finding the median is quite simple. After arranging the data in ascending or descending order, count from either end to the number in the middle. If the data set consists of an even number of data, there are two middle values, and the median is the number halfway between those two middle values. At this stage, either value or any number between them is acceptable.

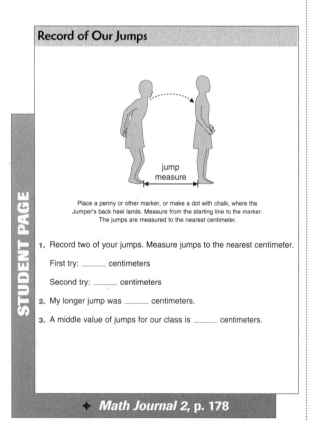

Record of Our Jumps

jump measure

Place a penny or other marker, or make a dot with chalk, where the Jumper's back heel lands. Measure from the starting line to the marker. The jumps are measured to the nearest centimeter.

1. Record two of your jumps. Measure jumps to the nearest centimeter.

First try: _____ centimeters

Second try: _____ centimeters

2. My longer jump was _____ centimeters.

3. A middle value of jumps for our class is _____ centimeters.

STUDENT PAGE

◆ *Math Journal 2*, p. 178

To find the median for the standing long jump data, use this routine:

1. Ask the children at each end of the line to take two large steps forward.

2. Identify the two children who are at each end of the line now, and ask them to take two large steps forward.

3. Continue to repeat this process. Each time that a child at each end steps forward, the original line of children is reduced by two. (See the margin.)

4. If you have an odd number of children in your class, there will be one remaining child on the line. The length of his or her jump is the median length.

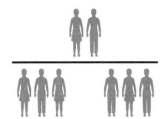

5. If you have an even number of children in your class, there will be two remaining children on the line. The lengths of their jumps are the middle values. The median is officially the number halfway between these two lengths. But either value or any number between them is an acceptable answer.

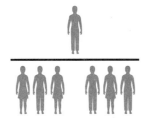

Ask children to record the median jump length on the journal page. Review the usefulness of finding a middle value: Since there are many differences in how far second graders jump, it is easier to talk about a median length than about many different lengths.

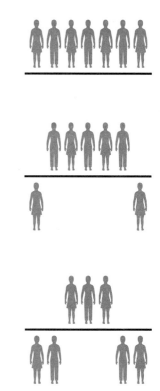

Each time the routine is repeated, the number of children standing on the line is reduced by two.

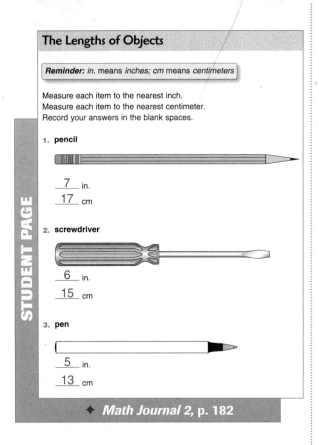

The Lengths of Objects

Reminder: *in.* means *inches*; *cm* means *centimeters*

Measure each item to the nearest inch.
Measure each item to the nearest centimeter.
Record your answers in the blank spaces.

1. **pencil**

   __7__ in.
   __17__ cm

2. **screwdriver**

   __6__ in.
   __15__ cm

3. **pen**

   __5__ in.
   __13__ cm

STUDENT PAGE

✦ *Math Journal 2*, p. 182

---

2 Ongoing Learning & Practice

✦ Measuring Objects
(*Math Journal 2*, pp. 182 and 183;
Math Masters, p. 498)

INDEPENDENT ACTIVITY

Children measure the lengths of various items to the
nearest inch and to the nearest centimeter. Then they list
the objects in order from shortest to longest.

 ONGOING ASSESSMENT
When children have completed Problem 6 on
journal page 183, have them answer the
following question on an Exit Slip or in their math
journal:

*Does it make any difference whether you order
the objects by inches or by centimeters? Explain.*

Expect children to understand that the unit used
to measure objects does not affect their lengths.
The longest object is still the longest object
whether it is measured in inches or centimeters.

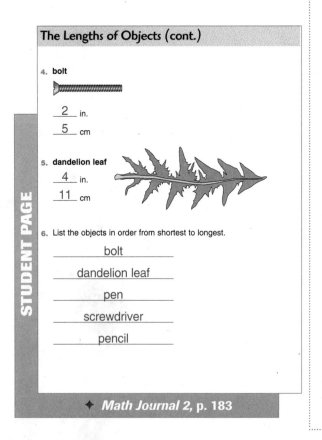

The Lengths of Objects (cont.)

4. **bolt**

   __2__ in.
   __5__ cm

5. **dandelion leaf**

   __4__ in.
   __11__ cm

6. List the objects in order from shortest to longest.

   _____ bolt _____

   _____ dandelion leaf _____

   _____ pen _____

   _____ screwdriver _____

   _____ pencil _____

STUDENT PAGE

✦ *Math Journal 2*, p. 183

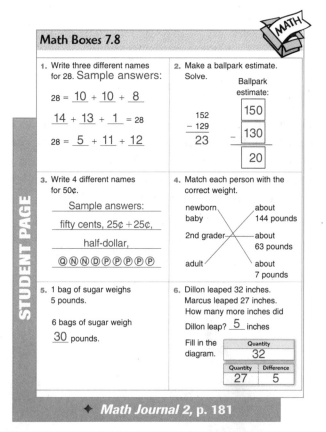

Math Boxes 7.8

1. Write three different names
   for 28. Sample answers:

   28 = __10__ + __10__ + __8__

   __14__ + __13__ + __1__ = 28

   28 = __5__ + __11__ + __12__

2. Make a ballpark estimate.
   Solve.

   Ballpark
   estimate:

   152
   − 129
   ___
   23

   [150]
   − [130]
   [20]

3. Write 4 different names
   for 50¢.

   Sample answers:

   fifty cents, 25¢ + 25¢,

   half-dollar,

   Ⓠ Ⓝ Ⓝ Ⓓ Ⓟ Ⓟ Ⓟ Ⓟ Ⓟ

4. Match each person with the
   correct weight.

   newborn   about
   baby   144 pounds

   2nd grader   about
                   63 pounds

   adult   about
                   7 pounds

5. 1 bag of sugar weighs
   5 pounds.

   6 bags of sugar weigh
   __30__ pounds.

6. Dillon leaped 32 inches.
   Marcus leaped 27 inches.
   How many more inches did
   Dillon leap? __5__ inches

   Fill in the
   diagram.

Quantity
32

Quantity	Difference
27	5

STUDENT PAGE

✦ *Math Journal 2*, p. 181

✦ Math Boxes 7.8 (*Math Journal 2*, p. 181)

Mixed Review This journal page provides opportunities for cumulative review or assessment of concepts and skills.

✦ Home Link 7.8 (*Math Masters*, pp. 339 and 340)

Home Connection Children sort data and find the median.

3 Options for Individualizing

✦ LANGUAGE DIVERSITY Discussing Meanings of the Word *Median*

SMALL-GROUP ACTIVITY   5–15 min

The median is the middle value of a set of data that have been put in order. Ask children if they have heard the word *median* used in other ways. Prompt with questions, such as the following:

- What is the median, median strip, or median area of a highway? The median divides the road in the middle— half the roadway is on one side, half on the other. The median may be a grassy strip, a concrete barrier, or just a painted line down the middle of the road.

- Who is the mediator in an argument or discussion? A person who takes the middle position or neutral ground between opposing sides. A mediator is said to "mediate" an argument or discussion.

Find the Middle Value

Home Link 7.8

Family Note In this lesson, your child has sorted data in order to find the median. *Median* is a term used for the middle value. To find the median of a set of data, arrange the data in ascending or descending order. Count from either end to the number in the middle. The middle value is the median. As your child finds the median in Problems 2 and 3, remind him or her that "in." is the abbreviation for inches and "cm" is the abbreviation for centimeters.

Please return this Home Link to school tomorrow.

List the data in order from smallest to largest.

Draw a circle around the median in your list.

1.

12 points	3 points	21 points	15 points	20 points	7 points	9 points

3 points **smallest**	7 points	9 points	(12) points	15 points	20 points	21 points **largest**

Math Masters, p. 339

Find the Middle Value (cont.)

Home Link 7.8

2.

Bob: 66 in. tall	Amy: 70 in. tall	Peter: 56 in. tall	Kate: 73 in. tall	Andy: 68 in. tall

56 in. **smallest**	66 in.	(68) in.	70 in.	73 in. **largest**

3.

Bob: 168 cm tall	Amy: 178 cm tall	Peter: 142 cm tall	Kate: 185 cm tall	Andy: 173 cm tall

142 cm **smallest**	168 cm	(173) cm	178 cm	185 cm **largest**

Math Masters, p. 340

7.9 Frequency Distributions

OBJECTIVES To make a frequency table, line plot, and bar graph for a set of data; and to find the median of a set of data.

Lesson 7.9 D.RE.02.01, D.RE.02.02, D.RE.02.03
Do Part 3, Extra Practice: Make this a pictograph. Use 4 colors. Have students place a crayon to represent their favorite color. Through discussion have students decide on a scale, eg. 1 crayon equals 2 votes for a color. Discuss, interpret, & analyze the data. (*The Graph Club* software).

summaries	materials

1 Teaching the Lesson

Children organize the class data on arm span length by making a frequency table, a line plot, and a bar graph.
[Data and Chance]

Children use a line plot to find the median arm span length.
[Data and Chance]

☐ *Math Journal 2*, pp. 179, 184, and 185

☐ Home Link 7.8

☐ Teaching Master (*Math Masters*, p. 135; optional)

☐ Teaching Master transparency (*Math Masters*, pp. 136 and 137; optional)

☐ Class Data Pad (optional)

☐ stick-on notes

See **Advance Preparation**

2 Ongoing Learning & Practice

Children add three or more 1-digit and 2-digit numbers by playing *Basketball Addition*. [Operations and Computation]

Children practice and maintain skills through Math Boxes and Home Link activities.

☐ *Math Journal 2*, p. 186

☐ Teaching Master (*Math Masters*, p. 130)

☐ Home Link Master (*Math Masters*, p. 341)

☐ 1 twenty-sided polyhedral die or 3 regular dice per small group of 3–5 children

3 Options for Individualizing

Extra Practice Children answer questions about data shown on a "quick graph." [Data and Chance]

☐ construction paper; ribbon

☐ pinch-style clothespins; overhead markers

☐ stapler, tape, or glue

See **Advance Preparation**

Additional Information

Advance Preparation You should plan to spend at least two days on this lesson.

Before beginning the Math Message, place a stack of stick-on notes next to the problem. For the Home Link 7.8 Follow-Up, make 1 copy of *Math Masters*, page 135 for every 2 children. Cut the copies apart.

For the arm span frequency table and the arm span bar graph activities in Part 1, you may want to make overhead transparencies of *Math Masters*, pages 136 and 137.

Before beginning the optional Extra Practice activity in Part 3, construct a "quick graph." See the Options for Individualizing section for instructions.

Vocabulary • **line plot**

Vocabulary (teacher) • **frequency** • **frequency table**

Getting Started

Mental Math and Reflexes

Write the following sets of numbers on the board. Ask children to find the median of each set. Remind children to first put the sets in ascending or descending order.

1, 9, 8, 5, 4   5

17, 34, 22, 15, 13   17

100, 500, 600, 200, 200   200

3, 9, 7, 15   7, 8, or 9

Math Message

Take 1 stick-on note. Turn to journal page 179.
Print your name and arm span on the stick-on note. Example:

$$47 \text{ in.}$$

Jack

Home Link 7.8 Follow-Up

Review answers. You may wish to use *Math Masters,* page 135 as an assessment tool. The problem on the *Math Masters* page is more challenging than the problems posed on Home Link 7.8 because there is no unique middle value. The two middle values are 48 and 50. The median is 49, but any of the answers 48, 49, or 50 are acceptable. Collect and assess children's responses.

1 Teaching the Lesson

DAY 1

◆ Math Message Follow-Up

WHOLE-CLASS DISCUSSION

Use a brief series of questions and answers to determine which child has the shortest arm span and what that length is. Repeat the process to determine which child has the longest arm span and what that length is. Write the shortest and longest arm spans on the board. (See the sample in margin.)

Draw a comparison diagram on the board. Fill in the known quantities, and write ? in the difference box. Working together, calculate the difference between the longest and shortest arm spans.

◆ Making a Frequency Table of Arm Spans
(*Math Journal 2,* p. 184; *Math Masters,* p. 136)

WHOLE-CLASS ACTIVITY

Draw a copy of the table on journal page 184 on the Class Data Pad or board. Alternately, use an overhead transparency of *Math Masters,* page 136.

Class Results
Shortest arm span is 42 in.
Longest arm span is 53 in.

Quantity
53 longest

Quantity	Difference
42 shortest	?

53 − 42 = 11
The difference is 11 in.

Arm Span (inches)	Frequency	
	Tallies	Number
42	//	2
43	/	1
44		0
45	//	2
46	////	4
47	//	2
48	~~////~~	5
49		0
50	/	1
51	/	1
52		0
53	/	1
	Total =	19

Table of Our Arm Spans

Make a table of the arm spans of your classmates.

Our Arm Spans

Arm span (inches)	Frequency	
	Tallies	Number
	Total =	

◆ *Math Journal 2*, p. 184

STUDENT PAGE

Work together to fill in the frequency table of arm spans. As children record their results on their journal pages, you should record the same information on the Class Data Pad or board. Use the following routine:

1. First, fill in the Arm Span column. Write the length of the shortest arm span in the class, followed by all other possible arm spans (to the nearest inch) up to the length of the longest arm span in the class. (Example: If the shortest span is 42 inches and the longest span is 53 inches, write 42, 43, 44, ..., 51, 52, 53 in the Arm Span column.)

2. Ask each child, in turn, to say what his or her arm span is. As each child speaks, everyone (including the speaker) makes a tally mark next to the arm span length reported.

3. After all measurements have been tallied, write a number for each set of tallies.

4. To check that no measurements have been omitted, add the frequency numbers and compare the sum to the number of children in the class.

Discuss the completed table. How many children had an arm span of 50 inches? Of 45 inches? What are the most popular arm spans for this class (the spans most often mentioned)? Look for the largest values in the Number column. Which arm spans did nobody mention? Look for a 0 in the Number column.

NOTE: **Frequency** means the number of times an event or value occurs in a set of data. The arm span table shows frequency in two ways: with a tally and with a number. The filled-in table is called a **frequency table** because it shows the frequencies for all possible arm spans in your data set. Use the terms *frequency* and *frequency table,* but do not expect children to use them at this time.

◆ Making a Line Plot of Arm Spans

WHOLE-CLASS ACTIVITY

Draw a long number line on the board, and make tick marks along the line about every 6 inches. Write the shortest arm span beneath the tick mark farthest to the left, followed by all other possible arm spans up to the length of the longest arm span in the class. (Example: If the shortest span is 42 inches and the longest span is 53 inches, write 42, 43, 44, ..., 51, 52, 53 beneath the tick marks.)

Children place their stick-on notes above the number line to create a **line plot** of the data. Use the following routine:

1. Have children come to the board in small groups of about 5.

2. Ask them to place their stick-on notes just above the tick mark on the number line for the number that is written on their stick-on note. (Example: Nicole's arm span is 51 inches, and her stick-on note reads "51." She attaches her stick-on note just above the tick mark on the number line that reads 51.)

3. If children discover that another child with the same arm span has previously attached a note, they should place their stick-on note directly above the note that is already attached.

Discuss the line plot of stick-on notes.

• What does it mean when there are a lot of stick-on notes above a number? Many children have that number of inches as their arm span.

• What about the numbers that have no stick-on notes above them? No child has that number of inches as an arm span.

• How many children have an arm span of 51 inches? Of 46 inches? Count the number of stick-on notes above those numbers.

DAY 2

◆ Making a Bar Graph of Arm Spans
(*Math Journal 2*, p. 185; *Math Masters*, p. 137)

INDEPENDENT ACTIVITY

If the stick-on notes were carefully placed, the line plot just created will also serve as a bar graph. The stick-on notes should form neat columns above the tick marks and numbers along the number line. (See the illustration in the margin above.)

Help children start the bar graph on the journal page. Ask, *Which numbers should you write below the horizontal axis?* The same numbers listed beneath the line plot

Show them how to draw one of the bars. For example, if there are 3 stick-on notes above 46 on the line plot, then 3 children have arm spans of 46 inches. Draw a bar 3 squares high above 46.

If children understand what to do, let them complete the graph as an independent activity. They should be able to check their own work because their completed graphs should look just like the line plot of stick-on notes.

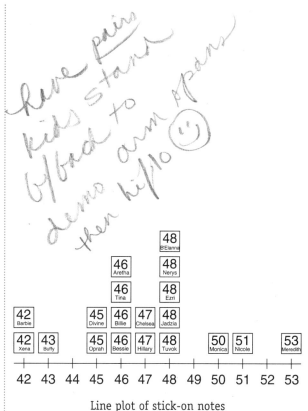

Line plot of stick-on notes

▼ *Math Masters,* page 137 is identical to the journal page below. You may use an overhead transparency of the *Math Masters* page to model drawing a bar graph as children follow along in their journals.

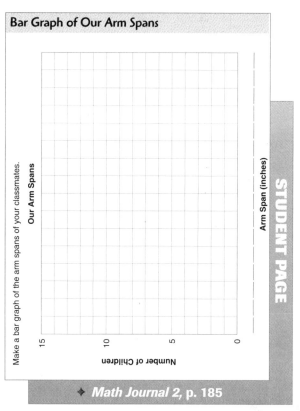

◆ *Math Journal 2*, p. 185

Record of Our Arm Spans

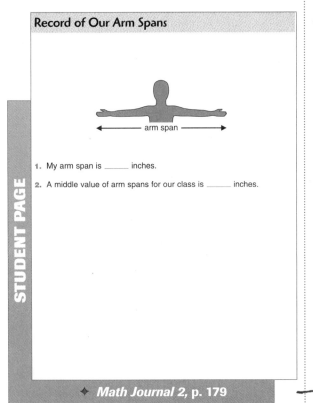

← arm span →

1. My arm span is _____ inches.

2. A middle value of arm spans for our class is _____ inches.

✦ *Math Journal 2, p. 179*

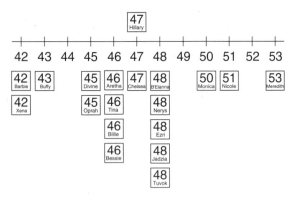

Reattaching the end stick-on notes below the
number line

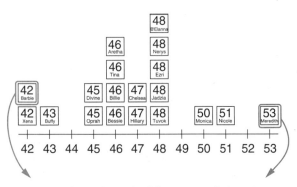

Line plot showing the median

✦ Finding the Median Length of Arm Spans
(Math Journal 2, p. 179)

WHOLE-CLASS ACTIVITY

Use the line plot of stick-on notes to find the median. Use the following routine:

1. Select two student helpers. Have them stand at the left and right ends of the line plot.

2. Ask each helper to remove the last stick-on note at his or her end and then to reattach it below the number line. (If there are several stick-on notes forming a column at one end of the line plot, the helper should remove the top one.)

3. Repeat this procedure over and over. Each time the stick-on notes at the ends are moved below the line, the number of notes above the line is reduced by two.

4. If you have an odd number of children in your class, there will be one remaining stick-on note above the line. The number on the note, and just below it, is the median arm span.

5. If you have an even number of children in your class, there will be two remaining stick-on notes above the line. The numbers on these notes, and just below, are the middle values. The official median is the number halfway between these middle values, but either value or any number between them is an acceptable answer.

Ask children to record the median arm span on the journal page.

② Ongoing Learning & Practice

✦ Playing *Basketball Addition*
(Math Masters, p. 130)

SMALL-GROUP ACTIVITY

This game gives children practice in adding three or more 1-digit and 2-digit numbers. Directions for the game appear in Lesson 7.4.

Math Boxes 7.9 (*Math Journal 2,* p. 186)

INDEShot...

INDEPENDENT ACTIVITY

Mixed Review This journal page provides opportunities for cumulative review or assessment of concepts and skills.

Home Link 7.9 (*Math Masters,* p. 341)

Home Connection Children answer questions about basketball players' heights based on a frequency table.

3 Options for Individualizing

◆ EXTRA PRACTICE Making a "Quick Graph" for Future Data Displays

SMALL-GROUP ACTIVITY 🚶🚶🚶🚶 5–15 min

Prepare a graph like the one pictured in the margin. Make the top part out of construction paper. Laminate it so that the title and column labels may be changed with an overhead marker each time the graph is used. Note that the top part may have room for as many column labels as you want, depending upon how big you decide to make it. Hang ribbons from the top, and have children use clothespins to mark entries on the graph.

Consider using the "quick graph" as a place for children to record responses to your own Math Message questions, such as, "What is your favorite color?" Discuss the display once all children have marked a response. Ask questions like the following:

• Which is the most popular/least popular response?

• How many children marked *x*?

• How many more children marked *x* than *y*?

• How many fewer children marked *a* than *b*?

• What is the total number of children who marked *c* and *d*?

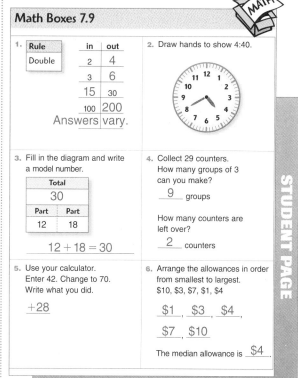

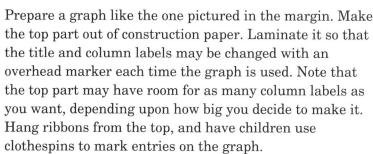

Favorite Color			
Blue	Green	Red	Other

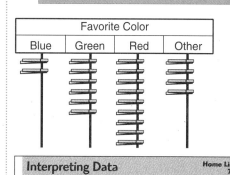

Interpreting Data

Home Link 7.9

Family Note Today your child represented data using a bar graph and a frequency table. The table below is called a *frequency table* because it shows how often different heights occurred. Help your child use the data to answer the questions. Remind your child that to find the median of a set of data, he or she should arrange the data in ascending or descending order and then count from either end to the number in the middle. The middle value is the median.

Please return this Home Link to school tomorrow.

Mr. Wilson is a basketball coach. He measured the height of each player. Then he made the data table shown below.

1. How many players are 50 inches tall? __2__ players

2. How many players are 47 inches tall? __0__ players

3. The shortest player is __46__ inches tall.

4. The tallest player is __52__ inches tall.

5. How many players did Mr. Wilson measure? __9__ players

6. Which height occurs most often? __48__ inches

7. Find the middle (median) height. __49__ inches

Players' Heights

Height (inches)	Number of Players
46	1
47	0
48	3
49	1
50	2
51	1
52	1

Math Masters, p. 341

Math Boxes 7.9

1. | Rule | | in | out |
   |---|---|---|---|
   | Double | | 2 | 4 |
   | | | 3 | 6 |
   | | | 15 | 30 |
   | | | 100 | 200 |

   Answers vary.

2. Draw hands to show 4:40.

3. Fill in the diagram and write a model number.

Total	
30	
Part	Part
12	18

   12 + 18 = 30

4. Collect 29 counters. How many groups of 3 can you make?

   __9__ groups

   How many counters are left over?

   __2__ counters

5. Use your calculator. Enter 42. Change to 70. Write what you did.

   +28

6. Arrange the allowances in order from smallest to largest. $10, $3, $7, $1, $4

   $1 , $3 , $4 ,

   $7 , $10

   The median allowance is $4.

Math Journal 2, p. 186

STUDENT PAGE

HOME LINK MASTER

7.10

Unit 7 Review and Assessment

OBJECTIVE To review and assess children's progress on the material covered in Unit 7.

1 Assess Progress

learning goals

7a **Developing Goal** Find missing addends for any multiple of 10. **(Lesson 7.3)**

7b **Developing Goal** Find the median (middle value) of a data set. **(Lesson 7.8)**

7c **Developing Goal** Add three 2-digit numbers mentally. **(Lesson 7.4)**

7d **Developing/Secure Goal** Measure to the nearest inch. **(Lesson 7.7)**

7e **Developing/Secure Goal** Measure to the nearest centimeter. **(Lesson 7.7)**

7f **Secure Goal** Know complements of 10. **(Lesson 7.3)**

7g **Secure Goal** Count by 2s, 5s, and 10s and describe the patterns. **(Lesson 7.1)**

7h **Secure Goal** Find missing addends for the next multiple of 10. **(Lesson 7.2)**

7i **Secure Goal** Solve number-grid puzzles. **(Lesson 7.2)**

7j **Secure Goal** Plot data on a bar graph. **(Lesson 7.9)**

activities

- ❑ Slate Assessment, Problem 5
- ❑ Written Assessment, Problem 2

- ❑ Slate Assessment, Problem 7
- ❑ Written Assessment, Problem 3

- ❑ Slate Assessment, Problem 6
- ❑ Written Assessment, Problem 4

- ❑ Written Assessment, Problem 5

- ❑ Written Assessment, Problem 6

- ❑ Slate Assessment, Problem 3

- ❑ Oral Assessment, Problem 1

- ❑ Slate Assessment, Problem 4
- ❑ Written Assessment, Problem 1

- ❑ Written Assessment, Problem 7

- ❑ Home Link 7.9 Follow-Up (*Math Masters,* p. 138)

materials

- ❑ Home Link 7.9
- ❑ Assessment Masters (*Math Masters,* pp. 429 and 430)
- ❑ Teaching Masters (*Math Masters,* pp. 22, 128, 130, and 138)

- ❑ object weighing about 10 pounds
- ❑ slate; calculator; ruler; counters; bath scale
- ❑ 1 twenty-sided polyhedral die or 3 regular dice
  See **Advance Preparation**

2 Build Background for Unit 8

summaries

Children practice and maintain skills through Math Boxes and Home Link activities.

materials

- ❑ *Math Journal 2,* p. 187
- ❑ Home Link Masters (*Math Masters,* pp. 342–345)

Each **learning goal** listed above indicates a level of performance that might be expected at this point in the *Everyday Mathematics* K–6 curriculum. For a variety of reasons, the levels indicated may not accurately portray your class's performance.

Getting Started

Math Message

Pick up the (object that weighs about 10 pounds). How much do you think it weighs?

Home Link 7.9 Follow-Up

Review the answers to the questions based on the data table. Ask children to describe the procedure that they used to find the median height. Be sure that children remember to arrange the data in ascending or descending order before counting to determine the middle value.

Provide each child with a blank bar graph from *Math Masters,* page 138. (See the margin below.) Have children plot the data from the table on the graph. Collect and assess children's ability to plot data on a bar graph.

1 Assess Progress

◆ Math Message Follow-Up

WHOLE-CLASS DISCUSSION

Children share their estimates for the weight of the object. Ask children how they decided upon their estimates. Place the object on a bath scale. Ask small groups of children to come and read the scale. Do all groups agree on the weight of the object?

◆ Oral and Slate Assessments

SMALL-GROUP ACTIVITY

Instead of doing the slate activities with the whole class, you might want to work with small groups of children, one group at a time, over several days. While you do this, the rest of the class can work on the written review pages.

It is not necessary to record every child's performance on every problem. Instead, you need keep a record of only those children who are struggling. You can go back later and enter positive comments.

Players' Heights

For the Home Link Follow-Up, children plot the data from the table on a bar graph, using *Math Masters,* page 138.

If the list of suggested problems below is not appropriate for your class's level of performance, adjust the numbers in the problems or adjust the problems themselves to better assess your children's abilities.

Oral Assessment Suggestions

1. Ask children to count by 2s, 5s, and 10s from any 2-digit number. Try some 3-digit numbers. Ask children to describe the patterns. **Goal 7g**

2. Encourage children to use counters or draw pictures to solve the following multiples of equal grouping number stories:

   - 3 packages of paper towels. 3 rolls per package. How many rolls? 9 rolls

   - 7 packages of pens. 2 pens in each package. How many pens? 14 pens

   - 6 goldfish per bowl. 4 bowls. How many goldfish? 24 goldfish

It might help children solve equal-group number stories if they visualize them.

3. Encourage children to use counters or draw pictures to solve the following equal-grouping and equal-sharing number stories:

   - 15 children. 5 children per group. How many groups? 3 groups How many children remaining? 0 children

   - 25 cents shared equally by 2 children. How much money per child? 12 cents How much money remaining? 1 cent

   - 20 trading cards shared equally by 4 children. How many cards for each child? 5 cards How many cards left over? 0 cards

Slate Assessment Suggestions

1. Say a number. Children record its double on their slates. 5 10   3 6   30 60   25 50

2. Say a number. Children record its half on their slates. 12 6   16 8   80 40   100 50

3. Write the following on the board. Children record the missing numbers on their slates. **Goal 7f**

- 7 + __ = 10 3
- 10 = 2 + __ 8
- 10 = __ + 5 5
- 1 + __ = 10 9
- __ + 4 = 10 6

4. Write the following on the board. Children record the missing numbers on their slates. **Goal 7h**

- 36 + __ = 40 4
- __ + 53 = 60 7
- 50 = 48 + __ 2
- 80 = __ + 71 9

5. Write the following on the board. Children record the missing numbers on their slates. **Goal 7a**

- 27 + __ = 90 63
- __ + 44 = 60 16
- 70 = __ + 42 28
- 50 = 29 + __ 21

6. Write the following on the board. Children record the sums on their slates. **Goal 7c**

- __ = 6 + 7 + 13 + 14 40
- 23 + 17 + 14 = __ 54
- 45 + 15 + 13 = __ 73

7. Write the following sets of numbers on the board. Ask children to find the median of each set. Remind them to first put the sets in ascending or descending order. **Goal 7b**

- 1, 7, 6, 5, 3 5
- 23, 17, 34, 22, 19 22
- 6, 8, 3, 10 6, 7, or 8

➤ Written Assessment
(*Math Masters*, pp. 429 and 430)

INDEPENDENT ACTIVITY

Read through the problems with the class. You may want to do examples with the class for some of the problems.

If appropriate, work through the problems together. Wait for children to complete a problem before reading the next one.

Unit 7 Checking Progress

1. Solve.

$23 + \underline{7} = 30$ $\underline{9} + 51 = 60$

$40 = \underline{8} + 32$ $70 = 66 + \underline{4}$

2. Solve.

$47 + \underline{13} = 60$ $90 = \underline{36} + 54$

$\underline{11} + 39 = 50$ $40 = 28 + \underline{12}$

3. Find the median.

7, 3, 4 $\underline{4}$ 27, 45, 63, 45, 50 $\underline{45}$

3, 9, 7, 14, 12 $\underline{9}$ 3, 5, 9, 7 $\underline{5, 6,}$ or 7

4. Add.

$15 + 13 + 17 = \underline{45}$ $\underline{50} = 15 + 25 + 10$

$\underline{75} = 26 + 24 + 25$ $22 + 18 + 15 + 14 = \underline{69}$

5. Measure each line to the nearest inch.

_____

about __5__ inches

_____

about __3__ inches

◆ *Math Masters*, p. 429

Unit 7 Checking Progress (cont.)

6. Measure each line to the nearest centimeter.

_____

about __8__ centimeters

_____

about __13__ cm

7. Solve the number-grid puzzles.

43	44	45
53		
63		

		438
446	447	
456	457	
466		468
476		
486		

231	232	233	234
241	242		244
251			
261	262	263	
271		273	
281			

◆ *Math Masters*, p. 430

If your class can work independently, have children work alone or with a partner. Circulate and assist as children work.

- Solve. (Problems 1 and 2) **Goals 7a and 7h**
- Find the median. (Problem 3) **Goal 7b**
- Add. (Problem 4) **Goal 7c**
- Measure each line to the nearest inch. (Problem 5) **Goal 7d**
- Measure each line to the nearest centimeter. (Problem 6) **Goal 7e**
- Solve the number-grid puzzles. (Problem 7) **Goal 7i**

◆ ALTERNATIVE ASSESSMENT OPTION
Play *Hit the Target* (*Math Masters*, p. 128)

PARTNER ACTIVITY

This game was introduced in Lesson 7.3. Use the record sheet for *Hit the Target* to assess children's ability to find the difference between 2-digit numbers and any higher multiple of 10. Identify children who can find the difference in one step and those who begin by finding the next-higher multiple of 10.

◆ ALTERNATIVE ASSESSMENT OPTION
Play *Basketball Addition*
(*Math Masters*, p. 130)

SMALL-GROUP ACTIVITY

This game was introduced in Lesson 7.4. Use the record sheet for the basketball game to assess children's ability to add three or more 1- and 2-digit numbers.

◆ ALTERNATIVE ASSESSMENT OPTION
Write a Doubles or Halves Story
(*Math Masters*, p. 22)

INDEPENDENT ACTIVITY

Children draw a picture of an imaginary animal or object that doubles or divides in half every hour. They also write a short story about their drawing.

Portfolio Ideas

2 ◆ Build Background for Unit 8

◆ Math Boxes 7.10 (*Math Journal 2*, p. 187)

INDEPENDENT ACTIVITY

Mixed Review This journal page provides opportunities for cumulative review or assessment of concepts and skills. Problem 6 is a prerequisite for Unit 8.

◆ Home Link 7.10: Unit 8 Family Letter
(*Math Masters*, pp. 342–345)

Home Connection This Home Link is a four-page newsletter that introduces parents and guardians to Unit 8's topics and terms. The letter also offers ideas for home-based mathematics activities that are supportive of classroom work.

Math Boxes 7.10

1. Count by 9s on the calculator. Start with 76.

   76, _85_, _94_, _103_, _112_

   What pattern do you see?
   Sample answer: The value in the tens place goes up, while the value in the ones place goes down.

2. Use your calculator. Enter 27. Change to 60. Write what you did.

   +33

3.
Rule	in	out
+9	32	41
	56	65
	45	54
	88	97
	89	98

   Answers vary.

4. Arrange the number of pets in order from smallest to largest.
   7, 0, 4, 1, 3, 5, 2

   _0_, _1_, _2_, _3_, _4_, _5_, _7_

   The median number of pets is _3_.

5. Write 5 names in the 90-box.

   | 90 |

   Sample answers:
   50 + 40, 108 − 18, ninety, *noventa*, 45 × 2

6. How many boxes are on this Math Boxes page?

   _6_ boxes

   How many boxes are on $\frac{1}{2}$ of this page?

   _3_ boxes

◆ *Math Journal 2*, p. 187

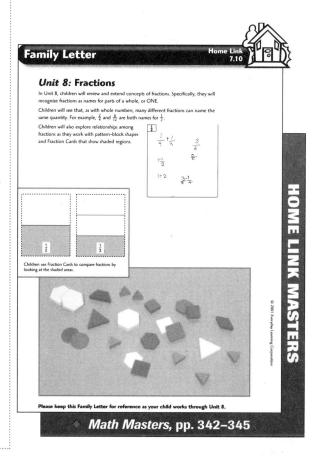

◆ *Math Masters*, pp. 342–345

Unit **8**
Fractions

Unit 8 emphasizes fractions of regions and collections of objects, as well as relationships between fractions (less than, equal to, greater than). While the focus of the unit is on fraction notation and equivalencies—not on fraction computation—the idea of "fraction of" does touch on division and multiplication concepts. Children's intuitive understanding of "half of" readily transfers to related fraction/multiples exercises, such as finding one-tenth of 20 and ten times 2. Addition and subtraction using fraction symbols are another matter: They should probably be deferred until children have a very firm grip on equivalence and find it natural to use such fractions as $\frac{2}{4}$, $\frac{3}{6}$, and $\frac{4}{8}$ in place of $\frac{1}{2}$.

contents

UNIT

8

learning goals in perspective

learning goals	links to the past	links to the future
8a **Beginning/Developing Goal** Compare fractions. **(Lessons 8.5–8.7)**	In first grade, children folded strips of paper to compare fractions. *(Related Grade 2 lesson: 7.5)*	In third grade, children will make a number line for fractions. Children will also use Fraction Cards to compare fractions to $\frac{1}{2}$. *(Related Grade 2 lesson: 9.3)*
8b **Developing Goal** Understand fractions as names for equal parts of a region or set. **(Lessons 8.1–8.3 and 8.7)**	Children were informally introduced to fractions in Kindergarten. In first grade, children used paper "crackers" and "pizzas" to investigate equal shares. *(Related Grade 2 lesson: 7.5)*	In third grade, children will use number stories to experience fractions as equal parts of regions or sets. *(Related Grade 2 lessons: 9.3, 10.7)*
8c **Developing Goal** Understand that the amount represented by a fraction depends on the size of the whole (ONE). **(Lessons 8.2, 8.3, and 8.7)**	This concept was informally introduced in first grade through activities and Explorations with sets and regions. *(Related Grade 2 lesson: 7.5)*	In third grade, children will review the "ONE" and fractional parts in a variety of situations. *(Related Grade 2 lessons: 9.3, 10.7)*
8d **Developing Goal** Shade a specified fractional part of a collection. **(Lessons 8.3 and 8.5)**	Children in *First Grade Everyday Mathematics* used a set of pennies to investigate fractional parts of a collection. *(Related Grade 2 lesson: 7.6)*	Children in *Third Grade Everyday Mathematics* will identify fractions of sets and will also be introduced to decimal equivalents. *(Related Grade 2 lesson: 10.2)*
8e **Developing Goal** Give the fraction name for the shaded part of a collection. **(Lesson 8.3)**	In first grade, the focus was on identifying unit fractions of collections.	Children will review fraction notation in third grade. *(Related Grade 2 lessons: 9.7, 10.6)*
8f **Developing Goal** Recognize equivalent fraction names. **(Lessons 8.4–8.6)**	In first grade, children folded strips of paper to illustrate equivalent fractions.	Children will continue to work with equivalent fractions in third grade and will extend the concept to include decimals and percents in later grades. *(Related Grade 2 lessons: 9.3, 9.7, 10.6)*
8g **Secure Goal** Shade a specified fractional part of a region. **(Lessons 8.1 and 8.4)**	Children in *First Grade Everyday Mathematics* used geoboards and folded paper to investigate fractional parts of a region.	Children in *Third Grade Everyday Mathematics* will use pattern blocks and a fraction number line to investigate fractional parts of regions. *(Related Grade 2 lessons: 9.3, 10.7)*
8h **Secure Goal** Give the fraction name for the shaded part of a region. **(Lessons 8.1, 8.3, and 8.5)**	In first grade, the focus was on identifying unit fractions of regions.	Children will review fraction notation in third grade. *(Related Grade 2 lessons: 9.3, 10.7)*

☑ Informal Assessment

Math Boxes These *Math Journal* pages provide opportunities for cumulative review or assessment of concepts and skills.

Ongoing Assessment: Kid Watching Use the Ongoing Assessment suggestions in the following lessons to make quick, on-the-spot observations about children's understanding of:
- Geometry **(Lesson 8.2)**
- Numeration **(Lessons 8.3 and 8.7)**

Portfolio Ideas Samples of children's work may be obtained from the following assignments:
- Making a Collection of "Collective Terms" **(Lesson 8.3)**
- Making Books of Fraction Number Stories **(Lesson 8.7)**
- Name Fractional Parts of a Region **(Lesson 8.8)**
- Describe Fractions Greater Than ONE **(Lesson 8.8)**
- Write and Solve Number Stories Involving Fractions **(Lesson 8.8)**

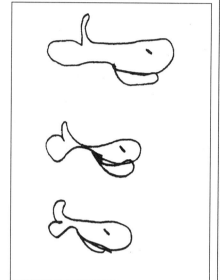

☑ Unit 8 Review and Assessment

Math Message Use the question in Lesson 8.8 to assess children's progress toward the following learning goal: Goal 8d

Oral and Slate Assessments Use oral or slate assessments during Lesson 8.8 to assess children's progress toward the following learning goals: Goals 8a, 8b, 8c, 8f, and 8h

Written Assessment Use a written review during Lesson 8.8 to assess children's progress toward the following learning goals: Goals 8b, 8d, 8e, 8g, and 8h

Performance/Group Assessment Use a partner activity in Lesson 8.8 to assess children's progress toward the following learning goals: Goals 8a and 8f

assessment handbook

For more information on how to use different types of assessment in Unit 8, see the Assessment Overview on pages 63–66 in the *Assessment Handbook*. The following Assessment Masters can be found in the *Math Masters* book:

- Unit 8 Checking Progress, p. 431
- Unit 8 Class Checklist, p. 462
- Unit 8 Individual Profile of Progress, p. 463
- Class Progress Indicator, p. 488
- Math Logs, pp. 493–495
- Self-Assessment Forms, pp. 496 and 497
- Interest Inventory, pp. 491 and 492

problemsolving

A process of modeling everyday situations using tools from mathematics

Encourage children to use a variety of strategies when attacking a given problem—and to explain those strategies. *Strategies children might use in this unit:*

- Acting out the problem
- Modeling with manipulatives
- Using a diagram (array)
- Using a drawing

Four Problem-Solving REPRESENTATIONS

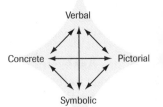

Verbal

Concrete ←→ Pictorial

Symbolic

Lessons that teach *through* problem solving, not just *about* problem solving

Lesson	Activity	Lesson	Activity
8.1	Solving multiplication and division number stories	8.2	Finding how many pattern blocks of one size cover a pattern block of another size
8.1	Dividing shapes into equal parts	8.7	Solving number stories involving fractions
8.3	Finding fractions of collections of things		

For more information about problem solving in *Everyday Mathematics,* see the *Teacher's Reference Manual,* pp. 197–208.

cross-curricularlinks

literature

- Read the following books about fractions: *Gator Pie, Eating Fractions,* and *Ed Emberley's Picture Pie: A Circle Drawing Book.* **(Lesson 8.1)**

- Read the book *Only One,* which discusses objects that compose a collection. **(Lesson 8.3)**

language arts

- Children make books of fraction number stories. **(Lesson 8.7)**

meeting INDIVIDUAL needs

✦ RETEACHING

The following features provide additional instructional support:

Adjusting the Activity

- **Lesson 8.1, Part 1**

Options for Individualizing

- **Lesson 8.4** Playing *Name That Number*

✦ ENRICHMENT

The following features suggest enrichment and extension activities:

Adjusting the Activity

- **Lesson 8.2, Part 1**
- **Lesson 8.3, Part 1**

Options for Individualizing

- **Lesson 8.1** Naming Equal Parts Situations Found in Literature
- **Lesson 8.5** Playing an Advanced Version of the *Equivalent Fractions Game*
- **Lesson 8.6** Playing the Advanced Version of *Fraction Top-It*

✦ LANGUAGE DIVERSITY

The following features suggest ways to support children who are acquiring proficiency in English:

Options for Individualizing

- **Lesson 8.1** Describing Fractions Displayed on a Fraction Poster
- **Lesson 8.3** Making a Collection of "Collective Terms"

✦ MULTIAGE CLASSROOM

The following chart lists related lessons from Grades 1 and 3 that can help you meet your instructional needs:

Grade 1	8.6 8.7 9.6	6.7 8.9	8.8	6.2 9.8	6.2 9.8	9.6 9.7	1.13 2.13 5.8
Grade 2	8.1	8.2	8.3	8.4	8.5	8.6	8.7
Grade 3	4.3 8.1	5.6 8.2	8.1	8.3 8.4	8.4	8.1 8.5	8.7

materials

lesson	📖 math masters pages	🧊 manipulative kit items	✂️ other items
8.1	Home Link Master, p. 346 Teaching Masters, pp. 139 and 140	slate pattern blocks (optional) geoboard rubber bands	8" by 8" paper squares straightedge various literature selections ***See* Advance Preparation, p. 578**

8.2	Home Link Master, p. 347
	Teaching Masters, pp. 117–119
	  and 141–143
	Teaching Aid Assessment
	  Master, p. 498
	***See* Advance Preparation, p. 584**
		pattern blocks
		Pattern-Block Template
		geoboard; rubber bands
		base-10 blocks; slate
		2 six-sided dice, 1 twelve-
		  sided die, or an egg-
		  carton number generator
		  per group
		1 twenty-sided die or number cards
		  1–20 per group
			straightedge

8.3	Home Link Master, p. 348	Pattern-Block Template	bills and coins
			a collection of 3 to 6 books and
			  various sets of objects, such as
			  crayons, chairs, or buttons
			49 pennies; straightedge
			Only One by Marc Harshman
			  (optional)
			***See* Advance Preparation, p. 590**

8.4	Home Link Master, p. 349 Teaching Master, p. 144 ***See* Advance Preparation, p. 594**	number cards 0–20	18 pennies or other counters (optional) glue
8.5	Home Link Master, p. 350	slate	paper clip blue crayon or pencil Fraction Cards
8.6	Home Link Master, p. 351	slate	Fraction Cards
8.7	Home Link Master, p. 352 Teaching Master, p. 22		16 pennies or other counters (optional) Fraction Cards
8.8	Home Link Masters, pp. 353–356 Assessment Master, p. 431	slate pattern blocks or Pattern-Block Template	20 counters (optional) Fractions Museum Fraction Cards

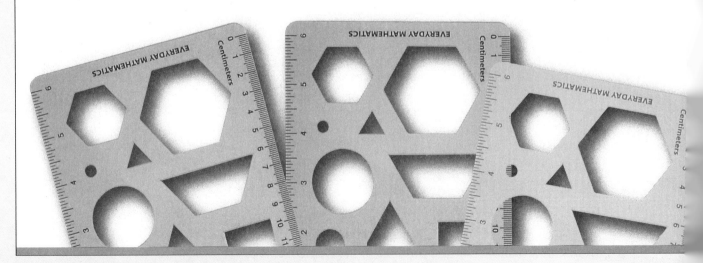

planningtips

Pacing

Pacing depends on a number of factors, such as children's individual needs and how long your school has been using *Everyday Mathematics*. At the beginning of Unit 8, review your Content by Strand Poster to help you set a monthly pace.

←——MOST CLASSROOMS——→		
FEBRUARY	MARCH	APRIL

Using the Projects

Both Projects recommended for use during Unit 8 are weather-related. Project 2 provides an opportunity for children to read thermometers and to observe and collect data on weather conditions. Project 5 is an experiment with paper folding, creating snowflakes that represent real 6-sided water crystals. The Projects can be found at the back of this book.

Home Communication

Share Home Links 8.1–8.7 with families to help them understand the content and procedures in this unit. At the end of the unit, use Home Link 8.8 to introduce Unit 9. Supplemental information can be found in the *Home Connection Handbook*.

NCTM Standards

Standard	1	2	3	4	5	6	7	8	9	10
Unit 8 Lessons	1–7	3, 5, 7	2, 5, 6	3–5	2	1–7	1–7	1–7	1–7	1–7

Content Standards
1 Number and Operation
2 Patterns, Functions, and Algebra
3 Geometry and Spatial Sense
4 Measurement
5 Data Analysis, Statistics, and Probability

Process Standards
6 Problem Solving
7 Reasoning and Proof
8 Communication
9 Connections
10 Representations

PRACTICE *through* Games

Everyday Mathematics uses games to help children develop good fact power and other math skills.

- Match numbers with the total number of dots in an array in *Array Bingo* **(Lesson 8.2)**
- Practice finding equivalent names for numbers in *Name That Number* **(Lesson 8.4)**
- Identify pairs of equivalent fractions with the *Equivalent Fractions Game* **(Lessons 8.5 and 8.6)**
- Compare fractions in *Fraction Top-It* **(Lessons 8.6 and 8.7)**

The notes below highlight the major content ideas presented in Unit 8. These notes may help you establish instructional priorities.

Fractions Museum (Lesson 8.1 and following)

Fractions were invented because counting numbers weren't sufficient to deal with the real world. An enjoyable way to emphasize the uses of fractions in everyday life is to create a Fractions Museum as a bulletin board or tabletop display. You might start it yourself to motivate children at the beginning of this unit and then ask them to bring things from home to add to the museum. (See Home Links 8.1 and 8.3.)

To begin, you might post newspaper and magazine clippings containing fraction words and symbols; draw regions and sets of objects on cards showing the "ONE" (whole) and the fraction; and display food packages (on which fraction words and symbols have been circled), measuring tools used in cooking, and recipes. Be sure to include rulers, scales, and other measuring tools as well. Fraction names are seldom shown on these tools, but you can point out that the marks between whole units represent fractions of whole units.

The primary task of school mathematics is to provide transitions from children's informal knowledge of the world around them to modeling of real-life situations through the skillful use of symbols. *Everyday Mathematics* uses paper folding, pattern blocks, and sets of objects to help children make the connections between fraction ideas and fraction symbols.

Equal Parts of ONE (Lesson 8.1 and following)

Establishing the ONE—otherwise known as the "whole"—is emphasized throughout Unit 8. This concept is necessary because a fraction, such as $\frac{1}{2}$, is meaningless by itself; for example, a length of half an inch is not the same as a distance of half a mile. You may recognize this concept as yet another way in which numbers are always about something, an idea that is emphasized throughout *Everyday Mathematics* through the use of context and unit boxes.

The idea of the "whole" or "ONE" is even more crucial in work with fractions than it is with whole numbers. It is important to remind children of the concept of ONE at every opportunity and to apply this concept through exercises, such as those in Lesson 8.1. In this lesson, you identify something as ONE and then ask children to name related things as fractions or multiples of ONE. Such exercises should be done frequently in this unit and revisited throughout the year in brisk oral drills, Mental Math and Reflexes problems, and Math Boxes exercises.

Marks between units represent fractions of whole units.

Explorations: Pattern Block Fractions, Geoboard Fences, Volumes of Base-10 Structures (Lesson 8.2)

Activities in Lesson 8.2 develop fraction concepts that are important in this unit, reinforce work with arrays that was done in Unit 7, and prepare children for work with volume to be done in Unit 9.

Relations between Fractions (Lessons 8.4–8.6)

Children cut out and use Fraction Cards from the back of *Math Journal 2*. The "picture side" of each card shows a region (the ONE) divided into equal parts, some of which may be shaded. These pictures make it possible to use pairs of cards to determine whether a given fraction is less than, equal to, or greater than another fraction.

In Lesson 8.5, children use Fraction Cards to compare pairs of fractions, to compare related fractions, and to observe the relationships between fractions having the same numerator or the same denominator.

The term *equivalent fractions* is introduced for fractions that name the same quantity, such as $\frac{1}{2}, \frac{2}{4}, \frac{3}{6}$, and so on.

Be sure to talk about fractions of the form $\frac{0}{n}$ (equivalent to 0) and $\frac{n}{n}$ (equivalent to 1). Although adults are often confused by these symbols, the symbols themselves are not inherently difficult. Children will not find them to be mysterious and confusing as long as they explore their meanings through lots of concrete experiences.

Equivalent names for fractions can be extended to include fraction names for whole numbers. For example, $\frac{1}{2}$ of 4 and fractions such as $\frac{4}{2}$ and $\frac{10}{5}$ can join $1 + 1$, $11 - 9$, and $8 \div 4$ in a name-collection box for 2.

Review and Assessment (Lesson 8.8)

Unit goals for fractions are assessed orally, on slates, and in review pages.

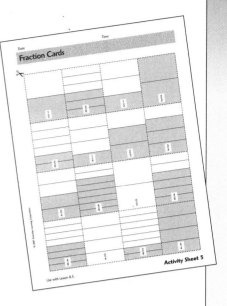

Children use the Fraction Cards to compare fractions by looking at the shaded areas.

Name-collection box for $\frac{1}{2}$.

For additional information on the following topics, see the *Teacher's Reference Manual*:

- fractions, decimals, and rational numbers
- notation for rational numbers
- teaching problem solving

8.1

Equal Parts of ONE

OBJECTIVE To review basic fraction concepts.

Lesson 8.1 (N.ME.02.18, N.ME.02.22)
Explicitly talk about **2/2, 3/3, 4/4 = 1 whole,** throughout unit.
Part 1, Math Message Follow-up: Include 3 strips of paper (3" x 6" each) to be folded in halves, thirds, & fourths. Label parts with correct fractions.

materials

1 Teaching the Lesson

Children fold square pieces of paper into 2, 4, and 8 equal parts in various ways; children color one or more parts of the folded squares and name the fractions for these parts.
[Numeration]

☐ *Math Journal 2,* p. 188
☐ slate
☐ three 8" by 8" paper squares (per child)
☐ straightedge
☐ scissors (optional)
☐ pattern blocks (optional)
See Advance Preparation

2 Ongoing Learning & Practice

Children solve multiplication and division number stories.
[Operations and Computation]

Children practice and maintain skills through Math Boxes and Home Link activities.

☐ *Math Journal 2,* pp. 189 and 190
☐ Home Link Master (*Math Masters,* p. 346)
See Advance Preparation

3 Options for Individualizing

Enrichment Children name fractions shown by pictures in literature selections. [Numeration]

Extra Practice Children divide geoboard shapes into equal parts. [Numeration]

Language Diversity Children describe fractions shown by pictures on the Fraction Poster. [Numeration]

☐ Teaching Masters (*Math Masters,* pp. 139 and 140)
☐ *Gator Pie*
☐ *Eating Fractions*
☐ *Ed Emberley's Picture Pie: A Circle Drawing Book*
☐ geoboard
☐ rubber bands
See Advance Preparation

Additional Information

Advance Preparation Before beginning the Math Message, place the 8" by 8" squares of paper near the problem.

Before distributing Home Link 8.1 in Part 2, read about the Fractions Museum on page 576.

Before beginning the optional Enrichment activity in Part 3, obtain these books: *Gator Pie* by Louise Matthews (Sundance, 1995); *Eating Fractions* by Bruce McMillan (Scholastic, 1991); and *Ed Emberley's Picture Pie: A Circle Drawing Book* by Ed Emberley (Little, Brown, 1984).

Vocabulary • ONE (the whole) • fraction • denominator • numerator

Getting Started

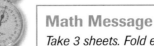

Mental Math and Reflexes

Say a number. Have children record its double on their slates. *Suggestions:*

6 8 10 15 40 100

Say a number. Have children record half of the number on their slates. *Suggestions:*

14 18 40 50 600

Math Message

Take 3 sheets. Fold each one into 4 equal squares. Carefully cut the squares apart along the folds.

1 Teaching the Lesson

◆ Math Message Follow-Up

WHOLE-CLASS ACTIVITY

Check that each child has 12 squares of approximately the same size.

◆ Folding Squares into Equal Parts

PARTNER ACTIVITY

Ask each child to fold one of his or her squares into 2 equal parts. Ask, *Is there more than one way to do this?*

Have children work with a partner to fold other squares into 4 equal parts in as many different ways as possible.

Finally, ask children to fold some of the remaining squares into 8 equal parts in as many ways as possible.

Invite children to share their work with the rest of the class. If children do not suggest all of the solutions shown above, ask them to look for other solutions or show the class the missing solutions.

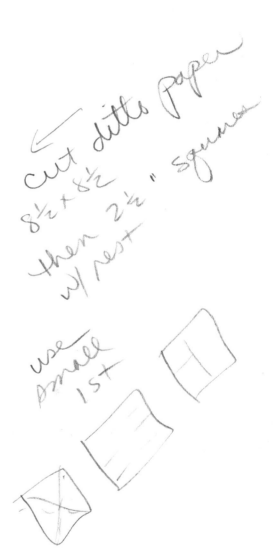

At the conclusion of the folding activity, have children sort their squares into piles according to the number of equal parts—squares showing two equal parts, four equal parts, and eight equal parts. If the squares are organized in this way, it will be easier for children to complete the following activity.

✦ Reviewing Basic Fraction Concepts

WHOLE-CLASS ACTIVITY

Ask children to take the square they folded into two equal parts and to color one of the parts. Review the following ideas:

- If you think of the square as representing **ONE** (**the whole**), then each part is half of ONE.
- The **fraction** $\frac{1}{2}$ names one of the parts.

Emphasize that the parts must be equal.

Continue with such activities as the following:

▷ Take one of the squares that you folded into four equal parts. Color one part of the square. Tell what fraction names the colored part. $\frac{1}{4}$ Tell what fraction names the part that is not colored. $\frac{3}{4}$

▷ Take another square that you folded into four equal parts. Color two of the parts. Tell what fraction names the colored part. $\frac{2}{4}$ or $\frac{1}{2}$

▷ Take another square that you folded into four equal parts. Color four of the parts. Tell what fraction names the colored part. $\frac{4}{4}$ Tell what fraction names the part that is not colored. $\frac{0}{4}$

▷ Take a square that you folded into eight equal parts. Color one of the parts. Tell what fraction names the colored part. $\frac{1}{8}$ Tell what fraction names the part that is not colored. $\frac{7}{8}$

▷ Repeat with other fractions, such as $\frac{3}{8}$ and $\frac{5}{8}$, using squares folded into eight equal parts.

NOTE: To help children learn to associate objects, pictures, and concrete models with fractions, write all fractions on the board during this activity.

As you write fractions on the board, mention the following:

- The number under the fraction bar is called the **denominator.** What does the denominator of $\frac{3}{4}$ tell you? The whole is divided into 4 equal parts. Emphasize again that the parts must be equal.

- The number above the fraction bar is called the **numerator.** What does the numerator of $\frac{3}{4}$ tell you? We are thinking about 3 equal parts of the whole.

Summary: The denominator of a fraction tells the total number of equal parts into which the whole is divided. The numerator of a fraction indicates the number of equal parts that you are thinking about.

NOTE: At this time, it is not necessary for children to use the words *numerator* and *denominator.* They will learn them over time with repeated exposure. Do, however, use these words, as well as the informal "the number on the top" and "the number on the bottom," when you discuss fractions.

◆ Writing Fractions for Parts of Regions
(*Math Journal 2,* p. 188)

INDEPENDENT ACTIVITY

Children divide shapes into equal parts and color one or two of the parts on each shape. Then children write fractions to name the colored and uncolored parts.

Adjusting the Activity The shape in each of the first three problems is a pattern-block shape. Children who are having difficulty dividing these shapes into equal parts might find it helpful to use pattern blocks.

2 Ongoing Learning & Practice

◆ Making up and Solving Multiplication and Division Number Stories
(*Math Journal 2,* p. 189)

INDEPENDENT ACTIVITY

Children can use arrays to help them solve multiplication and division number stories.

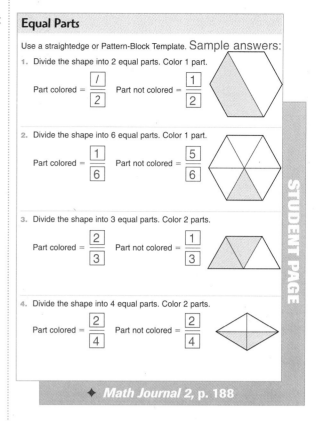

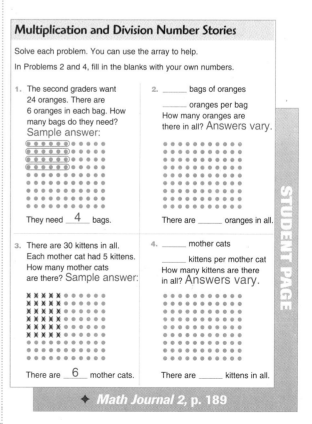

Math Boxes 8.1

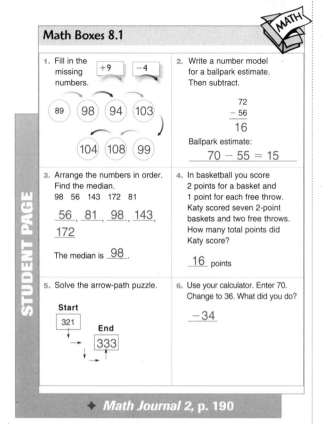

1. Fill in the missing numbers.

+9 **−4**

89 98 94 103
104 108 99

2. Write a number model for a ballpark estimate. Then subtract.

$$\begin{array}{r} 72 \\ -\ 56 \\ \hline 16 \end{array}$$

Ballpark estimate:
70 − 55 = 15

3. Arrange the numbers in order. Find the median.

98 56 143 172 81

56, 81, 98, 143, 172

The median is 98.

4. In basketball you score 2 points for a basket and 1 point for each free throw. Katy scored seven 2-point baskets and two free throws. How many total points did Katy score?

16 points

5. Solve the arrow-path puzzle.

Start
321
End
333

6. Use your calculator. Enter 70. Change to 36. What did you do?

−34

Math Journal 2, p. 190

Equal Parts

Home Link 8.1

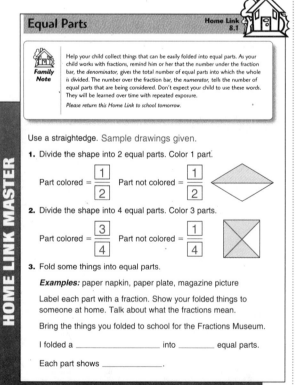

Family Note Help your child collect things that can be easily folded into equal parts. As your child works with fractions, remind him or her that the number under the fraction bar, the *denominator*, gives the total number of equal parts into which the whole is divided. The number over the fraction bar, the *numerator*, tells the number of equal parts that are being considered. Don't expect your child to use these words. They will be learned over time with repeated exposure.

Please return this Home Link to school tomorrow.

Use a straightedge. Sample drawings given.

1. Divide the shape into 2 equal parts. Color 1 part.

Part colored = $\dfrac{1}{2}$ Part not colored = $\dfrac{1}{2}$

2. Divide the shape into 4 equal parts. Color 3 parts.

Part colored = $\dfrac{3}{4}$ Part not colored = $\dfrac{1}{4}$

3. Fold some things into equal parts.

Examples: paper napkin, paper plate, magazine picture

Label each part with a fraction. Show your folded things to someone at home. Talk about what the fractions mean.

Bring the things you folded to school for the Fractions Museum.

I folded a _____ into _____ equal parts.

Each part shows _____.

Math Masters, p. 346

◆ Math Boxes 8.1 (*Math Journal 2*, p. 190)

INDEPENDENT ACTIVITY

Mixed Review This journal page provides opportunities for cumulative review or assessment of concepts and skills.

◆ Home Link 8.1 (*Math Masters*, p. 346)

Home Connection Children practice writing fractions for parts of regions in Problems 1 and 2. In Problem 3, children show someone at home how they can fold things, such as napkins, paper plates, or magazine pictures, into equal parts. Then children label each part of the whole with a fraction.

Children will bring the folded objects to school to include as part of a Fractions Museum.

3 Options for Individualizing

◆ ENRICHMENT Naming Equal Parts Situations Found in Literature

WHOLE-CLASS ACTIVITY   15–30 min

Literature Link Read the following books to children, or have them read the books themselves.

Gator Pie

Summary: Three alligators decide to share a pie. Before they can cut it, additional alligators arrive. They need to determine how to cut the pie into thirds, fourths, eighths, and finally hundredths. A circular model of the pie is shown for each new situation. Text like the following accompanies the illustration: "Three gators. That means three pieces. Cut three one-thirds."

Eating Fractions

Summary: Wholes, halves, thirds, and fourths are introduced through colorful photographs of such foods as bananas and muffins.

Ed Emberley's Picture Pie: A Circle Drawing Book

Summary: Circles cut into halves, fourths, or eighths are the basis for the artwork in the book. The circles are of various colors and form elaborate designs.

Children may wish to create their own circle designs, based on those in the book, and discuss the number of circles and fractional parts of circles that were used.

◆ EXTRA PRACTICE Dividing Shapes into Equal Parts (*Math Masters,* pp. 139 and 140)

INDEPENDENT ACTIVITY   **15–30 min**

Children make shapes on a geoboard and divide them into equal parts. You may want to have only advanced children do the Challenge problems. Take time for children to share different solutions for each problem.

◆ LANGUAGE DIVERSITY Describing Fractions Displayed on a Fraction Poster

SMALL-GROUP ACTIVITY   **5–15 min**

Construct a poster like the one below to remind children of the meanings of *numerator* and *denominator*.

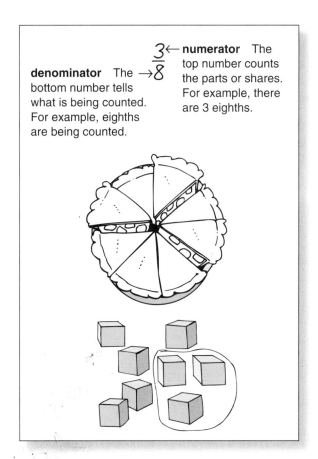

denominator The bottom number tells what is being counted. For example, eighths are being counted.

numerator The top number counts the parts or shares. For example, there are 3 eighths.

A fraction poster

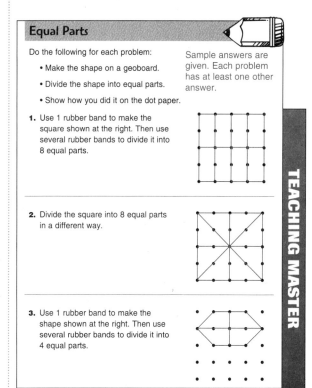

Equal Parts

Do the following for each problem:
- Make the shape on a geoboard.
- Divide the shape into equal parts.
- Show how you did it on the dot paper.

Sample answers are given. Each problem has at least one other answer.

1. Use 1 rubber band to make the square shown at the right. Then use several rubber bands to divide it into 8 equal parts.

2. Divide the square into 8 equal parts in a different way.

3. Use 1 rubber band to make the shape shown at the right. Then use several rubber bands to divide it into 4 equal parts.

Math Masters, p. 139

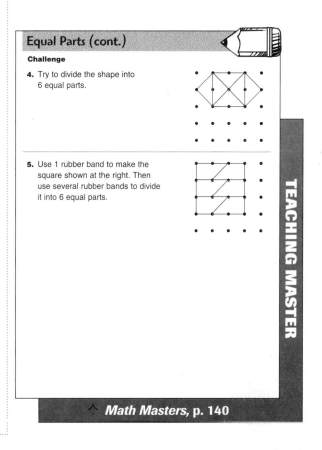

Equal Parts (cont.)

Challenge

4. Try to divide the shape into 6 equal parts.

5. Use 1 rubber band to make the square shown at the right. Then use several rubber bands to divide it into 6 equal parts.

Math Masters, p. 140

TEACHING MASTER

8.2 EXPLORATIONS
Exploring Fractions, Multiplication and Division, and Volume

OBJECTIVES To link a fraction amount to the size of the ONE, or whole; to prepare for multiplication and division; and to introduce the concept of volume.

summaries	materials

1 Teaching the Lesson

Exploration A: Children compare pairs of pattern-block shapes as fractions and multiples of each other. [Numeration]	☐ Home Link 8.1 **Exploration A:** Per partnership: ☐ *Math Journal 2*, pp. 191 and 192 ☐ Teaching Master (*Math Masters*, p. 141) ☐ pattern blocks; Pattern-Block Template
Exploration B: Children form rectangles or "fences" on geoboards; they also determine the total number of pegs inside the fences and the dimensions of the rectangles. [Operations and Computation]	**Exploration B:** Per group: ☐ *Math Journal 2*, p. 193 ☐ Teaching Master (*Math Masters*, p. 142) ☐ Teaching Aid Assessment Master (*Math Masters*, p. 498) ☐ geoboard; rubber bands; straightedge
Exploration C: Children use base-10 blocks to build structures; they also estimate and find the volumes of the structures in cubic centimeters. [Measurement and Reference Frames; Numeration]	**Exploration C:** Per group: ☐ Teaching Master (*Math Masters*, p. 143) ☐ base-10 blocks: several cubes, longs, flats; big cubes, if available ☐ slate ***See* Advance Preparation**

2 Ongoing Learning & Practice

Children practice finding the total number of items in an array by playing playing *Array Bingo*. [Operations and Computation; Numeration] Children practice and maintain skills through Math Boxes and Home Link activities.	☐ *Math Journal 2*, p. 194 ☐ Home Link Master (*Math Masters*, p. 347) ☐ Teaching Masters (*Math Masters*, pp. 118 and 119) ☐ 2 six-sided dice, 1 twelve-sided die, or an egg-carton number generator per group; scissors ☐ 9 cards labeled "A" cut from *Math Masters*, p. 117 ☐ 7 cards not labeled "A" cut from *Math Masters*, p. 117 (optional) ☐ 1 twenty-sided die or one number card for each of the numbers 1–20 per group (from the Everything Math Deck, if available)

3 Options for Individualizing

Extra Practice Children find parts of a whole. [Numeration]	☐ *Minute Math®*, p. 40

Additional Information

Advance Preparation Before starting the lesson, decide where to set up the Fractions Museum in your classroom.

Vocabulary • cubic centimeter • volume

Getting Started

Mental Math and Reflexes

Write the following sets of numbers on the board. Ask children to find the median of each set. Remind them to first put the sets in ascending or descending order.

- 2, 5, 8, 9, 0, 1, 1 2
- 56, 89, 34, 35, 82 56
- 5, 9, 11, 18 9, 11, or 10
- 100, 400, 700, 600 400, 500, or 600

Math Message

Martha ate $\frac{1}{4}$ of a large pizza. Joe ate $\frac{1}{4}$ of a small pizza. Did they eat the same amount of pizza?

How do you know?

Home Link 8.1 Follow-Up

Use the items children brought from home to start a Fractions Museum. Encourage children to bring additional items to add to the museum. Suggest that they look for written fractions in ads and on food packages and kitchen utensils. Children might, for example, bring a half-pint or half-gallon milk carton and measuring spoons or cups.

1 Teaching the Lesson

◆ Math Message Follow-Up

WHOLE-CLASS DISCUSSION

On the board, draw and label two pizzas.

As children share their answers, it is important to emphasize that a fraction is not meaningful if one does not know what it is a fraction of; that is, what is the ONE, or the whole. A fraction is always "a fraction of something."

◆ Comparing Pattern Blocks, One of Which Represents ONE

WHOLE-CLASS DISCUSSION

Hold up two pattern blocks, the larger of which is a multiple of the smaller. For example, hold a hexagon in one hand and a trapezoid in the other. Ask questions like the following:

- How many of these ⬡ do you need to cover one of these ⬡? 2
- If ⬡ is ONE (the whole), what fraction of ONE is ⬡? one-half
- How do we write this fraction? $\frac{1}{2}$

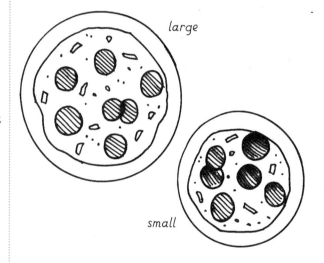

large

small

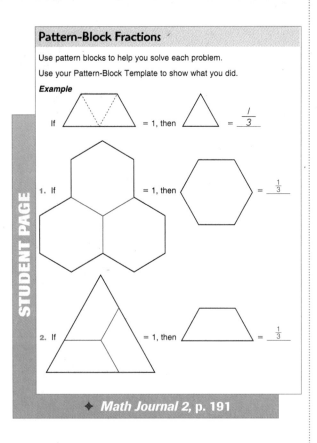

Pattern-Block Fractions

Use pattern blocks to help you solve each problem.
Use your Pattern-Block Template to show what you did.

Example

If ◻ = 1, then △ = $\frac{1}{3}$

1. If ⬡⬡⬡ = 1, then ⬡ = $\frac{1}{3}$

2. If △ = 1, then ◻ = $\frac{1}{3}$

✦ *Math Journal 2,* p. 191

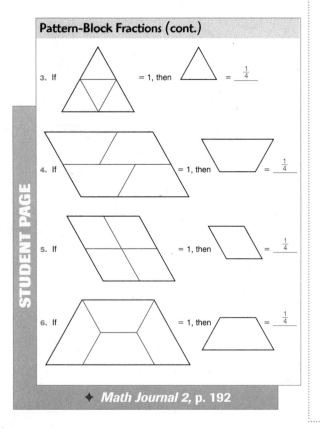

Pattern-Block Fractions (cont.)

3. If △ = 1, then △ = $\frac{1}{4}$

4. If ▱ = 1, then ◻ = $\frac{1}{4}$

5. If ▱ = 1, then ◇ = $\frac{1}{4}$

6. If ◻ = 1, then ◻ = $\frac{1}{4}$

✦ *Math Journal 2,* p. 192

Next, reverse the relationship between the pattern blocks. Ask:

• If ◻ is ONE, how much is ⬡? 2

Display and ask about other pattern blocks. *For example:*

• If △ is ONE, ◇ is what number? 2
• If ◇ is ONE, △ is what fraction? $\frac{1}{2}$
• If △ is ONE, ◻ is what number? 3
• If ◻ is ONE, △ is what fraction? $\frac{1}{3}$
• If △ is ONE, ⬡ is what number? 6
• If ⬡ is ONE, △ is what fraction? $\frac{1}{6}$
• If ◇ is ONE, ⬡ is what number? 3
• If ⬡ is ONE, ◇ is what fraction? $\frac{1}{3}$

◆ **Exploration A: Comparing Pairs of Shapes When One Shape Represents ONE**
(*Math Journal 2,* pp. 191 and 192;
Math Masters, p. 141)

PARTNER ACTIVITY

In each problem on the journal pages, children compare a pattern-block shape to a larger shape. Go over the example on journal page 191 with children. Ask them to cover the trapezoid with three triangle pattern blocks to reinforce the fact that a triangle pattern block is one-third of a trapezoid.

Do the first problem together. Children cover the larger shape with hexagon pattern blocks. Since it takes three hexagons to cover the larger shape, a hexagon is one-third of the larger shape. Children write the fraction $\frac{1}{3}$ in the answer space and use their Pattern-Block Templates or a straightedge to partition the larger shape.

Partners work together to complete the rest of the problems on journal pages 191 and 192. Circulate and offer help as needed.

When children have completed the journal pages and Problem 3 on *Math Masters,* page 141, bring the class together to share solutions. Emphasize that each of the smaller shapes on journal page 191 is represented by the fraction $\frac{1}{3}$. The fractions mean different things, however, since the wholes are not the same size and shape. Similarly, each of the smaller shapes on journal page 192 is $\frac{1}{4}$ of the larger shape.

Summary: The size of a fractional part of a whole depend on the size of the whole. A fraction has no meaning unles we know what it is a fraction of.

Adjusting the Activity You may want to challenge children to compare the sizes of the larger shapes in Problems 1 and 2 and also in 4 and 6 on journal pages 191 and 192. Since both shapes in Problems 4 and 6 can be covered with 4 trapezoids, the shapes are the same size.

The shape in Problem 1 can be covered with 6 trapezoids, and the shape in Problem 2 with 3 trapezoids. So, the shape in Problem 1 is twice as large as the shape in Problem 2.

◆ Exploration B: Making Arrays with Geoboard Fences

(*Math Journal 2*, p. 193; *Math Masters*, pp. 142 and 498)

SMALL-GROUP ACTIVITY

Children form a variety of rectangles on their geoboards, using one rubber band for each rectangle. They draw four of their rectangles at the top of the journal page.

NOTE: Exploration B reinforces the work with arrays done at the end of Unit 6.

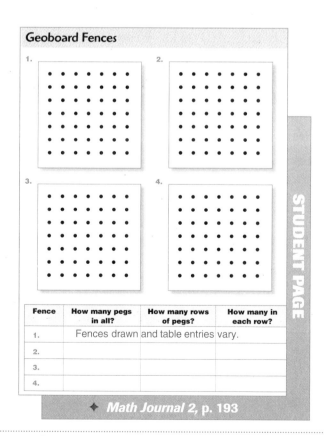

Pattern-Block Fractions

Work with a partner.

Materials
- *Math Journal 2*, pp. 191 and 192
- pattern blocks
- straightedge or Pattern-Block Template

Study the example at the top of journal page 191. Cover the △ with △s.

You need 3 triangles, so a △ is $\frac{1}{3}$ of a △.

1. Do Problem 1 on journal page 191.

   Cover the larger shape with hexagon blocks.

   The number of hexagons helps you find the fraction to write as the answer.

   Use your straightedge or Pattern-Block Template to divide the larger shape into hexagons.

2. Do the rest of the problems on journal pages 191 and 192 in the same way.

3. Get together with other partners in the class. Check one another's work.

   Each smaller shape on page 191 is $\frac{1}{3}$ of the larger shape.

   Are the smaller shapes all the same size? _____ no

   Each smaller shape on page 192 is $\frac{1}{4}$ of the larger shape.

   Are the smaller shapes all the same size? _____ no

Math Masters, p. 141

TEACHING MASTER

Geoboard Fences

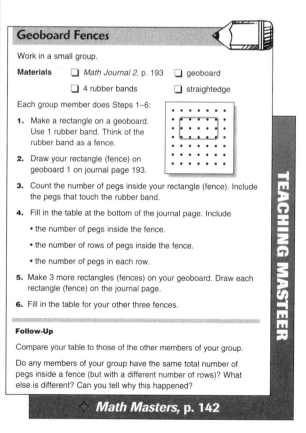

Fence	How many pegs in all?	How many rows of pegs?	How many in each row?
1.	Fences drawn	and table entries	vary.
2.			
3.			
4.			

STUDENT PAGE

Geoboard Fences

Work in a small group.

Materials
- *Math Journal 2*, p. 193
- geoboard
- 4 rubber bands
- straightedge

Each group member does Steps 1–6:

1. Make a rectangle on a geoboard. Use 1 rubber band. Think of the rubber band as a fence.

2. Draw your rectangle (fence) on geoboard 1 on journal page 193.

3. Count the number of pegs inside your rectangle (fence). Include the pegs that touch the rubber band.

4. Fill in the table at the bottom of the journal page. Include
   - the number of pegs inside the fence.
   - the number of rows of pegs inside the fence.
   - the number of pegs in each row.

5. Make 3 more rectangles (fences) on your geoboard. Draw each rectangle (fence) on the journal page.

6. Fill in the table for your other three fences.

Follow-Up

Compare your table to those of the other members of your group.

Do any members of your group have the same total number of pegs inside a fence (but with a different number of rows? What else is different? Can you tell why this happened?

TEACHING MASTER

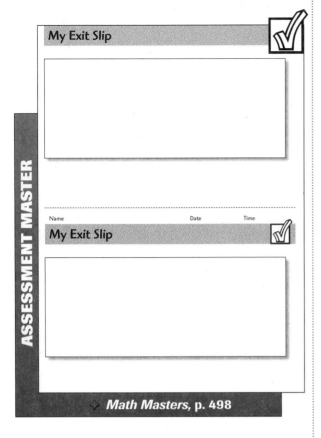

Name _____ Date _____ Time _____

My Exit Slip

Name _____ Date _____ Time _____

My Exit Slip

Math Masters, p. 498

Next, children find the total number of pegs within each "fence" (including the pegs touching the rubber band), the number of rows of pegs, and the number of pegs in each row. Children record this information in the table at the bottom of the journal page.

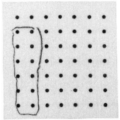

ONGOING ASSESSMENT

Ask members of each group to compare tables. Did any of the same totals within "fences" have a different number of rows with different numbers in each row? Can children explain how this is possible? Ask them to record their thoughts on an Exit Slip.

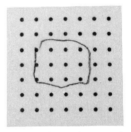 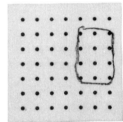

Children show how 6 × 2, 3 × 4, and 4 × 3 fences each enclose a total of 12 pegs.

◆ Exploration C: Finding the Volume of Base-10 Structures (*Math Masters,* p. 143)

SMALL-GROUP ACTIVITY

Two or three group members take turns building structures with base-10 blocks. Each group member studies the structure and then estimates the total number of centimeter cubes (**cubic centimeters**) in the structure. Children write their estimates on slates.

As they take the structures apart, children count the cubes and compare the actual totals to their estimates. They report the **volume** in the form of, "This structure has a volume of _____ cubic centimeters."

NOTE: Exploration C helps prepare children for work in Unit 9.

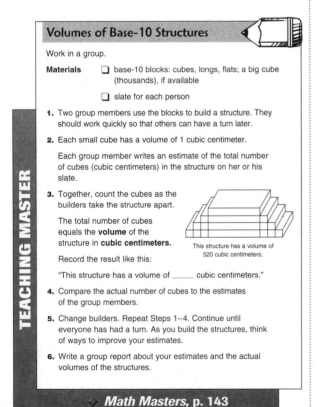

Volumes of Base-10 Structures

Work in a group.

Materials ☐ base-10 blocks: cubes, longs, flats; a big cube (thousands), if available

☐ slate for each person

1. Two group members use the blocks to build a structure. They should work quickly so that others can have a turn later.

2. Each small cube has a volume of 1 cubic centimeter.

   Each group member writes an estimate of the total number of cubes (cubic centimeters) in the structure on her or his slate.

3. Together, count the cubes as the builders take the structure apart.

   The total number of cubes equals the **volume** of the structure in **cubic centimeters**.

   This structure has a volume of 520 cubic centimeters.

   Record the result like this:

   "This structure has a volume of _____ cubic centimeters."

4. Compare the actual number of cubes to the estimates of the group members.

5. Change builders. Repeat Steps 1–4. Continue until everyone has had a turn. As you build the structures, think of ways to improve your estimates.

6. Write a group report about your estimates and the actual volumes of the structures.

Math Masters, p. 143

2 Ongoing Learning & Practice

◆ Playing *Array Bingo*
(*Math Masters,* pp. 117–119)

SMALL-GROUP ACTIVITY

This game was introduced in Lesson 6.10. The rules are found on *Math Masters,* pages 118 and 119. To make the game more challenging, have children use all 16 array cards and follow the suggestions for Another Way to Play.

◆ Math Boxes 8.2 (*Math Journal 2,* p. 194)

INDEPENDENT ACTIVITY

Mixed Review This journal page provides opportunities for cumulative review or assessment of concepts and skills.

◆ Home Link 8.2 (*Math Masters,* p. 347)

Home Connection Children write fractions to name parts of regions.

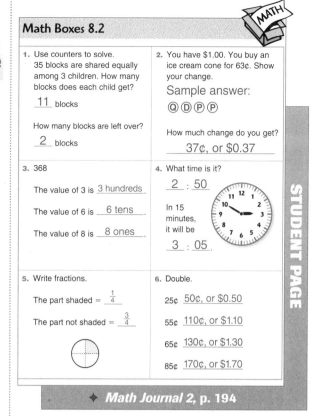

Math Boxes 8.2

1. Use counters to solve.
   35 blocks are shared equally among 3 children. How many blocks does each child get?

   __11__ blocks

   How many blocks are left over?

   __2__ blocks

2. You have $1.00. You buy an ice cream cone for 63¢. Show your change.
   Sample answer:

   Q D P P

   How much change do you get?

   __37¢, or $0.37__

3. 368

   The value of 3 is __3 hundreds__

   The value of 6 is __6 tens__

   The value of 8 is __8 ones__

4. What time is it?

   __2__ : __50__

   In 15 minutes, it will be

   __3__ : __05__

5. Write fractions.

   The part shaded = $\frac{1}{4}$

   The part not shaded = $\frac{3}{4}$

6. Double.

   25¢ __50¢, or $0.50__

   55¢ __110¢, or $1.10__

   65¢ __130¢, or $1.30__

   85¢ __170¢, or $1.70__

◆ *Math Journal 2, p. 194*

STUDENT PAGE

3 Options for Individualizing

◆ EXTRA PRACTICE Minute Math

SMALL-GROUP ACTIVITY **5–15 min**

To offer children more experience with finding parts of a whole, see the following page in *Minute Math:*

Operations: p. 40

Fractions of Shapes Home Link 8.2

Family Note As you work on this activity with your child, keep in mind that the shapes below the ONE are fractional parts of the ONE. Remind your child that the size of a fractional part of a whole depends on the size of the whole. It may be helpful for your child to separate the ONE into parts that are the size of the fractional part. For example, in Problem 1, your child can divide the square in half diagonally to determine that the triangle is $\frac{1}{2}$ of the square.

Please return this Home Link to school tomorrow.

1. If this is ONE,

   then what are these?

   Write a fraction for each shape. $\frac{1}{2}$ $\frac{1}{4}$ $\frac{1}{2}$ $\frac{3}{4}$

2. If this is ONE,

   then what are these?

   Write a fraction for each shape. $\frac{1}{4}$ $\frac{1}{2}$ $\frac{3}{4}$ $\frac{1}{2}$

3. If this is ONE,

   then what are these?

   Write a fraction for each shape. $\frac{1}{2}$ $\frac{1}{3}$ $\frac{1}{6}$ $\frac{5}{6}$

Math Masters, p. 347

HOME LINK MASTER

8.3 Collections of Things

OBJECTIVE To use fractions to name parts of collections.

summaries	materials
1 Teaching the Lesson	
Children identify fractions of collections of pennies; they also identify equal shares and translate them into fractions. Children color fractional parts of a set. [Numeration]	☐ *Math Journal 2*, pp. 195 and 196 ☐ Home Link 8.2 ☐ penny, nickel, dime, quarter, and dollar bill ☐ collection of 3 to 6 books and various sets of objects, such as crayons, chairs, or buttons ☐ 15 pennies ☐ red crayon or pencil
2 Ongoing Learning & Practice	
Children divide regions into equal parts, color some parts, and name fractions for the colored and uncolored parts. [Numeration; Geometry] Children practice and maintain skills through Math Boxes and Home Link activities.	☐ *Math Journal 2*, pp. 197 and 198 ☐ Home Link Master (*Math Masters*, p. 348) ☐ 49 pennies ☐ straightedge or Pattern-Block Template
3 Options for Individualizing	
Language Diversity Children make a display about collective terms; then they use fractions to name parts of those collections. [Numeration]	☐ *Only One* (optional) **See Advance Preparation**

Additional Information

Advance Preparation Before doing the optional Language Diversity activity in Part 3, you may want to obtain the book *Only One* by Marc Harshman (Cobblehill Books, 1993).

Getting Started

Mental Math and Reflexes

Illustrate the following questions by holding up coins and a $1 bill.

- How many nickels make one dime? 2

- If a dime is ONE, then what is a nickel? one-half How do we write this fraction? $\frac{1}{2}$

- If a dime is ONE, then what is $1? 10 What is a penny? $\frac{1}{10}$

- If a quarter is ONE, then what is $1? 4 A nickel? $\frac{1}{5}$

- If $1 is ONE, then what is a quarter? $\frac{1}{4}$ A dime? $\frac{1}{10}$

Math Message

Jack had 12 marbles. He gave $\frac{1}{3}$ of the marbles to Sue and $\frac{1}{4}$ of the marbles to Mike. How many marbles did he keep for himself? 5 marbles

Home Link 8.2 Follow-Up

As you review answers, emphasize the idea that the size of a fractional part depends on the size of the whole. A fraction has no meaning unless we know what it is a fraction of.

1 Teaching the Lesson

◆ Math Message Follow-Up

WHOLE-CLASS DISCUSSION

Have children share solution strategies. If necessary, model the story with 12 pennies or counters.

◆ Reviewing Fractions with Reference to Collections of Objects

WHOLE-CLASS DISCUSSION

Display a pile of books. Have someone count the books. Then, pointing to the pile of books, ask, *What fraction of the pile is 1 book? What fraction are 2 books?* Write each fraction on the board as you talk.

Follow the same procedure with other collections, such as a new box of crayons or chairs in rows.

NOTE: Because fractions of collections of things refer to the numbers of things, not their amounts, the things in a collection need not be identical. However, children might find it easier to understand the concept if you begin with collections made up of similar items.

◆ Identifying Fractions of Collections of Pennies

WHOLE-CLASS ACTIVITY

Each child should have about 15 pennies. Conduct brisk oral drills, such as the following:

- Make a pile of 4 pennies. What fraction of the pile is 1 penny? $\frac{1}{4}$ 2 pennies? $\frac{2}{4}$ or $\frac{1}{2}$ 4 pennies? $\frac{4}{4}$ 0 pennies? $\frac{0}{4}$

- Make a pile of 5 pennies. Show me $\frac{1}{5}$ of this pile. 1 penny $\frac{2}{5}$ of the pile. 2 pennies $\frac{5}{5}$ of the pile. 5 pennies How many pennies are in $\frac{0}{5}$ of the pile? 0 pennies

- Take 12 pennies. Show how you would share them equally with another person. How many pennies would each person get? 6 pennies Show equal shares among 3 people. How many pennies would each person get? 4 pennies

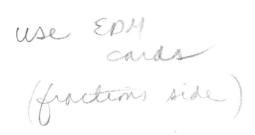

Adjusting the Activity To extend the activity, pose problems like the following: *There are 8 crayons in 1 box. How many crayons are there in 2 boxes?* 16 crayons *In $1\frac{1}{2}$ boxes?* There are 8 crayons in 1 box, so there are 4 crayons in half of a box. Therefore, there are 8 + 4, or 12 crayons in $1\frac{1}{2}$ boxes.

use EDM cards (fractions side)

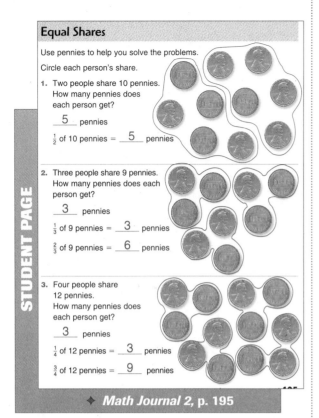

Equal Shares

Use pennies to help you solve the problems.
Circle each person's share.

1. Two people share 10 pennies.
   How many pennies does each person get?

   __5__ pennies

   $\frac{1}{2}$ of 10 pennies = __5__ pennies

2. Three people share 9 pennies.
   How many pennies does each person get?

   __3__ pennies

   $\frac{1}{3}$ of 9 pennies = __3__ pennies

   $\frac{2}{3}$ of 9 pennies = __6__ pennies

3. Four people share 12 pennies.
   How many pennies does each person get?

   __3__ pennies

   $\frac{1}{4}$ of 12 pennies = __3__ pennies

   $\frac{3}{4}$ of 12 pennies = __9__ pennies

✦ *Math Journal 2*, p. 195

ONGOING ASSESSMENT

Compare children's work on journal page 188 to their work on journal page 197 to assess progress in writing fractions for parts of regions.

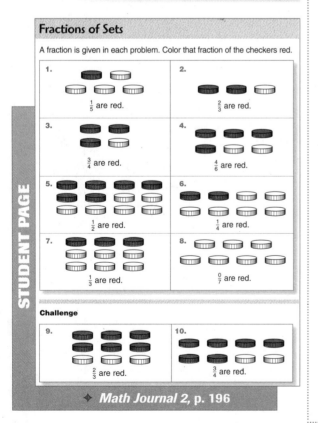

Fractions of Sets

A fraction is given in each problem. Color that fraction of the checkers red.

1. $\frac{1}{5}$ are red.
2. $\frac{2}{3}$ are red.
3. $\frac{3}{4}$ are red.
4. $\frac{4}{6}$ are red.
5. $\frac{1}{2}$ are red.
6. $\frac{1}{4}$ are red.
7. $\frac{1}{3}$ are red.
8. $\frac{0}{7}$ are red.

Challenge

9. $\frac{2}{3}$ are red.
10. $\frac{3}{4}$ are red.

✦ *Math Journal 2*, p. 196

• I am thinking of a pile of pennies. There are 4 pennies in $\frac{1}{2}$ of the pile. Show me the whole pile. 8 pennies What if 4 pennies are $\frac{1}{3}$ of the pile? How many pennies are in the whole pile now? 12 pennies

◆ Finding Fractions of Collections of Things
(*Math Journal 2*, pp. 195 and 196)

INDEPENDENT ACTIVITY

Most children should be able to complete these pages independently. You may need to go through the first problem on each page with the class to make sure that children understand what they are to do.

2 Ongoing Learning & Practice

◆ Writing Fractions for Parts of Regions
(*Math Journal 2*, p. 197)

INDEPENDENT ACTIVITY

Children divide regions into equal parts and color some of the parts. Then they write fractions to name both the colored and the uncolored parts.

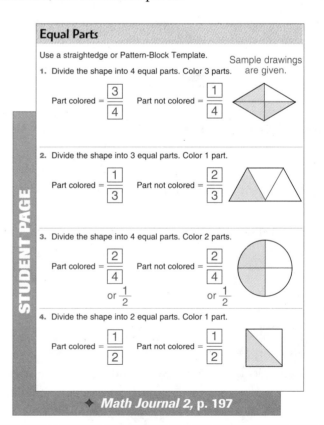

Equal Parts

Use a straightedge or Pattern-Block Template.
Sample drawings are given.

1. Divide the shape into 4 equal parts. Color 3 parts.

   Part colored = $\frac{3}{4}$ Part not colored = $\frac{1}{4}$

2. Divide the shape into 3 equal parts. Color 1 part.

   Part colored = $\frac{1}{3}$ Part not colored = $\frac{2}{3}$

3. Divide the shape into 4 equal parts. Color 2 parts.

   Part colored = $\frac{2}{4}$ Part not colored = $\frac{2}{4}$

   or $\frac{1}{2}$ or $\frac{1}{2}$

4. Divide the shape into 2 equal parts. Color 1 part.

   Part colored = $\frac{1}{2}$ Part not colored = $\frac{1}{2}$

✦ *Math Journal 2*, p. 197

◆ Math Boxes 8.3 (*Math Journal 2*, p. 198)

INDEPENDENT ACTIVITY

Mixed Review This journal page provides opportunities for cumulative review or assessment of concepts and skills.

◆ Home Link 8.3 (*Math Masters*, p. 348)

Home Connection Children solve an equal-sharing problem. Children also find additional items to add to the Fractions Museum.

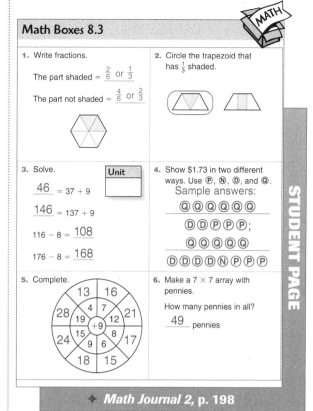

Math Boxes 8.3

1. Write fractions.

   The part shaded = $\frac{2}{6}$ or $\frac{1}{3}$

   The part not shaded = $\frac{4}{6}$ or $\frac{2}{3}$

2. Circle the trapezoid that has $\frac{1}{3}$ shaded.

3. Solve.   **Unit**

   $\underline{46} = 37 + 9$

   $\underline{146} = 137 + 9$

   $116 - 8 = \underline{108}$

   $176 - 8 = \underline{168}$

4. Show $1.73 in two different ways. Use Ⓟ, Ⓝ, Ⓓ, and Ⓠ.

   Sample answers:
   Ⓠ Ⓠ Ⓠ Ⓠ Ⓠ Ⓠ
   Ⓓ Ⓓ Ⓟ Ⓟ Ⓟ;
   Ⓠ Ⓠ Ⓠ Ⓠ Ⓠ
   Ⓓ Ⓓ Ⓓ Ⓝ Ⓟ Ⓟ Ⓟ

5. Complete.

   13 | 16
   28 | 4 | 7 | 21
   19 | +9 | 12
   24 | 15 | 8 | 17
   9 | 6
   18 | 15

6. Make a 7 × 7 array with pennies.

   How many pennies in all?

   $\underline{49}$ pennies

STUDENT PAGE

◆ *Math Journal 2*, p. 198

◆ LANGUAGE DIVERSITY Making a Collection of "Collective Terms"

SMALL-GROUP ACTIVITY   30+ min

Portfolio Ideas

The English language has many expressions to describe groups or collections: a school of fish, a pack of dogs, a litter of pups, a pride of lions, a swarm of bees, a flock of sheep, a colony of ants, a flight of stairs, a bouquet of flowers, a bunch of grapes, and so on. Children enjoy learning such expressions and using them in problems they make up. Some children might find it interesting to make a "collection of collective terms"—in book form or as a bulletin-board display. To reinforce the meaning of collective terms, children can illustrate collections and then write fractions to describe parts of collections.

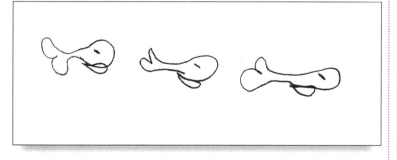

Collection (a pod of whales)

◯ Literature Link

The book *Only One* by Marc Harshman (Cobblehill Books, 1993) discusses objects that compose a collection. For example, "There may be a million stars, but there is only one sky."

Fractions of Collections   Home Link 8.3

Family Note In this lesson, your child learned to use fractions to name part of a collection of objects. For example, your child could identify 2 out of 4 objects as $\frac{2}{4}$ or $\frac{1}{2}$. Show your child how to use pennies to act out Problem 1. Help your child collect household items that can be separated into fractional parts—or any other items that have fractions written on them. Encourage your child to bring these items to school for the class's Fractions Museum.

Please return this Home Link to school tomorrow.

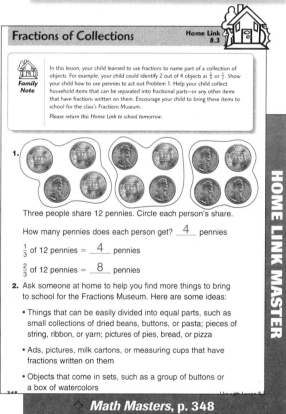

1.

Three people share 12 pennies. Circle each person's share.

How many pennies does each person get? $\underline{4}$ pennies

$\frac{1}{3}$ of 12 pennies = $\underline{4}$ pennies

$\frac{2}{3}$ of 12 pennies = $\underline{8}$ pennies

2. Ask someone at home to help you find more things to bring to school for the Fractions Museum. Here are some ideas:

   • Things that can be easily divided into equal parts, such as small collections of dried beans, buttons, or pasta; pieces of string, ribbon, or yarn; pictures of pies, bread, or pizza.

   • Ads, pictures, milk cartons, or measuring cups that have fractions written on them

   • Objects that come in sets, such as a group of buttons or a box of watercolors

HOME LINK MASTER

◆ *Math Masters*, p. 348

8.4 Equivalent Fractions

OBJECTIVE To investigate the idea that many different fractions can name the same fractional part of a whole.

Lesson 8.4 (N.ME.02.19, M.UN.02.06)
Part 1: Apply concepts of ½, ¼, ¾ to analog clocks and telling time.

summary	materials

1 Teaching the Lesson

Children find equivalent fractions by matching fractional parts of circles. [Numeration; Geometry]

- ☐ *Math Journal 2*, pp. 200 and 201
- ☐ Home Link 8.3
- ☐ Teaching Master (*Math Masters*, p. 144)
- ☐ 1 set of fraction circles cut out from *Math Masters*, p. 144 (optional)
- ☐ 18 pennies or other counters (optional)
- ☐ scissors
- ☐ glue

***See* Advance Preparation**

2 Ongoing Learning & Practice

Children practice and maintain skills through Math Boxes and Home Link activities.

- ☐ *Math Journal 2*, p. 199
- ☐ Home Link Master (*Math Masters*, p. 349)

3 Options for Individualizing

Reteaching Children identify sums and differences that match a given number by playing *Name That Number*.
[Operations and Computation; Numeration]

Per group:

- ☐ 4 number cards for each of the numbers 0–10 (from the Everything Math Deck, if available)
- ☐ 1 number card for each of the numbers 11–20 (from the Everything Math Deck, if available)

Additional Information

Advance Preparation Before beginning the Math Message, make one copy of *Math Masters,* page 144 for each child, as well as a few extras. Place them near the Math Message.

During the *Making a Display of Equivalent Fractions* activity in Part 1, you may want to use the overhead projector to display a set of fraction circles cut from *Math Masters,* page 144 or a set of fraction circles commercially made for the overhead.

Vocabulary • equivalent • equivalent fractions

Getting Started

Mental Math and Reflexes

Invite children to use pennies or other counters, as necessary, to solve the following problems:

- Make a pile of 12 pennies. Show me $\frac{1}{2}$ of this pile. How many pennies in $\frac{1}{2}$ of the pile? 6 pennies $\frac{1}{3}$ of the pile? 4 pennies $\frac{1}{4}$ of the pile? 3 pennies
- I am thinking of a pile of pennies. There are 9 pennies in $\frac{1}{2}$ of the pile. Show me the whole pile. 18 pennies
- I am thinking of a pile of pennies. What if 3 pennies are $\frac{1}{3}$ of the pile? How many pennies are in the pile? 9 pennies

Math Message

Take a copy of Math Masters, *page 144. Carefully cut out each circle.*

Home Link 8.3 Follow-Up

Discuss the objects that children brought from home for the Fractions Museum. Ask children how they want to place the items in the museum.

1 Teaching the Lesson

◆ Math Message Follow-Up
(*Math Masters*, p. 144)

WHOLE-CLASS ACTIVITY

Check that children have cut out all 4 circles. Give children who have made a mistake an extra copy of *Math Masters*, page 144 so that they can complete their collection of circles.

◆ Making a Display of Equivalent Fractions
(*Math Journal 2*, pp. 200 and 201)

WHOLE-CLASS ACTIVITY

Have children label the parts of each circle they cut out with the appropriate fraction—$\frac{1}{4}$, $\frac{1}{6}$, or $\frac{1}{8}$. Remind children that each circle represents ONE. If necessary, review the words for the fractions: *fourths, sixths,* and *eighths.*

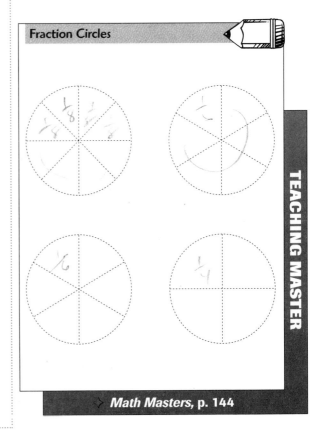

Fraction Circles

TEACHING MASTER

Math Masters, p. 144

Equivalent Fractions

Do the following:

- Use the circles you cut out of *Math Masters*, page 144.
- Cut these circles apart along the dashed lines.
- Glue the cutout pieces onto the circles on this page and the next, as directed.
- Write the missing numerators to complete the equivalent fractions.

1. Cover $\frac{1}{2}$ of the circle with fourths.

$$\frac{1}{2} = \frac{2}{4}$$

2. Cover $\frac{1}{4}$ of the circle with eighths.

$$\frac{1}{4} = \frac{2}{8}$$

[handwritten note] label pieces 4, 8, etc BEFORE cutting out

Equivalent Fractions (cont.)

3. Cover $\frac{2}{4}$ of the circle with eighths.

$$\frac{2}{4} = \frac{4}{8}$$

4. Cover $\frac{1}{2}$ of the circle with sixths.

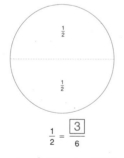

$$\frac{1}{2} = \frac{3}{6}$$

5. Cover $\frac{1}{3}$ of the circle with sixths.

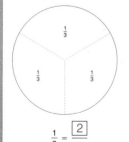

$$\frac{1}{3} = \frac{2}{6}$$

6. Cover $\frac{2}{3}$ of the circle with sixths.

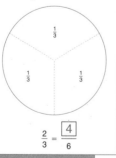

$$\frac{2}{3} = \frac{4}{6}$$

STUDENT PAGE

Work with the class to complete Problem 1 on journal page 200. You may want to use a set of fraction circles for the overhead. Model the following steps while children carry them out at their desks:

1. Cut the circle that has 4 equal parts into fourths along the dashed lines.

2. Glue two of the fourths onto the circle on journal page 200 so that half of the circle is covered. This shows that $\frac{2}{4}$ of the circle is **equivalent** to $\frac{1}{2}$ of the circle.

3. Say that $\frac{2}{4}$ and $\frac{1}{2}$ are called **equivalent fractions.** Both fractions name the same fractional part of the circle.

4. Fill in the missing numerator of the fraction that is equivalent to $\frac{1}{2}$. 2; $\frac{1}{2} = \frac{2}{4}$

Have children repeat this procedure on their own for the other circles on the two journal pages. For each problem, children:

1. find the appropriate fractions of a circle, cutting them apart along the dashed lines if necessary;

2. glue the correct number of pieces on part of the circle on the journal page; and

3. write the equivalent fraction below the circle.

For example, in Problem 2, children cut the circle that was divided into 8 equal parts into eighths and glue two of the eighths onto the circle so that $\frac{1}{4}$ of the circle is covered. This circle shows that $\frac{2}{8}$ is equivalent to $\frac{1}{4}$. Children fill in the missing numerator of the fraction equivalent to $\frac{1}{4}$. Circulate and offer help as needed.

After children have completed their equivalent-fractions displays, bring the class together to list the equivalent fractions on the board.

Summary: Remind children that numbers have many names. Similarly, a fractional part of a whole can be named in many different ways with equivalent fractions.

Ongoing Learning & Practice

◆ **Math Boxes 8.4** (*Math Journal 2,* p. 199)

INDEPENDENT ACTIVITY 👤

Mixed Review This journal page provides opportunities for cumulative review or assessment of concepts and skills.

◆ **Home Link 8.4** (*Math Masters,* p. 349)

Home Connection Children shade rectangles and squares to create equivalent fractions.

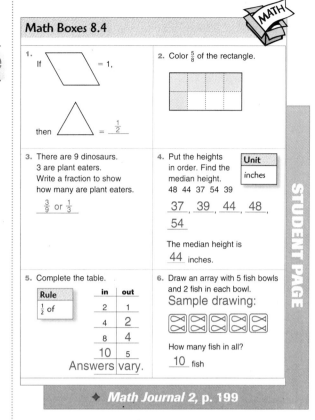

Math Boxes 8.4

1. If [parallelogram] = 1,

   then [triangle] = $\frac{1}{2}$

2. Color $\frac{5}{8}$ of the rectangle.

3. There are 9 dinosaurs. 3 are plant eaters. Write a fraction to show how many are plant eaters.

   $\frac{3}{9}$ or $\frac{1}{3}$

4. Put the heights in order. Find the median height.

   Unit: inches

   48 44 37 54 39

   $\underline{37}$, $\underline{39}$, $\underline{44}$, $\underline{48}$, $\underline{54}$

   The median height is $\underline{44}$ inches.

5. Complete the table.

Rule $\frac{1}{2}$ of	in	out
	2	1
	4	2
	8	4
	10	5

   Answers vary.

6. Draw an array with 5 fish bowls and 2 fish in each bowl.
   Sample drawing:

   How many fish in all?
   $\underline{10}$ fish

◆ *Math Journal 2,* p. 199

Options for Individualizing

◆ **RETEACHING** Playing *Name That Number*

SMALL-GROUP ACTIVITY 👥👥 15–30 min 🕐

Since this lesson focuses on equivalent fractions, it may be helpful to remind children that all numbers have many names. *Name That Number* reinforces this idea. Directions for the game are found in Lessons 2.9 and 2.10 on pages 130 and 136, respectively.

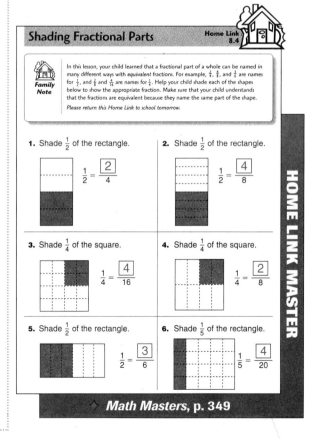

Shading Fractional Parts

Home Link 8.4

Family Note In this lesson, your child learned that a fractional part of a whole can be named in many different ways with *equivalent* fractions. For example, $\frac{2}{4}$, $\frac{4}{8}$, and $\frac{4}{8}$ are names for $\frac{1}{2}$, and $\frac{4}{8}$ and $\frac{4}{16}$ are names for $\frac{1}{4}$. Help your child shade each of the shapes below to show the appropriate fraction. Make sure that your child understands that the fractions are equivalent because they name the same part of the shape.

Please return this Home Link to school tomorrow.

1. Shade $\frac{1}{2}$ of the rectangle.

   $\frac{1}{2} = \frac{\boxed{2}}{4}$

2. Shade $\frac{1}{2}$ of the rectangle.

   $\frac{1}{2} = \frac{\boxed{4}}{8}$

3. Shade $\frac{1}{4}$ of the square.

   $\frac{1}{4} = \frac{\boxed{4}}{16}$

4. Shade $\frac{1}{4}$ of the square.

   $\frac{1}{4} = \frac{\boxed{2}}{8}$

5. Shade $\frac{1}{2}$ of the rectangle.

   $\frac{1}{2} = \frac{\boxed{3}}{6}$

6. Shade $\frac{1}{5}$ of the rectangle.

   $\frac{1}{5} = \frac{\boxed{4}}{20}$

◆ *Math Masters,* p. 349

8.5 Equivalent Fractions Using Fraction Cards

OBJECTIVE To find pairs of equivalent fractions by using region models.

Hershey's candy bar fraction on scholastic $5.95

summaries	materials

1 Teaching the Lesson

Children identify equivalent fractions by using Fractions Cards and playing the *Equivalent Fractions Game*. [Numeration]

- ☐ *Math Journal 2*, p. 202 and Activity Sheet 5
- ☐ Home Link 8.4
- ☐ slate
- ☐ scissors
- ☐ paper clip

***See* Advance Preparation**

2 Ongoing Learning & Practice

Children find fractions of collections. [Numeration]

Children practice and maintain skills through Math Boxes and Home Link activities.

- ☐ *Math Journal 2*, pp. 204–206
- ☐ Home Link Master (*Math Masters*, p. 350)
- ☐ blue crayon or pencil

3 Options for Individualizing

Enrichment Children identify equivalent fractions by playing an advanced version of the *Equivalent Fractions Game*. [Numeration]

- ☐ *Math Journal 2*, p. 203
- ☐ 16 Fraction Cards (cut from *Math Journal 2*, Activity Sheet 5)

Additional Information

Advance Preparation Before beginning the lesson, place a box of paper clips near the Math Message.

Getting Started

Mental Math and Reflexes

Write sets of numbers on the board. Have children record the median of each set on their slates. *Suggestions:*

- 47, 53, 92, 12, 51 51
- 150, 200, 175, 300, 250 200
- 2, 10, 15, 12 10, 11, or 12

Math Message

Take a paper clip.

Find Math Journal 2, *Activity Sheet 5. Cut apart the Fraction Cards.*

Then solve this problem:

Which is more: $\frac{1}{2}$ of a granola bar or $\frac{3}{6}$ of the same granola bar?

Home Link 8.4 Follow-Up

Review answers. Stress the idea that a fractional part of a whole can be named in many different ways with equivalent fractions. You may wish to challenge children by asking them to name other fractions that are equivalent to $\frac{1}{2}$ and $\frac{1}{4}$.

1 Teaching the Lesson

◆ Math Message Follow-Up
(*Math Journal 2,* Activity Sheet 5)

WHOLE-CLASS DISCUSSION

Check that children have cut out all 16 Fraction Cards. Then go over the answer to the problem. You might draw a picture of a granola bar and ask someone to divide it into 6 equal parts. Each part is $\frac{1}{6}$ of the granola bar. Ask a volunteer to divide the granola bar in half. *How many pieces (sixths) are in half of the granola bar?* $\frac{3}{6}$ This activity shows that $\frac{1}{2}$ and $\frac{3}{6}$ of the same granola bar are the same amount.

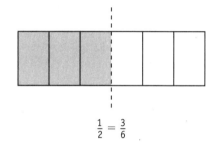

$$\frac{1}{2} = \frac{3}{6}$$

◆ Using Fraction Cards to Review and Extend Fraction Concepts

WHOLE-CLASS ACTIVITY

Ask children to turn their cards to the picture side. Share observations, such as the following:

- Each Fraction Card represents ONE. All Fraction Cards are the same size.

- The number of strips (or bars) varies from card to card. Some of the strips are shaded. Others are unshaded.

- The fraction shown on the card represents the fractional part of ONE that is shaded.

- The denominator tells the total number of strips on the card. The numerator tells the number of shaded strips.

Guide the class through the following activities:

1. Find the cards that are divided into 4 equal strips (the fourths family). Ask, *How many cards show fourths?* 5

Pick out the card from this family that has 3 of the strips shaded. *What fraction names the shaded part?* $\frac{3}{4}$ *What fraction names the unshaded part?* $\frac{1}{4}$

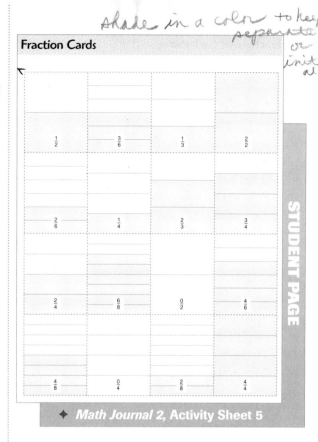

◆ *Math Journal 2,* Activity Sheet 5

▼ This journal page accompanies the *Equivalent Fractions Game* activity on the following page.

The *Equivalent Fractions Game*

Materials ❑ 32 Fraction Cards (2 sets cut from *Math Journal 2,* Activity Sheet 5)

Players 2

Directions

1. Mix the Fraction Cards and put them in a stack with the picture sides (the sides with the strips) facedown.

2. Turn the top card over so that the picture side faces up. Put it on the table near the stack of cards.

3. Take turns with your partner. When it is your turn, take the top card from the stack. Turn it over and put it on the table. Try to match this card with a picture-side-up card on the table. (If there are no other picture-side-up cards on the table, turn over the next card on the stack and put it on the table.)

4. Look for a match. If two cards match, take both of them. If there is a match that you don't see, the other player can take the matching cards. If there is no match, your turn is over.

5. The game ends when each card has been matched with another card. The player who took more cards wins the game.

Example

1. The top card is turned over. The picture shows $\frac{4}{6}$.

2. Ruth turns over the next card. It shows $\frac{2}{3}$. This matches $\frac{4}{6}$. Ruth takes both cards.

3. Justin turns over the top card on the stack. It shows $\frac{6}{8}$. Justin turns over the next card. It shows $\frac{0}{4}$. There is no match. Justin places $\frac{0}{4}$ next to $\frac{6}{8}$.

4. Ruth turns over the top card on the stack.

◆ *Math Journal 2,* p. 202

Fractions of Collections

1. Five people share 15 pennies.

   How many pennies does each person get? __3__ pennies

   $\frac{1}{5}$ of 15 pennies = __3__ pennies

   $\frac{2}{5}$ of 15 pennies = __6__ pennies

2. Six people share 12 pennies.

   How many pennies does each person get? __2__ pennies

   $\frac{1}{6}$ of 12 pennies = __2__ pennies

   $\frac{4}{6}$ of 12 pennies = __8__ pennies

3. Four people share 16 pennies.

   How many pennies does each person get? __4__ pennies

   $\frac{1}{4}$ of 16 pennies = __4__ pennies

   $\frac{4}{4}$ of 16 pennies = __16__ pennies

   $\frac{2}{4}$ of 16 pennies = __8__ pennies

   $\frac{3}{4}$ of 16 pennies = __12__ pennies

   $\frac{0}{4}$ of 16 pennies = __0__ pennies

◆ *Math Journal 2,* p. 204

NOTE: Before putting the cards away in their tool kits, children should sort them into two decks and fasten each deck with a paper clip. The *Equivalent Fractions Game* should be played often so that everyone can progress to the advanced version of the game.

Fractions of Collections (cont.)

Color the fractions of circles blue.

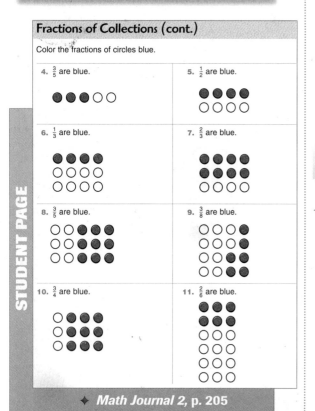

4. $\frac{3}{5}$ are blue.

5. $\frac{1}{2}$ are blue.

6. $\frac{1}{3}$ are blue.

7. $\frac{2}{3}$ are blue.

8. $\frac{3}{5}$ are blue.

9. $\frac{3}{8}$ are blue.

10. $\frac{3}{4}$ are blue.

11. $\frac{2}{6}$ are blue.

◆ *Math Journal 2,* p. 205

---

2. Find the cards on which all of the strips are shaded. *What do you notice about the fractions on these cards?* Each fraction has the same numerator and denominator.

3. Find the cards on which none of the strips are shaded. *What do you notice about the fractions on these cards?* Each fraction has 0 in the numerator.

4. Find the cards that are divided into 2 equal strips (the halves family). *How many cards show halves?* 3

   Ask children to take the card showing $\frac{1}{2}$ and find all of the cards that have exactly the same amount of shading. Demonstrate side-by-side comparisons for exact matches. As children name fractions equivalent to $\frac{1}{2}$, record them on the board. $\frac{1}{2}, \frac{2}{4}, \frac{3}{6}, \frac{4}{8}$

   Repeat with each of the other 2 cards in the halves family. Record equivalent fractions on the board. $\frac{0}{2}$ and $\frac{0}{4}$; $\frac{2}{2}$ and $\frac{4}{4}$

5. So far, eight fractions have been matched. Ask children to match the remaining eight fractions. Record each pair of equivalent fractions on the board. $\frac{1}{4}$ and $\frac{2}{8}$; $\frac{1}{3}$ and $\frac{2}{6}$; $\frac{2}{3}$ and $\frac{4}{6}$, $\frac{3}{4}$ and $\frac{6}{8}$

◆ Playing the *Equivalent Fractions Game*
(*Math Journal 2,* p. 202)

PARTNER ACTIVITY

Demonstrate how to play the game, while children follow the rules on journal page 202. Go through the example with children.

![2] **Ongoing Learning & Practice**

◆ Fractions of Collections of Things
(*Math Journal 2,* pp. 204 and 205)

INDEPENDENT ACTIVITY 👤

Most children should be able to complete these pages independently. You may want to go over Problems 1 and 3 with the class to make sure that children understand what they are to do.

◆ Math Boxes 8.5 (*Math Journal 2*, p. 206)

INDEPENDENT ACTIVITY

Mixed Review This journal page provides opportunities for cumulative review or assessment of concepts and skills.

◆ Home Link 8.5 (*Math Masters*, p. 350)

Home Connection Children circle pictures that are equivalent to a given fraction.

---

③ Options for Individualizing

◆ ENRICHMENT Playing an Advanced Version of the *Equivalent Fractions Game* (*Math Journal 2*, p. 203)

PARTNER ACTIVITY 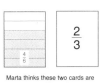   15–30 min

In this version of the game, players try to match the fraction on one card with the picture showing on another card.

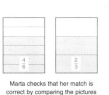

The *Equivalent Fractions Game* (cont.)

Advanced Version

1. Mix the Fraction Cards and put them in a stack with the picture sides facedown.

2. Turn the top card over so that the picture side faces up. Put it on the table with the picture side faceup.

3. Players take turns. When it is your turn, take the top card from the stack, but *do not* turn it over. Keep the picture side down. Try to match the fraction on the card with one of the picture-side-up cards on the table.

4. If you find a match, turn your card over. Check that your match is correct by comparing the two pictures. If your match is correct, take both cards.

   If there is no match, place your card next to the other cards, picture side face-up. Your turn is over. If the other player can find a match, he or she can take the matching cards.

5. If there are no picture cards showing when Player 2 begins his or her turn, take the top card from the stack. Place it on the table with the picture side showing. Then Player 2 takes the next card in the stack and doesn't turn that card over.

Marta thinks these two cards are a matching pair.

Marta checks that her match is correct by comparing the pictures of the fractions.

STUDENT PAGE

◆ *Math Journal 2*, p. 203

Math Boxes 8.5

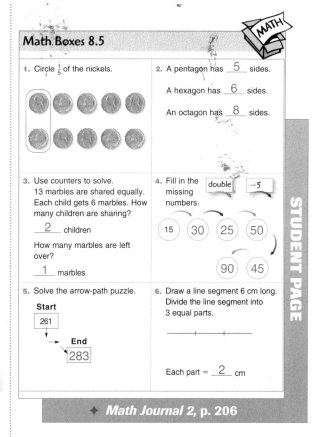

1. Circle $\frac{1}{5}$ of the nickels.

2. A pentagon has __5__ sides.
   A hexagon has __6__ sides.
   An octagon has __8__ sides.

3. Use counters to solve. 13 marbles are shared equally. Each child gets 6 marbles. How many children are sharing?
   __2__ children
   How many marbles are left over?
   __1__ marbles

4. Fill in the missing numbers. double →5
   15 30 25 50
   90 45

5. Solve the arrow-path puzzle.
   Start
   261
   End
   283

6. Draw a line segment 6 cm long. Divide the line segment into 3 equal parts.
   Each part = __2__ cm

STUDENT PAGE

◆ *Math Journal 2*, p. 206

NOTE: Since the game calls for combining two decks of cards, you might ask children to put their initials in the same place on each of their cards. This will help them re-sort the cards quickly at a later time.

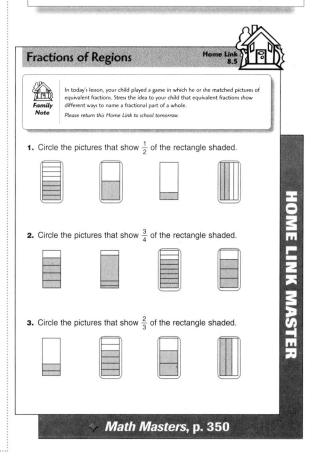

Fractions of Regions   Home Link 8.5

Family Note In today's lesson, your child played a game in which he or she matched pictures of equivalent fractions. Stress the idea to your child that equivalent fractions show different ways to name a fractional part of a whole.
Please return this Home Link to school tomorrow.

1. Circle the pictures that show $\frac{1}{2}$ of the rectangle shaded.

2. Circle the pictures that show $\frac{3}{4}$ of the rectangle shaded.

3. Circle the pictures that show $\frac{2}{3}$ of the rectangle shaded.

HOME LINK MASTER

◆ *Math Masters*, p. 350

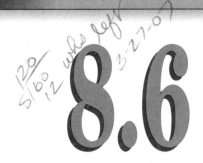

8.6 Comparing Fractions

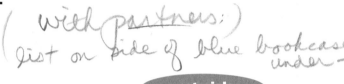

OBJECTIVE To compare fractions by using region models.

(with partners :)
list on side of blue bookcase under TV

summaries	materials

1 Teaching the Lesson

Children sort Fraction Cards into three categories: fractions less than $\frac{1}{2}$, greater than $\frac{1}{2}$, and equivalent to $\frac{1}{2}$. [Numeration; Patterns, Functions, and Algebra]

Children compare fractions by playing *Fraction Top-It*. [Numeration]

☐ *Math Journal 2,* p. 208
☐ Home Link 8.5
☐ Fraction Cards cut out from *Math Journal 2,* Activity Sheet 5
☐ slate

2 Ongoing Learning & Practice

Children identify equivalent fractions by playing the *Equivalent Fractions Game.* [Numeration]

Children practice and maintain skills through Math Boxes and Home Link activities.

☐ *Math Journal 2,* pp. 202, 203, and 207
☐ Home Link Master (*Math Masters,* p. 351)

3 Options for Individualizing

Enrichment Children compare fractions by playing the advanced version of *Fraction Top-It.* [Numeration]

Extra Practice Children estimate regions that are less than $\frac{1}{2}$, greater than $\frac{1}{2}$, or about $\frac{1}{2}$ of a shape. [Numeration]

☐ *Math Journal 2,* p. 209
☐ Fraction Cards cut out from *Math Journal 2,* Activity Sheet 5

Getting Started

② ✓ 3-26-02

Mental Math and Reflexes

Write addition problems on the board. Have children record the sums on their slates. *Suggestions:*

• 12 + 18 + 15 = ? 45
• 25 + 15 + 18 = ? 58
• 17 + 16 + 14 + 15 = ? 62

Math Message

Take out your Fraction Cards. Find the cards that show fourths. Line them up side by side. Which is more, $\frac{1}{4}$ of something or $\frac{3}{4}$ of the same thing? $\frac{4}{4}$ or $\frac{2}{4}$?

Home Link 8.5 Follow-Up

Review answers. Watch for children having difficulty with the concept of *equal* parts. For example, in Problem 1, some children may have circled the third rectangle. The third rectangle is divided into 2 parts, and one of those parts has been shaded. The rectangle was not divided into *equal* parts, however, so $\frac{1}{2}$ of the rectangle is *not* shaded. Look for similar errors in Problems 2 and 3.

Teaching the Lesson

✦ Math Message Follow-Up

WHOLE-CLASS DISCUSSION

Children share answers and discuss how they found them. *For example:*

- When I lined up my $\frac{1}{4}$ and $\frac{3}{4}$ cards, I found that more of the $\frac{3}{4}$ card is shaded. So $\frac{3}{4}$ of the card is more than $\frac{1}{4}$ of the card.

- Both cards show fourths of the same whole, so the fourths are the same on both cards. Therefore, 3 fourths is more than 1 fourth.

✦ Identifying Fractions That Are Less Than, More Than, and Equivalent to $\frac{1}{2}$
(*Math Journal 2*, p. 208)

WHOLE-CLASS DISCUSSION

Ask the class to turn to the top of journal page 208 and to list the Fraction Cards in three categories—cards in which:

▷ less than half of ONE is shaded

▷ more than half of ONE is shaded

▷ exactly half of ONE is shaded

Encourage children to devise their own methods for sorting the cards with as little help from you as possible.

After everyone has completed this task, bring the class together to share strategies. *For example:*

- I found the $\frac{1}{2}$ card. Then I lined up each of the other cards side by side with the $\frac{1}{2}$ card. That way I could tell which cards have less than $\frac{1}{2}$ of the card shaded, which have more than $\frac{1}{2}$ shaded, and which have exactly $\frac{1}{2}$ shaded.

With children's help, list the three groups of fractions on the board. Ask: *Can anyone suggest a way of telling to which group a fraction belongs by just looking at the fraction?* If the numerator is less than half of the denominator, then the fraction is less than $\frac{1}{2}$; if the numerator is more than half of the denominator, then the fraction is greater than $\frac{1}{2}$; if the numerator is half of the denominator, then the fraction is the same as, or equivalent to, $\frac{1}{2}$. Remind children that there are many names for "half" of something.

Halves—More or Less?

Use your Fraction Cards. List all the fractions that are:

less than $\frac{1}{2}$. $\quad \frac{1}{3} \quad \frac{2}{6} \quad \frac{0}{2} \quad \frac{1}{4} \quad \frac{1}{4} \quad \frac{2}{8}$

more than $\frac{1}{2}$. $\quad \frac{2}{2} \quad \frac{2}{3} \quad \frac{3}{4} \quad \frac{6}{8} \quad \frac{4}{6} \quad \frac{4}{4}$

the same as $\frac{1}{2}$. $\quad \frac{3}{6} \quad \frac{2}{4} \quad \frac{4}{8}$

Fraction Top-It

Materials ❑ 32 Fraction Cards (2 sets cut from *Math Journal 2*, Activity Sheet 5)

Players 2

Directions

1. Mix the Fraction Cards and put them in a stack so that all the picture sides (the sides with the strips) are facedown.

2. Each player turns over a card from the top of the stack. Players compare the shaded parts of their cards. The player with the larger (higher) fraction takes both cards.

3. If the shaded parts are equal, the fractions are equivalent. Each player turns over another card. The player with the larger fraction takes all the cards from both plays.

4. The game ends when all of the cards have been taken from the stack. The player who took more cards wins.

$\frac{1}{2}$ is greater than $\frac{1}{3}$.

✦ *Math Journal 2*, p. 208

$\frac{1}{3}$ is less than $\frac{1}{2}$.

$\frac{6}{8}$ is greater than $\frac{1}{2}$.

$\frac{3}{6}$ is equal to $\frac{1}{2}$.

The *Equivalent Fractions Game*

Materials ❑ 32 Fraction Cards (2 sets cut from
Math Journal 2, Activity Sheet 5)

Players 2

Directions

1. Mix the Fraction Cards and put them in a stack with the picture sides (the sides with the strips) facedown.

2. Turn the top card over so that the picture side faces up. Put it on the table near the stack of cards.

3. Take turns with your partner. When it is your turn, take the top card from the stack. Turn it over and put it on the table. Try to match this card with a picture-side-up card on the table. (If there are no other picture-side-up cards on the table, turn over the next card on the stack and put it on the table.)

4. Look for a match. If two cards match, take both of them. If there is a match that you don't see, the other player can take the matching cards. If there is no match, your turn is over.

5. The game ends when each card has been matched with another card. The player who took more cards wins the game.

Example

1. The top card is turned over. The picture shows $\frac{4}{6}$.

2. Ruth turns over the next card. It shows $\frac{2}{3}$. This matches $\frac{4}{6}$. Ruth takes both cards.

3. Justin turns over the top card on the stack. It shows $\frac{6}{8}$. Justin turns over the next card. It shows $\frac{0}{4}$. There is no match. Justin places $\frac{0}{4}$ next to $\frac{6}{8}$.

4. Ruth turns over the top card on the stack.

✦ *Math Journal 2,* p. 202

▲ The advanced version of the *Equivalent Fractions Game* is found on journal page 203.

Math Boxes 8.6

1. Color $\frac{1}{2}$ of the set green.

2. Complete the diagram.

Quantity	
64	

Quantity	Difference
28	36

Write a number model.
$64 - 28 = 36$ or $28 + 36 = 64$

3. Use the partial-sums algorithm to solve. Show your work.

$$
\begin{array}{r}
78 \\
+\ 26 \\
\hline
90 \\
+\ 14 \\
\hline
104
\end{array}
$$

4. Circle the digits in the hundreds place.

①2 8   ⑨7 2   ④6 3

2, ④6 5   3, ⑩9 1

6 6, ②5 0

5. 10 balloons are shared equally among 3 children. How many balloons does each child get?

_3_ balloons

How many are left over?

_1_ balloons

6. Count 20 pennies.

$\frac{1}{2}$ = _10_ pennies

$\frac{1}{4}$ = _5_ pennies

$\frac{1}{5}$ = _4_ pennies

✦ *Math Journal 2,* p. 207

✦ Playing *Fraction Top-It*
(*Math Journal 2,* p. 208)

PARTNER ACTIVITY

Demonstrate how to play the game while children follow the rules on journal page 208.

NOTE: Before children put their cards away in their tool kits, they should sort them into two decks and fasten each deck with a paper clip. Children should play *Fraction Top-It* often so that everyone can progress to the advanced version of the game.

2 Ongoing Learning & Practice

✦ Playing the *Equivalent Fractions Game*
(*Math Journal 2,* pp. 202 and 203)

PARTNER ACTIVITY

This game was introduced in Lesson 8.5 and gives children practice in identifying pairs of equivalent fractions. You may want to pair children of the same ability level. Some partnerships can play the regular version, while more capable children can play the advanced version.

✦ Math Boxes 8.6 (*Math Journal 2,* p. 207)

INDEPENDENT ACTIVITY 🧑

Mixed Review This journal page provides opportunities for cumulative review or assessment of concepts and skills.

Home Link 8.6 (*Math Masters*, p. 351)

Home Connection Children use number tiles to create fractions that are less than or greater than $\frac{1}{2}$.

Options for Individualizing

► ENRICHMENT Playing the Advanced Version of *Fraction Top-It* (*Math Journal 2*, p. 209)

PARTNER ACTIVITY   15–30 min

Begin this version of the game like the basic game. Place the 32 cards in a stack with the pictures facedown. The game rules are on journal page 209.

► EXTRA PRACTICE Estimating Regions That Are Less Than $\frac{1}{2}$, Greater Than $\frac{1}{2}$, or About $\frac{1}{2}$

SMALL-GROUP ACTIVITY   5–15 min

Draw shapes like the following on the board. Ask children to explain why they think the shaded part of the picture is less than $\frac{1}{2}$, greater than $\frac{1}{2}$, or about $\frac{1}{2}$.

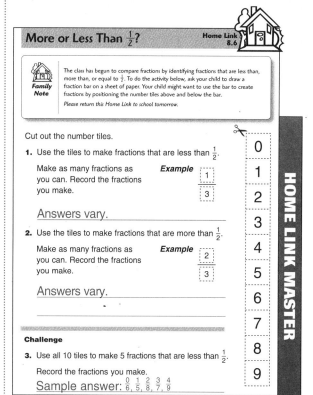

More or Less Than $\frac{1}{2}$?   Home Link 8.6

Family Note The class has begun to compare fractions by identifying fractions that are less than, more than, or equal to $\frac{1}{2}$. To do the activity below, ask your child to draw a fraction bar on a sheet of paper. Your child might want to use the bar to create fractions by positioning the number tiles above and below the bar.
Please return this Home Link to school tomorrow.

Cut out the number tiles.

1. Use the tiles to make fractions that are less than $\frac{1}{2}$.

   Make as many fractions as you can. Record the fractions you make.   **Example** $\frac{1}{3}$

   Answers vary.

2. Use the tiles to make fractions that are more than $\frac{1}{2}$.

   Make as many fractions as you can. Record the fractions you make.   **Example** $\frac{2}{3}$

   Answers vary.

Challenge

3. Use all 10 tiles to make 5 fractions that are less than $\frac{1}{2}$.

   Record the fractions you make.
   Sample answer: $\frac{0}{6}, \frac{1}{5}, \frac{2}{8}, \frac{3}{7}, \frac{4}{9}$

Number tiles: 0 1 2 3 4 5 6 7 8 9

◆ *Math Masters*, p. 351

HOME LINK MASTER

Fraction Top-It (cont.)

Advanced Version

1. Mix the Fraction Cards and put them in a stack so that all the picture sides (the sides with the strips) are facedown.

2. Each player takes a card from the top of the stack but does *not* turn it over.

3. Players take turns. When it is your turn, compare the fractions on the two cards. Say one of the following:
   - My fraction is more than your fraction.
   - My fraction is less than your fraction.
   - The fractions are equivalent.

   $\frac{2}{3}$ $\frac{6}{8}$

   John's card   Barb's card
   John says that his fraction is less than Barb's fraction.

4. Turn the cards over and compare the shaded parts. If you were correct, take both cards. If you were not correct, the other player takes both cards.

   $\frac{2}{3}$ $\frac{6}{8}$

   John's card   Barb's card
   Less of John's card is shaded: $\frac{2}{3}$ is less than $\frac{6}{8}$. John takes both cards.

◆ *Math Journal 2*, p. 209

STUDENT PAGE

8.7 Fraction Number Stories

OBJECTIVE To solve number stories involving fractions.

summaries	materials
1 Teaching the Lesson	
Children make up and solve number stories involving fractions of collections. [Numeration; Operations and Computation]	☐ *Math Journal 2*, pp. 210 and 211 ☐ Home Link 8.6 ☐ 16 pennies or other counters (optional) *See* **Advance Preparation**
2 Ongoing Learning & Practice	
Children compare fractions by playing *Fraction Top-It.* [Numeration] Children practice and maintain skills through Math Boxes and Home Link activities.	☐ *Math Journal 2*, pp. 208, 209, and 212 ☐ Home Link Master (*Math Masters*, p. 352) ☐ Fraction Cards cut out from *Math Journal 2*, Activity Sheet 5
3 Options for Individualizing	
Extra Practice Children compile their number stories in individual or whole-class books. [Numeration; Operations and Computation]	☐ Teaching Master (*Math Masters*, p. 22)

Additional Information

Advance Preparation Before children solve problems independently on journal pages 210 and 211 in Part 1, create and pose additional fraction number stories, as needed. Use similar number stories in future Mental Math and Reflexes sessions.

Getting Started

Mental Math and Reflexes

Invite children to use pennies or other counters, as necessary, to solve the following problems:

- Make a pile of 16 pennies. Show me $\frac{1}{2}$ of this pile. How many pennies are in $\frac{1}{2}$ of this pile? 8 pennies $\frac{1}{4}$ of the pile? 4 pennies $\frac{3}{4}$ of the pile? 12 pennies
- I am thinking of a pile of pennies. There are 4 pennies in $\frac{1}{3}$ of the pile. Show me the whole pile. 12 pennies
- I am thinking of a pile of pennies. What if 2 pennies are $\frac{1}{4}$ of the pile? How many pennies are in the whole pile? 8 pennies

Math Message

Think of a game you like to play. Would you rather play it for $\frac{1}{2}$ of an hour or for $\frac{1}{3}$ of an hour?

Home Link 8.6 Follow-Up

Children share the fractions they made up that are more than and less than $\frac{1}{2}$.

Teaching the Lesson

✦ Math Message Follow-Up

WHOLE-CLASS DISCUSSION

Children share solution strategies. *For example:*

▷ Use Fraction Cards to compare $\frac{1}{2}$ and $\frac{1}{3}$.

▷ Draw two clock faces. Divide one into 2 equal parts and the other into 3 equal parts. Compare the sizes of the parts.

▷ One hour has 60 minutes, so $\frac{1}{2}$ hour is 30 minutes, and $\frac{1}{3}$ hour is 20 minutes.

▷ $\frac{1}{3}$ means that the ONE is divided into 3 equal parts; $\frac{1}{2}$ means that the ONE is divided into 2 equal parts. When ONE is divided into more parts, the parts are smaller.

✦ Making up and Solving Fraction Number Stories

WHOLE-CLASS DISCUSSION

You and children make up number stories involving fractions of sets. Children solve the problems in any way they can—by using pennies or counters, looking at Fraction Cards, drawing pictures, and so on. You might want to begin with stories like the following:

- 5 birds were in a tree. 1 flew away. What fraction of the birds flew away? $\frac{1}{5}$ What fraction of the birds stayed? $\frac{4}{5}$

- Bob had 12 cards. He spilled juice on $\frac{1}{3}$ of them. How many cards were spoiled? 4 How many were not? 8

- A pizza was cut in 10 equal slices. Each friend got 2 slices. What fraction of the pizza did each person get? $\frac{2}{10}$

- There are 10 children on the bus. That's $\frac{1}{2}$ of all the people on the bus. How many people are on the bus? 20

After working through a few examples, ask volunteers to make up stories for the class to solve.

✦ Solving Fraction Number Stories
(*Math Journal 2,* pp. 210 and 211)

INDEPENDENT ACTIVITY

Children solve number stories on the journal pages using counters, pictures, or other aids as needed. Circulate and assist those who need help.

Fraction Number Stories

Solve these number stories. To help, you can use pennies or other counters, or you can draw pictures.

1. Mark has 4 shirts to wear.
   3 of them have short sleeves.
   What fraction of the shirts have short sleeves? $\frac{3}{4}$

2. 8 birds are sitting on a tree branch.
   6 of the birds are sparrows.
   What fraction of the birds are sparrows? $\frac{6}{8}$

3. June has 15 fish in her fish tank.
   $\frac{1}{3}$ of the fish are guppies.
   How many guppies does she have? __5__

4. Mr. Sharp has 7 neckties.
   $\frac{3}{7}$ of the neckties are blue.
   How many neckties are blue? __3__

5. Sam ate $\frac{0}{5}$ of a candy bar.
   How much of the candy bar did he eat? __None of it__

6. If you were thirsty, would you rather have $\frac{2}{2}$ of a carton of milk or $\frac{4}{4}$ of that same carton? Explain.
   Sample answer: Either amount of milk would be fine because both fractions are equal to 1 whole carton of milk.

Math Journal 2, p. 210

✔ ONGOING ASSESSMENT

As you evaluate Problem 8, look for:

▷ a whole; for example, "8 birds in all" or "1 cake"

▷ a fraction of the whole; for example, "6 of the birds are crows" or "$\frac{1}{5}$ of the cake eaten"

Fraction Number Stories (cont.)

7. Joan and Terrell brought a 6-pack of soda to the picnic.
   They drank $\frac{2}{3}$ of the 6-pack. How many cans did they drink? __4__
   What fraction of the 6-pack was left? $\frac{1}{3}$

8. Write a fraction story. Ask your partner to solve it.
   Stories and solutions vary.

Challenge

9. Keesha's mother bought a dozen doughnuts. Keesha and her 2 brothers each ate 2 of the doughnuts for breakfast.
   How many doughnuts were left? __6__
   What fraction of the doughnuts was left? $\frac{6}{12}$ or $\frac{1}{2}$

Math Journal 2, p. 211

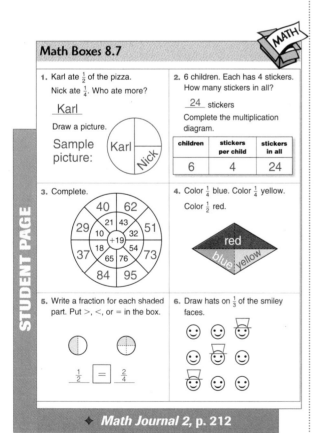

Halves—More or Less?

Use your Fraction Cards. List all the fractions that are:

less than $\frac{1}{2}$. $\quad \frac{1}{3} \quad \frac{2}{6} \quad \frac{0}{2} \quad \frac{0}{4} \quad \frac{1}{4} \quad \frac{2}{8}$

more than $\frac{1}{2}$. $\quad \frac{2}{3} \quad \frac{2}{4} \quad \frac{3}{4} \quad \frac{4}{6} \quad \frac{4}{4}$

the same as $\frac{1}{2}$. $\quad \frac{3}{6} \quad \frac{2}{4} \quad \frac{4}{8}$

Fraction Top-It

Materials ☐ 32 Fraction Cards (2 sets cut from *Math Journal 2*, Activity Sheet 5)

Players 2

Directions

1. Mix the Fraction Cards and put them in a stack so that all the picture sides (the sides with the strips) are facedown.

2. Each player turns over a card from the top of the stack. Players compare the shaded parts of their cards. The player with the larger (higher) fraction takes both cards.

3. If the shaded parts are equal, the fractions are equivalent. Each player turns over another card. The player with the larger fraction takes all the cards from both plays.

4. The game ends when all of the cards have been taken from the stack. The player who took more cards wins.

$$\frac{1}{2} \qquad \frac{1}{3}$$

$\frac{1}{2}$ is greater than $\frac{1}{3}$.

✦ *Math Journal 2, p. 208*

▲ The advanced version of *Fraction Top-It* is found on journal page 209.

---

2 Ongoing Learning & Practice

◆ Playing *Fraction Top-It* (*Math Journal 2*, pp. 208 and 209)

PARTNER ACTIVITY

This game was introduced in Lesson 8.6 and gives children practice in comparing pairs of fractions. You may wish to pair children of the same ability level. Some partnerships can play the regular version while more capable children can play the advanced version.

◆ Math Boxes 8.7 (*Math Journal 2*, p. 212)

INDEPENDENT ACTIVITY

 Mixed Review This journal page provides opportunities for cumulative review or assessment of concepts and skills.

◆ Home Link 8.7 (*Math Masters*, p. 352)

 Home Connection Children use objects or draw pictures to solve number stories about fractions.

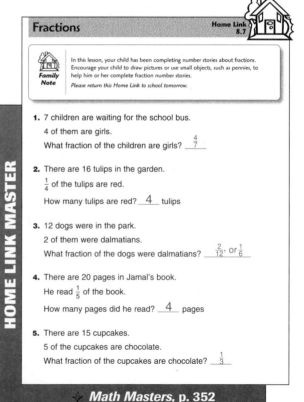

Fractions — Home Link 8.7

Family Note In this lesson, your child has been completing number stories about fractions. Encourage your child to draw pictures or use small objects, such as pennies, to help him or her complete fraction number stories. Please return this Home Link to school tomorrow.

1. 7 children are waiting for the school bus.
   4 of them are girls.
   What fraction of the children are girls? $\frac{4}{7}$

2. There are 16 tulips in the garden.
   $\frac{1}{4}$ of the tulips are red.
   How many tulips are red? 4 tulips

3. 12 dogs were in the park.
   2 of them were dalmatians.
   What fraction of the dogs were dalmatians? $\frac{2}{12}$ or $\frac{1}{6}$

4. There are 20 pages in Jamal's book.
   He read $\frac{1}{5}$ of the book.
   How many pages did he read? 4 pages

5. There are 15 cupcakes.
   5 of the cupcakes are chocolate.
   What fraction of the cupcakes are chocolate? $\frac{1}{3}$

✦ *Math Masters, p. 352*

Math Boxes 8.7

1. Karl ate $\frac{1}{2}$ of the pizza. Nick ate $\frac{1}{4}$. Who ate more?

   Karl

   Draw a picture.

   Sample picture: [circle divided into Karl/Nick sections]

2. 6 children. Each has 4 stickers. How many stickers in all?

   24 stickers

   Complete the multiplication diagram.

children	stickers per child	stickers in all
6	4	24

3. Complete.

   [number wheel with +19 in center; 40, 62, 29, 21, 43, 32, 51, 10, 54, 37, 18, 65, 76, 73, 84, 95]

4. Color $\frac{1}{4}$ blue. Color $\frac{1}{4}$ yellow. Color $\frac{1}{2}$ red.

   [diamond shape labeled red, blue, yellow]

5. Write a fraction for each shaded part. Put >, <, or = in the box.

   $\frac{1}{2}$ $=$ $\frac{2}{4}$

6. Draw hats on $\frac{1}{3}$ of the smiley faces.

   [nine smiley faces]

✦ *Math Journal 2, p. 212*

Options for Individualizing

✦ EXTRA PRACTICE Making Books of Fraction Number Stories (*Math Masters*, p. 22)

INDEPENDENT ACTIVITY   30+ min

Language Arts Link Compile children's number stories and their solutions in individual or whole-class books. Children can look at these books in their free time or check the books out to take home. Comparing the content of books made at different times of the year offers a clear picture of children's progress.

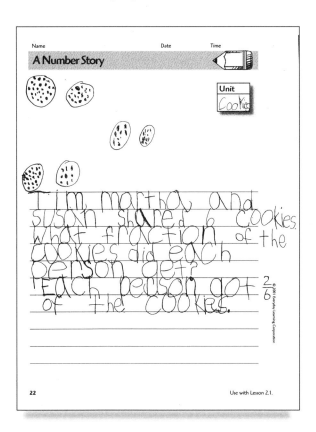

A child's number story and illustration representing the fraction of cookies received

TEACHING MASTER

Math Masters, p. 22

8.8 Unit 8 Review and Assessment

OBJECTIVE To review and assess children's progress on the material covered in Unit 8.

1 Assess Progress

learning goals

8a **Beginning/Developing Goal** Compare fractions. **(Lessons 8.5–8.7)**

8b **Developing Goal** Understand fractions as names for equal parts of a region or set. **(Lessons 8.1–8.3 and 8.7)**

8c **Developing Goal** Understand that the amount represented by a fraction depends on the size of the whole (ONE). **(Lessons 8.2, 8.3, and 8.7)**

8d **Developing Goal** Shade a specified fractional part of a collection. **(Lessons 8.3 and 8.5)**

8e **Developing Goal** Give the fraction name for the shaded part of a collection. **(Lesson 8.3)**

8f **Developing Goal** Recognize equivalent fraction names. **(Lessons 8.4–8.6)**

8g **Secure Goal** Shade a specified fractional part of a region. **(Lessons 8.1 and 8.4)**

8h **Secure Goal** Give the fraction name for the shaded part of a region. **(Lessons 8.1, 8.3, and 8.5)**

activities

- ☐ Oral Assessment, Problem 6

- ☐ Oral Assessment, Problems 1 and 2
- ☐ Slate Assessment, Problems 1 and 2
- ☐ Written Assessment, Problem 1

- ☐ Oral Assessment, Problems 1, 2, and 4
- ☐ Slate Assessment, Problem 3

- ☐ Written Assessment, Problems 8 and 9

- ☐ Written Assessment, Problems 2 and 5

- ☐ Oral Assessment, Problems 3 and 5

- ☐ Written Assessment, Problems 6 and 7

- ☐ Slate Assessment, Problem 3
- ☐ Written Assessment, Problems 1, 3, and 4

materials

- ☐ Home Link 8.7
- ☐ *Math Journal 2*, pp. 202, 203, 208, and 209
- ☐ Assessment Master (*Math Masters*, p. 431)
- ☐ 20 counters (optional)
- ☐ pattern blocks or Pattern-Block Template; slate
- ☐ 16 Fraction Cards (cut from *Math Journal 2*, Activity Sheet 5)
- ☐ Fractions Museum

***See* Advance Preparation**

2 Build Background for Unit 9

summaries

Children practice and maintain skills through Math Boxes and Home Link activities.

materials

- ☐ *Math Journal 2*, p. 213
- ☐ Home Link Masters (*Math Masters*, pp. 353–356)

Each **learning goal** listed above indicates a level of performance that might be expected at this point in the *Everyday Mathematics* K–6 curriculum. For a variety of reasons, the levels indicated may not accurately portray your class's performance.

Getting Started

Math Message

Fold a half-sheet of paper into 8 equal parts. Write $\frac{1}{8}$ in each part. Color half of the sheet. How many eighths did you color? 4 eighths

Home Link 8.7 Follow-Up

Review answers as necessary. Consider using counters to illustrate the solutions.

1 Assess Progress

◆ Math Message Follow-Up

WHOLE-CLASS DISCUSSION

Review the idea of equivalent fractions. When children colored $\frac{1}{2}$ of the sheet, they colored 4 of the 8 parts. $\frac{1}{2}$ is equivalent to $\frac{4}{8}$.

◆ Oral and Slate Assessments

SMALL-GROUP ACTIVITY

If the following list of suggested problems is not appropriate for your class's level of performance, adjust the numbers in the problems or adjust the problems themselves to better assess your children's abilities.

Oral Assessment Suggestions

For each problem, invite children to use counters, draw pictures, or use Fraction Cards. Ask children to describe the strategies that they use.

1. How much is $\frac{1}{2}$ of 12 cents? 6 cents $\frac{1}{3}$ of 12 cents? 4 cents $\frac{1}{4}$ of 12 cents? 3 cents **Goals 8b and 8c**

2. There are 8 pennies in $\frac{1}{2}$ of a pile. How many are in the whole pile? 16 There are 3 pennies in $\frac{1}{5}$ of the pile. How many are in the whole pile? 15 **Goals 8b and 8c**

3. Which is more, $\frac{1}{2}$ of a granola bar or $\frac{2}{4}$ of the same bar? Neither; they are the same. **Goal 8f**

4. Jenna ate $\frac{1}{2}$ of a Choco-Delight bar. Tawisha ate $\frac{1}{2}$ of a Nutty Dream bar. They both ate $\frac{1}{2}$ of a candy bar. Did they eat the same amount of candy? Unable to determine. As children share their ideas, it is important for them to understand that a fraction is not meaningful if one does not know what it is a fraction of—that is, the ONE. **Goal 8c**

5. Name a fraction equivalent to $\frac{1}{2}$, $\frac{2}{4}$, $\frac{3}{6}$, and so on; to $\frac{1}{3}$, $\frac{2}{6}$, $\frac{3}{9}$, and so on; and to $\frac{3}{4}$, $\frac{6}{8}$, $\frac{9}{12}$, and so on. **Goal 8f**

6. Name a fraction less than $\frac{1}{2}$. $\frac{1}{3}$, $\frac{1}{4}$, $\frac{0}{2}$, $\frac{2}{8}$, and so on
Goal 8a

 Name a fraction more than $\frac{1}{2}$. $\frac{2}{2}$, $\frac{3}{4}$, $\frac{6}{8}$, $\frac{4}{6}$, and so on
Goal 8a

Slate Assessment Suggestions

1. Write the following as fractions: one-half, one-fourth, two halves, one-third, two-thirds, three-quarters, five-eighths. $\frac{1}{2}$, $\frac{1}{4}$, $\frac{2}{2}$, $\frac{1}{3}$, $\frac{2}{3}$, $\frac{3}{4}$, $\frac{5}{8}$ **Goal 8b**

2. Divide your slate in half. How many halves? 2 Erase. Divide your slate into thirds. How many thirds? 3 (Continue with fourths and other fractions.) **Goal 8b**

3. For each of the following problems, display the appropriate pattern blocks. Children record answers on their slates. **Goals 8c and 8h**
 • If ⬡ is ONE, then what is ⬭ ? $\frac{1}{2}$
 • If ⬡⬡ is ONE, then what is ⬭ ? $\frac{1}{4}$
 • If ⬡ is ONE, then what is △ ? $\frac{1}{6}$
 • If ⬭ is ONE, then what is △ ? $\frac{1}{3}$

♦ **Written Assessment**
(*Math Masters,* p. 431)

INDEPENDENT ACTIVITY

Read the instructions aloud, repeating as needed. Children respond on the masters.

• Which shows $\frac{1}{4}$ shaded? Fill in the oval. (Problem 1) **Goals 8b and 8h**

• Which shows $\frac{2}{3}$ shaded? Fill in the oval. (Problem 2) **Goal 8e**

• Which fraction shows how much is shaded? Fill in the oval. (Problems 3–5) **Goals 8e, 8h**

• Color $\frac{5}{8}$. (Problem 6) **Goal 8g**

• Color $\frac{1}{5}$. (Problem 7) **Goal 8g**

• Color $\frac{7}{8}$. (Problem 8) **Goal 8d**

• Color $\frac{1}{2}$. (Problem 9) **Goal 8d**

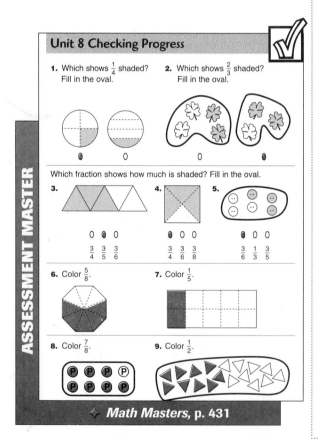

Unit 8 Checking Progress

1. Which shows $\frac{1}{4}$ shaded? Fill in the oval.
2. Which shows $\frac{2}{3}$ shaded? Fill in the oval.

Which fraction shows how much is shaded? Fill in the oval.

3. $\frac{3}{5}$ $\frac{3}{5}$ $\frac{3}{6}$
4. $\frac{3}{4}$ $\frac{3}{3}$ $\frac{3}{6}$
5. $\frac{3}{6}$ $\frac{1}{3}$ $\frac{3}{5}$

6. Color $\frac{5}{8}$.
7. Color $\frac{1}{5}$.
8. Color $\frac{7}{8}$.
9. Color $\frac{1}{2}$.

✔ *Math Masters,* p. 431

INDEPENDENT ACTIVITY

Have children use one of the shapes on a Pattern-Block Template to draw a design. The design is the ONE. Children write what fraction each part of the design represents. *Example:*

Portfolio
Ideas

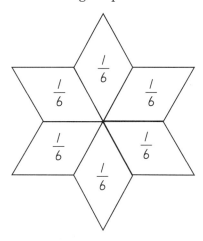

◆ **ALTERNATIVE ASSESSMENT OPTION**
Describe Fractions Greater Than ONE

INDEPENDENT ACTIVITY

Children respond, in writing, to the following question:

Can fractions name things that are more or bigger than ONE? Give two examples. Draw a picture of one of your examples.

Portfolio
Ideas

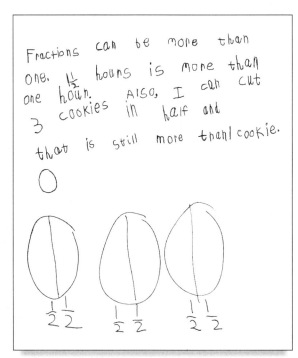

The *Equivalent Fractions Game*

Materials ❏ 32 Fraction Cards (2 sets cut from *Math Journal 2*, Activity Sheet 5)

Players 2

Directions

1. Mix the Fraction Cards and put them in a stack with the picture sides (the sides with the strips) facedown.

2. Turn the top card over so that the picture side faces up. Put it on the table near the stack of cards.

3. Take turns with your partner. When it is your turn, take the top card from the stack. Turn it over and put it on the table. Try to match this card with a picture-side-up card on the table. (If there are no other picture-side-up cards on the table, turn over the next card on the stack and put it on the table.)

4. Look for a match. If two cards match, take both of them. If there is a match that you don't see, the other player can take the matching cards. If there is no match, your turn is over.

5. The game ends when each card has been matched with another card. The player who took more cards wins the game.

Example

1. The top card is turned over. The picture shows $\frac{4}{6}$.

2. Ruth turns over the next card. It shows $\frac{2}{3}$. This matches $\frac{4}{6}$. Ruth takes both cards.

3. Justin turns over the top card on the stack. It shows $\frac{6}{8}$. Justin turns over the next card. It shows $\frac{0}{4}$. There is no match. Justin places $\frac{0}{4}$ next to $\frac{6}{8}$.

4. Ruth turns over the top card on the stack.

✦ *Math Journal 2*, p. 202

Halves—More or Less?

Use your Fraction Cards. List all the fractions that are:

less than $\frac{1}{2}$. $\frac{1}{3}$ $\frac{2}{6}$ $\frac{0}{2}$ $\frac{0}{4}$ $\frac{1}{4}$ $\frac{2}{8}$

more than $\frac{1}{2}$. $\frac{2}{2}$ $\frac{2}{3}$ $\frac{3}{4}$ $\frac{6}{6}$ $\frac{4}{4}$ $\frac{4}{4}$

the same as $\frac{1}{2}$. $\frac{3}{6}$ $\frac{2}{4}$ $\frac{4}{8}$

Fraction Top-It

Materials ❏ 32 Fraction Cards (2 sets cut from *Math Journal 2*, Activity Sheet 5)

Players 2

Directions

1. Mix the Fraction Cards and put them in a stack so that all the picture sides (the sides with the strips) are facedown.

2. Each player turns over a card from the top of the stack. Players compare the shaded parts of their cards. The player with the larger (higher) fraction takes both cards.

3. If the shaded parts are equal, the fractions are equivalent. Each player turns over another card. The player with the larger fraction takes all the cards from both plays.

4. The game ends when all of the cards have been taken from the stack. The player who took more cards wins.

$\frac{1}{2}$ is greater than $\frac{1}{3}$.

✦ *Math Journal 2*, p. 208

Write and Solve Number Stories Involving Fractions

INDEPENDENT ACTIVITY

Use the Fractions Museum to generate number stories for children to solve, or have children write and solve their own number stories.

Portfolio Ideas

✦ **ALTERNATIVE ASSESSMENT OPTION**

Play the *Equivalent Fractions Game* or *Fraction Top-It*
(*Math Journal 2*, pp. 202, 203, 208, and 209)

PARTNER ACTIVITY

Circulate and observe as children play these games. Assess children's ability to find pairs of equivalent fractions and to compare fractions. Do they accomplish these tasks with or without the aid of a region model?

NOTE: Advanced versions of these games are found on journal pages 203 and 209.

---

2 Build Background for Unit 9

✦ **Math Boxes 8.8** (*Math Journal 2*, p. 213)

INDEPENDENT ACTIVITY

Mixed Review This journal page provides opportunities for cumulative review or assessment of concepts and skills. The skill in Problem 4 is a prerequisite for Unit 9.

Home Link 8.8: Unit 9 Family Letter
(*Math Masters,* pp. 353–356)

Home Connection This Home Link is a four-page newsletter that introduces parents and guardians to Unit 9's topics and terms. The letter also offers ideas for home-based mathematics activities that are supportive of classroom work.

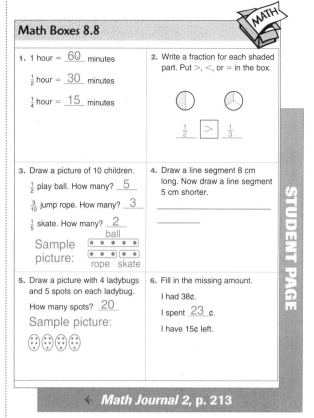

Math Boxes 8.8

1. 1 hour = __60__ minutes

$\frac{1}{2}$ hour = __30__ minutes

$\frac{1}{4}$ hour = __15__ minutes

2. Write a fraction for each shaded part. Put >, <, or = in the box.

$\frac{1}{2}$ [>] $\frac{1}{3}$

3. Draw a picture of 10 children.

$\frac{1}{2}$ play ball. How many? __5__

$\frac{3}{10}$ jump rope. How many? __3__

$\frac{1}{5}$ skate. How many? __2__

Sample picture:

ball
rope skate

4. Draw a line segment 8 cm long. Now draw a line segment 5 cm shorter.

5. Draw a picture with 4 ladybugs and 5 spots on each ladybug.

How many spots? __20__

Sample picture:

6. Fill in the missing amount.

I had 38¢.

I spent __23__ ¢.

I have 15¢ left.

Math Journal 2, p. 213

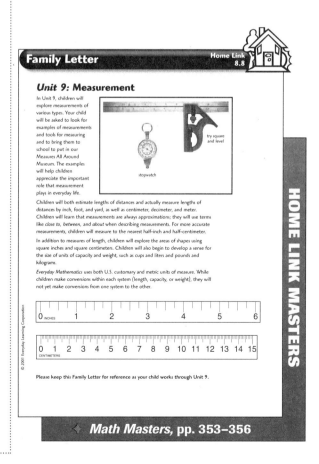

Family Letter Home Link 8.8

Unit 9: Measurement

In Unit 9, children will explore measurements of various types. Your child will be asked to look for examples of measurements and tools for measuring and to bring them to school to put in our Measures All Around Museum. The examples will help children appreciate the important role that measurement plays in everyday life.

Children will both estimate lengths of distances and actually measure lengths of distances by inch, foot, and yard, as well as centimeter, decimeter, and meter. Children will learn that measurements are always approximations; they will use terms like *close to, between,* and *about* when describing measurements. For more accurate measurements, children will measure to the nearest half-inch and half-centimeter.

In addition to measures of length, children will explore the areas of shapes using square inches and square centimeters. Children will also begin to develop a sense for the size of units of capacity and weight, such as cups and liters and pounds and kilograms.

Everyday Mathematics uses both U.S. customary and metric units of measure. While children make conversions within each system (length, capacity, or weight), they will not yet make conversions from one system to the other.

Please keep this Family Letter for reference as your child works through Unit 9.

Math Masters, pp. 353–356

Lesson 8.8   **615**

Unit **9**
Measurement

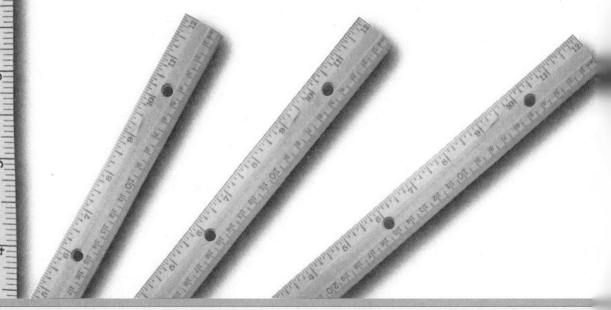

overview

We live in a world filled with numbers, many of which pertain to measures of things. It is not surprising, therefore, that measures play an important role in *Everyday Mathematics.* Measures have been used in various ways practically every day since the beginning of Kindergarten. Occasionally, *Everyday Mathematics* pauses to discuss and summarize these everyday experiences with measures. Unit 9 is one such pause.

contents

UNIT

9

learning goals in perspective

learning goals	links to the past	links to the future
9a **Beginning/Developing Goal** Identify equivalencies for millimeters, centimeters, decimeters, and meters. **(Lessons 9.2, 9.3, 9.5, and 9.9)**	The metric system was informally introduced in Kindergarten and first grade. Children used base-10 blocks (longs) to measure and compare lengths in first grade. *(Related Grade 2 lessons: 4.7, 7.7)*	Children will continue to explore the relationships among metric units beyond second grade. *(Related Grade 2 lesson: 10.4)*
9b **Developing Goal** Measure to the nearest $\frac{1}{2}$ inch. **(Lesson 9.3)**	Children measured themselves and classroom items using inches and feet in first grade. *(Related Grade 2 lessons: 4.7, 7.7)*	Children in third grade are expected to express units as fractions of larger units and to identify the $\frac{1}{8}$-inch marks on their tape measures.
9c **Developing Goal** Measure to the nearest $\frac{1}{2}$ centimeter. **(Lesson 9.3)**	Children measured classroom items using centimeters in first grade. *(Related Grade 2 lessons: 4.7, 7.7)*	Children will begin to measure to the nearest millimeter in third grade. *(Related Grade 2 lesson: 12.7)*
9d **Developing Goal** Use appropriate units for measurement and recognize sensible measurements. **(Lessons 9.1-9.6, 9.9, and 9.10)**	In Kindergarten and first grade, children used both standard and nonstandard units. In first grade, children were asked to choose and use appropriate measuring tools. *(Related Grade 2 lessons: 2.7, 4.7, 7.7)*	In third grade, children will review and be asked to demonstrate their ability to choose the most appropriate units for measuring various items.
9e **Developing Goal** Find area concretely. **(Lessons 9.7 and 9.8)**	Children were informally exposed to the idea of area in Kindergarten and first grade by covering areas with shapes. *(Related Grade 2 lesson: 4.7)*	In third grade, children will review area through experiences that will standardize area units as square units. They will count unit squares within rectangles to extend the concept to include multiplying length times width. *(Related Grade 2 lesson: 10.7)*
9f **Developing Goal** Find perimeter concretely. **(Lessons 9.4, 9.5, and 9.8)**	Children in first grade measured perimeters using a tape measure.	Children will continue to explore and determine perimeters using various units.
9g **Developing/Secure Goal** Identify equivalencies for inches, feet, and yards. **(Lessons 9.2 and 9.9)**	In first grade, children measured themselves and classroom items using inches and feet. *(Related Grade 2 lessons: 4.7, 7.7)*	Children in third grade will continue to practice the relationships among U.S. customary units. *(Related Grade 2 lesson: 10.4)*
9h **Secure Goal** Use a ruler, tape measure, and meter/yardstick correctly. **(Lessons 9.1–9.4)**	Measuring tools were introduced in Kindergarten and used in activities and Projects in first grade. *(Related Grade 2 lessons: 4.7, 7.7)*	Children will continue to use measuring tools throughout the grades. *(Related Grade 2 lesson: 12.7)*

assessment

ongoing • product • periodic

☑ Informal Assessment

Math Boxes These *Math Journal* pages provide opportunities for cumulative review or assessment of concepts and skills.

Ongoing Assessment: Kid Watching Use the Ongoing Assessment suggestions in the following lessons to make quick, on-the-spot observations about children's understanding of:
• Measurement and Reference Frames **(Lessons 9.1 and 9.6)**
• Geometry **(Lesson 9.7)**

Portfolio Ideas Samples of children's work may be obtained from the following assignments:
• Solving Road-Map Stories **(Lesson 9.5)**
• Researching a Pretend Trip **(Lesson 9.5)**
• Making a Measuring Tools Booklet **(Lesson 9.6)**
• Finding the Area of Grid-Paper Drawings **(Lesson 9.8)**

☑ Unit 9 Review and Assessment

Math Message Use the question in Lesson 9.11 to assess children's progress toward the following learning goal: Goal 9d

Oral and Slate Assessments Use oral or slate assessments during Lesson 9.11 to assess children's progress toward the following learning goals: Goals 9a, 9d, and 9g

Written Assessment Use a written review during Lesson 9.11 to assess children's progress toward the following learning goals: Goals 9b, 9c, 9d, 9e, 9f, and 9h

Performance/Group Assessment Use a small-group activity in Lesson 9.11 to assess children's progress toward the following learning goals: Goals 9a and 9g

assessment handbook

For more information on how to use different types of assessment in Unit 9, see the Assessment Overview on pages 67–69 in the *Assessment Handbook*. The following Assessment Masters can be found in the *Math Masters* book:

• Unit 9 Checking Progress, p. 432
• Unit 9 Class Checklist, p. 464
• Unit 9 Individual Profile of Progress, p. 465
• Class Progress Indicator, p. 488
• Math Logs, pp. 493–495
• Self-Assessment Forms, pp. 496 and 497
• Interest Inventories, pp. 491 and 492

problemsolving

A process of modeling everyday situations using tools from mathematics

Encourage children to use a variety of strategies when attacking a given problem—and to explain those strategies. *Strategies children might use in this unit:*

- Using estimation
- Acting out the problem
- Using computation

- Using a picture (map)
- Making a list

Four Problem-Solving REPRESENTATIONS

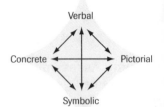

Lessons that teach *through* problem solving, not just *about* problem solving

Lesson	Activity	Lesson	Activity
9.1	How long is our classroom?	9.4	Solve perimeter problems.
9.5	Solve and write road-map number stories.	9.7	Which cylinder holds more?
9.8	Find the area and perimeter of various designs.	9.10	How many pennies weigh 1 ounce?

For more information about problem solving in *Everyday Mathematics,* see the *Teacher's Reference Manual,* pp. 197–208.

cross-curricularlinks

literature

- Read *How Big Is a Foot?* and *Counting on Frank,* two books that illustrate nonstandard units of measure. **(Lesson 9.1)**

- Read *Twelve Snails to One Lizard: A Tale of Mischief and Measurement,* a book that introduces U.S. customary measures of length. **(Lesson 9.2)**

- Read *Pigs in the Pantry: Fun with Math and Cooking,* the adventures of a pig who must measure ingredients to make firehouse chili. **(Lesson 9.9)**

language arts

- Discuss the origins of *meter* and *peri-*. **(Lesson 9.4)**

- Discuss the origins of the prefix *kilo-* and the word *mile.* **(Lesson 9.5)**

social studies

- Children interview someone at home about the longest trip taken by that person and write a report about the person's trip. **(Lesson 9.5)**

science

- Children explore the fractions involved in the Hubble telescope. **(Lesson 9.3)**

meeting
INDIVIDUAL needs
UNIVERSAL ACCESS

✦ RETEACHING

The following features provide additional instructional support:

Adjusting the Activity

- **Lesson 9.3, Part 1**
- **Lesson 9.4, Part 1**
- **Lesson 9.5, Part 2**
- **Lesson 9.8, Part 1**
- **Lesson 9.9, Part 1**

✦ ENRICHMENT

The following features suggest enrichment and extension activities:

Adjusting the Activity

- **Lesson 9.1, Part 1**
- **Lesson 9.2, Part 1**
- **Lesson 9.4, Part 1**
- **Lesson 9.8, Part 2**
- **Lesson 9.9, Part 1**

Options for Individualizing

- **Lesson 9.1** Measurement in Literature
- **Lesson 9.2** Exploring Equivalent U.S. Customary Linear Measures in Literature
- **Lesson 9.3** Comparing Units of Metric Linear Measure
- **Lesson 9.4** Measuring Perimeter in Paces
- **Lesson 9.5** Researching a Pretend Trip
- **Lesson 9.8** Finding the Areas of Grid-Paper Drawings
- **Lesson 9.9** Measuring the Capacity of Irregular Containers

✦ LANGUAGE DIVERSITY

The following features suggest ways to support children who are acquiring proficiency in English:

Options for Individualizing

- **Lesson 9.6** Making a Measuring Tools Booklet
- **Lesson 9.9** Creating a Class Equivalencies Poster

✦ MULTIAGE CLASSROOM

The following chart lists related lessons from Grades 1 and 3 that can help you meet your instructional needs:

Grade 1	4.2–4.7 6.6	2.7 4.2–4.7		4.6		2.2 4.1–4.7 9.5	3.4 5.4 9.5	3.4 5.4	9.5	5.4
Grade 2	9.1	9.2	9.3	9.4	9.5	9.6	9.7	9.8	9.9	9.10
Grade 3	3.1–3.3	3.1–3.3	3.2 10.1	3.4 3.5 5.6	4.9	1.4 3.2 10.6	3.6 5.6 10.6	3.5–3.7 9.3	10.6	10.4 10.5

materials

lesson	math masters pages	manipulative kit items	other items
9.1	Home Link Master, p. 357	meterstick	Class Data Pad (optional) stick-on notes; masking tape yardstick *How Big Is a Foot* by Rolf Myller *Counting on Frank* by Rod Clement **See Advance Preparation, p. 630**
9.2	Home Link Masters, pp. 358 and 359 Teaching Master, p. 145	tape measure pattern blocks meterstick	counters (optional) Class Data Pad items for demonstration purposes *Twelve Snails to One Lizard: A Tale of Mischief and Measurement* by Susan Hightower **See Advance Preparation, p. 636**
9.3	Home Link Masters, pp. 360 and 361 Teaching Masters, pp. 148–150 transparencies of Teaching Masters, pp. 146 and 147 (optional) **See Advance Preparation, p. 642**	tape measure meterstick	tool-kit ruler length of string or ribbon inch ruler centimeter ruler
9.4	Home Link Masters, pp. 362 and 363 Teaching Masters, pp. 151–153	tape measure	inch and centimeter rulers box in the shape of a rectangular prism masking tape
9.5	Home Link Master, p. 364	tape measure	calculator map(s) for a pretend trip
9.6	Home Link Master, p. 365	tape measure	Class Data Pad 18 counters (optional) ruler
9.7	Home Link Master, p. 366 Teaching Masters, pp. 86 and 154–159	number cards pattern blocks Pattern-Block Template	construction paper; masking tape 8–10 squares of posterboard or cardboard about 2 pounds of small macaroni small items, such as slates or crayon boxes
9.8	Home Link Master, p. 367 Teaching Masters, pp. 86 and 158	geoboard rubber bands	grid paper
9.9	Home Link Master, p. 368 Teaching Masters, pp. 160 and 161		containers for demonstration funnel; tray 1 gallon of water, rice, or sand water-resistant write-on tape pitcher of water food coloring (optional) *Pigs in the Pantry: Fun with Math and Cooking* by Amy Axelrod (optional) **See Advance Preparation, p. 672**
9.10	Home Link Master, p. 369	spring scale	measuring spoons and cups bath scale objects that differ in weight objects with the same weight pennies
9.11	Home Link Masters, pp. 370–373 Teaching Master, p. 162 Assessment Masters, p. 432	slate tape measure or yardstick	2 objects weighing less than 1 lb each object weighing more than 1 lb rulers; string; index cards **See Advance Preparation, p. 683**

planningtips

Pacing

Pacing depends on a number of factors, such as children's individual needs and how long your school has been using *Everyday Mathematics*. At the beginning of Unit 9, review your Content by Strand Poster to help you set a monthly pace.

FEBRUARY	←——MOST CLASSROOMS——→ MARCH	APRIL

Home Communication

Share Home Links 9.1–9.10 with families to help them understand the content and procedures in this unit. At the end of the unit, use Home Link 9.11 to introduce Unit 10. Supplemental information can be found in the *Home Connection Handbook*.

NCTM Standards

Standard	1	2	3	4	5	6	7	8	9	10
Unit 9 Lessons	2, 3, 5, 7, 9, 10	3–5, 7, 9, 10	4–9	1–10	5	1–10	1–10	1–10	1–10	1–10

Content Standards
1 Number and Operation
2 Patterns, Functions, and Algebra
3 Geometry and Spatial Sense
4 Measurement
5 Data Analysis, Statistics, and Probability

Process Standards
6 Problem Solving
7 Reasoning and Proof
8 Communication
9 Connections
10 Representations

PRACTICE through Games

Everyday Mathematics uses games to help children develop good fact power and other math skills.

- Identify pairs of equivalent fractions in the *Equivalent Fractions Game* **(Lesson 9.7)**
- Compare fractions when playing *Fraction Top-It*. **(Lesson 9.7)**

unit 9 content highlights

The notes below highlight the major content ideas presented in Unit 9. These notes may help you establish instructional priorities.

The purpose of this unit is to look at measurement concepts in a more formal way. Just as counts answer the question "How many...?," measures answer the question "How much...?" Measures tell us how much something weighs, how fast it travels, how much time it requires to reach a destination, and how much space it takes up.

Counts are discrete—without connected meaning—whereas measures are continuous. For example, when someone counts people, the count may jump from 4 to 5 people; whereas when someone measures a length, the measure may be any number between 4 and 5 inches, or 4 and 5 centimeters.

No matter how precise a measurement is, in theory it can always be refined. Because of this, a measurement is never exact; it is always an approximation. The precision of a measurement is dependent both on the precision of the available measuring tools and on judgments about how much precision is called for in any given situation. Although it may get tiresome at times, you should insist that children use such phrases as *close to ____, between ____ and ____,* and *about ____* whenever they talk about specific measurements. Every once in a while, discuss the reasons for using the language of approximation.

Everyday Mathematics uses both metric and U.S. customary units of measure. Because equivalencies exist among the units within each system of measure (for example, 1 m = 100 cm and 1 pt = 2 c), measurements can be converted from one unit to another. But it is rarely necessary to convert from one system to the other; such conversions should, for the most part, be avoided in second grade.

Hands-on Activities

Since measurement takes place in the real world, the discussions and activities in this unit are all related to concrete experiences. You can find some of these activities in Explorations in previous units; you will find others in the Explorations in this unit and in parts of other lessons in this unit as well. The results of the activities are discussed, and measurement concepts are formalized in the process.

Measures All Around Museum

On Home Link 9.1, children are asked to look for and bring to school items related to some kinds of measures for use as resources in upcoming discussions. These measures can be circled with a felt-tip marker, either in class or at home, by parents and children. Children can report on what they discussed with their parents, or small groups can speculate on the meanings of the numbers and units, especially those that are unusual.

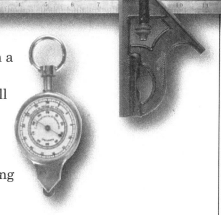

The authors encourage you to make the Measures All Around Museum a top priority and to keep reminding children to add interesting items to the museum. Children can, for example, collect containers, packages, and pictures that have measures printed on them. You and children's parents can add items to the museum that children are not likely to find. You might also ask parents to tell their children about unusual measures they know of; they can send notes about these measures to class.

Children might bring such diverse measuring tools as a stopwatch and a combination square to class.

Parents might also lend such measuring instruments as blood pressure measurers, altimeters, barometers, wind-speed indicators, rain gauges, stopwatches, calipers, trundle wheels, surveyor transits, or navigational quadrants to take star sightings. If the instrument is fragile or expensive, invite parents to class to demonstrate it themselves. As a rule of thumb, nothing should be lent to the museum that its owner would miss if damaged or lost.

Measure Sense

Through repeated experiences with measures, it is hoped that children will gradually develop "measure sense," a sense of the magnitude of a specific measurement. For example, in Lesson 9.1 children estimate how many children can lie head-to-foot along a wall of the classroom. Then, they actually measure the length of the wall with a yardstick. The goal is for children to be able to estimate a length in inches or centimeters, as well as in feet, yards, or meters.

Children do similar activities with weight. After they have found sets of things that weigh a specific amount (1 pound in Unit 2; 5, 10, and 15 pounds in Unit 7), children decide which of two objects weighs more by holding one object in each hand (see Lesson 9.10). At the next stage, they are given several possible weights an object might weigh and choose which might be the most reasonable. Ultimately, children may be able to estimate how much an object actually weighs.

Measuring with Yards and Meters (Lesson 9.1)

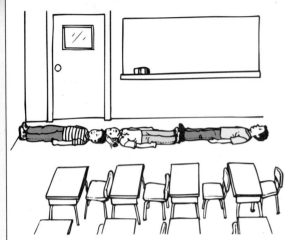

This lesson briefly revisits measuring with a nonstandard unit—children themselves. They lie down along the wall to measure the longest side of the classroom. Since measuring such a long distance with inches or centimeters (which children have been using up to this time) would take more time and result in larger numbers of units, the standard units of yard and meter are introduced.

Linear Measures (Lesson 9.2)

Measuring to the nearest inch and centimeter is used to quickly review how to use a ruler. The activity focuses on measuring not only to the nearest inch and centimeter, but also revisits the foot and the decimeter. Using a combination of large and small units, children report the measurements as a number of feet and inches or decimeters and centimeters. With the introduction of the yard and the meter, children have experienced the basic units of linear measure for both the U.S. customary system and the metric system. A table of equivalent measures is started in this lesson and later extended to include millimeters, kilometers, and miles, as well as equivalent measures for capacity and weight.

Fractional Units of Length (Lesson 9.3)

The size of the unit of measure one uses depends on how precise the measurement needs to be: The more precise the measurement, the smaller the unit. One doesn't measure a table in miles or the distance between cities in centimeters. Lesson 9.3 reviews the marks between inches and between centimeters on measuring tools as representations of fractional parts of these units. Children are asked to identify the $\frac{1}{2}$-inch, $\frac{1}{4}$-inch, $\frac{1}{8}$-inch and $\frac{1}{16}$-inch marks on their rulers. In the metric system, the marks between centimeters stand for millimeters (10 mm = 1 cm). You might discuss situations in which it may be necessary to measure things in millimeters or sixteenths of inches or in even smaller parts of a unit. At this time, children are asked to measure only to the nearest half-inch and half-centimeter.

Perimeter (Lesson 9.4)

Perimeter is the distance around the edge of something. In the course of this lesson, be sure to discuss situations that call for measuring perimeters. You might ask children to suggest ways of measuring the perimeter of something whose border is curved. For example, partners can try to measure the distance around all of the fingers of a spread-out hand. The measurer starts the tape measure at the partner's wrist and then continues around the first finger. The partner holds the tape measure in place with a finger on the other hand while the measurer continues the path. Or an easier task might be to measure the perimeter of the sole of a shoe. In third grade, children will learn to find the circumference of a circle.

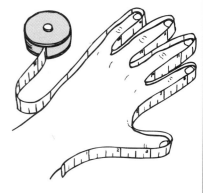

Children find the perimeter of a curved object using a tape measure.

Measuring Longer Distances (Lesson 9.5)

Since measuring miles and kilometers with children would be difficult, try to find distances between landmarks in your area that are about a mile or a kilometer. The distances could be from school to some place in the neighborhood. For example, you might use a distance from outside the classroom window to a specific grocery store or the distance between other landmarks, such as the distance between the entrance to a city park and a fire station. The number of miles between cities shown on a map is used for solving number stories.

Measures All Around (Lesson 9.6)

This lesson is an open-ended discussion of measuring tools and of units used in measuring objects of all kinds. As children examine and discuss a variety of measuring tools, be sure to point out the features shared by most of these instruments. It is nearly always necessary to establish a "zero," or starting point, and, in many cases, the instrument must be calibrated so that it really does begin at zero. One usually starts to measure at that zero point and then reads the value at an endpoint. In weighing things, one may have to subtract the weight of the container from the total weight to get the actual net weight of the contents. You might remind children of an extension to Exploration A in Unit 7, in which the weight of a child is subtracted from the total weight of the child and the object the child is holding. In measuring capacity, a container is filled to the top or to a fill mark.

You cannot remind children often enough that a measurement must have two parts: a number and a unit of measure. Most measurements are expressed in terms of just a few base units, which are very precisely standardized by an official "bureau of standards." In Lesson 9.2, a table of equivalent measures was started among the units in each system. For example, 1 m = 10 dm and 1 yd = 3 ft. Encourage children to practice conversions within systems, but not from one system to another system.

Explorations (Lesson 9.7)

Besides providing some hands-on experience with the capacity of two cylinders, Exploration A should help children become aware of how deceiving appearances can be. Exploration B continues the work with area started in Exploration E of Unit 4 by not only counting whole square inches and whole square centimeters, but by estimating the area of the remaining portion of the surface. Drawing a wall built with pattern blocks in Exploration C gives children an opportunity to experience a 2-dimensional representation of a 3-dimensional object.

Area (Lesson 9.8)

Area is the measure of a surface or region bounded by a border, as opposed to perimeter, which is the length of that border. Children have measured area by "tiling" a surface with regions that are the same size and shape. Any shape that can cover a region without overlaps or gaps can be used as an area unit. This tiling can be done with any triangle, quadrilateral, regular hexagon, or countless irregular shapes. The tessellations of the artist M. C. Escher provide wonderful examples of tilings with odd shapes.

Because the environment that humans construct for themselves is very much a rectangular one, it is convenient to measure areas in square units. These standard units of area are derived from the standard units of length with which we are familiar—square feet, square meters, square miles, and so on. In third grade, children will learn that square units make area calculations easy; for example, the area of a rectangle is the product of its length times its width. If you make overhead transparencies with square inches or square centimeters, children can use these grids as area-measuring instruments, much like they would use a ruler. Simply cover the region to be measured with the grid, and then count the squares. For area estimates, count as "1" any part of the region covered by more than half of a square unit; disregard any part of the region covered by less than half of a square unit.

Fish vignette. One of the many wood-engraving tessellation designs done by M. C. Escher

Measures of Capacity (Lesson 9.9)

Sometimes we want to measure the amount of a substance that can be poured, such as liquids, sand, rice, and so on—things that take the shapes of their containers. For these measurements we use units of capacity, which are special units of volume. (Volume is a measure of a finite amount of 3-dimensional space.)

The focus of Lesson 9.9 is on equivalencies among units of capacity. In discussing these, take advantage of children's previous experiences with milk cartons, soft-drink bottles, and measuring cups and spoons. Plan on demonstrating the relationships among the capacities of cup, pint, quart, half-gallon, and gallon containers. Children will benefit by participating in the optional activity of making a measuring container and using it to measure the capacities of irregular containers.

Measures of Weight (Lesson 9.10)

This lesson reviews equivalencies among units of weight and various weighing instruments. If you have a pan balance and weights, you might want to demonstrate how they may be used to weigh objects. Discuss how the pan balance differs from other weighing instruments. Provide children with experience using various types of scales (bath scale, spring scale, letter scale) so that they can become familiar with how the scales work. Children should learn to identify appropriate scales to weigh certain objects.

Review and Assessment (Lesson 9.11)

The best way to assess children's understanding of measurement is through ongoing observation as they participate in various measuring activities and discussions. To supplement your observations, Lesson 9.11 assesses children's ability to use appropriate units of measures and to recognize sensible measurements through a fill-in-the-blank activity.

For **additional information** on the following topics, see the *Teacher's Reference Manual:*

- area
- length
- measurement systems
- museums
- personal measures
- rulers and tape measures
- volume
- weight and mass

9.1

Measuring with Yards and Meters

OBJECTIVES To revisit the concept of nonstandard units of measure; and to introduce *yard* and *meter*.

summaries	materials

1 Teaching the Lesson

Children find the length of a classroom wall by using their heights and by measuring with a yardstick. Children also compare a yardstick and a meterstick. [Measurement and Reference Frames]

- □ *Math Journal 2,* p. 214
- □ Class Data Pad (optional)
- □ stick-on notes
- □ yardstick
- □ meterstick
- □ floor covering (optional)

***See* Advance Preparation**

2 Ongoing Learning & Practice

Children practice and maintain skills through Math Boxes and Home Link activities.

- □ *Math Journal 2,* p. 215
- □ Home Link Master (*Math Masters,* p. 357)

3 Options for Individualizing

Enrichment Children read and discuss stories involving nonstandard units of measure. [Measurement and Reference Frames]

Extra Practice Children discuss nonstandard units that could be used to measure length. [Measurement and Reference Frames]

- □ *How Big Is a Foot?*
- □ *Counting on Frank*
- □ *Minute Math*®, p. 62

***See* Advance Preparation**

Additional Information

Advance Preparation For the activities in Part 1, the yardstick and meterstick need to be two separate measuring tools. The yardstick should be 36 inches long, not 39 inches as on the back of a meterstick. For the *Measuring Length with a Nonstandard Unit* activity, several children lie down on part of the classroom floor. You may want to cover this part of the floor with blankets or a rug.

Before beginning the optional Enrichment activity in Part 3, obtain the books *How Big Is a Foot?* by Rolf Myller (Dell Publishing, 1991) and *Counting on Frank* by Rod Clement (Gareth Stevens Children's Books, 1991).

Vocabulary • **standard unit** • **yard** • **meter**

Math Message

About how many children in our class can lie head-to-foot along the longest wall of our classroom?

Write your estimate on a stick-on note. Write large! Keep your stick-on note.

1 Teaching the Lesson

◆ Math Message Follow-Up

WHOLE-CLASS ACTIVITY 👥👥👥👥

Put children's estimates in order by having them bring their stick-on notes to the board or Class Data Pad. Have children find the median (middle value) of the estimates. Summarize the activity by saying: *Our class estimate of the length of the classroom is* ___ *second graders.*

Discuss what it means to estimate the number of units in a specific length. To make an estimate, one uses a mental picture of the unit and imagines how many units would match the length.

◆ Measuring Length with a Nonstandard Unit

WHOLE-CLASS ACTIVITY 👥👥👥👥

Ask volunteers to measure the length of the classroom. Have children lie down head-to-foot along the longest side of the classroom.

1. The first child lies on the floor with his or her feet at one end of the room.

2. The second child lies down head-to-head next to the first child, the third child lies down feet-to-feet next to the second child's feet, and so on.

Tell children that the length of the classroom could be given as ___ second graders long. Since second graders are different sizes, however, suggest measuring the length of the classroom using only one child.

The length of the classroom is measured using second graders as the unit.

The length of the classroom is measured using one class member as the unit.

NOTE: Some children may remember the historic yard used in *First Grade Everyday Mathematics*. It is the distance (for an adult) from the tip of the nose to the end of the longest finger when the arm is outstretched.

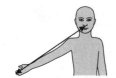

Ask for a volunteer. Select someone who is neither the shortest nor the tallest child in the class. Measure the length of the classroom using the volunteer as the unit.

1. The child lies on the floor with his or her feet at one end of the room.

2. Use the corner of a yardstick to mark the place at the top of the child's head while the child gets up and moves. Mark the second length and so on.

The class keeps a count as the volunteer moves along the length of the classroom. Tell children that the length of the classroom could be given as ____ (number) ____ (child's name given in plural) long.

Ask the class: *How could we tell someone in another city or state how long our classroom is?* Discuss some of the difficulties with using people as a unit of measure:

• Unless the same person is used each time, we may get a different measurement each time we measure.

• Even if only one person is used to measure, we can't take that person with us whenever we want to measure something. Besides, the person will grow, so the measurement will change.

A **standard unit** is one that is accessible to most people and does not keep changing. If different people measure the same object using the same standard unit, they will get the same measurement.

◆Introducing *Yard* and *Meter* as Standard Lengths

WHOLE-CLASS DISCUSSION

Children have previously used the standard units of inch and centimeter to measure length. Inches and centimeters are good for measuring short lengths. For longer lengths, such as the length of the classroom, there are other standard units that can be used.

Talk about the stick you used earlier as a marker when measuring the length of the room with a person. In the U.S. customary system, a **yard** is 36 inches long. A yard makes it easier to measure longer lengths, and it is a standard unit of measure that is used by most people in the United States.

In the metric system, the most commonly used standard unit of length that is longer than a centimeter is a meter. A **meter** is 100 centimeters long. Show the class a meterstick. Compare it to a yardstick.

NOTE: In the metric system, all of the linear units are defined in terms of a meter.

Both the metric system and the U.S. customary system are used in the United States. The U.S. customary system is used for everyday purposes; the metric system is used for science and industry. Most labels on canned and packaged food show both metric and U.S. customary units of measure.

Most of the other countries in the world use only the metric system.

Talk about lengths and distances that might be measured in yards or meters. Some examples include the length of a hallway, the width of a playground, the length and width of a piece of fabric, the distance traveled by runners in a race, the distance an object is thrown in sports, and various lengths marked on sports fields.

Yards

Materials   ❑ yardstick

Directions

Record each step in the table below.

1. Choose a distance.
2. Estimate the distance in yards.
3. Use a yardstick to measure the distance to the nearest yard. Compare this measurement to your estimate. Answers vary.

Distance I Estimated and Measured	My Estimate	My Yardstick Measurement
	about _____ yards	about _____ yards
	about _____ yards	about _____ yards
	about _____ yards	about _____ yards
	about _____ yards	about _____ yards
	about _____ yards	about _____ yards

✦ *Math Journal 2,* p. 214

✦Checking Estimates by Measuring Distances with Yardsticks (*Math Journal 2,* p. 214)

PARTNER ACTIVITY 👥

Standing near the longest wall of the classroom, hold up a yardstick and ask children to estimate the length of the wall in yards. Then use the yardstick to measure that same distance to the nearest yard. Compare the estimate to the measurement in yards.

On the journal page, children select distances in or near the classroom, estimate the number of yards for each distance, and then measure each distance using a yardstick. When children measure with a yardstick, they should measure to the nearest yard. You may wish to have children measure several distances before assigning the journal page so that you can observe that they are measuring correctly.

NOTE: Many children are hesitant to make estimates. Some will try to avoid doing so by measuring first and then recording a number close to the actual measurement as their "estimate." Others will estimate first and then measure. However, they will then erase their first estimate and record a new "estimate" that is closer to the actual measurement. To avoid these problems and to get a more accurate assessment of a child's ability to estimate, ask children to record each estimate in pen before measuring the distance with a yardstick.

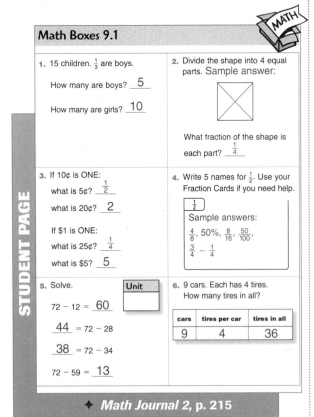

STUDENT PAGE

Math Boxes 9.1

1. 15 children. $\frac{1}{3}$ are boys.

   How many are boys? __5__

   How many are girls? __10__

2. Divide the shape into 4 equal parts. Sample answer:

   What fraction of the shape is each part? __$\frac{1}{4}$__

3. If 10¢ is ONE:

   what is 5¢? __$\frac{1}{2}$__

   what is 20¢? __2__

   If $1 is ONE:

   what is 25¢? __$\frac{1}{4}$__

   what is $5? __5__

4. Write 5 names for $\frac{1}{2}$. Use your Fraction Cards if you need help.

   $\boxed{\frac{1}{2}}$

   Sample answers:

   $\frac{4}{8}$, 50%, $\frac{8}{16}$, $\frac{50}{100}$,

   $\frac{3}{4} - \frac{1}{4}$

5. Solve.

Unit

   $72 - 12 =$ __60__

   __44__ $= 72 - 28$

   __38__ $= 72 - 34$

   $72 - 59 =$ __13__

6. 9 cars. Each has 4 tires. How many tires in all?

cars	tires per car	tires in all
9	4	36

◆ *Math Journal 2, p. 215*

HOME LINK MASTER

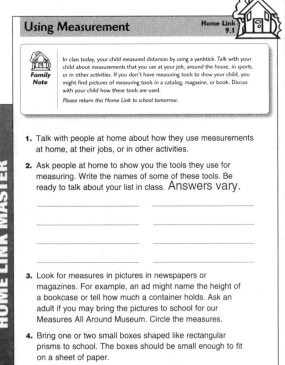

Using Measurement   Home Link 9.1

Family Note

In class today, your child measured distances by using a yardstick. Talk with your child about measurements that you use at your job, around the house, in sports, or in other activities. If you don't have measuring tools to show your child, you might find pictures of measuring tools in a catalog, magazine, or book. Discuss with your child how these tools are used.

Please return this Home Link to school tomorrow.

1. Talk with people at home about how they use measurements at home, at their jobs, or in other activities.

2. Ask people at home to show you the tools they use for measuring. Write the names of some of these tools. Be ready to talk about your list in class. Answers vary.

   _____   _____

   _____   _____

   _____   _____

3. Look for measures in pictures in newspapers or magazines. For example, an ad might name the height of a bookcase or tell how much a container holds. Ask an adult if you may bring the pictures to school for our Measures All Around Museum. Circle the measures.

4. Bring one or two small boxes shaped like rectangular prisms to school. The boxes should be small enough to fit on a sheet of paper.

◆ *Math Masters, p. 357*

Adjusting the Activity To extend the activity, have children measure the distances with a meterstick. Ask children if the number of meters would be larger or smaller than the number of yards when measuring distances like a long hallway or large playground. Since a meter is a larger unit than a yard, the number of meters would be smaller than the number of yards.

ONGOING ASSESSMENT

Choose a few items that all children must measure and record on the journal page so that you can quickly assess whether or not children are making accurate measurements.

2 Ongoing Learning & Practice

◆ **Math Boxes 9.1** (*Math Journal 2*, p. 215)

INDEPENDENT ACTIVITY

Mixed Review This journal page provides opportunities for cumulative review or assessment of concepts and skills.

◆ **Home Link 9.1** (*Math Masters,* p. 357)

Home Connection Children talk with people at home about how they use measurements at home, at their jobs, or during other activities.

Children bring to class pictures of items labeled with measures for the Measures All Around Museum. Encourage children to also bring other items dealing with measurement—tools, labeled containers, and so on. Children also bring small boxes shaped like rectangular prisms to school. These boxes will be used in Lesson 9.4.

Options for Individualizing

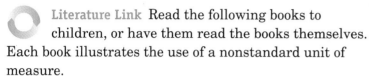

◆ ENRICHMENT Measurement in Literature

SMALL-GROUP ACTIVITY   5–15 min

Literature Link Read the following books to children, or have them read the books themselves. Each book illustrates the use of a nonstandard unit of measure.

How Big Is a Foot?

Summary: The king decides to have a bed made for the queen's birthday. He marks off the dimensions of the bed with his feet and gives them to the head carpenter who gives them to his apprentice. When the bed is delivered, it is too small. The apprentice must figure out why this has happened.

Counting on Frank

Summary: Frank (a dog) and his young owner estimate numbers and measures using nonstandard units, such as piles of "Franks" and green peas.

◆ EXTRA PRACTICE Minute Math

SMALL-GROUP ACTIVITY   5–15 min

To offer children more experience with using nonstandard units of measure, see the following page in *Minute Math:*

Measurement: p. 62

PLANNING AHEAD

For Lesson 9.2, gather the items for the Measures All Around Museum.

Linear Measures

9.2

OBJECTIVES To review measuring with inches, feet, centimeters, and decimeters; and to begin a table of equivalent linear measures.

summaries	materials
1 Teaching the Lesson	
Children use a ruler to measure in inches, feet, centimeters, and decimeters. Children also begin to identify equivalent U.S. customary and metric measures. [Measurement and Reference Frames; Numeration]	☐ *Math Journal 2*, p. 216 ☐ Home Link 9.1 ☐ Teaching Master (*Math Masters*, p. 145) ☐ counters (optional) ☐ tape measure ☐ Class Data Pad ☐ items for demonstration purposes: posterboard, 12-inch ruler, yardstick, 1-inch square pattern block, meterstick, longs from base-10 blocks, and centimeter cube **See Advance Preparation**
2 Ongoing Learning & Practice	
Children practice and maintain skills through Math Boxes and Home Link activities.	☐ *Math Journal 2*, p. 217 ☐ Home Link Masters (*Math Masters*, pp. 358 and 359)
3 Options for Individualizing	
Enrichment Children read and discuss a story about equivalent U.S. customary units of measure. [Measurement and Reference Frames; Numeration] **Extra Practice** Children identify objects and distances that might be measured with various measuring tools. [Measurement and Reference Frames]	☐ *Twelve Snails to One Lizard: A Tale of Mischief and Measurement* ☐ *Minute Math®*, p. 61 **See Advance Preparation**

Additional Information

Advance Preparation Begin a display of the items and pictures you and children have collected for a Measures All Around Museum. Tape a yardstick, a 12-inch ruler, a 1-inch-square pattern block, a meterstick, a long from the base-10 blocks, and a centimeter cube to a posterboard to create a display showing the relative sizes of these six measurement units. (See the top of the margin on page 638.)

Before beginning the optional Enrichment activity in Part 3, obtain a copy of the book *Twelve Snails to One Lizard: A Tale of Mischief and Measurement* by Susan Hightower (Simon and Schuster Books for Young Readers, 1997).

Vocabulary • **inch** • **centimeter** • **foot** • **decimeter**

Getting Started

Mental Math and Reflexes

Children use counters, as necessary, to solve problems like the following:

- Make a pile of 14 pennies. Show me $\frac{1}{2}$ of this pile. 7 pennies $\frac{1}{7}$ of the pile. 2 pennies $\frac{3}{7}$ of the pile. 6 pennies

- I am thinking of a pile of pennies. There are 6 pennies in $\frac{1}{3}$ of the pile. How many pennies are in the pile? 18 pennies

- I am thinking of a pile of pennies. 2 pennies are $\frac{1}{8}$ of the pile. How many pennies are in the pile? 16 pennies

Math Message

Yards and meters are good units to use for measuring long lengths. What units are good to use for measuring short lengths?

Home Link 9.1 Follow-Up

Conduct a brief show-and-tell session. Ask children to talk about the items they brought from home and about the tools people at home use for measuring. Display items you collected for the Measures All Around Museum. Encourage children to bring in additional items for the museum over the next few days. Clothing sizes, temperatures, wind speeds, numbers on a camera lens, sizes of nails and screws, and weights of cars are all good sources.

Teaching the Lesson

◆ Math Message Follow-Up

WHOLE-CLASS DISCUSSION

Most children will name inches and centimeters since those units have been used previously in second grade activities. Some children may remember measuring with the foot-long foot in *First Grade Everyday Mathematics*.

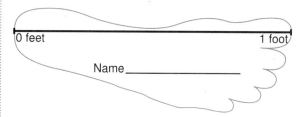

The foot-long foot used in *First Grade Everyday Mathematics*

Measuring to the Nearest Inch and Centimeter

WHOLE-CLASS DISCUSSION

Ask children to describe how to measure to the nearest **inch** or **centimeter.** Their descriptions should include the following:

▷ Line up the 0-mark on the ruler with one edge of the object being measured.

▷ The inch (or centimeter) mark nearest to the other edge of the object is the measurement.

▷ Use the mark halfway between inches (or centimeters) to decide which mark the edge is closer to.

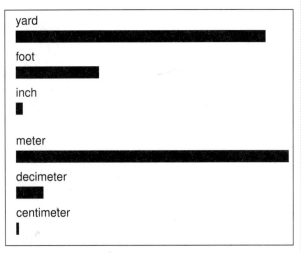

yard

foot

inch

meter

decimeter

centimeter

Display showing the relationships among U.S. customary and metric units

---

▷ Measure objects longer than the ruler by putting a mark on the object where the end of the ruler meets it and then moving the ruler so that the 0-mark is at that mark.

▷ If one end of the object is not lined up with the 0-mark, the measurement is equal to the difference between the beginning and end numbers.

Remind the class that a measurement is meaningful only when it is labeled with an appropriate unit. Ask what is wrong with the statement, "The average second grader is 46 centimeters tall." Children may show a length of 46 centimeters with their tape measures to illustrate their answers. Ask them to make up other silly statements that use inappropriate units.

◆ Revisiting Foot and Decimeter

WHOLE-CLASS DISCUSSION

Remind children that in first grade they used two other units to measure length, the **foot** and the **decimeter.** Children may remember using the foot-long foot to measure lengths and that a foot is equal to 12 inches. The other unit they used was the base-10 block called a *long.* A long has a length of 10 centimeters. It is the same length as a decimeter, another metric unit. A decimeter is equal to 10 centimeters.

Use the poster (see Advance Preparation on page 636) displaying lengths in yards, feet, and inches, as well as meters, decimeters, and centimeters to help children to see the relative sizes of the six units.

◆ Beginning a Table of Equivalent Measures

WHOLE-CLASS ACTIVITY

Have children look at the inch side of their tape measures. Remind them that this side is numbered in inches and that the marks between inches show fractions of an inch. *Does this side of the tape measure have any other marks?* Some tape measures have a star (or other symbol) at the 12-inch and 36-inch marks. Ask questions like the following about equivalent measures:

- How many inches are in 1 foot? 12 inches How many inches are in 1 yard? 36 inches

- How many feet are in 1 yard? 3 feet (You can demonstrate this by laying three 12-inch rulers on top of a yardstick.)

- How many inches long is the tape measure? How many feet is that?

Table of Equivalent Measures

U.S. Customary System

1 yard (yd) $= 36$ inches (in.)

$\quad\quad\quad\quad\quad = 3$ feet (ft)

1 foot $= 12$ inches

$\quad\quad\quad = \frac{1}{3}$ yard

1 inch $= \frac{1}{12}$ foot

$\quad\quad\quad = \frac{1}{36}$ yard

Metric System

1 meter (m) $= 100$ centimeters (cm)

$\quad\quad\quad\quad\quad = 10$ decimeters (dm)

1 decimeter $= 10$ centimeters

$\quad\quad\quad\quad = \frac{1}{10}$ meter

1 centimeter $= \frac{1}{10}$ decimeter

$\quad\quad\quad\quad = \frac{1}{100}$ meter

Begin a Table of Equivalent Measures on the Class Data Pad (see the lower margin on the facing page). Save the table for future discussions. Plan to add equivalencies to the table as they are introduced in subsequent lessons.

 Adjusting the Activity To extend the activity, ask questions like the following:

- What part of a yard is 1 inch? $\frac{1}{36}$
- What part of a yard is 1 foot? $\frac{1}{3}$
- What part of a foot is 1 inch? $\frac{1}{12}$

Ask children to turn over their tape measures to the centimeter side. The numbers name whole centimeters, and the marks between centimeters are used to name fractions of centimeters. Ask: *Are there any other marks on this side?* There is probably a symbol at 100 centimeters to name 1 meter. Place longs from the base-10 blocks on a tape measure or meterstick to show that 1 meter is equal to 10 decimeters (10 longs).

Tell children that the prefix *deci-* means "one-tenth of" and *centi-* means "one-hundredth of"—in this case, of a meter:

- What fraction of a meter is 1 decimeter? $\frac{1}{10}$
- What fraction of a meter is 1 centimeter? $\frac{1}{100}$

Finally, help children see that 1 meter is a little more than 1 yard, a decimeter is a little less than 4 inches, and 1 centimeter is less than $\frac{1}{2}$ inch. Children can compare these measurements by finding the metric measure on the tape measure, turning the tape measure over, and identifying the closest U.S. customary measure.

◆ Measuring in Feet and Inches, Decimeters and Centimeters
(*Math Journal 2*, p. 216; *Math Masters*, p. 145)

SMALL-GROUP ACTIVITY

Children cut out the foot and decimeter rulers from *Math Masters*, page 145. Working in small groups, children measure objects or distances to the nearest foot and then to the nearest inch. Then children measure the same objects or distances with metric units.

Bring the class together to compare measurements. Help children see that using smaller units gives more exact measurements.

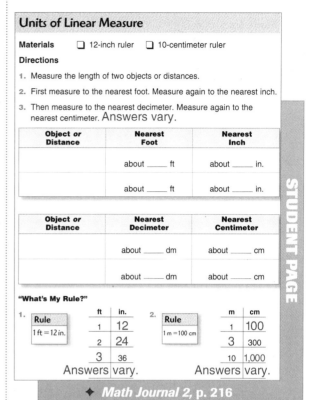

Units of Linear Measure

Materials ☐ 12-inch ruler ☐ 10-centimeter ruler

Directions

1. Measure the length of two objects or distances.
2. First measure to the nearest foot. Measure again to the nearest inch.
3. Then measure to the nearest decimeter. Measure again to the nearest centimeter. Answers vary.

Object *or* Distance	Nearest Foot	Nearest Inch
	about _____ ft	about _____ in.
	about _____ ft	about _____ in.

Object *or* Distance	Nearest Decimeter	Nearest Centimeter
	about _____ dm	about _____ cm
	about _____ dm	about _____ cm

"What's My Rule?"

1. Rule 1 ft = 12 in.

ft	in.
1	12
2	24
3	36

Answers vary.

2. Rule 1 m = 100 cm

m	cm
1	100
3	300
10	1,000

Answers vary.

◆ *Math Journal 2, p. 216*

STUDENT PAGE

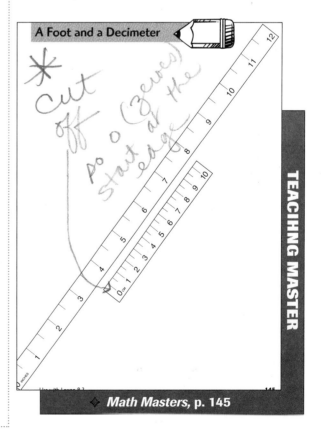

A Foot and a Decimeter

◆ *Math Masters, p. 145*

TEACHING MASTER

Math Boxes 9.2

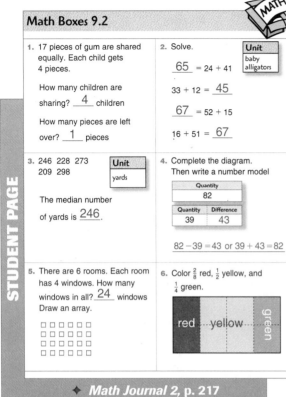

1. 17 pieces of gum are shared equally. Each child gets 4 pieces.

How many children are sharing? __4__ children

How many pieces are left over? __1__ pieces

2. Solve.

Unit
baby alligators

__65__ = 24 + 41

33 + 12 = __45__

__67__ = 52 + 15

16 + 51 = __67__

3. 246 228 273
209 298

Unit
yards

The median number of yards is __246__.

4. Complete the diagram. Then write a number model

Quantity
82

Quantity	Difference
39	43

82 − 39 = 43 or 39 + 43 = 82

5. There are 6 rooms. Each room has 4 windows. How many windows in all? __24__ windows
Draw an array.

□ □ □ □ □ □
□ □ □ □ □ □
□ □ □ □ □ □
□ □ □ □ □ □

6. Color $\frac{2}{8}$ red, $\frac{1}{2}$ yellow, and $\frac{1}{4}$ green.

red — yellow — green

✦ *Math Journal 2, p. 217*

STUDENT PAGE

2 Ongoing Learning & Practice

 Math Boxes 9.2 (*Math Journal 2*, p. 217)

INDEPENDENT ACTIVITY 👤

Mixed Review This journal page provides opportunities for cumulative review or assessment of concepts and skills.

✦ **Home Link 9.2** (*Math Masters*, pp. 358 and 359)

Home Connection Children measure objects with rulers using U.S. customary and metric units.

Linear Measurements

Home Link 9.2

Family Note
Today your child reviewed how to use a ruler to measure objects and distances in inches and feet and in centimeters and decimeters. Your child's class also began making a Table of Equivalencies for both the U.S. customary and the metric systems. Ask your child to show you how to measure some of the objects or distances that he or she selects to complete the tables below.

Please return this Home Link to school tomorrow.

1. Cut out the 6-inch ruler on the next page. Measure two objects or distances. Measure to the nearest foot. Then measure again to the nearest inch. Some things you might measure are the width of the refrigerator door, the length of the bathtub, or the height of a light switch from the floor. Sample answers:

Object *or* Distance	Nearest Foot	Nearest Inch
length of bed	about _7_ ft	about _79_ in.
	about ___ ft	about ___ in.

2. Cut out the 10-inch centimeter ruler on the next page. Measure the same objects or distances. Measure to the nearest decimeter. Then measure again to the nearest centimeter.

Object *or* Distance	Nearest Decimeter	Nearest Centimeter
	about ___ dm	about ___ cm
	about ___ dm	about ___ cm

✦ *Math Masters, p. 358*

HOME LINK MASTER

Linear Measurements (cont.)

Home Link 9.2

Complete each sentence.

3. One foot is equal to __12__ inches.

4. One yard is equal to __3__ feet.

5. One decimeter is equal to __10__ centimeters.

6. One meter is equal to __100__ centimeters.

7. Two feet are equal to __24__ inches.

8. Three yards are equal to __9__ feet.

9. Four decimeters are equal to __40__ centimeters.

10. Seven meters are equal to __700__ centimeters.

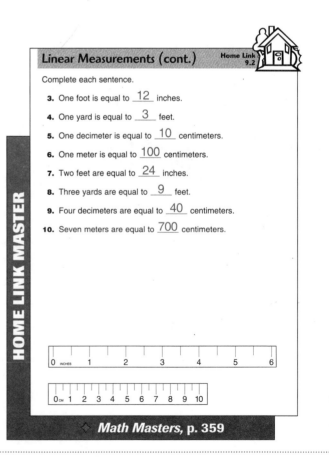

✦ *Math Masters, p. 359*

HOME LINK MASTER

Options for Individualizing

◆ ENRICHMENT Exploring Equivalent U.S. Customary Linear Measures in Literature

SMALL-GROUP ACTIVITY   5–15 min

 Literature Link Read the following story to children, or have them read the book themselves. It introduces U.S. customary measures of length and the relationships among the units.

Twelve Snails to One Lizard: A Tale of Mischief and Measurement

Summary: This book is the story of Milo Beaver and Bubba Bullfrog and how they solve the problem of fixing a hole in the dam.

◆ EXTRA PRACTICE Minute Math

SMALL-GROUP ACTIVITY   5–15 min

To offer children more experience with using measuring tools, see the following page in *Minute Math:*

Measurement: p. 61

PLANNING AHEAD

Collect the boxes shaped like rectangular prisms that children have brought to school. Check that each box fits on a sheet of paper. Make sure that children have written their names on the boxes. Remind children who have not yet brought in boxes to do so. The boxes will be used in Lesson 9.4.

9.3

Fractional Units of Length

OBJECTIVES To investigate the idea of accuracy; to identify $\frac{1}{8}$ inch, $\frac{1}{16}$ inch, and $\frac{1}{2}$ centimeter on a ruler; and to measure to the nearest half-inch and half-centimeter.

summaries | materials

1 Teaching the Lesson

Children discuss accuracy, identify subdivisions on tape measures and rulers, and measure to the nearest half-inch and half-centimeter. [Numeration; Measurement and Reference Frames]

- ☐ *Math Journal 2*, pp. 218 and 219
- ☐ Home Link 9.2
- ☐ Teaching Master transparencies (*Math Masters*, pp. 146 and 147; optional)
- ☐ tape measure
- ☐ tool-kit ruler
- ☐ Table of Equivalent Measures (started in Lesson 9.2)

***See* Advance Preparation**

2 Ongoing Learning & Practice

Children practice and maintain skills through Math Boxes and Home Link activities.

- ☐ *Math Journal 2*, p. 220
- ☐ Home Link Masters (*Math Masters*, pp. 360 and 361)

3 Options for Individualizing

Extra Practice Children measure objects of their choice to the nearest half-inch and half-centimeter. [Numeration; Measurement and Reference Frames]

Enrichment Children compare the metric units of meter, decimeter, and centimeter by measuring the same objects with all three units. [Numeration; Measurement and Reference Frames]

- ☐ Teaching Masters (*Math Masters*, pp. 148–150)
- ☐ length of string or ribbon
- ☐ inch ruler
- ☐ centimeter ruler
- ☐ tape measure
- ☐ meterstick

***See* Advance Preparation**

Additional Information

Advance Preparation For the *Introducing Fractional Units of Length* activity in Part 1, you may want to make overhead transparencies of *Math Masters*, pages 146 and 147.

For the optional Enrichment activity in Part 3, cut lengths of string or ribbon that are a whole number of meters long, such as 2 meters or 5 meters.

Vocabulary • millimeter

Getting Started

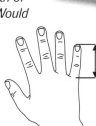

Teaching the Lesson

◆ Math Message Follow-Up

WHOLE-CLASS DISCUSSION

Ask children to raise their hands if their little fingers are about 1 inch long. About 2 inches long. About 3 inches long. Can children tell from their responses whose little finger is the longest? The shortest? Might they be able to tell if they had taken more exact measurements?

◆ Discussing the Need for Accurate Measurements

WHOLE-CLASS DISCUSSION

People take measurements using tools made by people. Because there is a limit to what people can observe and what tools can do, it is likely that any measurement differs somewhat from the "exact" or "true" value of the quantity being measured.

An accurate measurement is one that is equal to, or close to, the "exact" value. Accuracy can be improved by using high-quality tools, reading the tools carefully, and measuring in small units or fractional parts of units.

NOTE: The precision with which measuring tools are manufactured is often based on intended use, materials, and cost. So the tolerance, or difference, between a standard unit and a particular measuring tool can vary.

Science Link

When the Hubble telescope was first sent into space (after years of research at a cost of billions of dollars), it did not work properly due to an error in measurement of about $\frac{1}{10}$ centimeter. Ask children to find $\frac{1}{10}$ centimeter (1 millimeter) on their tape measures.

NOTE: It is assumed that children are using tape measures with eighth-inch marks on one side and half-centimeter and millimeter marks on the other side, as well as rulers with sixteenth-inch marks on the inch scale and half-centimeter and millimeter marks on the centimeter scale. Please adjust the discussion of fractional units to match the tools that your class is using.

NOTE: Since children will benefit from repeated exposures to fraction notation, write the fractions on the board as children name them. You might also draw a unit box to remind children of the unit associated with the fractions.

Discuss the following ideas with children:

▷ Some situations require very accurate measurements. For example, people who build cars must measure accurately to be sure that the parts fit together properly. Prescription drugs are usually dispensed in milligrams.

▷ Other situations require less accurate measurements. For example, it wouldn't make sense to give the length of a football field in inches or the weight of a truck in milligrams.

▷ Sometimes an estimate is good enough. For example, is the distance from home to school farther than the distance from home to the fire station?

Have children share examples of measurement situations. Which situations call for very accurate measurements? For which situations is a less accurate measurement, or an estimate, good enough?

◆ Introducing Fractional Units of Length
(*Math Masters,* pp. 146 and 147)

WHOLE-CLASS DISCUSSION

Tell children that they can make more accurate measurements if they measure in fractional parts of inches or centimeters. Ask children to examine the inch side of their tape measures. *How many spaces are marked between inch marks?* 8 *Are all marks equally spaced?* yes

---

 Adjusting the Activity If children have difficulty finding the dividing marks within an inch, use an overhead transparency of *Math Masters,* page 146 to help them.

Next, ask children to look for the mark that divides an inch on the tape measure into two equal parts. Check to see that they have found the $\frac{1}{2}$-inch mark. *How long is the part between the 0-inch mark and the $\frac{1}{2}$-inch mark?* $\frac{1}{2}$ inch *The part between the $\frac{1}{2}$-inch mark and the 1-inch mark?* $\frac{1}{2}$ inch

Have children find the marks that divide an inch into eight equal parts. *How long is the part between two such marks?* $\frac{1}{8}$ inch Count the divisions of an inch in unison: $\frac{1}{8}, \frac{2}{8}, \frac{3}{8}, ..., \frac{8}{8}$ *inch.* Then follow the same procedure with quarter-inches. Encourage children to find equivalent names for the same fractional measurement units.

Next, have children examine the inch side of the ruler in their tool kits. Children should notice that the inches are divided into even more (smaller) parts than on the tape measure. *How many such parts are there in an inch?* 16 As before, count the marks in an inch space in unison: $\frac{1}{16}, \frac{2}{16}, \frac{3}{16}, \ldots \frac{16}{16}$ inch.

Finally, ask children to find the 1-centimeter marks on their rulers. Ask them how many equal parts a centimeter is divided into. 10 Tell them that the name for one of the ten parts of a centimeter is a **millimeter** (mm). *How many millimeters are in 1 centimeter?* 10 A millimeter is $\frac{1}{10}$ of a centimeter. Mention that the prefix *milli-* means "thousandth of" and that there are 1,000 millimeters in a meter. A millimeter is $\frac{1}{1,000}$ of a meter.

Point out the half-centimeter marks on the ruler. These marks are a little longer than the millimeter marks.

 Adjusting the Activity If children have difficulty finding the dividing marks within a centimeter, use an overhead transparency of *Math Masters,* page 147 to help them.

Add millimeters to the Table of Equivalent Measures on the Class Data Pad (see below). Save the table for future discussions.

```
1 meter (m)  = 1,000 millimeters
1 decimeter  =  100 millimeters
1 centimeter =   10 millimeters
```

Update the Table of Equivalent Measures on the Class Data Pad.

◆ Measuring to the Nearest Half-Inch and Half-Centimeter
(*Math Journal 2,* pp. 218 and 219)

PARTNER ACTIVITY 👬

Children use a ruler to measure the lengths of objects in full-size drawings.

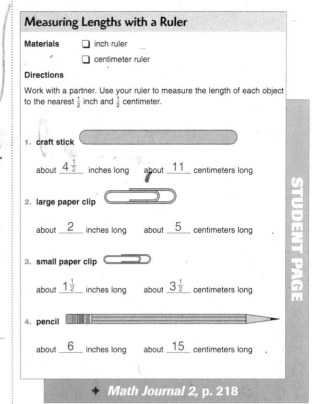

Measuring Lengths with a Ruler

Materials ☐ inch ruler
           ☐ centimeter ruler

Directions

Work with a partner. Use your ruler to measure the length of each object to the nearest $\frac{1}{2}$ inch and $\frac{1}{2}$ centimeter.

1. **craft stick**
   about $4\frac{1}{2}$ inches long   about 11 centimeters long

2. **large paper clip**
   about 2 inches long   about 5 centimeters long

3. **small paper clip**
   about $1\frac{1}{2}$ inches long   about $3\frac{1}{2}$ centimeters long

4. **pencil**
   about 6 inches long   about 15 centimeters long

Math Journal 2, p. 218

STUDENT PAGE

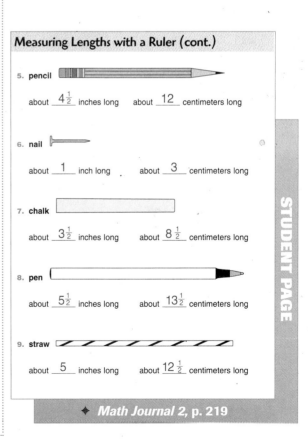

Measuring Lengths with a Ruler (cont.)

5. **pencil**
   about $4\frac{1}{2}$ inches long   about 12 centimeters long

6. **nail**
   about 1 inch long   about 3 centimeters long

7. **chalk**
   about $3\frac{1}{2}$ inches long   about $8\frac{1}{2}$ centimeters long

8. **pen**
   about $5\frac{1}{2}$ inches long   about $13\frac{1}{2}$ centimeters long

9. **straw**
   about 5 inches long   about $12\frac{1}{2}$ centimeters long

Math Journal 2, p. 219

STUDENT PAGE

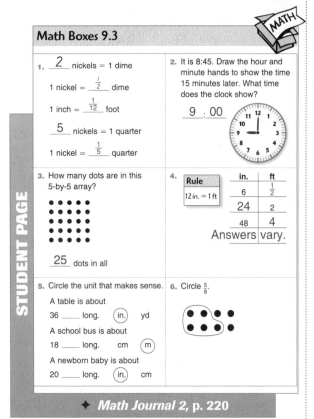

Math Boxes 9.3

1. __2__ nickels = 1 dime

   1 nickel = __$\frac{1}{2}$__ dime

   1 inch = __$\frac{1}{12}$__ foot

   __5__ nickels = 1 quarter

   1 nickel = __$\frac{1}{5}$__ quarter

2. It is 8:45. Draw the hour and minute hands to show the time 15 minutes later. What time does the clock show?

   __9__ : __00__

3. How many dots are in this 5-by-5 array?

   • • • • •
   • • • • •
   • • • • •
   • • • • •
   • • • • •

   __25__ dots in all

4.
Rule	in.	ft
12 in. = 1 ft	6	$\frac{1}{2}$
	24	2
	48	4

   Answers vary.

5. Circle the unit that makes sense.

   A table is about

   36 ____ long. (in.) yd

   A school bus is about

   18 ____ long. cm (m)

   A newborn baby is about

   20 ____ long. (in.) cm

6. Circle $\frac{5}{8}$.

Math Journal 2, p. 220

STUDENT PAGE

---

2 Ongoing Learning & Practice

◆ **Math Boxes 9.3** (*Math Journal 2*, p. 220)

INDEPENDENT ACTIVITY 👤

Mixed Review This journal page provides opportunities for cumulative review or assessment of concepts and skills.

◆ **Home Link 9.3** (*Math Masters*, pp. 360 and 361)

Home Connection Children measure objects around their homes to the nearest half-inch or half-centimeter. They draw a picture and record the measurements.

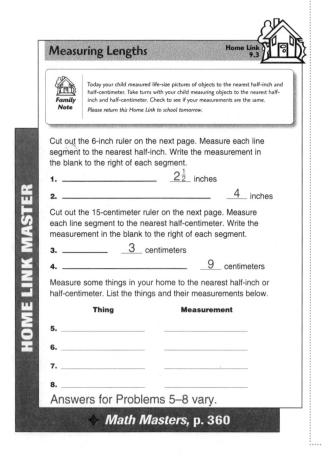

Measuring Lengths — Home Link 9.3

Family Note Today your child measured life-size pictures of objects to the nearest half-inch and half-centimeter. Take turns with your child measuring objects to the nearest half-inch and half-centimeter. Check to see if your measurements are the same.

Please return this Home Link to school tomorrow.

Cut out the 6-inch ruler on the next page. Measure each line segment to the nearest half-inch. Write the measurement in the blank to the right of each segment.

1. _____ __$2\frac{1}{2}$__ inches

2. _____ __4__ inches

Cut out the 15-centimeter ruler on the next page. Measure each line segment to the nearest half-centimeter. Write the measurement in the blank to the right of each segment.

3. _____ __3__ centimeters

4. _____ __9__ centimeters

Measure some things in your home to the nearest half-inch or half-centimeter. List the things and their measurements below.

Thing	Measurement
5. _____	_____
6. _____	_____
7. _____	_____
8. _____	_____

Answers for Problems 5–8 vary.

Math Masters, p. 360

HOME LINK MASTER

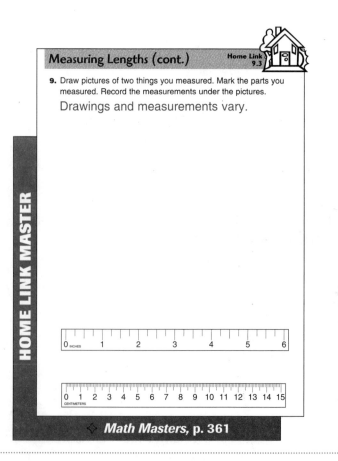

Measuring Lengths (cont.) — Home Link 9.3

9. Draw pictures of two things you measured. Mark the parts you measured. Record the measurements under the pictures.

Drawings and measurements vary.

Math Masters, p. 361

HOME LINK MASTER

---

3 Options for Individualizing

◆ EXTRA PRACTICE Measuring to the Nearest Half-Inch and Half-Centimeter
(*Math Masters,* p. 148)

PARTNER ACTIVITY   15–30 min

Partners measure five objects in the classroom to the nearest half-inch and half-centimeter. Children draw a picture of each object and record its measurement.

◆ ENRICHMENT Comparing Units of Metric Linear Measure
(*Math Masters,* pp. 149 and 150)

SMALL-GROUP ACTIVITY   15–30 min

Children practice finding linear measures of objects using metric units. They should see a pattern showing the relationships among the three metric units used: 10 centimeters = 1 decimeter; 10 decimeters = 1 meter; and 100 centimeters = 1 meter.

If decimeters and meters are not marked on children's tape measures and metersticks, children can mark these increments using crayons.

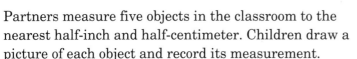

Metric Units of Linear Measure

Work with 1 or 2 people.

Materials   ❑ tape measures
          ❑ metersticks
          ❑ string or ribbon from your teacher

Directions

1. Check your measuring tools. Look for these units:
   • 1 meter (100 centimeters)
   • decimeters (10 centimeters each)
   If the units are hard to see, mark them with a crayon.

2. Measure the string or ribbon you get from your teacher. Measure it 3 times.
   Use meters the first time you measure. Use decimeters the next time. Use centimeters the last time.
   Answers vary.

   _____ meters

   _____ decimeters

   _____ centimeters

Math Masters, p. 149

TEACHING MASTER

Measures around the Classroom

Materials   ❑ tape measure

Directions
   • Measure five things. Draw a picture of each item and show which part you measured.
   • Measure to the nearest half-inch. Then measure again to the nearest half-centimeter. Answers vary.

Example	1.
_14_ inches _35½_ centimeters	_____ inches _____ centimeters
2.	**3.**
_____ inches _____ centimeters	_____ inches _____ centimeters
4.	**5.**
_____ inches _____ centimeters	_____ inches _____ centimeters

◆ *Math Masters,* p. 148

TEACHING MASTER

PLANNING AHEAD

In Lesson 9.4, each child will need a box in the shape of a rectangular prism, with bases smaller than a sheet of paper.

Metric Units (cont.)

3. Choose a different item to measure. *For example:*
   • the width of a door, the classroom, or a window
   • the length of someone's arm or leg
   • the length and width of a rug, a table, or the hall

   Measure the item 3 times. Use meters the first time you measure, decimeters the next time, and centimeters the last time. Answers vary.

   _____ meters

   _____ decimeters

   _____ centimeters

4. Talk about the measurements in Problems 2 and 3. Can anyone see any patterns among the 3 measurements? Is the measure in centimeters about 10 times the measure in decimeters? About 100 times the measure in meters?

5. Name some things that would best be measured in …
   a. meters Answers for parts a–c vary.

   b. centimeters _____

   c. decimeters _____

◆ *Math Masters,* p. 150

TEACHING MASTER

Perimeter

9.4

OBJECTIVE To find perimeters by measuring to the nearest half-centimeter or half-inch.

summaries	materials
1 Teaching the Lesson	
Children measure the distances around their thumbs, wrists, necks, ankles, and other objects to the nearest centimeter. They also find the perimeters of rectangles and polygons by measuring to the nearest half-inch or half-centimeter. [Measurement and Reference Frames; Geometry]	☐ *Math Journal 2*, p. 221 ☐ Home Link 9.3 ☐ Teaching Master (*Math Masters*, p. 151; 1 copy per 4 children) ☐ inch and centimeter rulers; tape measure ☐ box in the shape of a rectangular prism ***See* Advance Preparation**
2 Ongoing Learning & Practice	
Children practice and maintain skills through Math Boxes and Home Link activities.	☐ *Math Journal 2*, p. 222 ☐ Home Link Masters (*Math Masters*, pp. 362 and 363)
3 Options for Individualizing	
Enrichment Children estimate their pace lengths in feet and use the estimate to solve a perimeter problem. [Measurement and Reference Frames]	☐ Teaching Masters (*Math Masters*, pp. 152 and 153) ☐ masking tape

---

Additional Information

Advance Preparation For the Math Message, copy and cut apart *Math Masters*, page 151. Place the slips next to the message.

Vocabulary • **perimeter**

Getting Started

Mental Math and Reflexes
Pose problems like the following:
- Seven children are in the playground. Two children went home. What fraction of the children went home? $\frac{2}{7}$ What fraction stayed? $\frac{5}{7}$
- Julian had 9 candies. He ate $\frac{1}{3}$ of them. How many candies did he eat? 3 How many were left? 6

Math Message
Take a slip of paper. Follow the instructions on it. Work with a partner.

Home Link 9.3 Follow-Up
Briefly go over the measurements of the line segments.

1 Teaching the Lesson

◆ Math Message Follow-Up
(*Math Masters,* p. 151)

WHOLE-CLASS DISCUSSION

Ask children in each group to compare their thumb and wrist measurements. Do larger thumbs seem to go with larger wrists?

◆ Measuring Distances around Shapes
(*Math Journal 2,* p. 221)

PARTNER ACTIVITY

Partners first measure the distances around each other's necks and ankles, and then around a book, slate, and/or various objects from the Measures All Around Museum. They should measure all distances to the nearest centimeter and record measurements on journal page 221.

Have children share their results and what they did to measure each distance. *Some key points:*

▷ Why did children choose a specific measuring tool? For example: Rigid measuring tools are inappropriate for measuring curved surfaces; a yardstick is easier to use than a 12-inch ruler when measuring a longer object.

▷ Name different ways of measuring distances around objects, such as a book. Measure the distance by wrapping a tape measure around the book's edges or by measuring the lengths of the edges and finding the sum.

▷ Children suggest situations in which one needs to find the distance around something. Sample answers: When buying wood for a picture frame or material for a fence

◆ Investigating Perimeters of Rectangles

WHOLE-CLASS ACTIVITY

In previous activities, children measured to the nearest centimeter. For this and the following activity, children measure to the nearest half-centimeter and half-inch.

Each child should have a box in the shape of a rectangular prism. Each face of the box should be smaller than a sheet of paper. Each child should proceed as follows:

1. Place the box on a sheet of paper and trace the edges around one face of the box.

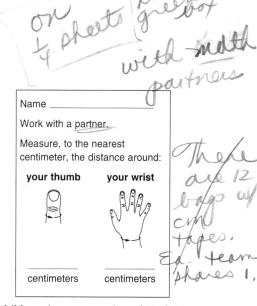

Name _____

Work with a partner.

Measure, to the nearest centimeter, the distance around:

your thumb   **your wrist**

_____ centimeters   _____ centimeters

Each child receives one section of *Math Masters,* page 151.

○ Language Arts Link

The word *meter* comes from the Greek word *metron,* which means "measure." The prefix *peri-* comes from the Greek word for "around." So perimeter means "the measure around something." Some children may remember the meaning of pe**rim**eter by focusing on the word "rim."

Distance Around and Perimeter

Measure the distance around the following to the nearest centimeter.

1. Your neck: _____ cm   **2.** Your ankle: _____ cm

Measure the distance around two other objects to the nearest centimeter.

Answers for Problems 1–4 vary.

3. Object: _____ Measurement: _____ cm

4. Object: _____ Measurement: _____ cm

Measure the sides of each figure to the nearest ½ inch. Write the length next to each side. Then find the perimeter.

5. Perimeter: __8 or 9__ inches

3 inches

1 inch or 1½ inches   [ ]   1 inch or 1½ inches

3 inches

6. Perimeter: __$6\frac{1}{2}$__ inches

1½ inches

1 inch

1 inch

1 inch

2 inches

◆ *Math Journal 2,* p. 221

STUDENT PAGE

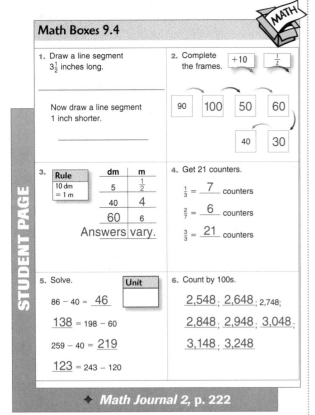

Math Boxes 9.4

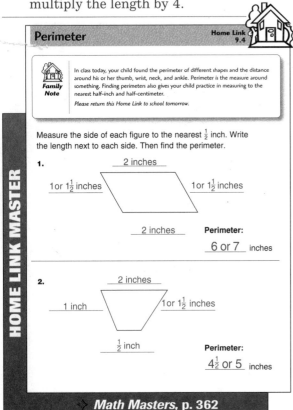

1. Draw a line segment $3\frac{1}{2}$ inches long.

Now draw a line segment 1 inch shorter.

_____

2. Complete the frames. $+10$ | $\frac{1}{2}$

90 | 100 | 50 | 60

40 | 30

3. Rule: 10 dm = 1 m

dm	m
5	$\frac{1}{2}$
40	4
60	6

Answers vary.

4. Get 21 counters.

$\frac{1}{3}$ = __7__ counters

$\frac{2}{7}$ = __6__ counters

$\frac{3}{3}$ = __21__ counters

5. Solve.

$86 - 40 =$ __46__

Unit

__138__ $= 198 - 60$

$259 - 40 =$ __219__

__123__ $= 243 - 120$

6. Count by 100s.

2,548 ; 2,648 ; 2,748 ;

2,848 ; 2,948 ; 3,048 ;

3,148 ; 3,248

✦ *Math Journal 2*, p. 222

Adjusting the Activity To extend the polygon perimeter activity, draw a square on the board. Ask children how they could find the perimeter of a square without measuring all four sides. Measure one side and then add its length four times; or multiply the length by 4.

Perimeter

Home Link 9.4

Family Note

In class today, your child found the perimeter of different shapes and the distance around his or her thumb, wrist, neck, and ankle. Perimeter is the measure around something. Finding perimeters also gives your child practice in measuring to the nearest half-inch and half-centimeter.

Please return this Home Link to school tomorrow.

Measure the side of each figure to the nearest $\frac{1}{2}$ inch. Write the length next to each side. Then find the perimeter.

1.

2 inches

1 or $1\frac{1}{2}$ inches   1 or $1\frac{1}{2}$ inches

2 inches

Perimeter: __6 or 7__ inches

2.

2 inches

1 inch   1 or $1\frac{1}{2}$ inches

$\frac{1}{2}$ inch

Perimeter: __$4\frac{1}{2}$ or 5__ inches

✦ *Math Masters, p. 362*

---

2. Find the distance around the tracing to the nearest half-centimeter or half-inch. Record this measurement below the tracing.

Help children add several half-centimeter or half-inch measurements. Ask children to explain how they found the distance around. *Did anyone do so without measuring all four sides?* Sample answer: Measure two sides with different lengths; then add each measurement twice.

How many different-size faces does the box have? Since the boxes are rectangular prisms, at most three.

Repeat Steps 1 and 2 with different-size faces of the box.

Define the word **perimeter.** The perimeter of something is the distance around it.

 Adjusting the Activity If children are having difficulty adding half-centimeter or half-inch measurements, use manipulatives to demonstrate how to put together pairs of halves to make a whole.

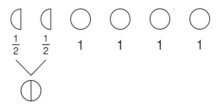

$\frac{1}{2}$ $\frac{1}{2}$ 1 1 1 1

5 circles in all

✦ **Investigating Perimeters of Polygons**
(*Math Journal 2*, p. 221)

INDEPENDENT ACTIVITY

Children measure the sides of polygons and find the perimeter. In Problem 5, point out to children that since each of the 2 shorter sides of the rectangle is $1\frac{1}{4}$ inches long, either 1 or $1\frac{1}{2}$ inches is an accurate measurement to the nearest $\frac{1}{2}$ inch.

Ongoing Learning & Practice

✦ **Math Boxes 9.4** (*Math Journal 2*, p. 222)

INDEPENDENT ACTIVITY

 Mixed Review This journal page provides opportunities for cumulative review or assessment of concepts and skills.

Home Connection Children solve perimeter problems.

Options for Individualizing

♦ **ENRICHMENT** **Measuring Perimeter in Paces** (*Math Masters*, pp. 152 and 153)

SMALL-GROUP ACTIVITY 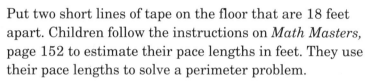 **15–30 min**

Put two short lines of tape on the floor that are 18 feet apart. Children follow the instructions on *Math Masters*, page 152 to estimate their pace lengths in feet. They use their pace lengths to solve a perimeter problem.

Perimeter (cont.) Home Link 9.4

Solve the number story. Write a number model.

3. Mr. McGreggor is putting a fence around his vegetable garden. The garden is shaped liked a rectangle. The longer sides are 14 feet long and the shorter sides are $9\frac{1}{2}$ feet long. How much fencing should Mr. McGreggor buy?

Answer: __47__ feet

Number model: $14 + 14 + 9\frac{1}{2} + 9\frac{1}{2} = 47$ or

$2 \times 14 + 2 \times 9\frac{1}{2} = 47$

4. Draw a quadrangle below. Measure the sides to the nearest $\frac{1}{2}$ inch. Write the length next to each side. Find the perimeter.

The perimeter of my quadrangle is _____ inches.

Answers vary.

| 0 INCHES | 1 | 2 | 3 | 4 | 5 | 6 |

♦ *Math Masters, p. 363*

Measuring Perimeter in Paces

Your teacher will put two lines of tape on the floor that are 18 feet apart.

1. Start with your toes on one line. Count the number of paces you take to reach the other line. Each time your foot hits the floor counts as 1 pace.

Number of paces: _____

2. Use this table to find out how long your pace is.

Number of Steps Taken	Length of Your Pace Is About ...
15 or more	1 foot
11 to 14	$1\frac{1}{2}$ feet
8 to 10	2 feet
7	$2\frac{1}{2}$ feet
6	3 feet

The length of my pace is about _____ feet.

♦ *Math Masters, p. 152*

Measuring Perimeter in Paces (cont.)

3. Mr. Dean's garden is square. Each side is 30 feet long.

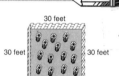

30 feet (top)
30 feet (left) 30 feet (right)
30 feet (bottom)

a. How many paces would you take to walk along one side of the garden?

_____ paces

b. How many paces would you take to walk around the whole garden?

_____ paces

c. The perimeter of the garden is __120__ feet.

d. The perimeter of the garden is _____ of my paces.

♦ *Math Masters, p. 153*

9.5 Measuring Longer Distances

OBJECTIVES To identify the mile and the kilometer as standard units for longer distances; and to solve problems about road-map distances.

| summaries | materials |

1 Teaching the Lesson

Children discuss the kilometer and the mile as units used for measuring longer distances and add these units to the Table of Equivalent Measures. Children also make up and solve number stories about road-map distances given in miles. [Measurement and Reference Frames; Operations and Computation]

- ☐ *Math Journal 2*, p. 223
- ☐ Home Link 9.4
- ☐ Table of Equivalent Measures (started in Lesson 9.2)
- ☐ tape measure
- ☐ calculator

2 Ongoing Learning & Practice

Children find the perimeters of block letters on a centimeter grid. [Measurement and Reference Frames]

Children practice and maintain skills through Math Boxes and Home Link activities.

- ☐ *Math Journal 2*, pp. 224 and 225
- ☐ Home Link Master (*Math Masters*, p. 364)

3 Options for Individualizing

Enrichment Children use a map to determine the number of miles they would travel on a pretend trip. [Measurement and Reference Frames]

- ☐ map(s) for a pretend trip

Additional Information
Vocabulary • **mile** • **kilometer**

Getting Started

Mental Math and Reflexes

Pose problems like the following:

- A group of children shared 15 books equally. Each child got 3 books. What fraction of the books did each child get? $\frac{1}{5}$
- Six children ate pepperoni pizza. That is $\frac{1}{2}$ of all of the children that ate pizza. How many children ate pizza? 12

Math Message

Three children measured the width of a door. Could they all be correct?

Maria: about 1 meter

George: about 9 decimeters

Suki: about 92 centimeters

Home Link 9.4 Follow-Up

Briefly review results.

Teaching the Lesson

✦ Math Message Follow-Up

WHOLE-CLASS DISCUSSION

To compare the three measurements, children can find the mark for each one on their tape measures. Ask: *Which measurement do you think is closest to the actual width of the door?* Remind children that when smaller units are used, the measurement can be more exact.

✦ Introducing Units Used to Measure Longer Distances

WHOLE-CLASS DISCUSSION

Ask: *Would it make sense to measure the distance to [name a nearby city or place] in inches? Can someone suggest a better unit?*

Children are likely to suggest the **mile** as a unit for measuring longer distances.

In the U.S. customary system, 1 mile is equivalent to 1,760 yards or 5,280 feet. Record these equivalencies on the Class Data Pad. Mention a few locations that are about 1 mile from school. Ask children about how long it would take them to walk a mile. Probably 20–30 minutes

Children may not know that the **kilometer** is the metric unit for longer distances. Say that 1 kilometer is equivalent to 1,000 meters, and record this equivalency on the Class Data Pad. Mention that a kilometer is shorter than a mile (about $\frac{6}{10}$ of a mile) and that people in most countries (except the United States) measure road distances in kilometers.

Save the Table of Equivalent Measures (on the Class Data Pad) for future discussions. Plan to augment the table by adding new equivalencies as they are introduced in subsequent lessons.

Language Arts Link The prefix *kilo-* comes from the Greek word for "thousand," and the word *mile* comes from Old English and Latin words for "thousand." Long ago, a mile was said to be equivalent to 1,000 "paces." Therefore, a pace was a little more than 5 feet. Since the average adult's stride is about 1 yard, or 3 feet, a pace probably meant two consecutive strides.

1 kilometer (km) = 1,000 meters
1 mile = 1,760 yards
= 5,280 feet

Update the Table of Equivalent Measures on the Class Data Pad.

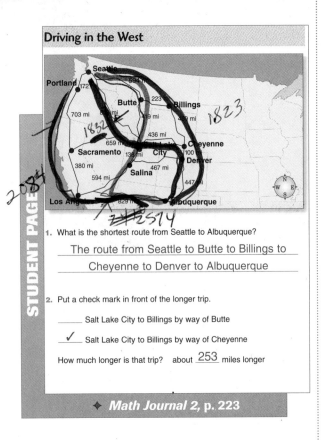

Driving in the West

1. What is the shortest route from Seattle to Albuquerque?

The route from Seattle to Butte to Billings to
Cheyenne to Denver to Albuquerque

2. Put a check mark in front of the longer trip.

_____ Salt Lake City to Billings by way of Butte

✓ Salt Lake City to Billings by way of Cheyenne

How much longer is that trip?   about __253__ miles longer

♦ Math Journal 2, p. 223

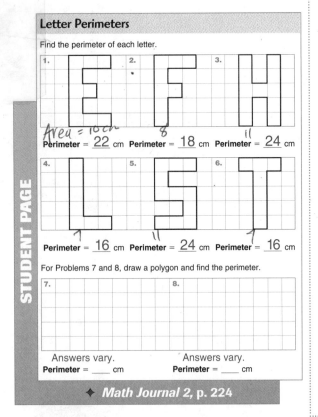

Letter Perimeters

Find the perimeter of each letter.

1.	2.	3.
E	F	H
Perimeter = __22__ cm	Perimeter = __18__ cm	Perimeter = __24__ cm

4.	5.	6.
L	S	T
Perimeter = __16__ cm	Perimeter = __24__ cm	Perimeter = __16__ cm

For Problems 7 and 8, draw a polygon and find the perimeter.

7.	8.
Answers vary.	Answers vary.
Perimeter = ____ cm	Perimeter = ____ cm

♦ Math Journal 2, p. 224

◆ Introducing Road-Map Stories
(*Math Journal 2*, p. 223)

PARTNER ACTIVITY 👥

Explain to the class that the road map on journal page 223 shows the driving distances in miles between cities in the western United States. Give children some number stories based on the map. Partners work together to solve the number stories, with or without calculators. Discuss the solutions. *Suggestions:*

Easy

H... ...acramento? About
87...

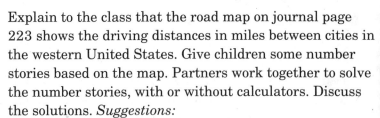

Av...

Mr... ...Los Angeles by
way... ...from Salt Lake
City... ...o drove more
mile... ...? About 307 more
mile...

Wha... ...les to Cheyenne?
The...

Cha...

The ... ...amily drove from Seattle to Los Angeles by way of Butte, Billings, Cheyenne, Denver, and Albuquerque. They drove about 400 miles a day. About how many days did the trip take them? About 7 days

◆ Solving Road-Map Stories
(*Math Journal 2*, p. 223)

PARTNER ACTIVITY 👥

Children solve two road-map stories on journal page 223. Encourage children to make up other stories based on the map and to record them on half-sheets of paper. Partners solve each other's stories.

Portfolio Ideas

2 Ongoing Learning & Practice

◆ Finding Perimeters (Math Journal 2, p. 224)

INDIVIDUAL

Children find t
centimeter gri

Adjusting t counting t
perimeters
sides with

Monday
4-23-07
Math

◆ Math Boxes

INDEPENDEN

M
op
as

◆ Home Link

H
so
ta
ab

Math Boxes 9.5

1. Measure each side of the triangle to the nearest inch. Find the perimeter.

   The perimeter is 5 inches.

2. Ginny had 16 baseball cards. She traded $\frac{1}{4}$ of them.

   How many cards did she trade? 4 cards

   How many did she keep? 12 cards

3. Draw a line segment $4\frac{1}{2}$ cm long.

   ______

   Now draw a line segment 2 cm longer.

   ______

4. If 25¢ is ONE:

   what is 5¢? $\frac{1}{5}$

   what is 50¢? 2

   If $2 is ONE:

   what is 50¢? $\frac{1}{4}$

   what is $4? 2

5. Rule: 1 yd = 3 ft

yd	ft
2	6
3	9
5	15
10	30
Answers	vary.

6. Solve. Unit

   22 − 14 = 8

   62 − 14 = 48

   162 − 14 = 148

   278 = 292 − 14

   388 = 402 − 14

STUDENT PAGE

◆ *Math Journal 2*, p. 225

Travel Interview Home Link 9.5

Family Note: Our class is studying measurement of longer distances. If the traveler your child talks to had experiences with the metric system in another country, have your child include this information to share with the class.

Please return this Home Link to school tomorrow.

Ask someone at home to tell you about the longest trip he or she ever took. Write about the trip. Here are some questions you might want to ask that person:

- When did you take the trip?
- Where did you go?
- What interesting or unusual things did you see or do?
- How did you travel? By car? By plane? By train?
- How long did the trip take?
- How far did you travel?

Answers vary.

HOME LINK MASTER

◇ *Math Masters*, p. 364

3 Options for Individualizing

◆ ENRICHMENT Researching a Pretend Trip

INDEPENDENT ACTIVITY **15–30 min**

Portfolio Ideas

Children determine a location in the United States that they would like to visit and use a map to determine the number of miles from their home to the location. Some children may be interested in comparing the road miles of their trip to the air miles. Encourage children to give a brief report to the class about their pretend trip.

9.6 Measures All Around

OBJECTIVE To identify appropriate tools and units of measure for determining length, weight, volume, and capacity.

summaries	materials

1 Teaching the Lesson

Children list things that can be measured; measuring tools; and units of measure for linear measures, weights, volume and capacity. [Measurement and Reference Frames]

- ☐ *Math Journal 2*, p. 226
- ☐ Home Link 9.5
- ☐ Class Data Pad
- ☐ 18 counters (optional)
- ☐ tape measure or ruler

See **Advance Preparation**

2 Ongoing Learning & Practice

Children practice and maintain skills through Math Boxes and Home Link activities.

- ☐ *Math Journal 2*, p. 227
- ☐ Home Link Master (*Math Masters*, p. 365)

3 Options for Individualizing

Language Diversity Children make a booklet displaying a variety of measuring tools and items that might be measured with each tool. [Measurement and Reference Frames]

Additional Information

Advance Preparation Before beginning the activities in Part 1, write the headings Linear Measures, Measures of Weight, and Measures of Volume and Capacity on three separate sheets of the Class Data Pad. Divide each sheet into three columns and label the columns Things, Tools, and Units. (See page 659.)

Have on hand as many kinds of measuring tools as possible.

Vocabulary • **linear measures** • **measures of weight** • **measures of volume and capacity** • **units of measure**

Getting Started

Mental Math and Reflexes

Children use counters, as necessary, to solve the following problems:

- Make a pile of 14 pennies. Show me $\frac{1}{2}$ of this pile. 7 pennies $\frac{1}{7}$ of this pile. 2 pennies $\frac{3}{7}$ of this pile. 6 pennies
- I am thinking of a pile of pennies. There are 6 pennies in $\frac{1}{3}$ of the pile. How many pennies are in the pile?
  18 pennies
- I am thinking of a pile of pennies. What if 2 pennies are $\frac{1}{8}$ of the pile? How many pennies are in the pile? 16 pennies

Home Link 9.5 Follow-Up

This Home Link presents an opportunity for a social studies connection. Take as much time as you can spare for children to share their reports.

1 Teaching the Lesson

◆ Math Message Follow-Up

WHOLE-CLASS ACTIVITY

Ask a volunteer to demonstrate how to measure the journal. Emphasize the need to start at the 0-mark on the ruler or measuring tape and to measure along the edges of the journal. You can also ask the class to find the perimeter of the journal. $8\frac{1}{2}" + 8\frac{1}{2}" + 10\frac{3}{4}" + 10\frac{3}{4}" = 38\frac{1}{2}"$

use slates to add

◆ Listing Things That Can Be Measured, Measuring Tools, and Units of Measure
(*Math Journal 2*, p. 226)

review

PARTNER ACTIVITY

Review the three kinds of measures listed on the Class Data Pad. Encourage children to explain each type of measure in their own words, or give examples.

▷ **linear measures:** length, width, height, distance between, distance around (perimeter)

▷ **measures of weight:** how heavy a thing is; how hard it is to move

▷ **measures of volume and capacity:** how much of something there is; how much a container will hold

NOTE: Both volume and capacity are measures of the amount of space something occupies. Volume is a measure for 3-dimensional objects; capacity is a measure for items that take the shape of their containers, such as liquids, sand, and rice.

Things to Measure

1. List 5 things you can measure with a ruler, a tape measure, a meterstick, or a yardstick.

   Sample answers: table

   wall

   car

   book

   window

2. List 5 things you can weigh with a scale.

   Sample answers: letter

   apple

   book

   person

   dog

3. List 5 things you can measure with a measuring cup, a measuring spoon, or some other container.

   Sample answers: milk

   sugar

   oil

   salt

   honey

STUDENT PAGE

◆ *Math Journal 2, p. 226*

Ask partners to make lists of things that can be measured with linear measuring tools, weighing scales, and containers that measure capacity. Partners write their lists in their journals. Mention that they may write the same thing on more than one list. For example, a desk might appear on all three lists:

▷ The desk's height, length, and width can be measured with a tape measure, ruler, yardstick, or meterstick.

▷ The desk's weight can be measured with a large scale.

▷ Another possible measure, but a less likely one, is to find the capacity of a desk drawer. A measuring cup can be used to fill the drawer with a pourable substance (preferably not water!), such as rice or sand.

After children have had time to work, bring the class together. Ask volunteers to name the things on their lists. Have them describe the parts of each thing that can be measured and tell which tool could be used to make those measurements. Ask children to name an appropriate unit that would be used to make each measurement. For example, if a tape measure is used to measure neck size, either inch or centimeter is an appropriate unit.

List the items, the tools, and the **units of measure** on the Class Data Pad under the proper headings (Linear, Weight, or Volume and Capacity). Keep the discussion open and informal so that children have an opportunity to share some of the things they have learned from everyday experiences, previous Explorations, and Projects.

Discuss the measuring tools on the three lists.

▷ Whenever possible, display the measuring tools under discussion and ask children to demonstrate or describe how they would use them.

▷ Ask children to name other measuring tools they know about. They might mention such items as odometers, trundle wheels, measuring cups, measuring spoons, and truck scales. Add these tools to the lists.

NOTE: Emphasize the importance of the following:

▷ Begin measurements at the 0-mark when using standard measuring tools, such as rulers and tape measures.

▷ Adjust a bath scale to 0; adjust a balance scale at the even balance point.

▷ Fill containers to the top or to the appropriate mark and pour carefully when filling a container.

▷ When using measuring spoons, make sure the substance measured is level with the top of the spoon.

A partial list for linear measures on the Class Data Pad might look like this:

Linear Measures		
Things	Tools	Units
calculator	ruler	inch
neck	tape measure (sewing)	centimeter
rug	tape measure (carpenter's)	yard
cloth	yardstick	inch
hallway	meterstick	meter
width of a building	trundle wheel	foot
city block	surveyor's level	mile
distance from home to school	odometer	kilometer
distance between cities	odometer	mile

Post the lists for several weeks so that items can be added as they come up in class.

ONGOING ASSESSMENT

To summarize, ask questions like the following:

· **What kinds of tools are used to measure short distances?** Tape measure, ruler, yardstick, meterstick **Longer distances?** Tape measure, trundle wheel, surveyor's level, odometer

· **What kinds of tools are used to weigh light objects?** Postal scale, spring scale **Heavy objects?** Bath scale, truck scale

· **In what situations are various tools used?** Sample answer: In cooking, measuring spoons and cups

STUDENT PAGE

Math Boxes 9.6

1. Write the number that is 100 less.

465	365
700	600
960	860
4,391	4,291

2. Write 5 names for $1.50.

Sample answers:
150¢, 75¢ + 75¢
$2.00 − 50¢
$1.25 + $0.25
300¢ − $1.50

3. Circle the unit that makes sense.

Grandma's house is
5 _____ away. **(km)** dm

Amy's goldfish is
8 _____ long. **(cm)** m

Ahmed's dad is
68 _____ tall. **(in.)** cm

4. Solve.
Unit: km

$6 + 5 =$ ___11___

$60 + 50 =$ ___110___

$600 + 500 =$ ___1,100___

$6,000 + 5,000 =$ ___11,000___

5. Measure each side to the nearest cm. Find the perimeter.

The perimeter is ___18___ cm.

6. Trade first. Then solve.
Unit: miles

```
  87
− 39
————
  48
```

Math Journal 2, p. 227

---

2 Ongoing Learning & Practice

◆ **Math Boxes 9.6** (*Math Journal 2*, p. 227)

INDEPENDENT ACTIVITY

Mixed Review This journal page provides opportunities for cumulative review or assessment of concepts and skills.

◆ **Home Link 9.6** (*Math Masters*, p. 365)

Home Connection Children determine which unit of measure is best suited to measure various linear distances. The selected units include inch, foot, yard, mile, centimeter, meter, and kilometer.

---

3 Options for Individualizing

◆ **LANGUAGE DIVERSITY** **Making a Measuring Tools Booklet**

PARTNER ACTIVITY   **30+ min**

Children make a booklet to display different types of measuring tools. Have children draw pictures of the tools and label them. If possible, have children cut out pictures or take photographs of measuring tools and mount them in the booklet. You might also want children to draw or cut out pictures of items that could be measured with each tool. Children can circle or draw an arrow to show the part of each item that would be measured.

HOME LINK MASTER

Units of Measure   Home Link 9.6

 Family Note Today in class, your child identified appropriate measuring tools and units of measure for various items. All of the items below may be measured with any of the given units. There are, however, some units that are best suited for measuring short distances and some units that are best suited for measuring longer distances. Help your child decide which unit is best for each situation.

Please return this Home Link to school tomorrow.

Circle the unit that you would use to measure each item.

1. distance from Orlando, Florida, to Boston, Massachusetts

inch
foot
(mile)

2. length of a paper clip

(centimeter)
meter
kilometer

3. height of your teacher

yard
(foot)
mile

4. perimeter of your bedroom

centimeter
(meter)
kilometer

5. width of a deck of cards

(inch)
foot
yard

6. length of a bus

inch
(foot)
(yard)

Math Masters, p. 365

9.7 Exploring Capacity, Area, and Pattern-Block Walls

EXPLORATIONS

Lesson 9.7 (M.UN.02.03, M.UN.02.04)
Exploration, Measuring Area with a Centimeter Grid and an Inch Grid: Before using grid paper, give students concrete experiences with tiles.

OBJECTIVES To explore the capacities of cylinders; to find the areas of shapes by using inch and centimeter grids; and to develop spatial abilities.

materials

---

1 Teaching the Lesson

Exploration A: Children make two different cylinders from identical sheets of paper and use macaroni to determine whether one cylinder holds more than the other or whether both cylinders hold the same amount. [Geometry; Measurement and Reference Frames]

Exploration B: Children trace small objects and estimate the areas of shapes using centimeter and inch grids. [Geometry; Measurement and Reference Frames]

Exploration C: Children build a wall with pattern blocks and then represent the structure on paper. [Geometry; Patterns, Functions, and Algebra]

- ☐ Home Link 9.6
- ☐ *Math Journal 2*, p. 228 (for Explorations A and B)

Exploration A: Per small group:
- ☐ Teaching Masters (*Math Masters*, pp. 154 and 155)
- ☐ 6 sheets of $8\frac{1}{2}$" by 11" construction paper
- ☐ pair of rectangular pieces of construction paper smaller than $8\frac{1}{2}$" by 11"
- ☐ 8–10 squares of posterboard or cardboard
- ☐ masking tape; about 2 pounds of small macaroni

Exploration B: Per small group:
- ☐ Teaching Masters (*Math Masters*, pp. 156 and 157; and pp. 86 and 158, at least 2 copies per child)
- ☐ Everything Math Deck, if available
- ☐ small items, such as slates, pattern blocks, crayon boxes, and objects from the Measures All Around Museum

Exploration C: Per small group:
- ☐ Teaching Master (*Math Masters*, p. 159)
- ☐ pattern blocks; Pattern-Block Template
- ☐ red, yellow, and blue crayons or colored pencils

***See* Advance Preparation**

---

2 Ongoing Learning & Practice

Children identify equivalent fractions by playing the *Equivalent Fractions Game* and *Fraction Top-It*. [Numeration]

Children practice and maintain skills through Math Boxes and Home Link activities.

- ☐ *Math Journal 2*, pp. 202, 203, 208, 209, and 229
- ☐ Home Link Master (*Math Masters*, p. 366)
- ☐ Fraction Cards (cut from *Math Journal 2*, Activity Sheet 5)

---

3 Options for Individualizing

Extra Practice Children identify measures of capacity that could be determined using various measuring tools. [Measurement and Reference Frames]

- ☐ *Minute Math*®, p. 61

Additional Information

Advance Preparation Plan to spend most of your time working with children on Exploration A. You will want to make copies of *Math Masters*, pages 154–157 and 159 for each child unless you plan to guide children through each activity.

Vocabulary • **area** • **square centimeter** • **square inch**

Getting Started

Mental Math and Reflexes

Name a fraction equivalent to:

- $\frac{1}{2}$ $\frac{3}{6}$, $\frac{5}{10}$, $\frac{150}{300}$, ...
- $\frac{1}{4}$ $\frac{3}{12}$, $\frac{10}{40}$, $\frac{25}{100}$, ...

Math Message

Look at the top of journal page 228. Which shape do you think is the "biggest" (has the largest area)? Think about how you might find out.

Home Link 9.6 Follow-Up

Briefly discuss children's choice of units.

---

1 Teaching the Lesson

◆ Math Message Follow-Up

WHOLE-CLASS DISCUSSION

Discuss answers and children's strategies for determining which shape is the "biggest." Tell children that the activities they do in this lesson will suggest an answer and that one measure of a shape is called the *area*.

◆ Exploration A: Discovering Which Cylinder Holds More (*Math Journal 2*, p. 228; *Math Masters*, pp. 154 and 155)

SMALL-GROUP ACTIVITY

Children complete the steps given on *Math Masters*, pages 154 and 155 to make two cylinders from identical paper rectangles. Then they predict and verify whether both cylinders hold the same amount of macaroni or whether one holds more.

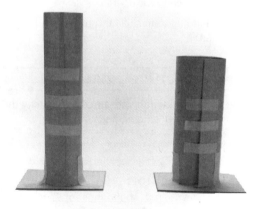

Using 2 paper rectangles that are the same size, children make 2 cylinders. Then they explore which will hold more.

Cylinders

Estimate: Which shape is the "biggest" (has the largest area)? Circle it.

Think: How might you measure the shapes to find out?

Exploration A: Which Cylinder Holds More?

Which holds more macaroni—the tall and narrow cylinder or the short and wide cylinder?

My prediction: _____ Answers vary. _____

Actual result: _____ The short and wide cylinder _____

Exploration B: Measuring Area Answers vary.

The area of my tracing of the deck of cards is about _____ square centimeters.

The area of my tracing of the deck of cards is about _____ square inches.

I traced _____ .

It has an area of about _____ .
                                      (unit)

228 (two hundred twenty-eight)   Use with Lesson 9.7.

◆ *Math Journal 2, p. 228*

STUDENT PAGE

4-1-03
8½ × 11 paper
overlap 1" tape -
label A & B + same
u cubes

Which Cylinder Holds More?

Work with a small group.

Materials
- [ ] *Math Journal 2*, p. 228
- [ ] rulers; masking tape; macaroni
- [ ] pieces of cardboard
- [ ] 2 sheets of 8½" × 11" construction paper
- [ ] 2 same-size sheets of construction paper (not 8½" × 11")

Directions

1. Draw a line 1 inch from a long edge on one construction paper rectangle.
   - Roll the rectangle into a long cylinder and tape the paper along the line.
   - Then tape the cylinder to a piece of cardboard.

2. Draw a line 1 inch from a short edge on the other rectangle.
   - Roll the rectangle into a short cylinder and tape the paper along the line.
   - Then tape the cylinder to a piece of cardboard.

TEACHING MASTER

◆ *Math Masters, p. 154*

Which Cylinder Holds More? (cont.)

3. Talk about these questions with your group.
   - Suppose that you fill both containers with macaroni. Will one of the cylinders hold more macaroni than the other?
   - If so, which one? Why? Record your prediction on journal page 228.

4. Find out. Fill the tall cylinder with macaroni.

   Then carefully pour the macaroni from the tall cylinder into the short cylinder.

   Record what happened on journal page 228.

5. Make another pair of cylinders. Use two paper rectangles that are the same size. The rectangles should be a different size from the ones you used in Steps 1 and 2. Repeat Steps 1–4.

Follow-Up

Plan how to make two cylinders that will hold about the same amount of macaroni. Try your plan. Record the results.

TEACHING MASTER

◆ *Math Masters, p. 155*

Measuring Area

Work in a small group.

Materials
- ❏ centimeter grid paper
- ❏ inch grid paper
- ❏ Everything Math Deck, if available
- ❏ for tracing: slate, Pattern-Block Template, crayon box, and other objects
- ❏ *Math Journal 2*, p. 228

Directions

1. Place the deck of cards on the centimeter grid paper.

   Trace around the deck. The tracing shows the border of the deck.

2. Count the squares that cover the space inside the border.
   - If more than half of a square is inside the border, count the whole square.
   - If less than half of a square is inside the border, do not count the square at all.

3. The amount of space inside the border is called the **area.**

   The number of squares you counted is a measurement of the area in **square centimeters.**

✦ Math Masters, p. 156

Measuring Area (cont.)

4. Repeat Steps 1 and 2 using inch grid paper.

5. Find the area of four or five more objects.

   You might trace things like …
   - a Pattern-Block Template
   - pattern blocks
   - a crayon box
   - objects from the Measures All Around Museum

6. Record the areas you measured on journal page 228.

Follow-Up

Work together as a group. Explain why your results are estimates and not exact measurements. How are the units used to measure area different from those used to measure perimeter?

✦ Math Masters, p. 157

✦ Exploration B: Measuring Area with a Centimeter Grid and an Inch Grid

(*Math Journal 2,* p. 228; *Math Masters,* pp. 86, 156–158)

SMALL-GROUP ACTIVITY 👥👥👥👥

Children trace around a deck of cards on centimeter grid paper and inch grid paper. They count the squares inside their drawings. The amount of space inside the borders is called the **area** (of that side of the card deck). The number of squares children count is a measurement of the area in **square centimeters** or **square inches,** respectively. Children then trace around other objects on grid paper and count squares to find the areas.

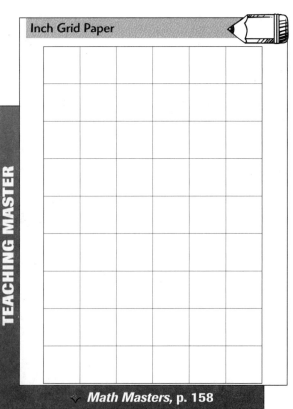

✦ Math Masters, p. 158

✦ Exploration C: Building and Drawing a Pattern-Block Wall (*Math Masters*, p. 159)

INDEPENDENT ACTIVITY

Children use pattern blocks to build a vertical wall. Their walls may show a pattern, a design, or random structures. Using their Pattern-Block Templates, children copy their walls onto a sheet of paper. They color the picture to match the pattern blocks.

ONGOING ASSESSMENT

As children do this activity, ask them to name each of the pattern-block shapes. Also ask questions about the characteristics of the shapes. For example: *Which sides of the trapezoid are parallel? How do you know?*

Build a Wall

Materials
- ❑ pattern blocks
- ❑ Pattern-Block Template
- ❑ sheet of paper
- ❑ crayons or coloring pencils

Directions

1. Make a wall with pattern blocks. Make your wall as high as you can. Here is one idea:

2. Draw your wall on your paper. Use your Pattern-Block Template.

3. Color the shapes to match the blocks.

Follow-Up

Look at the walls made by other children in your class.

How many different pattern-block shapes were used in each wall?

Were all of the shapes used? Which were not used? Why not?

Math Masters, p. 159

---

2 Ongoing Learning & Practice

✦ Playing the *Equivalent Fractions Game* or *Fraction Top-It*
(*Math Journal 2*, pp. 202, 203, 208, and 209)

PARTNER ACTIVITY

Children use Fraction Cards to practice identifying equivalent fractions and comparing pairs of fractions to determine the larger. For detailed instructions, see Lessons 8.5 and 8.6.

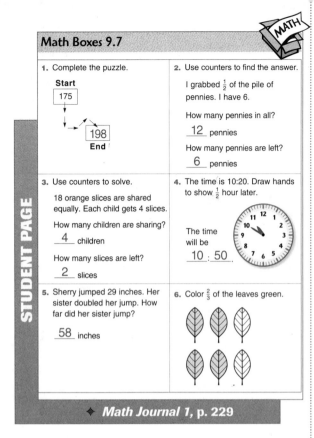

Math Boxes 9.7

1. Complete the puzzle.

   Start

   175

   198

   End

2. Use counters to find the answer.

   I grabbed $\frac{1}{2}$ of the pile of pennies. I have 6.

   How many pennies in all?

   _12_ pennies

   How many pennies are left?

   _6_ pennies

3. Use counters to solve.

   18 orange slices are shared equally. Each child gets 4 slices.

   How many children are sharing?

   _4_ children

   How many slices are left?

   _2_ slices

4. The time is 10:20. Draw hands to show $\frac{1}{2}$ hour later.

   The time will be

   _10_ : _50_

5. Sherry jumped 29 inches. Her sister doubled her jump. How far did her sister jump?

   _58_ inches

6. Color $\frac{2}{3}$ of the leaves green.

◆ *Math Journal 1, p. 229*

◆ **Math Boxes 9.7** (*Math Journal 2*, p. 229)

INDEPENDENT ACTIVITY

Mixed Review This journal page provides opportunities for cumulative review or assessment of concepts and skills.

◆ **Home Link 9.7** (*Math Masters*, p. 366)

Home Connection Children explore capacity as they predict and then check whether one glass of water holds more than another. They also count squares to find areas.

3 Options for Individualizing

◆ **EXTRA PRACTICE** Minute Math

SMALL-GROUP ACTIVITY 5–15 min

To offer children more experience with using measuring tools for volume, see the following page in *Minute Math*:

Measurement: p. 61

PLANNING AHEAD

Bring a checkerboard to class for children to use when solving Challenge problems in Lesson 9.8.

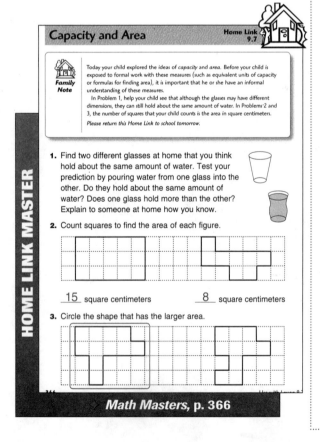

Capacity and Area

Home Link 9.7

Family Note

Today your child explored the ideas of *capacity* and *area*. Before your child is exposed to formal work with these measures (such as equivalent units of capacity or formulas for finding area), it is important that he or she have an informal understanding of these measures.

In Problem 1, help your child see that although the glasses may have different dimensions, they can still hold about the same amount of water. In Problems 2 and 3, the number of squares that your child counts is the area in square centimeters.

Please return this Home Link to school tomorrow.

1. Find two different glasses at home that you think hold about the same amount of water. Test your prediction by pouring water from one glass into the other. Do they hold about the same amount of water? Does one glass hold more than the other? Explain to someone at home how you know.

2. Count squares to find the area of each figure.

   _15_ square centimeters   _8_ square centimeters

3. Circle the shape that has the larger area.

Math Masters, p. 366

9.8 Area

OBJECTIVES To develop the concept of area; to distinguish between area and perimeter; and to find areas of rectangular figures by counting squares.

summaries	materials

1 Teaching the Lesson

Children discuss the concept of area; compare area and perimeter, including the different units used for each measure; and identify rectangles with the same area but different perimeters. [Measurement and Reference Frames]

☐ Home Link 9.7

☐ per group: 3 copies of Teaching Master (*Math Masters,* p. 86; optional) or 3 sheets of centimeter grid paper

2 Ongoing Learning & Practice

Children find the areas of block letters by counting centimeter squares. [Measurement and Reference Frames]

Children solve checkerboard problems. [Patterns, Functions, and Algebra]

Children practice and maintain skills through Math Boxes and Home Link activities.

☐ *Math Journal 2,* pp. 230 and 231

☐ Home Link Master (*Math Masters,* p. 367)

1st- have students draw a 3×4 array on their slates

3 Options for Individualizing

Extra Practice Children use rubber bands to create rectangles on a geoboard and then find the areas of those rectangles. [Measurement and Reference Frames]

Enrichment Children draw designs on grid paper and find the area of each design. [Measurement and Reference Frames]

☐ geoboard

☐ rubber bands

☐ grid paper or Teaching Masters (*Math Masters,* pp. 86 and 158)

Additional Information

Vocabulary • surface • area • square unit

3-30-06 use ED Math cards to make a 4×4 array count for area... (cover ED math book w. cards -- how many?

Getting Started

Mental Math and Reflexes

Pose problems like the following:

Which fraction is greater?

- $\frac{6}{10}$ or $\frac{3}{10}$ $\frac{6}{10}$
- $\frac{1}{2}$ or $\frac{3}{4}$ $\frac{3}{4}$

Math Message

A checkerboard has 8 rows of squares. There are 8 squares in each row. How many squares does the checkerboard have in all? 64 squares

Home Link 9.7 Follow-Up

Ask volunteers to share their findings.

◆ Math Message Follow-Up

WHOLE-CLASS DISCUSSION

Ask children to share their solution strategies. Some possibilities: Make an 8-by-8 array; count by 8s; find 8×8 from memory, by using a facts table, or by using a calculator.

◆ Developing the Concept of Area

WHOLE-CLASS DISCUSSION

Begin an informal discussion about **surfaces.**

• What is a surface? The top or outside of an object

• What are some examples of a surface? A tabletop, the floor, a checkerboard, the cover of a book, the top of a lake, and so on

• Most surfaces have boundaries, or borders. Boundaries give a surface its shape. Use the examples from the question above to help children understand boundaries.

• When we measure the amount of surface inside of a shape, we are finding the **area** of the shape.

Remind children of the different ways in which they have tiled surfaces. (See Exploration E in Lesson 4.7.) They covered surfaces without gaps or overlaps using multiples of identical shapes—pattern blocks, Everything Math Deck cards, and quarter-sheets of paper. Point out that they were finding the areas of the surfaces.

Tell children that units of area can have all kinds of shapes but are usually square. Ask: *What are the advantages of* **square units** *over other shapes (like the trapezoid pattern block) for measuring area?* Many surfaces around us have square corners; therefore, one is more likely to cover a surface more completely without gaps or overlaps using unit squares.

Area can be measured in square "standard" units, such as square inches (squares measuring 1 inch on each side), square feet, square centimeters, or square meters.

As a follow-up to Exploration B in Lesson 9.7, ask children to describe or demonstrate how to measure area using a square grid.

✦ Comparing Units Used to Measure Area and Perimeter

WHOLE-CLASS DISCUSSION

Refer to the Math Message problem.

- If the sides of each square on the checkerboard are 1 inch long, what is the area of each square? 1 square inch

- What is the area of the checkerboard? 64 square inches

- How long is each side of the checkerboard? 8 inches

- What is the perimeter of the checkerboard? 32 inches

Call attention to the difference between the units for area and the units for perimeter.

- Since 32 is half of 64, does it make sense to say that the perimeter of the checkerboard is half its area? No; perimeter and area are measured using different units and cannot be compared in this way.

- How are the units for measuring area different from the units used for measuring perimeter? The units for perimeter measure the distance between points along a line segment; the units for area measure a surface.

If children have difficulty understanding the last point, you might tell the following story:

- A man is 32 years old and weighs 64 kilograms. What is half of the man's weight? 32 kilograms Does it make sense to say that his age is half of his weight? No, half his weight is 32 kilograms, not 32 years.

✦ Investigating the Relationships between Perimeter and Area (*Math Masters*, p. 86)

SMALL-GROUP ACTIVITY

Divide the class into small groups or partnerships and distribute several sheets of centimeter grid paper to each group. Ask children to draw as many different rectangles as they can whose area is 12 square centimeters each. Then ask them to find the perimeter of each rectangle.

After children complete this task, bring the class together and go over the answers. There are three rectangles whose sides have whole-number lengths: 1 cm-by-12 cm, 3 cm-by-4 cm, and 2 cm-by-6 cm. Some children may suggest other rectangles, for example, $1\frac{1}{2}$ cm-by-8 cm.

Over the next few days, encourage children who are interested in this activity to draw as many rectangles as

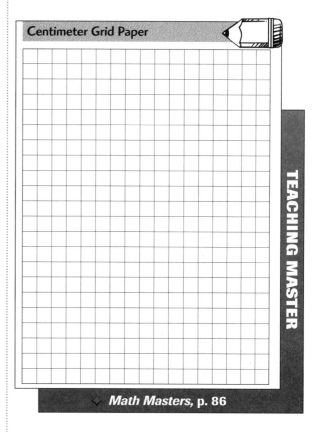

Math Masters, p. 86

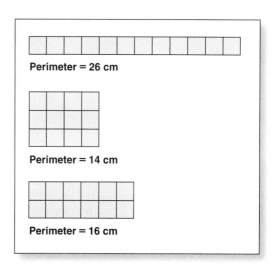

Rectangles with an area of 12 square centimeters

Adjusting the Activity If children are having difficulty drawing the rectangles on centimeter grid paper, have them use centimeter cubes to create the rectangles instead. Each centimeter cube represents one square on the grid paper.

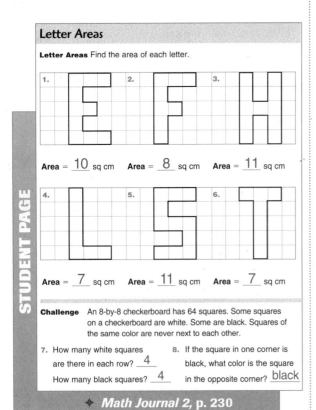

Letter Areas

Letter Areas Find the area of each letter.

1. E   2. F   3. H

Area = 10 sq cm   Area = 8 sq cm   Area = 11 sq cm

4. L   5. S   6. T

Area = 7 sq cm   Area = 11 sq cm   Area = 7 sq cm

Challenge An 8-by-8 checkerboard has 64 squares. Some squares on a checkerboard are white. Some are black. Squares of the same color are never next to each other.

7. How many white squares are there in each row? 4

How many black squares? 4

8. If the square in one corner is black, what color is the square in the opposite corner? black

✦ *Math Journal 2,* p. 230

Math Boxes 9.8

1. Write 4 names for $\frac{1}{2}$. Use your Fraction Cards to help.
Sample answers:
$\frac{2}{4}$, $\frac{10}{20}$, $1 - \frac{1}{2}$, $\frac{1}{4} + \frac{1}{4}$

Write 2 fractions that are:
greater than $\frac{1}{2}$. $\frac{2}{3}$, $\frac{3}{5}$
less than $\frac{1}{2}$. $\frac{1}{3}$, $\frac{2}{5}$

2. Solve.   Unit

$8 + 6 = 14$

$8 + 6 + 7 = 21$

$8 + 6 + 7 + 5 = 26$

$8 + 6 + 7 + 5 + 9 = 35$

3. Count by quarters to $3.00.
$0.50, $0.75, $1.00,
$1.25, $1.50, $1.75,
$2.00, $2.25, $2.50,
$2.75, $3.00

4. Draw two ways to show $\frac{2}{3}$.
Sample answers:

5. Circle $\frac{3}{8}$.

6. 5 nickels = 1 quarter
1 nickel = $\frac{1}{5}$ of a quarter
36 inches = 1 yard
1 inch = $\frac{1}{36}$ of a yard
24 inches = 2 feet
1 inch = $\frac{1}{24}$ of 2 feet

✦ *Math Journal 2,* p. 231

---

they can for other areas. Make a bulletin board of the results and discuss patterns children may have observed.

 Adjusting the Activity To extend the perimeter and area activity, children draw as many different rectangles and squares as they can that each have a perimeter of 12 centimeters (rather than an area of 12 square centimeters).

2 Ongoing Learning & Practice

✦ Finding the Area of Block Letters
(*Math Journal 2,* p. 230)

INDEPENDENT ACTIVITY

Children find the areas of block letters. They can compare the areas of the block letters on journal page 230 to their perimeters on journal page 224.

✦ Challenge: Solving Checkerboard Problems
(*Math Journal 2,* p. 230)

INDEPENDENT ACTIVITY

Have children work on the Challenge problems at the bottom of the page. You might want to display a checkboard or model one on the board.

Adjusting the Activity As an extra challenge, you migh want to point out that in addition to the 1-by-1 black and white squares on a checkerboard, there are large squares: 2-by-2 squares (containing 4 of the 1-by-1 squares), 3-by-3 squares, and so on. *If you counted all of the different sizes of squares, how many squares are there in all?* 204: sixty-four 1-by-1 squares, forty-nine 2-by-2 squares, thirty-six 3-by-3 squares, twenty-five 4-by-4 squares, sixteen 5-by-5 squares, nine 6-by-6 squares, four 7-by-7 squares, and one 8-by-8 square

✦ Math Boxes 9.8 (*Math Journal 2,* p. 231)

INDEPENDENT ACTIVITY

Mixed Review This journal page provides opportunities for cumulative review or assessment of concepts and skills.

Home Connection Children find the areas and perimeters of letters. Then they count the squares that tile a surface at home.

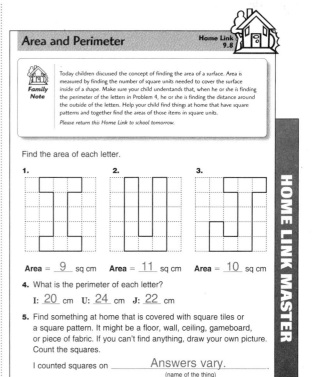

Area and Perimeter

Home Link
9.8

Family Note

Today children discussed the concept of finding the area of a surface. Area is measured by finding the number of square units needed to cover the surface inside of a shape. Make sure your child understands that, when he or she is finding the perimeter of the letters in Problem 4, he or she is finding the distance around the outside of the letters. Help your child find things at home that have square patterns and together find the areas of those items in square units.

Please return this Home Link to school tomorrow.

Find the area of each letter.

1.

2.

3.

Area = __9__ sq cm   Area = __11__ sq cm   Area = __10__ sq cm

4. What is the perimeter of each letter?

I: __20__ cm   U: __24__ cm   J: __22__ cm

5. Find something at home that is covered with square tiles or a square pattern. It might be a floor, wall, ceiling, gameboard, or piece of fabric. If you can't find anything, draw your own picture. Count the squares.

I counted squares on _____Answers vary._____
(name of the thing)

Number of squares: Answers vary.

Math Masters, p. 367

---

3 Options for Individualizing

✦ EXTRA PRACTICE Finding the Areas of Geoboard Rectangles

INDEPENDENT ACTIVITY   5–15 min

Children use a rubber band to make various rectangles on a geoboard. When counting the number of squares in a rectangle, it may be helpful for children to place a penny in each of the square units.

Example

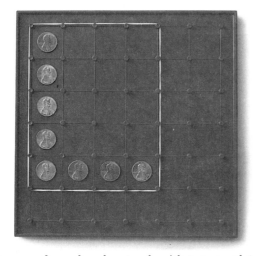

Finding the area of a geoboard rectangle with 5 rows and 4 columns

ENRICHMENT Finding the Areas of Grid-Paper Drawings
(*Math Masters,* pp. 86 and 158)

INDEPENDENT ACTIVITY   15–30 min

Children draw designs on grid paper and color them. Then they calculate the area of each design. Display children's work on a bulletin board.

Portfolio Ideas

PLANNING AHEAD

To do the demonstration in Lesson 9.9, you will need labeled containers, such as milk cartons and beverage bottles, with these capacities: half-pint, pint, quart, half-gallon, gallon, and liter. Use a colored marker or a hole in the container to show the fill level of each container. You will also need a funnel, a pan, and at least 1 gallon of a pourable substance, such as water, sand, or rice.

In Lesson 9.10, children will weigh pennies on a spring scale. Attach a paper or plastic cup to the spring scale to hold the pennies. Each group will need about 40 pennies in a container.

9.9

Capacity

OBJECTIVES To observe relationships among units of capacity; and to identify equivalent measures of capacity.

for Tues.
4-4-06

1 Teaching the Lesson

Children name and order units of capacity, observe relationships among units of capacity, and name equivale measures of capacity. [Measurement and Reference Frames; Numeration]

7 (optional)

pint (cup),
nal liter cube

on 9.2)

2 Ongoing Learning & Practice

Children practice and maintain skills through Math Boxes and Home Link activities.

- [ ] *Math Journal 2*, p. 233
- [ ] Home Link Master (*Math Masters*, p. 368)

3 Options for Individualizing

Enrichment Children measure the capacities of irregular containers. [Measurement and Reference Frames]

Language Diversity Children help create a Class Equivalencies Poster in both English and Spanish. [Measurement and Reference Frames]

- [ ] Teaching Masters (*Math Masters*, pp. 160 and 161)
- [ ] open-mouth half-gallon container (such as a plastic milk or juice container with the top cut off)
- [ ] water-resistant, write-on tape; pen or marker
- [ ] half-cup (4 oz) container; pitcher of water; tray
- [ ] irregular containers from the Measures All Around Museum that will hold liquids
- [ ] a few drops of food coloring for the water (optional)

***See* Advance Preparation**

Additional Information

Advance Preparation For the Math Message Follow-Up, you may want to obtain the book *Pigs in the Pantry: Fun with Math and Cooking* by Amy Axelrod (Simon & Schuster Books for Young Readers, 1997). To do the Part 1 demonstration, write the capacity on each container, or circle the capacity if it is printed on the container. Use a colored marker or a hole in the container to show the fill level of each container.

For the optional Enrichment activity in Part 3, set up one or more workstations with the materials listed above. *Math Masters*, page 160 provides directions for the activity. Copy it unless you plan to guide children through the activity yourself.

Vocabulary • capacity • cup • pint • quart • gallon • liter

Getting Started

Mental Math and Reflexes

Encourage children to refer to the Table of Equivalent Measures as necessary.

- How many inches are in 1 foot? 12
- How many inches are in $\frac{1}{2}$ of a foot? 6
- How many inches are in 1 yard? 36
- How many inches are in $\frac{1}{2}$ of a yard? 18

Math Message

Write some of the units of measure you have seen on milk cartons, soft-drink cans, bottles, and other containers. Example: quart

Home Link 9.8 Follow-Up

Children tell where they found square patterns. They can use the size of the squares and the number of squares to describe each pattern.

---

1 Teaching the Lesson

◆ Math Message Follow-Up

WHOLE-CLASS DISCUSSION

Ask children to name the units on their lists while you write them on the board. Together, name and list things that can be measured using these units. The list might include water, milk, juice, and soft drinks. Focus on the units of **capacity.** Tell children that these units are used in measuring how much liquid or other pourable substance (such as macaroni, rice, or sand) a container can hold.

Circle the U.S. customary units of capacity on the list. Ask children to put the U.S. customary units of capacity in order from smallest to largest. Write their list on the board. If they name some of the units out of order, do not correct them at this time.

Show the half-pint (or **cup**), **pint, quart,** half-gallon, and **gallon** containers. Point out the labels. Ask the class to check the list and to make corrections if some units are out of order.

NOTE: You may want to point out that while *fluid ounce* sounds like a unit of weight, it is actually a unit of capacity.

◯ Literature Link

Pigs in the Pantry: Fun with Math and Cooking by Amy Axelrod (Simon & Schuster Books for Young Readers, 1997) is the story of Mr. Pig and the firehouse chili that he prepares. As Mr. Pig adds ingredients to the pots, the reader sees that he has mixed up the measures of different ingredients and that he does not understand what are reasonable amounts of certain ingredients.

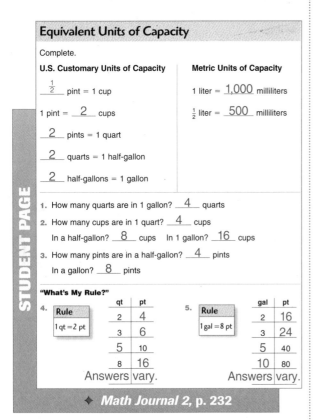

Equivalent Units of Capacity

Complete.

U.S. Customary Units of Capacity	Metric Units of Capacity

$\frac{1}{2}$ pint = 1 cup

1 liter = __1,000__ milliliters

1 pint = __2__ cups

$\frac{1}{2}$ liter = __500__ milliliters

__2__ pints = 1 quart

__2__ quarts = 1 half-gallon

__2__ half-gallons = 1 gallon

1. How many quarts are in 1 gallon? __4__ quarts

2. How many cups are in 1 quart? __4__ cups
   In a half-gallon? __8__ cups   In 1 gallon? __16__ cups

3. How many pints are in a half-gallon? __4__ pints
   In a gallon? __8__ pints

"What's My Rule?"

4.
Rule	qt	pt
1 qt = 2 pt	2	4
	3	6
	5	10
	8	16

Answers vary.

5.
Rule	gal	pt
1 gal = 8 pt	2	16
	3	24
	5	40
	10	80

Answers vary.

◆ *Math Journal 2*, p. 232

Table of Equivalent Measures

U.S. Customary Units of Capacity

1 cup (c) = $\frac{1}{2}$ pint
1 pint (pt) = 2 cups
1 quart (qt) = 2 pints
1 half-gallon ($\frac{1}{2}$ gal) = 2 quarts
1 gallon (gal) = 4 quarts

◆ Demonstrating Equivalent U.S. Customary Units of Capacity (*Math Journal 2*, p. 232)

WHOLE-CLASS ACTIVITY

You will need at least 1 gallon of water or other pourable substance for the following demonstration. You might place a tray under the containers to make it easier to clean up spills.

Do the following steps to show equivalent measures:

1. Begin with the half-pint and pint containers. Tell children that cup is another name for *half-pint*.

2. Fill the half-pint (cup) container with the pourable substance. Pour the substance from the half-pint carton into the pint carton. Do this again to demonstrate that 1 pint is equivalent to 2 cups.

3. Start a list of equivalencies on the Class Data Pad while children record this equivalence on journal page 232.

4. Repeat the demonstration, using the pint and quart containers.

5. Repeat the demonstration, using the quart and half-gallon containers and then the half-gallon and gallon containers.

6. Continue to record the equivalencies in the Table of Equivalent Measures on the Class Data Pad. Children continue to record the equivalencies in their journals.

Adjusting the Activity If children have difficulty remembering equivalencies, use the accompanying sketch:

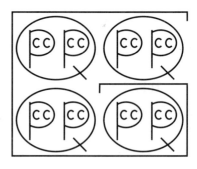

The G represents *gallon*.
The Q represents *quart*.
The P represents *pint*.
The C represents *cup*.

✦ Reviewing Equivalent Metric Units of Capacity (*Math Journal 2*, p. 232)

WHOLE-CLASS ACTIVITY

Display and identify a liter bottle and ask which U.S. customary unit seems to be closest to the **liter** in size. The quart Ask: *Is 1 liter more or less than 1 quart?* more Check children's guesses by filling the quart or liter container with a pourable substance and then pouring the contents into the empty container.

Mention that the other commonly used metric unit of capacity is the milliliter. Remind children that they have seen the prefix *milli-* before.

• How many milliliters are in 1 liter? 1,000

• How many milliliters are in half of a liter? 500

Add these equivalencies to the Table of Equivalent Measures while children record them in their journals.

Adjusting the Activity You can extend the demonstration if a liter cube is available. A liter cube measures 10 cm by 10 cm by 10 cm and holds 1 liter. Therefore, 1 cubic decimeter (10 cm = 1 dm) is equivalent to 1 liter, and 1 cubic centimeter is equivalent to 1 milliliter.

✦ Completing "What's My Rule?" Tables of Equivalent Measures of Capacity
(*Math Journal 2*, p. 232)

INDIVIDUAL ACTIVITY

Children complete "What's My Rule?" tables in Problems 4 and 5. Remind children that the last row of each table is blank and that they are to make up their own entries according to the given rule.

2 Ongoing Learning & Practice

✦ Math Boxes 9.9 (*Math Journal 2*, p. 233)

INDEPENDENT ACTIVITY

Mixed Review This journal page provides opportunities for cumulative review or assessment of concepts and skills.

NOTE: You might want to do this demonstration at another time.

Metric Units of Capacity
1 liter (L) = 1,000 milliliters (mL)
$\frac{1}{2}$ liter = 500 milliliters

Update the Table of Equivalent Measures on the Class Data Pad.

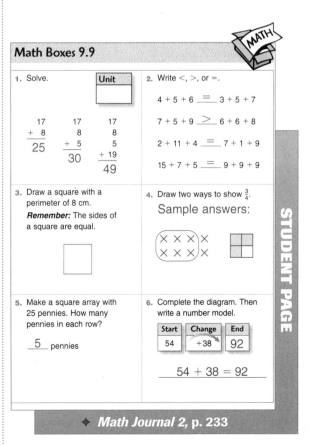

Math Boxes 9.9

1. Solve.

	Unit	

17	17	17
+ 8	8	8
25	+ 5	5
	30	+ 19
		49

2. Write <, >, or =.

$4 + 5 + 6 \; = \; 3 + 5 + 7$

$7 + 5 + 9 \; > \; 6 + 6 + 8$

$2 + 11 + 4 \; = \; 7 + 1 + 9$

$15 + 7 + 5 \; = \; 9 + 9 + 9$

3. Draw a square with a perimeter of 8 cm.
Remember: The sides of a square are equal.

4. Draw two ways to show $\frac{3}{4}$.
Sample answers:

5. Make a square array with 25 pennies. How many pennies in each row?

___5___ pennies

6. Complete the diagram. Then write a number model.

Start	Change	End
54	+38	92

$54 + 38 = 92$

STUDENT PAGE

✦ *Math Journal 2*, p. 233

Capacity

Family Note

Today children discussed units of capacity. Capacity is a measure of how much liquid (or other pourable substance, such as sand or rice) a container can hold. Your child recorded equivalent U.S. customary units of capacity (cup, pint, quart, half-gallon, gallon) and equivalent metric units of capacity (milliliter, liter). Please help your child pick out a recipe and identify the units of capacity in the list of ingredients.

Please return this Home Link to school tomorrow.

Ask someone at home to help you find a recipe that uses units of capacity. Copy those ingredients and the amounts called for by the recipe. Bring your list to school.

Example: $\frac{3}{4}$ *cup of milk*

Answers vary.

"What's My Rule?"

Rule	
1 gal = 4 qt	

gal	qt
2	8
4	16
6	24
10	40

Answers vary.

Rule	
1 pt = 2 c	

pt	c
2	4
3	6
5	10
7	14

Answers vary.

Rule	
1 qt = 2 pt	

qt	pt
2	4
4	8
6	12
8	16

Answers vary.

◆ ***Math Masters,* p. 368**

Measuring Capacity

Materials
- ☐ half-gallon container
- ☐ tape
- ☐ measuring cup
- ☐ water

1. Make a measuring container.

- Attach a piece of tape from the bottom to the top of an empty half-gallon container.

- Fill a measuring cup with a half-cup of water.

- Pour the water into the container. Do all of your pouring on a tray to catch the drips.

- Mark the tape to show how high the water is inside the container.

- Write $\frac{1}{2}$ **c** next to the mark.

- Pour another half-cup of water into the container.

- Mark the tape and write **1 c** next to the mark.

- Continue. Mark the tape $1\frac{1}{2}$ **c** to show 3 half-cups, **2 c** for 4 half-cups, and so on. Fill the container.

- Pour the water back into the pitcher.

◆ ***Math Masters,* p. 160**

◆ Home Link 9.9 (*Math Masters,* p. 368)

Home Connection Children copy units of capacity found in recipes and complete "What's My Rule?" tables.

3 Options for Individualizing

◆ ENRICHMENT Measuring the Capacity of Irregular Containers
(*Math Masters,* pp. 160 and 161)

SMALL-GROUP ACTIVITY 15–30 min

Groups take turns at the workstations that have been set up. They complete the steps on *Math Masters,* pages 160 and 161 to make a measuring container, estimate the capacities of irregularly shaped containers, and use the measuring container to verify those estimates.

When all of the groups have finished, bring the class together for a discussion.

NOTE: As children do this activity, show them how to position themselves to keep the top of the liquid at eye level as they read and mark off their measuring containers. This will help make their marks more accurate.

◆ LANGUAGE DIVERSITY Creating a Class Equivalencies Poster

WHOLE-CLASS ACTIVITY   15–30 min

Both children learning English and native English speakers will enjoy creating a class equivalencies poster that can be taped to the classroom wall for future reference.

Write the following measurements on the left side of a large piece of construction paper or posterboard. Invite volunteers to either draw the suggested picture, paste magazine pictures, or attach empty containers to the right of each pair of measurements.

$1 \text{ cup } (c) = \frac{1}{2} \text{ pint}$

$1 \text{ taza} = \frac{1}{2} \text{ pinta}$

1 pint (pt) = 2 cups

1 pinta = 2 tazas

1 quart (qt) = 2 pints

1 cuarto de galón = 2 pintas

$1 \text{ half-gallon } (\frac{1}{2} \text{ gal}) = 2 \text{ quarts}$

1 medio galón = 2 cuartos de galón

1 gallon (gal) = 4 quarts

1 galón = 4 cuartos de galón

PLANNING AHEAD

In Lesson 9.10, you will need a set of measuring spoons and measuring cups for the Follow-Up to Home Link 9.9, as well as a spring scale (or letter scale or diet scale) and a bath scale for the activities.

Lesson 9.10 also calls for children to weigh pennies on a spring scale. Attach a paper or plastic cup to a spring scale to hold the pennies. Each group will need about 40 pennies.

Measuring Capacity (cont.)

2. In the first column of the table below, write the names or draw pictures of several containers in the Measures All Around Museum. In the second column, estimate the capacity of each container. Answers vary.

Container (description or picture)	Estimated Capacity	Measured Capacity
	_____ c	_____ c
	_____ c	_____ c
	_____ c	_____ c
	_____ c	_____ c

3. Measure the capacity of each container.

- Fill the container with water.
- Pour the water into your measuring container.
- See how high the water is on the tape. Write the number of the nearest mark in the third column above.
- Pour the water back into the pitcher.

◆ *Math Masters*, p. 161

TEACHING MASTER

9.10 Weight

OBJECTIVES To compare weights by feel; to identify purposes of various scales; to know units of weight and equivalent measures; and to weigh objects.

summaries	materials
1 Teaching the Lesson	
Children use a bath scale and spring scale to weigh objects; identify U.S. customary and metric units of weight and equivalent measures; determine how many pennies weigh 1 ounce; and identify objects of equal weight. [Measurement and Reference Frames; Numeration]	☐ *Math Journal 2*, p. 234 ☐ Home Link 9.9 ☐ measuring spoons and cups; bath scale and spring scale ☐ two objects that differ in weight by feel ☐ two objects that feel about the same in weight ☐ Table of Equivalent Measures (started in Lesson 9.2) ☐ 40 pennies and a collection of objects to weigh per group ***See* Advance Preparation**
2 Ongoing Learning & Practice	
Children solve problems about weight. [Measurement and Reference Frames; Operations and Computation] Children practice and maintain skills through Math Boxes and Home Link activities.	☐ *Math Journal 2*, pp. 235–237 ☐ Home Link Master (*Math Masters,* p. 369)
3 Options for Individualizing	
Extra Practice Children list things that each weigh about 1 pound or about 1 kilogram. [Measurement and Reference Frames]	

Additional Information

Advance Preparation For the Math Message, choose two objects that weigh less than 1 pound each but have very different weights—such as an apple and a calculator.

Collect a variety of objects for each workstation that weigh less than 1 pound each, such as an apple, orange, chalkboard eraser, deck of cards, or calculator. If children will be using a spring scale for the *Determining How Many Pennies Weigh 1 Ounce* activity in Part 1, attach a paper or plastic cup to hold the pennies. If children will be using a spring scale for *Deciding Which Objects Weigh the Same Amount,* attach a plastic bag to hold the objects.

Vocabulary • weigh • scale • weight • ounce • pound • gram • kilogram

Getting Started

Mental Math and Reflexes

Have children answer each question. Encourage them to refer to the Table of Equivalent Measures, as necessary.

• How many quarts are in 1 gallon? 4 In 2 gallons? 8   • How many cups are in 1 pint? 2 In 3 pints? 6

Math Message

*Pick up the [first object]
in one hand. Pick up the [second
object] in your other hand. Decide
which object weighs more.*

Home Link 9.9 Follow-Up

Children share the amounts of ingredients in their recipes. As they name these amounts, display the measuring spoons and measuring cups that are used to measure the ingredients. You may want to point out that 1 tablespoon (tbs or T) is equivalent to 3 teaspoons (tsp or t), 1 fluid ounce (fl oz) is equivalent to 6 teaspoons, and 8 fluid ounces is equivalent to 1 cup. About how many teaspoons are in 1 cup? 48 teaspoons About how many tablespoons are in 1 cup? 16 tablespoons

1 Teaching the Lesson

◆ Math Message Follow-Up

WHOLE-CLASS DISCUSSION

Ask: *What are we measuring when we* **weigh** *something?*
Sample answers: How heavy it is, how hard it is to lift, or how hard it is to move *Which weighs more, the [first object] or the [second object]?*

Give a volunteer two objects that weigh about the same amount, and ask him or her to lift each one. Ask the volunteer whether it is easy to decide which object weighs more.

◆ Discussing the Spring Scale and the Bath Scale

PARTNER ACTIVITY

Point out that lifting objects is not a reliable way to compare the weights of objects or to tell someone how much an object weighs. A **scale** is the measuring tool that tells the **weight** of an object by using a number.

Display a bath scale and a spring scale (or letter scale or diet scale). Gather children around the scales and discuss the features of both scales. Ask such questions as:

• What are some things you might weigh with a spring scale? Sample answer: Food items

• What are some things you might weigh with a bath scale? Sample answer: people

U.S. Customary Units of Weight
1 pound (lb) = 16 ounces (oz)

Metric Units of Weight
1 kilogram (kg) = 1,000 grams (g)

Update the Table of Equivalent Measures on the Class Data Pad.

Weight

Weighing Pennies

Use a spring scale, letter scale, or diet scale to weigh pennies. Find the number of pennies that weigh about 1 ounce.

I found that _____ pennies weigh about 1 ounce.

Answers for Problems 1 and 2 vary.

Which Objects Weigh about the Same?

Work in a small group. Your group will be given several objects that weigh less than 1 pound.

1. Choose two objects. Hold one object in each hand and compare their weights. Try to find two objects that weigh about the same.

   Two objects that weigh about the same:

   _____   _____

2. After everyone in the group has chosen two objects that weigh about the same, weigh all of the objects. Record the weights below.

Object	Weight (include the unit)
_____	_____
_____	_____
_____	_____
_____	_____

Math Journal 2, p. 234

- Can you name some things that could not be weighed with either of these scales? Sample answer: Very heavy objects or animals, such as a car or an elephant

- What other weighing tools can you name? What would you weigh with them? Grocery scales for fruits and vegetables, scales for trucks, scales for packages, laboratory balances for small amounts

◆ Discussing Units of Weight

WHOLE-CLASS DISCUSSION

Discuss questions like the following as children weigh several objects with each scale:

- What do the marks and the numbers on the spring scale mean? On the bath scale?

- How many ounces are shown on the spring scale? How many grams (if shown)?

- How many pounds are shown on the bath scale? How many kilograms (if shown)?

- How do you read the scale?

Remind children that the **ounce** and **pound** are units of weight in the U.S. customary system; the **gram** and the **kilogram** are units of weight in the metric system.

- How many ounces are there in 1 pound? 16 ounces

- What is the symbol for ounce? oz For pound? lb

- What does the prefix *kilo-* stand for? thousand How many grams in 1 kilogram? 1,000

- What is the symbol for gram? g For kilogram? kg

Add units of weight to the Table of Equivalent Measures on the Class Data Pad.

◆ Determining How Many Pennies Weigh 1 Ounce (*Math Journal 2*, p. 234)

SMALL-GROUP ACTIVITY

Have groups take turns at a workstation or stations. Tell them to use the spring, letter, or diet scale to find out how many pennies it takes to weigh 1 ounce. They record this number on journal page 234.

Bring the class together to compare answers. Since answers will probably vary, this presents another opportunity to remind children that measurements are not exact. Emphasize the importance of such words and phrases as "about," "a little over," and "close to" when talking about measurements.

✦ Deciding Which Objects Weigh the Same Amount (*Math Journal 2*, p. 234)

SMALL-GROUP ACTIVITY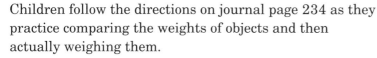

Children follow the directions on journal page 234 as they practice comparing the weights of objects and then actually weighing them.

Demonstrate the procedure they should follow. Have groups take turns at a workstation or stations. Suggested questions for a follow-up discussion:

▷ Could everyone feel when two objects weighed about the same amount?

▷ What was the smallest difference in weight someone was able to feel?

▷ How much was the weight difference before it was easy to feel that one object weighed more than the other?

Ask children whether it became easier to compare weights with practice.

2 Ongoing Learning & Practice

✦ Solving Problems about Weight
(*Math Journal 2*, pp. 235 and 236)

INDEPENDENT ACTIVITY

Children solve problems about the costs of food based on their weights and estimate how much different items weigh.

Thinking about Weight

For Problems 1–4, fill in the blanks.

1. Are all boxes of cereal that weigh the same also the same size and shape?
   _no_

2. Which weighs more, 1 pound of potato chips or 1 pound of potatoes?
   They weigh the same amount.

   Which takes up more space?
   The pound of potato chips

3. A phone book for the city of Chicago weighs about 4 pounds.

   I weigh about _____ pounds. Answers vary.

   I weigh about _____ times as much as a Chicago phone book.
   Answers vary.

4. If 1 pound of bananas costs 50 cents, how much do 2 pounds cost?
   _$1.00_

   How much does half of a pound cost? _25¢_

   How much do 1½ pounds cost? _75¢_

✦ *Math Journal 2*, p. 235

STUDENT PAGE

Thinking about Weight (cont.)

Circle the best answer.

5. A small dog might weigh about …

   4 feet   (4 pounds)   4 gallons   4 grams

6. A letter might weigh about …

   (5 ounces)   5 grams   5 meters   5 kilograms

7. A bunch of 5 bananas might weigh about …

   3 ounces   3 grams   3 liters   (3 pounds)

8. A whole watermelon might weigh about …

   (6 kilograms)   6 ounces   6 quarts   6 decimeters

✦ *Math Journal 2*, p. 236

STUDENT PAGE

Student Page

1. The total cost is 60¢.
You pay with a $1 bill.

How much change do you get?
__40¢__

Show the change using
Ⓠ, Ⓓ, and Ⓝ.

Sample answer:
Ⓠ Ⓝ Ⓓ

2. Show 8 groups of 2 ☐s.

☐☐ ☐☐ ☐☐ ☐☐
☐☐ ☐☐ ☐☐ ☐☐

How many ☐s in all? __16__

3. Estimate. Then solve.

Jen drove 127 miles the first day. She drove 154 miles the second day. How many miles did she drive in all?

Estimate: __280__ miles

Answer: __281__ miles

4.

Area = __6__ sq cm

Perimeter = __10__ cm

5.

Rule	cm	dm
10 cm = 1 dm	5	½
	30	3
	60	6

Answers vary.

6. Match.

5 ft ⟍⟋ 3 yd
24 in. ⟋⟍ 60 in.
9 ft 2 ft

✦ *Math Journal 2*, p. 237

✦ **Math Boxes 9.10** (*Math Journal 2,* p. 237)

INDEPENDENT ACTIVITY

Mixed Review This journal page provides opportunities for cumulative review or assessment of concepts and skills.

✦ **Home Link 9.10** (*Math Masters,* p. 369)

Home Connection Children weigh things at home or identify cans and packages with weights written on them.

Options for Individualizing

✦ **EXTRA PRACTICE** Assembling a Pound and Kilogram "Collection"

SMALL-GROUP ACTIVITY   5–15 min

Children work together to make a list of things that weigh about 1 pound or about 1 kilogram each.

Home Link Master

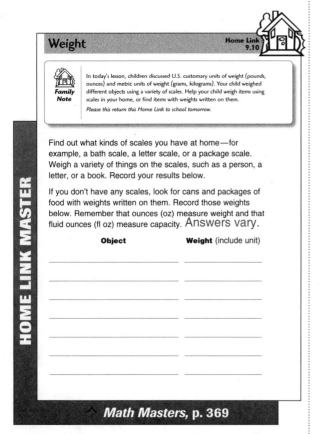

Weight   Home Link 9.10

Family Note In today's lesson, children discussed U.S. customary units of weight (pounds, ounces) and metric units of weight (grams, kilograms). Your child weighed different objects using a variety of scales. Help your child weigh items using scales in your home, or find items with weights written on them.

Please this return this Home Link to school tomorrow.

Find out what kinds of scales you have at home—for example, a bath scale, a letter scale, or a package scale. Weigh a variety of things on the scales, such as a person, a letter, or a book. Record your results below.

If you don't have any scales, look for cans and packages of food with weights written on them. Record those weights below. Remember that ounces (oz) measure weight and that fluid ounces (fl oz) measure capacity. Answers vary.

Object	Weight (include unit)
_____	_____
_____	_____
_____	_____
_____	_____
_____	_____
_____	_____

^ *Math Masters*, p. 369

9.11

Unit 9 Review and Assessment

OBJECTIVE To review and assess children's progress on the material covered in Unit 9.

---

1 ⎯ Assess Progress

learning goals

9a **Beginning/Developing Goal** Identify equivalencies for mm, cm, dm, and m. **(Lessons 9.2, 9.3, 9.5, and 9.9)**

9b **Developing Goal** Measure to the nearest $\frac{1}{2}$ inch. **(Lesson 9.3)**

9c **Developing Goal** Measure to the nearest $\frac{1}{2}$ cm. **(Lesson 9.3)**

9d **Developing Goal** Use appropriate units for measurement and recognize sensible measurements. **(Lessons 9.1–9.6, 9.9, 9.10)**

9e **Developing Goal** Find area concretely. **(Lessons 9.7 and 9.8)**

9f **Developing Goal** Find perimeter concretely. **(Lessons 9.4, 9.5, and 9.8)**

9g **Developing/Secure Goal** Identify equivalencies for inches, feet, and yards. **(Lessons 9.2 and 9.9)**

9h **Secure Goal** Use a ruler, tape measure, and meter/yardstick correctly. **(Lessons 9.1–9.4)**

activities

❑ Slate Assessment, Problem 2

❑ Written Assessment, Problems 1 and 2

❑ Written Assessment, Problem 3

❑ Oral Assessment, Problems 1–3, 6, and 7
❑ Written Assessment, Problems 5 and 6

❑ Written Assessment, Problems 7 and 8

❑ Written Assessment, Problems 4, 7, and 8

❑ Slate Assessment, Problem 1

❑ Written Assessment, Problems 1–3

materials

☐ Home Link 9.10

☐ Assessment Master (*Math Masters*, p. 432)

☐ Teaching Master (*Math Masters*, p. 162, 1 copy per group)

☐ 2 objects weighing less than a pound each; 1 object weighing more than a pound

☐ slate

☐ inch and centimeter rulers

☐ string; tape measure or yardstick

☐ index cards; tape; scissors

***See* Advance Preparation**

---

2 ⎯ Build Background for Unit 10

summaries

Children practice and maintain skills through Math Boxes and Home Link activities.

materials

☐ *Math Journal 2*, p. 238

☐ Home Link Masters (*Math Masters*, pp. 370–373)

Each **learning goal** listed above indicates a level of performance that might be expected at this point in the *Everyday Mathematics* K–6 curriculum. For a variety of reasons, the levels indicated may not accurately portray your class's performance.

Advance Preparation For the Math Message, choose two objects that weigh less than 1 pound each and one object that weighs more than 1 pound. If possible, the object that weighs more than 1 pound should have smaller dimensions than at least one of the objects that weighs less than 1 pound.

For additional information on assessment for Unit 9, see the *Assessment Handbook*, pages 67–69. For assessment checklists, see *Math Masters*, pages 464–465 and 485–488.

Getting Started

Math Message

Pick up each object. Which one do you think weighs more than 1 pound?

Home Link 9.10 Follow-Up

Have children talk about some of the scales that they found in their homes and/or on packages of food with weights written on them.

NOTE: Many of these assessment suggestions relate to learning goals that have been addressed in previous units. Now is a good time to evaluate children's progress toward these goals.

1 Assess Progress

✦Math Message Follow-Up

WHOLE-CLASS DISCUSSION

By a show of hands, find out which objects children think weigh more than 1 pound. Watch for children who incorrectly assume that the larger an object is, the more it must weigh. Weigh the objects.

✦Oral and Slate Assessments

SMALL-GROUP ACTIVITY

If the list of suggested problems below is not appropriate for your class's level of performance, adjust the numbers in the problems or adjust the problems themselves to better assess your children's abilities.

Oral Assessment Suggestions

Give children the following directions:

I have a story in which some information is missing. Before I read the story to you, I will ask you to make up information to put in place of the missing information. Some of the time, I will ask you for a number and the name of an object. At other times, I will ask you for a measurement.

After you have made up all of the missing information, I will put the information in the story and then read the story to you. It's going to be a very silly story, but we will correct it together so that it makes sense.

Using the directions in the margin, ask children to make up the missing story information. Write it on the board.

Read the following story; complete it with the information children made up from the list in the margin. Ask them to correct the information so that the story makes sense.

Today I walked about (1) to school. I was carrying my lunch box that weighed about (2). By accident, I dropped it and it fell (3). Oh, no! Everything fell out. I dropped my 2 cookies, my (4), my (5), and my thermos. They were all over the sidewalk, and it took me (6) to pick them all up again. Most of them were ruined, and the (7) of juice from my thermos was leaking all over. To make matters worse, I had only (8) with me to buy another lunch. Luckily, my friend Jorge shared his lunch with me.

Slate Assessment Suggestions

1. How many inches in 1 foot? 12 How many feet in 1 yard? 3 How many inches in 1 yard? 36 **Goal 9g**

2. How many millimeters in a centimeter? 10 How many centimeters in a meter? 100 How many millimeters in a meter? 1,000 How many centimeters in a decimeter? 10 How many decimeters in a meter? 10 **Goal 9a**

3. Eight children are on the basketball court. 2 of the children are wearing white shirts. What fraction of the children are wearing white shirts? $\frac{2}{8}$ or $\frac{1}{4}$ What fraction are not? $\frac{6}{8}$ or $\frac{3}{4}$

4. Tenisha brought 10 cupcakes to school to share with her friends. She gave away $\frac{1}{5}$ at snack time. How many did she give away? 2 How many were left? 8

Written Assessment (*Math Masters,* p. 432)

INDEPENDENT ACTIVITY

Read the instructions aloud, repeating as needed. Children respond on the master.

- Measure each line segment to the nearest $\frac{1}{2}$ inch. (Problems 1 and 2) **Goals 9b and 9h**

- Measure the sides of the trapezoid to the nearest $\frac{1}{2}$ centimeter. (Problem 3) **Goals 9c and 9h**

- The perimeter of the trapezoid is about ____ centimeters. (Problem 4) **Goal 9f**

- Circle the best answer. (Problems 5 and 6) **Goal 9d**

- Find the area and perimeter of each shape. (Problems 7 and 8) **Goals 9e and 9f**

1. Tell me a measurement, such as 4 miles or 2 pounds. **Goal 9d**

2. Tell me another measurement. **Goal 9d**

3. Tell me one more measurement. **Goal 9d**

4. Tell me a number of objects, such as 3 pencils or 20 apples.

5. Tell me another number of objects.

6. Tell me a measurement. **Goal 9d**

7. Tell me another measurement. **Goal 9d**

8. Tell me an amount of money.

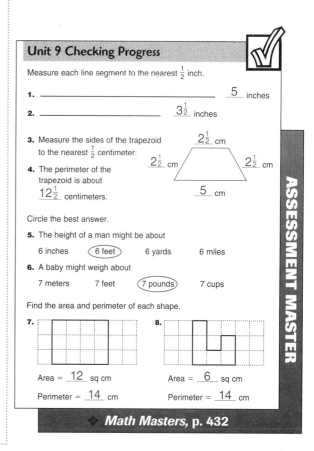

Math Masters, p. 432

Complete a Missing Measurements Story

SMALL-GROUP ACTIVITY 👥👥👥👥

Using the following directions, ask children to make up the missing story information. Write it on the board.

1. Tell me a time measurement.
2. Tell me a number of objects and the name of the object.
3. Tell me a number of objects and the name of the object.
4. Tell me a number of objects and the name of the object.
5. Tell me a time measurement.
6. Tell me a weight measurement.
7. Tell me a weight measurement.
8. Tell me an amount of money.

Read the following story, inserting the information children made up from the list above. Then ask them to correct the information so that the story makes sense.

Yesterday I spent (1) at the zoo. While visiting the zoo, I saw 3 giraffes, (2), (3), and (4), but my favorite part was visiting the mother elephant and her baby, Lolly, who is (5) old. Lolly is so cute! Unlike human babies, which might weigh about (6), Lolly weighs (7). I bet she eats a lot! After watching Lolly and her mother for awhile, I decided to go home. I waited for the bus, paid the driver (8), and rode home.

♦ **ALTERNATIVE ASSESSMENT OPTION**

Construct a Display of Fish Lengths
(*Math Masters,* p. 162)

SMALL-GROUP ACTIVITY 👥👥👥👥

Small groups of children measure and cut out lengths of string that correspond to the lengths of fish on the Fish Poster. For example, if the poster reports Fish H's length as 30 inches, children use their tape measures or yardsticks to mark off and cut a 30-inch length of string. They tape this string to an index card and write "Fish H–30 inches" on the card.

Fish Poster

Fish A
1 lb
12 in.

Fish B
3 lb
14 in.

Fish C
4 lb
18 in.

Fish D
5 lb
24 in.

Fish E
6 lb
24 in.

Fish F
8 lb
30 in.

Fish G
10 lb
30 in.

Fish H
14 lb
30 in.

Fish I
15 lb
30 in.

Fish J
24 lb
36 in.

Fish K
35 lb
42 in.

Fish L
100 lb
72 in.

♦ *Math Masters,* p. 162

TEACHING MASTER

When children have repeated this routine for all of the fish shown on the poster, display their string models in the classroom. Children arrange the strings from shortest to longest in the display.

Fish A - 12 inches   Fish B - 14 inches   Fish C - 18 inches   Fish D - 24 inches

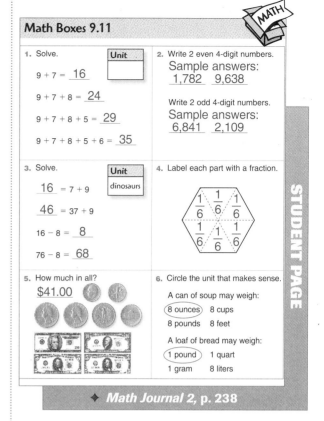

Math Boxes 9.11

1. Solve.

   Unit

   $9 + 7 =$ _16_

   $9 + 7 + 8 =$ _24_

   $9 + 7 + 8 + 5 =$ _29_

   $9 + 7 + 8 + 5 + 6 =$ _35_

2. Write 2 even 4-digit numbers.
   Sample answers:
   _1,782_ _9,638_

   Write 2 odd 4-digit numbers.
   Sample answers:
   _6,841_ _2,109_

3. Solve.

   Unit
   dinosaurs

   _16_ $= 7 + 9$

   _46_ $= 37 + 9$

   $16 - 8 =$ _8_

   $76 - 8 =$ _68_

4. Label each part with a fraction.

   | $\frac{1}{6}$ | $\frac{1}{6}$ | $\frac{1}{6}$ |
   | $\frac{1}{6}$ | $\frac{1}{6}$ | $\frac{1}{6}$ |

5. How much in all?

   $41.00

6. Circle the unit that makes sense.

   A can of soup may weigh:
   (8 ounces)   8 cups
   8 pounds   8 feet

   A loaf of bread may weigh:
   (1 pound)   1 quart
   1 gram   8 liters

Math Journal 2, p. 238

Build Background for Unit 10

◆ Math Boxes 9.11 (*Math Journal 2*, p. 238)

INDEPENDENT ACTIVITY

Mixed Review This journal page provides opportunities for cumulative review or assessment of concepts and skills. The skill in Problem 5 is a prerequisite for Unit 10.

Home Link 9.11: Unit 10 Family Letter
(*Math Masters*, pp. 370–373)

Home Connection This Home Link is a four-page newsletter that introduces parents and guardians to Unit 10's topics and terms. The letter also offers ideas for home-based mathematics activities that are supportive of classroom work.

Family Letter

Home Link 9.11

Unit 10: Decimals and Place Value

In this unit, children will review money concepts, such as names of coins and bills, money exchanges, and equivalent amounts. They will pretend to pay for items and to make change.

The unit also focuses on extending work with fractions and money by using decimal notation. Children will use calculators for money problems and estimation.

Later in this unit, children will work with place-value notation for 5-digit numbers. Here, as previously, the focus remains on strategies that help children automatically think of any digit in a numeral in terms of its value as determined by its place. For example, children will learn that in a number like 7,843, the 8 stands for 800, not 8, and the 4 for 40, not 4.

50¢

50 cents

$\frac{1}{2}$ of a dollar

$0.50

fifty cents

Ⓓ Ⓓ Ⓓ Ⓓ Ⓓ

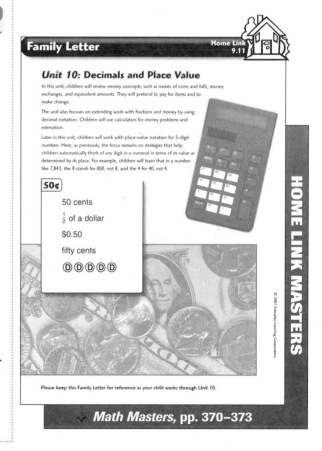

Please keep this Family Letter for reference as your child works through Unit 10.

Math Masters, pp. 370–373

Unit 10
Decimals and Place Value

overview

The first part of Unit 10 extends previous work with money and fractions to decimal notation for dollars-and-cents amounts. The second part of this unit, Lessons 10.9 and 10.10, extends place-value concepts to 5-digit numbers.

Children, as well as many adults, often do not realize that both fractions and decimals can be used to name the same number. Perhaps this is because one form is usually preferred over the other, depending on the situation. Fractions are often used in measurement situations that involve U.S. customary units—in cooking and in the construction trades, for example. Decimals are the notation of the metric system; they occur universally in science and technology applications. Until the second half of the year 2000, fractions were used in stock market reports. Decimals are now used in practically all areas of finance. With a few exceptions, calculators and computers display decimals.

contents

UNIT
10

learning goals
in perspective

learning goals	links to the past	links to the future

10a **Beginning Goal** Use parentheses in number models. **(Lesson 10.11)**

Throughout first and second grades, children solved three-number problems involving addition and/or subtraction. *(Related Grade 2 lessons: 3.8, 5.3, 7.3)*

Third grade children will continue to work with number models that include parentheses. Order of operations and the use of parentheses extends into algebra.

10b **Developing Goal** Solve money stories involving change. **(Lessons 10.6 and 10.8)**

Children used change-to-less diagrams to model subtraction. They also modeled subtraction problems using coins, pictures, doodles, and tallies. *(Related Grade 2 lessons: 1.2, 1.6, 3.2, 3.7, 3.8, 4.3, 4.6, 5.3)*

Children will purchase items and make change from a variety of sources, including store and vending machine posters. *(Related Grade 2 lessons: 11.1, 11.2)*

10c **Developing Goal** Estimate totals for "ballpark" check of exact answers. **(Lessons 10.5, 10.6, 10.8, and 10.9)**

In Kindergarten, children were introduced to the idea of estimation. In first grade, estimation was extended to include money, measurement, and time. *(Related Grade 2 lessons: 4.5, 4.6, 4.8)*

In subsequent grades, children will continue to hone their estimation skills by "purchasing" items from merchants, making magnitude estimates, and rounding numbers. *(Related Grade 2 lessons: 11.1, 11.2)*

10d **Developing Goal** Know and express automatically the values of digits in 5-digit numbers. **(Lessons 10.10 and 10.11)**

In first grade, children were introduced to place value for 10s and 1s using base-10 blocks (longs and cubes). Previously in second grade, children worked with place value for hundreds and thousands. *(Related Grade 2 lessons: 1.9, 6.5, 6.6)*

In third grade, children will read, write, and compare 6- and 7-digit whole numbers and decimals to the hundredths. *(Related Grade 2 lesson: 11.2.)*

10e **Secure Goal** Read and write money amounts in decimal notation. **(Lessons 10.2–10.4 and 10.6)**

Children read and wrote money amounts by counting a number of coins, entering amounts on a calculator, and exchanging combinations of coins. *(Related Grade 2 lessons: 1.2, 1.6, 3.2, 3.7, 3.8, 4.3, 4.6, 5.3)*

Children will continue to work with money through the use of such routines as "What's My Rule?" and Frames-and-Arrows diagrams. Children will also work with money in equal-sharing and equal-grouping situations. *(Related Grade 2 lessons: 11.1, 11.2)*

10f **Secure Goal** Use equivalent coins to show money amounts in different ways. **(Lesson 10.1)**

Children were introduced to coins and bills in Kindergarten and counted combinations of coins in first grade. *(Related Grade 2 lessons: 1.2, 1.6, 3.2, 3.7, 3.8, 4.3, 4.6, 5.3)*

Children will practice using equivalent coin amounts in problem-solving situations, such as vending machine problems. *(Related Grade 2 lesson: 11.7)*

10g **Secure Goal** Use a calculator to compute money amounts. **(Lessons 10.3, 10.4, and 10.7)**

Children were introduced to calculators in Kindergarten and have used them in a variety of contexts through second grade. *(Related Grade 2 lessons: 1.11, 4.6)*

In third grade, children will review how to use a calculator to compute money amounts in simulated shopping activities.

10h **Secure Goal** Know exchange values of U.S. coins. **(Lessons 10.2, 10.8, and 10.10)**

Children exchanged coins as they played *Coin-Dice*. *(Related Grade 2 lessons: 1.2, 1.6, 3.2, 3.7, 3.8, 4.3, 4.6, 5.3)*

Children will continue to work with coins and bills in a variety of problem-solving situations, such as maintaining the fewest possible number of coins and bills in their possession. *(Related Grade 2 lesson: 11.2)*

10i **Secure Goal** Know and express automatically the values of digits in 2-, 3-, and 4-digit numbers. **(Lessons 10.8–10.11)**

In first grade, children were introduced to place value for 10s and 1s using base-10 blocks (longs and cubes). Previously in second grade, children worked with place value for hundreds and thousands. *(Related Grade 2 lessons: 1.9, 6.5, 6.6)*

In third grade, children will read, write, and compare 6- and 7-digit whole numbers and decimals to the hundredths.

assessment
ongoing • product • periodic

☑ Informal Assessment

Math Boxes These *Math Journal* pages provide opportunities for cumulative review or assessment of concepts and skills.

Ongoing Assessment: Kid Watching Use the Ongoing Assessment suggestions in the following lessons to make quick, on-the-spot observations about children's understanding of:
• Numeration **(Lessons 10.3 and 10.10)**
• Geometry **(Lesson 10.7)**
• Measurement and Reference Frames **(Lessons 10.1 and 10.6)**

Portfolio Ideas Samples of children's work may be obtained from the following assignments:
• Write about Mathematics **(Lesson 10.12)**
• Write Number Stories **(Lesson 10.12)**

☑ Unit 10 Review and Assessment

Oral and Slate Assessments Use oral or slate assessments during Lesson 10.12 to assess children's progress toward the following learning goals: Goals 10a, 10e, 10g, and 10i

Written Assessment Use a written review during Lesson 10.12 to assess children's progress toward the following learning goals: Goal 10b, 10c, 10d, 10e, 10f, 10g, 10h, and 10i

Performance/Group Assessment Use a small-group activity in Lesson 10.12 to assess children's progress toward the following learning goals: Goals 10b, 10g, and 10h

assessment handbook

For more information on how to use different types of assessment in Unit 10, see the Assessment Overview on pages 70–72 in the *Assessment Handbook*. The following Assessment Masters can be found in the *Math Masters* book:

• Unit 10 Checking Progress, pp. 433 and 434
• Unit 10 Class Checklist, p. 466
• Unit 10 Individual Profile of Progress, p. 467
• Class Progress Indicator, p. 488
• Math Logs, pp. 493–495
• Self-Assessment Forms, pp. 496 and 497
• Interest Inventories, pp. 491 and 492

problemsolving

A process of modeling everyday situations using tools from mathematics

Encourage children to use a variety of strategies when attacking a given problem—and to explain those strategies. *Strategies children might use in this unit:*

- Using computation
- Using logical reasoning
- Using information in a picture
- Identifying necessary information
- Using estimation
- Using number models

Four Problem-Solving REPRESENTATIONS

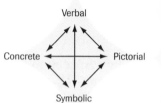

Lessons that teach *through* problem solving, not just *about* problem solving

Lesson	Activity	Lesson	Activity
10.1	Finding different ways to pay for a grocery item	10.6	Finding the exact cost of a purchase
10.3	Making strategy choices when playing *Pick-a-Coin*	10.6	Calculating how much change is received when making purchases
10.4	Writing and solving then-and-now comparison problems	10.7	Finding the areas of your hand and of your foot
10.6	Determining if you have enough money to make a purchase	10.11	Solving parentheses puzzles

For more information about problem solving in *Everyday Mathematics,* see the *Teacher's Reference Manual,* pp. 197–208.

cross-curricularlinks

social studies

- Investigate money from other countries. **(Lesson 10.1)**
- Children list states' areas from largest to smallest. **(Lesson 10.10)**

language arts

- Compare number models with word sentences. **(Lesson 10.11)**

language

- Discuss the Latin word *centum* and explore English-language words that emanate from *centum.* **(Lesson 10.2)**

literature

- Read *26 Letters and 99 Cents,* a book that gives practice finding equivalent amounts of change. **(Lesson 10.1)**
- Read the following books about money: *Pigs Will Be Pigs* and *Alexander Who Used to Be Rich Last Sunday.* **(Lesson 10.6)**

meeting INDIVIDUAL needs

UNIVERSAL ACCESS

◆ RETEACHING

The following features provide additional instructional support:

Adjusting the Activity

- **Lesson 10.1, Part 1**
- **Lesson 10.4, Part 1**
- **Lesson 10.5, Part 1**
- **Lesson 10.6, Part 1**
- **Lesson 10.8, Part 1**
- **Lesson 10.9, Part 1**
- **Lesson 10.11, Part 1**

Options for Individualizing

- **Lesson 10.2** Reviewing the Relationships among Pennies, Dimes, and Dollars
- **Lesson 10.6** Finding Differences between Pairs of Numbers on the Number Grid
- **Lesson 10.10** Counting through Transitions Using a Calculator

◆ ENRICHMENT

The following features suggest enrichment and extension activities:

Adjusting the Activity

- **Lesson 10.1, Part 1**
- **Lesson 10.3, Part 1**
- **Lesson 10.5, Part 1**
- **Lesson 10.7, Part 1**
- **Lesson 10.8, Part 1**

Options for Individualizing

- **Lesson 10.1** Investigating Money from Other Countries
- **Lesson 10.3** Using Mental Arithmetic and a Calculator to Find *Pick-a-Coin* Totals
- **Lesson 10.3** Variations of *Pick-a-Coin*
- **Lesson 10.6** Using Money in Literature
- **Lesson 10.10** Ordering 5-Digit Numbers
- **Lesson 10.11** Making Up and Solving Parentheses Puzzles

◆ LANGUAGE DIVERSITY

The following features suggest ways to support children who are acquiring proficiency in English:

Adjusting the Activity

- **Lesson 10.4, Part 1**

Options for Individualizing

- **Lesson 10.4** Comparing Prices
- **Lesson 10.11** Comparing Number Models to Word Sentences

◆ MULTIAGE CLASSROOM

The following chart lists related lessons from Grades 1 and 3 that can help you meet your instructional needs:

Grade 1	3.12 6.9 8.2	8.3 10.7	3.10	8.4	8.4 10.3 10.4	8.5	3.4 5.4 6.7	5.1 8.3 10.7	5.1 5.2 10.7	8.3 10.7	
Grade 2	10.1	10.2	10.3	10.4	10.5	10.6	10.7	10.8	10.9	10.10	10.11
Grade 3	1.9	1.9 5.11	1.8 1.10	1.8 1.10 10.9	7.7 9.5	1.9 9.7	3.5 8.2 9.3	5.1 5.3		5.1 5.3	7.4

materials

lesson	math masters pages	manipulative kit items	other items

10.1	Home Link Master, p. 374
	Teaching Masters, p. 38;
	   and pp. 37 and 164 (optional)
	transparency of Teaching
	   Master, p. 163 (optional)
	See Advance Preparation, p. 698
		slate	calculator (optional)
			coins and bills
			foreign coins and bills (optional)
			encyclopedias and magazines
			spinners
			26 Letters and 99 Cents by Tana Hoban

10.2	Home Link Master, p. 375 Teaching Masters, pp. 165–167 transparency of Teaching Master, p. 163 (optional) **See Advance Preparation, p. 702**	slate	coins and bills paste, glue, or tape
10.3	Home Link Master, p. 376 Teaching Master, p. 168 (optional) transparency of Teaching Master, p. 168 (optional) **See Advance Preparation, p. 708**	slate dice	calculator
10.4	Home Link Master, p. 377 Teaching Master, p. 168 (optional) transparency of Teaching Master, p. 169 **See Advance Preparation, p. 714**	1 die per group	calculator
10.5	Home Link Master, p. 378 Teaching Masters, pp. 163 and 170 transparency of Teaching Master, p. 163 (optional) **See Advance Preparation, p. 718**	slate	calculator

10.6	Home Link Master, p. 379
	Teaching Masters, pp. 163 and
	   171 (optional)
	transparency of Teaching
	   Master, p. 163
	See Advance Preparation, p. 722
		slate	coins and bills
			calculator
			Class Number Grid Poster
			*Pigs Will Be Pigs: Fun with Math
			   and Money* by Amy Axelrod
			*Alexander, Who Used to Be Rich
			   Last Sunday* by Judith Viorst

10.7	Home Link Master, p. 380 Teaching Masters, pp. 168 and 172–175	slate; dice pattern blocks Pattern-Block Template geoboard and rubber bands	calculator
10.8	Home Link Master, p. 381 Teaching Master, p. 176 transparency of Teaching Master, p. 176 (optional) **See Advance Preparation, p. 732**	slate base-10 blocks dice	coins and bills quarter-sheets of paper

10.9	Home Link Master, p. 382
	Teaching Masters, pp. 177–180,
	   or 181 and 182, or 181 and 183;
	   and pp. 184–190 (optional)
			paper clips, stapler, box (optional)
			calculator (optional)
			place-value tools
			overhead base-10 blocks (optional)

10.10	Home Link Master, p. 383 Teaching Master, p. 191	dice number cards	place-value tool coins and bills; calculator
10.11	Home Link Master, p. 384		place-value tool
10.12	Home Link Masters, pp. 385–388 Teaching Masters, pp. 22, 38, and 168 Assessment Masters, pp. 433 and 434	slate dice	calculator coins and bills

planning tips

Pacing

Pacing depends on a number of factors, such as children's individual needs and how long your school has been using *Everyday Mathematics.* At the beginning of Unit 10, review your Content by Strand Poster to help you set a monthly pace.

	←——MOST CLASSROOMS——→	
MARCH	APRIL	MAY

Using the Projects

Use Project 8 during or after Unit 10 to provide a real-world data collection situation. Children measure the distances they can run in 10 seconds. The Projects can be found at the back of this book.

Home Communication

Share Home Links 10.1–10.11 with families to help them understand the content and procedures in this unit. At the end of the unit, use Home Link 10.12 to introduce Unit 11. Supplemental information can be found in the *Home Connection Handbook.*

NCTM Standards

Standard	1	2	3	4	5	6	7	8	9	10
Unit 10 Lessons	1–11	7–11	7	1–9	3, 10	1–11	1–11	1–11	1–11	1–11

Content Standards
1 Number and Operation
2 Patterns, Functions, and Algebra
3 Geometry and Spatial Sense
4 Measurement
5 Data Analysis, Statistics, and Probability

Process Standards
6 Problem Solving
7 Reasoning and Proof
8 Communication
9 Connections
10 Representations

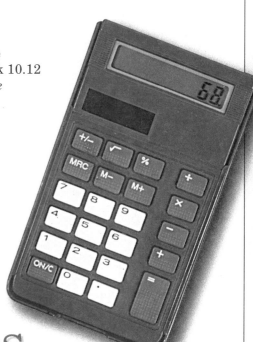

PRACTICE *through* Games

Everyday Mathematics uses games to help children develop good fact power and other math skills.

- Count money and make money exchanges in *Spinning for Money* **(Lesson 10.1)**
- Find the value of coins and add money using a calculator in *Pick-a-Coin* **(Lessons 10.3, 10.4, and 10.7)**
- Identify pairs of equivalent fractions with the *Equivalent Fractions Game* **(Lesson 10.6)**
- Compare fractions with *Fraction Top-It* **(Lesson 10.6)**
- Practice place-value exchanges by playing the *Money Exchange Game* **(Lessons 10.8 and 10.10)**
- Form and compare numbers with up to 5 digits in the *Digit Game* **(Lesson 10.10)**

The notes below highlight the major content ideas presented in Unit 10. These notes may help you establish instructional priorities.

Decimal Notation for Dollars-and-Cents Amounts
(Lesson 10.1 and following)

Unit 10 begins with a review of the money concepts taught previously: names and values of various coins and bills, money exchanges, and equivalencies. Children use a Good Buys Poster about groceries to practice finding alternate ways of paying for purchases.

After a review of decimal notation used to represent money amounts, children explore various names, fractional and decimal, for a penny and a dime (Lesson 10.2). Then they use decimal notation for dollars-and-cents amounts in a variety of situations.

In Lesson 10.3, they learn to enter money amounts into a calculator; in Lesson 10.4, they solve problems in which they compare prices of items in 1897 to current prices. The Good Buys Poster is revisited in Lessons 10.5 and 10.6; children estimate the total cost of several items, check their estimates by finding the exact costs of the items, and find the change owed on their purchases. All of these transactions are completed on a calculator. In Unit 11, children will solve similar types of problems, using paper and pencil instead of calculators. The focus of Unit 10 is on notation and applications in preparation for the work in Unit 11, which will emphasize computational strategies.

Explorations: Areas of Handprints and Footprints, Polygons Formed from Trapezoids, and Geoboard Fractions (Lesson 10.7)

In Exploration A, children find areas of irregular shapes by tracing each other's hands and feet on centimeter grids and then counting full and partial square centimeters. In Exploration B, children form and identify polygons and other shapes from one basic shape (a trapezoid). Exploration C involves forming shapes on a geoboard and trying to divide them into equal parts.

Place-Value Skills (Lessons 10.8–10.10)

A Place-Value Book

In Unit 10, work on whole-number notation begins with a review of representations of 3- and 4-digit numbers with base-10 blocks (Lesson 10.8). Children then make a place-value tool (Lesson 10.9) to use in more formal work with place value. These place-value skills are extended to 5-digit numbers in Lesson 10.10.

If children are to perform multidigit arithmetic intelligently, it is vitally important that they think automatically of any digit in a numeral in terms of its value, as determined by its place in the numeral, not as a single digit. For example, the 9 in 2,592 stands for 90, not 9. When children share strategies or otherwise talk about multidigit numbers, insist that they refer to digits by their values whenever appropriate. After children have become comfortable with their place-value tools, ask for the values of specific digits when numbers are displayed.

Be sure to include examples in which zero serves as a placeholder. Children understand that although the value of the digit 0 is always 0, its presence affects the value of the other digits in a numeral. For example, the 5 in 53 stands for 50, but in 503, it stands for 500.

Equivalent Names (Lesson 10.11)

There are nearly always several ways, and often a great many ways, to express the same number or measure. For example, 40 hundreds and 400 tens are both names for 4 thousands. The "many names for a number" idea plays an important part in almost all of the lessons in this unit and is a focus of Lesson 10.11.

A name-collection box for 50¢

Unit 10 Review and Assessment (Lesson 10.12)

A good understanding of decimals and place value for whole numbers is very helpful in developing sound strategies for computation. You should emphasize these topics in your review and assessment activities.

Addition and subtraction are related operations, as are multiplication and division. That is, one operation undoes the result of the other. For example, 1 dollar is 100 cents (100×1 cent) and 1 cent is $\frac{1}{100}$ of 1 dollar. This reversibility of actions comes into play as children observe that a digit in any place in a number is worth 10 times as much as the same digit in the place to its right and $\frac{1}{10}$ of the same digit in the place to its left. Thus, the value of the digit 2 in the hundreds place (200) is 10 times that of 2 in the tens place (20) and $\frac{1}{10}$ of 2 in the thousands place (2,000).

> **For additional information on the following topics, see the Teacher's Reference Manual:**

- decimal notation
- decimals
- estimation and number sense
- fractions, decimals, and percents
- notation
- number models and number sentences
- place value
- relations

10.1

Money

Unit 10 (D.RE.02.01, D.RE. 02.02, D.RE.02.03)
Do Project, " Dates on Pennies": Follow project script for observing dates & tallying dates. Decide on scale for graphing, eg, 1 penny picture equals 5 pennies. After developing pictograph on *The Graph Club,* refer to questions under "Tallying Dates..." to discuss, interpret, & analyze data.

OBJECTIVE To review notation and equivalencies for money amounts.

Lesson 10.1 (N.FL.02.06)
Part 1, Extend: Include buying items that cost less than $1 and determining how much change they would receive from $1. Have students write a # model/# sentence for each situation.

1 Teaching th...

summary

Children review values of coins and bills, money exchanges, and equivalencies. They find two equivalent ways of paying for a grocery item. [Measurement and Reference Frames; Numeration]

materials

☐ *Math Journal 2*, pp. 240 and 241

☐ Teaching Master transparency (*Math Masters,* p. 163; optional)

☐ slate; calculator (optional)

☐ 7 pennies, 5 nickels, 5 dimes, 4 quarters, and six $1 bills

See **Advance Preparation**

2 Ongoing Learning & Practice

Children practice and maintain skills through Math Boxes and Home Link activities.

☐ *Math Journal 2,* p. 239

☐ Home Link Master (*Math Masters,* p. 374)

3 Options for Individualizing

Enrichment Children investigate and describe money from other countries. [Measurement and Reference Frames]

Extra Practice Children play *Spinning for Money* to practice identifying coins and exchanging a collection of coins for an equivalent coin or bill. [Measurement and Reference Frames; Numeration]

Extra Practice Children practice making equivalent amounts of money. [Measurement and Reference Frames; Numeration]

☐ Teaching Masters (*Math Masters,* p. 38; and pp. 37 and 164, optional)

☐ foreign coins and currency; resources such as encyclopedias and magazines

☐ 1 Money-Game Spinner per group

☐ 7 pennies, 5 nickels, 5 dimes, 4 quarters, and one $1 bill

☐ *26 Letters and 99 Cents* (optional)

See **Advance Preparation**

Additional Information

Advance Preparation Revise the Math Message instructions if children do not have the money in their tool kits. You may want to make an overhead transparency of *Math Masters,* page 163 for the equivalent amounts activity in Part 1.

For the first optional Extra Practice activity in Part 3, Money-Game Spinners can be reused from Unit 3 or made from *Math Masters,* page 37. For the second optional Extra Practice activity, you may want to obtain the book *26 Letters and 99 Cents* by Tana Hoban (Greenwillow Books, 1987).

Getting Started

Mental Math and Reflexes

Have children tell which fraction is greater.
Suggestions: $\frac{4}{5}$ or $\frac{2}{5}$ $\frac{1}{2}$ or $\frac{1}{4}$ $\frac{7}{8}$ or $\frac{2}{3}$

Math Message

Take the following tool-kit bills and coins to your seat: 6 $1, 4 Ⓠ, 5 Ⓓ, 5 Ⓝ, *and* 7 Ⓟ.
Write the total amount of money on your slate.

Teaching the Lesson

◆ Math Message Follow-Up

WHOLE-CLASS DISCUSSION

Briefly share strategies used to find the total amount.
$7.82 Some children may need to review coin recognition.
Ask: *Why do people use paper money or bills as well as coins?* Sample answer: Paper money is not as heavy.

◆ Assessing Knowledge of Values of Coins and Bills

WHOLE-CLASS DISCUSSION

Ask questions like the following. Children write answers on their slates.

- How many pennies in a nickel? 5 In a dime? 10
- How many pennies in a quarter? 25 In a half-dollar? 50
- How many pennies in a dollar? 100 In 2 dollars? 200 In 10 dollars? 1,000

◆ Assessing Understanding of Exchange Values

WHOLE-CLASS DISCUSSION

Ask questions like the following. Children write answers on their slates. If they need help, partners can use coins to count out the exchanges.

- How many dimes in a dollar? 10 In 60 cents? 6 In $1.20? 12 In 10 dollars? 100
- How many nickels in a quarter? 5 In a half-dollar? 10 In a dollar? 20
- How many quarters in a half-dollar? 2 In a dollar? 4 In 10 dollars? 40

◆ Making Equivalent Amounts with Coins and Bills
(*Math Journal 2*, pp. 240 and 241; *Math Masters,* p. 163)

PARTNER ACTIVITY

Ask children to examine the Good Buys Poster on journal page 240. If you want, display an overhead transparency of the poster made from *Math Masters,* page 163. Check that children know how to read the prices of the items.

Good Buys Poster

Fruit/Vegetables Group

Seedless Grapes 99¢ lb
Carrots 1-lb bag 3/$1.00
Plums 69¢ lb
Oranges $1.49 lb
Bananas 59¢ lb
Watermelons $2.99 ea.
Celery 59¢ lb

Meat Group

U.S.D.A. Choice Fresh Ground Beef $1.99 lb
American Cheese 8 oz $1.49
Chunk Light Tuna 6.5 oz 69¢
Peanut Butter 18-oz jar $1.29
Lunch Meat 1-lb package $1.39

Milk Group

Gallon Milk $2.39
½ Gallon Ice Cream $2.49
6-pack Yogurt $2.09

Grain Group

Wheat Bread 16 oz 99¢
Potato Chips 8 oz 89¢
Pork & Beans 16 oz 2/89¢
Saltines 1 lb 69¢
Hamburger Buns 16 oz 69¢

Miscellaneous Items

Mayonnaise 32 oz $1.99
Catsup 32 oz $1.09
Grape Jelly 2-lb jar $1.69

◆ *Math Journal 2, p. 240*

Adjusting the Activity To extend the Math Message Follow-Up activity, ask children to estimate how much money the whole class has. Children can use their calculators to find the exact amount and compare it to their estimates.

Ways to Pay

Choose 4 items from the Good Buys Poster on page 240. List the items and how much they cost in the table below.

For each item:
- Count out coins and bills to show several different ways of paying for each item.
- Record two ways by drawing coins and bills in the table. Use ⓆⒹⓃⓅ, and $1.

Example

You buy 1 pound of bananas. They cost 59¢ a pound. You pay with:
ⓆⓆⓃⓅⓅⓅⓅ or ⒹⒹⒹⒹⓃⓅⓅⓅⓅ

1. You buy _____. Cost: _____ Pay with _____ or _____

2. You buy _____. Cost: _____ Pay with _____ or _____

3. You buy _____. Cost _____ Pay with _____ or _____

4. You buy _____. Cost: _____ Pay with _____ or _____

◆ *Math Journal 2, p. 241*

Math Boxes 10.1

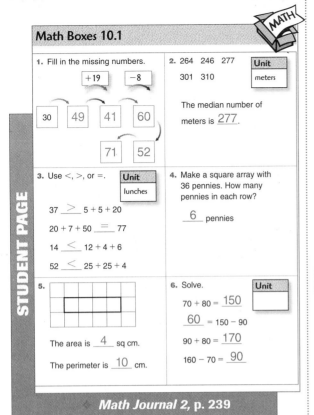

1. Fill in the missing numbers.

30	49	41	60

+19   −8

71	52

2. 264   246   277
301   310

Unit
meters

The median number of
meters is 277.

3. Use <, >, or =.

Unit
lunches

37 > 5 + 5 + 20

20 + 7 + 50 = 77

14 < 12 + 4 + 6

52 < 25 + 25 + 4

4. Make a square array with
36 pennies. How many
pennies in each row?

6   pennies

5.

The area is 4 sq cm.

The perimeter is 10 cm.

6. Solve.

Unit

70 + 80 = 150

60 = 150 − 90

90 + 80 = 170

160 − 70 = 90

Math Journal 2, p. 239

STUDENT PAGE

Coin Combinations

Home Link 10.1

Family Note

In today's lesson, your child practiced writing amounts of money. For example, in Problem 1, 10 pennies can be written as 10¢ or $0.10. Your child also showed different groups of coins that have the same monetary value. For example, your child could show 62¢ with 2 quarters, 1 dime, and 2 pennies; or 4 dimes, 4 nickels, and 2 pennies. For Problem 2, help your child find items in newspaper or magazine ads and think of different combinations of coins and bills to pay for the items.

Please return this Home Link to school tomorrow.

1. Pretend that you have 10 of each kind of coin.
How much is that in all?

10 pennies = 10¢, or $0.10

10 nickels = 50¢, or $0.50

10 dimes = $1.00

10 quarters = $2.50

10 half-dollars = $5.00

Total = $9.10

2. Find two ads in a newspaper or magazine for items that
cost less than $3.00 each.

- Ask for permission to cut out the ads.
- Cut them out and glue them onto the back of this page.
- Draw coins to show the cost of each item.

(If you can't find ads, draw pictures of items and prices on
the back of this page.)

Math Masters, p. 374

HOME LINK MASTER

Partners choose 4 items from the poster to "buy." Using their coins and bills, they count out several equivalent ways of paying for each item. They record two ways for each item by drawing coins and bills on journal page 241.

 Adjusting the Activity If children are having difficulty, choose 3 items for them to buy and ask partners to choose 1 additional item on their own.

---

2 Ongoing Learning & Practice

◆ Math Boxes 10.1 (*Math Journal 2,* p. 239)

INDEPENDENT ACTIVITY

Mixed Review This journal page provides opportunities for cumulative review or assessment of concepts and skills.

◆ Home Link 10.1 (*Math Masters,* p. 374)

Home Connection Children find the total value of 10 pennies, 10 nickels, 10 dimes, 10 quarters, and 10 half-dollars. Then they cut out two ads for items costing less than $3.00 each and draw coin combinations that could be used to pay for each item.

---

3 Options for Individualizing

◆ ENRICHMENT Investigating Money from Other Countries

SMALL-GROUP ACTIVITY   **30+ min**

Social Studies Link Children may collect coins and paper money from other countries. Family members or neighbors who travel may be able to help. Children can also use encyclopedias and magazines to learn about other types of currency. Children can share their findings about money names and equivalencies verbally or through diagrams with descriptions.

◆ EXTRA PRACTICE Playing *Spinning for Money* (*Math Masters*, pp. 37 and 38)

SMALL-GROUP ACTIVITY **15–30 min**

Children practice money-counting and money-exchange skills by playing *Spinning for Money*. For detailed instructions, see Lesson 3.2.

◆ EXTRA PRACTICE Making Equivalent Amounts (*Math Masters*, p. 164)

PARTNER ACTIVITY **5–15 min**

Draw a name-collection box for 75 cents on the board. Ask children to suggest other names for that amount, and enter their suggestions in the box. Continue until you have listed many names. Partners may use coins to help them come up with coin combinations.

Suggestions for other amounts: 32¢, 45¢, 77¢, $1.35, $2.59

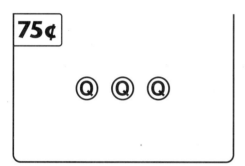

ONGOING ASSESSMENT

Use the name-collection boxes on *Math Masters*, page 164 to assess children's facility with finding equivalent money amounts. Fill in the amounts in the tags, copy, and distribute.

Literature Link The book *26 Letters and 99 Cents* by Tana Hoban (Greenwillow Books, 1987) shows photographs of the numbers 1–30, 35, 40, 45, 50, 60, 70, 80, 90, and 99 represented by coins. Sometimes more than one combination is shown, but often the least possible number of coins is shown. This book can provide children with practice representing the same value in different ways.

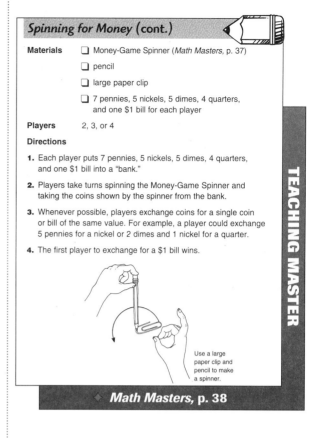

Spinning for Money (cont.)

Materials	☐ Money-Game Spinner (*Math Masters*, p. 37)
	☐ pencil
	☐ large paper clip
	☐ 7 pennies, 5 nickels, 5 dimes, 4 quarters, and one $1 bill for each player
Players	2, 3, or 4

Directions

1. Each player puts 7 pennies, 5 nickels, 5 dimes, 4 quarters, and one $1 bill into a "bank."

2. Players take turns spinning the Money-Game Spinner and taking the coins shown by the spinner from the bank.

3. Whenever possible, players exchange coins for a single coin or bill of the same value. For example, a player could exchange 5 pennies for a nickel or 2 dimes and 1 nickel for a quarter.

4. The first player to exchange for a $1 bill wins.

Use a large paper clip and pencil to make a spinner.

◆ *Math Masters*, p. 38

TEACHING MASTER

NOTE: Children may have already created the Money-Game Spinner from *Math Masters*, page 37. If so, reuse those spinners at this time.

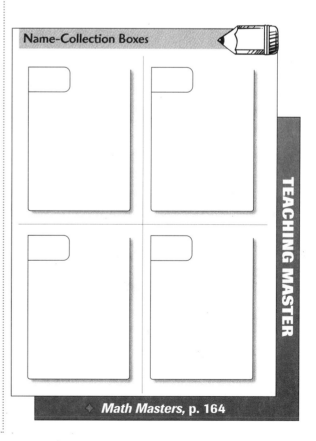

Name-Collection Boxes

◆ *Math Masters*, p. 164

TEACHING MASTER

10.2 Decimal Notation for Pennies and Dimes

OBJECTIVE To review estimation; dollars-and-cents notation; and names for a dollar, a dime, and a penny.

Lesson 10.2 (N.FL.02.06)
Do Part 3: Working as partners place 100 pennies/counters on double copy of Master 167. One partner removes some complete & partial rows, the 2nd partner counts blank cells on grid & lists # on white board, then counts # of items on grid and writes a # model/# sentence that will add up to 100.

summary **materials**

1 Teaching the Lesson

Children use estimation to identify two grocery items that could be bought for $2.00. They review decimal notation for dollars-and-cents amounts and identify various names for dollars, dimes, and pennies. They investigate pennies and dimes as fractional parts of a dollar. [Measurement and Reference Frames; Numeration]

☐ *Math Journal 2,* p. 240
☐ Home Link 10.1
☐ Teaching Masters (*Math Masters,* pp. 165 and 166)
☐ Teaching Master transparency (*Math Masters,* p. 163; optional)
☐ 100 pennies, 10 dimes, and one $1 bill
☐ scissors; slate
☐ paste, glue, or tape
***See* Advance Preparation**

2 Ongoing Learning & Practice

Children practice adding whole-dollar amounts by calculating word values. [Operations and Computation]

Children practice and maintain skills through Math Boxes and Home Link activities.

☐ *Math Journal 2,* pp. 242 and 243
☐ Home Link Master (*Math Masters,* p. 375)

3 Options for Individualizing

Reteaching Children use a 100-grid to review the relationships among pennies, dimes, and dollars. [Measurement and Reference Frames; Numeration]

Extra Practice Children identify coins equivalent to $1.00. [Measurement and Reference Frames]

☐ Teaching Master (*Math Masters,* p. 167)
☐ 100 pennies and 10 dimes
☐ *Minute Math*®, p. 64
***See* Advance Preparation**

Additional Information

Advance Preparation You may want to make an overhead transparency of *Math Masters,* page 163 for the Math Message Follow-Up in Part 1.

For the optional Reteaching activity in Part 3, make 2 copies of *Math Masters,* page 167 and paste or tape them together to create a 10 × 10 grid.

Vocabulary • decimal point

Getting Started

Mental Math and Reflexes

Pose questions about money equivalencies. *Suggestions:*

- How many pennies are in a nickel? 5 What fraction of a nickel is 1 penny? $\frac{1}{5}$
- How many nickels are in a dime? 2 What fraction of a dime is 1 nickel? $\frac{1}{2}$
- How many dimes are in a dollar? 10 What fraction of a dollar is 1 dime? $\frac{1}{10}$

Math Message

Look at journal page 240. Find two items you could buy with $2.00.

Home Link 10.1 Follow-Up

Review the answers to Problem 1. For Problem 2, ask volunteers to name an item and its cost. Have the class suggest combinations of coins and dollar bills to pay for the item.

1 Teaching the Lesson

◆ Math Message Follow-Up

(*Math Journal 2*, p. 240; *Math Masters*, p. 163)

WHOLE-CLASS DISCUSSION

You may want to display an overhead transparency of the Good Buys Poster. Ask children to share their answers and tell how they know that $2.00 would be enough to buy both items. Some will have found exact answers and some will have estimated. Briefly discuss why estimation is appropriate, but don't try to teach any particular method. (In Lesson 10.5, children will learn to estimate by rounding to the nearest 10¢.) Continue by asking children whether $2.00 is enough for the following:

- 1 loaf of wheat bread and 1 pound of grapes yes

- 1 pound of saltines and one 1-pound package of lunch meat no

- 1 pound of ground beef and one 16-ounce package of hamburger buns no

If children ask about sales tax, explain that they should pretend there is none. Tell children that finding sales tax involves percent, which they will study at a later time.

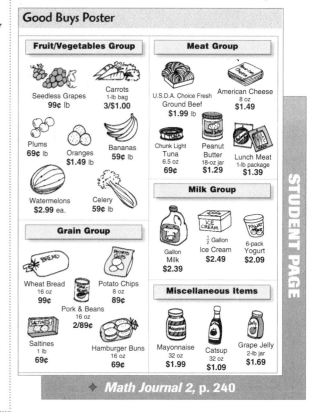

Good Buys Poster

Fruit/Vegetables Group

Seedless Grapes 99¢ lb

Carrots 1-lb bag 3/$1.00

Plums 69¢ lb

Oranges $1.49 lb

Bananas 59¢ lb

Watermelons $2.99 ea.

Celery 59¢ lb

Grain Group

Wheat Bread 16 oz 99¢

Potato Chips 8 oz 89¢

Pork & Beans 16 oz 2/89¢

Saltines 1 lb 69¢

Hamburger Buns 16 oz 69¢

Meat Group

U.S.D.A. Choice Fresh Ground Beef $1.99 lb

American Cheese 8 oz $1.49

Chunk Light Tuna 6.5 oz 69¢

Peanut Butter 18-oz jar $1.29

Lunch Meat 1-lb package $1.39

Milk Group

Gallon Milk $2.39

½ Gallon Ice Cream $2.49

6-pack Yogurt $2.09

Miscellaneous Items

Mayonnaise 32 oz $1.99

Catsup 32 oz $1.09

Grape Jelly 2-lb jar $1.69

◆ *Math Journal 2*, p. 240

STUDENT PAGE

Language Link

The word *cent* is derived from the Latin word *centum,* meaning one hundred. Many other words come from this Latin word: *century,* for example, means 100 years. In some words, *cent-* means one hundred; in others it means one-hundredth. Ask children to name other words with *cent-* in them. Sample answers: centimeter, centennial, centipede, centurion, centigrade, percent

---

NOTE: Although amounts of 1 dollar or more can be written as cents ($1.25 = 125¢), this isn't usually done.

---

penny	1¢	$0.01	$\frac{1}{100}$ of a dollar
dime	10¢	$0.10	$\frac{10}{100}$ of a dollar
			$\frac{1}{10}$ of a dollar

◆Reviewing Decimal Notation for Money

WHOLE-CLASS DISCUSSION

Write an amount like $12.37 on the board. Remind children that the period after the 12 is called the **decimal point.** The digits before the decimal point stand for whole dollar amounts; the digits after the decimal point stand for cents amounts. Point out that in decimal money notation, there are always two digits after the decimal point.

Ask someone to read the amount shown on the board. Sample answers: twelve dollars and thirty-seven cents; twelve dollars thirty-seven cents; twelve dollars thirty-seven; twelve thirty-seven The "and" in "twelve dollars and thirty-seven cents" denotes the decimal point.

With children, practice reading and writing money amounts in decimal notation. *Suggestions:*

▷ Write amounts like $1.25 and $3.05 on the board. Ask children to read the amounts. One dollar and twenty-five cents; three dollars and five cents

▷ Ask: *In $1.25, what does the 1 stand for?* 1 dollar *What does the 25 stand for?* 25 cents

▷ Write amounts less than one dollar, such as $0.48 and $0.06. Ask: *How do you read this?* $0.48 can be read as "zero dollars and 48 cents," but it is usually read simply as "48 cents."

▷ Dictate amounts like "5 dollars and 64 cents," "32 cents," and "3 cents." Children write them in decimal notation on their slates.

◆Pennies and Dimes as Fractional Parts of a Dollar

WHOLE-CLASS DISCUSSION

Use pennies, dimes, and dollars to illustrate the relationships among these coins and $1.00. Ask questions like the following:

• How many pennies are in one dollar? 100 pennies

• What part of a dollar is a penny? $\frac{1}{100}$ of a dollar

• How do you write 1 penny in decimal notation? $0.01

Or like these:

• How many dimes are in one dollar? 10 dimes

• What part of a dollar is a dime? $\frac{1}{10}$ of a dollar

• How do you write 1 dime in decimal notation? $0.10

◆ Matching a Dollar, a Dime, and a Penny with Their Names (*Math Masters,* pp. 165 and 166)

INDEPENDENT ACTIVITY

Children cut out the names from *Math Masters,* page 166 and paste them in the proper columns on *Math Masters,* page 165.

S-9-05

2 Ongoing Learning & Practice

◆ Calculating Word Values
(*Math Journal 2,* p. 242)

INDEPENDENT ACTIVITY

Children pretend that the letters of the alphabet have been assigned the dollar values shown at the top of the journal page. They calculate the values of words. *For example:*

▷ What is the value of cat? $3 + $1 + $20 = $24

▷ What is the value of dog? $4 + $15 + $7 = $26

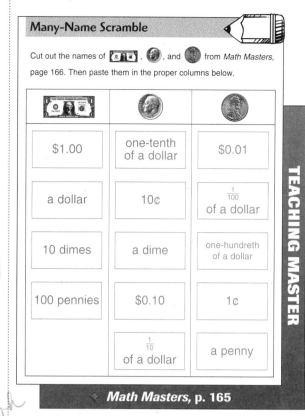

Many-Name Scramble

Cut out the names of 🫰, 🪙, and 🪙 from *Math Masters,* page 166. Then paste them in the proper columns below.

$1.00	one-tenth of a dollar	$0.01
a dollar	10¢	$\frac{1}{100}$ of a dollar
10 dimes	a dime	one-hundreth of a dollar
100 pennies	$0.10	1¢
	$\frac{1}{10}$ of a dollar	a penny

❖ *Math Masters,* p. 165

TEACHING MASTER

Word Values

Pretend the letters of the alphabet have the dollar values shown in the table. For example, the letter **g** is worth $7; the letter **v** is worth $22. The word **jet** is worth $10 + $5 + $20 = $35.

	a	b	c	d	e	f	g	h	i	j	k	l	m
Value	$1	$2	$3	$4	$5	$6	$7	$8	$9	$10	$11	$12	$13

	n	o	p	q	r	s	t	u	v	w	x	y	z
Value	$14	$15	$16	$17	$18	$19	$20	$21	$22	$23	$24	$25	$26

1. Which is worth more, **dog** or **cat**? ___dog___
2. Which is worth more, **whale** or **zebra**? ___zebra___
3. How much is your first name worth? Answers vary.
4. Write 2 spelling words you are trying to learn. Find their values.
   Word: Answers vary. Value: $_____
   Word: _____ Value: $_____
5. What is the cheapest word you can make? It must have at least 2 letters. Sample answer:
   Word: ___ad___ Value: $___5___
6. What is the most expensive word you can make? Answers vary.
   Word: _____ Value: $_____
7. Think of the letter values as dimes. For example, **m** is worth 13 dimes; **b** is worth 2 dimes. Find out how much each word is worth.
   dog: $2.60 cat: $2.40 zebra: $5.20 whale: $4.90
   candy: $4.70 your last name: $Answers vary.

STUDENT PAGE

❖ *Math Journal 2,* p. 242

Many-Name Scramble (cont.)

$1.00	$\frac{1}{100}$ of a dollar
$0.01	100 pennies
a dollar	10 dimes
one-tenth of a dollar	$\frac{1}{10}$ of a dollar
10¢	one-hundredth of a dollar
a dime	1¢
$0.10	a penny

TEACHING MASTER

❖ *Math Masters,* p. 166

Math Boxes 10.2

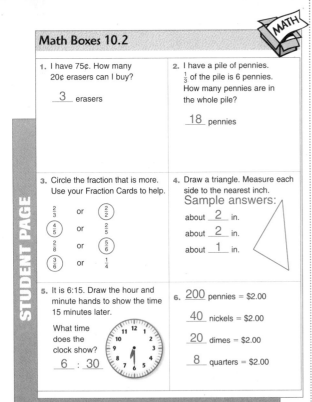

1. I have 75¢. How many 20¢ erasers can I buy?

__3__ erasers

2. I have a pile of pennies. $\frac{1}{3}$ of the pile is 6 pennies. How many pennies are in the whole pile?

__18__ pennies

3. Circle the fraction that is more. Use your Fraction Cards to help.

$\frac{2}{3}$ or $\left(\frac{2}{2}\right)$

$\left(\frac{4}{5}\right)$ or $\frac{2}{5}$

$\frac{2}{8}$ or $\left(\frac{5}{6}\right)$

$\left(\frac{3}{6}\right)$ or $\frac{1}{4}$

4. Draw a triangle. Measure each side to the nearest inch.

Sample answers:

about __2__ in.

about __2__ in.

about __1__ in.

5. It is 6:15. Draw the hour and minute hands to show the time 15 minutes later.

What time does the clock show?

__6__ : __30__

6. __200__ pennies = $2.00

__40__ nickels = $2.00

__20__ dimes = $2.00

__8__ quarters = $2.00

◆ *Math Journal 2*, p. 243

STUDENT PAGE

NOTE: Before children begin the Reteaching activity, provide each group with the 10×10 grid by taping together two 10×5 grids (*Math Masters*, page 167).

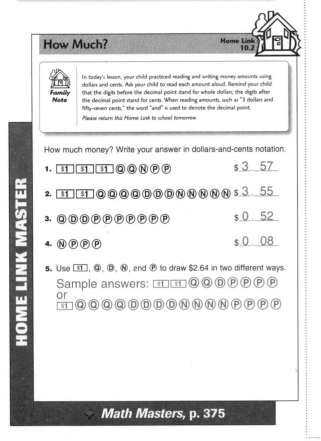

How Much?

Home Link 10.2

Family Note

In today's lesson, your child practiced reading and writing money amounts using dollars and cents. Ask your child to read each amount aloud. Remind your child that the digits before the decimal point stand for whole dollars; the digits after the decimal point stand for cents. When reading amounts, such as "3 dollars and fifty-seven cents," the word "and" is used to denote the decimal point.

Please return this Home Link to school tomorrow.

How much money? Write your answer in dollars-and-cents notation.

1. $1 $1 $1 Ⓠ Ⓠ Ⓝ Ⓟ Ⓟ $ __3__ . __57__

2. $1 $1 Ⓠ Ⓠ Ⓠ Ⓠ Ⓓ Ⓓ Ⓝ Ⓝ Ⓝ Ⓝ $ __3__ . __55__

3. Ⓠ Ⓓ Ⓓ Ⓟ Ⓟ Ⓟ Ⓟ Ⓟ Ⓟ Ⓟ $ __0__ . __52__

4. Ⓝ Ⓟ Ⓟ Ⓟ $ __0__ . __08__

5. Use $1, Ⓠ, Ⓓ, Ⓝ, and Ⓟ to draw $2.64 in two different ways.

Sample answers: $1 $1 Ⓠ Ⓠ Ⓓ Ⓟ Ⓟ Ⓟ Ⓟ
or
$1 Ⓠ Ⓠ Ⓠ Ⓠ Ⓓ Ⓓ Ⓓ Ⓝ Ⓝ Ⓝ Ⓟ Ⓟ Ⓟ Ⓟ

HOME LINK MASTER

▽ *Math Masters*, p. 375

◆ Math Boxes 10.2 (*Math Journal 2*, p. 243)

INDEPENDENT ACTIVITY

Mixed Review This journal page provides opportunities for cumulative review or assessment of concepts and skills.

◆ Home Link 10.2 (*Math Masters*, p. 375)

Home Connection Children write amounts of money in dollars-and-cents notation, and they represent an amount of money in two different ways.

---

3 Options for Individualizing

◆ RETEACHING Reviewing the Relationships among Pennies, Dimes, and Dollars (*Math Masters*, p. 167)

SMALL-GROUP ACTIVITY   **5–15 min**

Have children arrange 100 pennies on the 10×10 grid. Ask:

- How many dollars are on your grid? 1 dollar
- How many pennies are on your grid? 100 pennies
- What part of a dollar is a penny? $\frac{1}{100}$ of a dollar
- How do you write 1 penny in decimal notation? $0.01

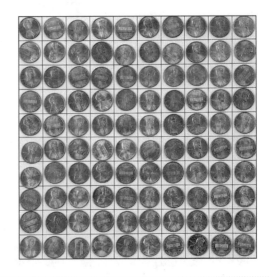

Tell children to replace each row of 10 pennies with a dime. Ask:

- How many dollars are on your grid? 1 dollar
- How many dimes are on your grid? 10 dimes
- What part of a dollar is a dime? $\frac{10}{100}$ or $\frac{1}{10}$ of a dollar
- How do you write 1 dime in decimal notation? $0.10

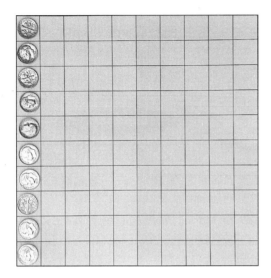

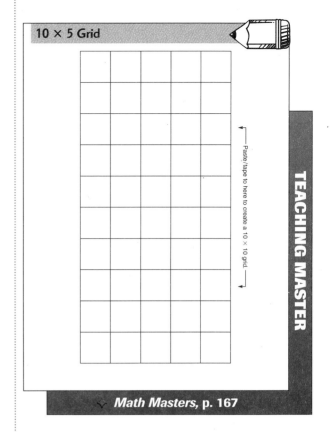

Math Masters, p. 167

TEACHING MASTER

◆ EXTRA PRACTICE Minute Math

SMALL-GROUP ACTIVITY   **5–15 min**

To offer children more experience with identifying groups of coins equivalent to $1.00, see the following page in *Minute Math:*

Measurement: p. 64

10.3 Money Amounts with a Calculator

OBJECTIVES To enter money amounts into a calculator; and to interpret calculator displays.

---

summaries | materials

1 Teaching the Lesson

Children enter money amounts in decimal form into their calculators and interpret calculator displays. [Measurement and Reference Frames; Numeration]

Children practice entering money amounts and finding totals on the calculator by playing *Pick-a-Coin*. [Measurement and Reference Frames; Operations and Computation]

- ☐ *Math Journal 2*, pp. 244–247
- ☐ Home Link 10.2
- ☐ Teaching Master (*Math Masters*, p. 168; optional)
- ☐ Teaching Master transparency (*Math Masters*, p. 168; optional)
- ☐ slate
- ☐ calculator
- ☐ 1 die per group

***See* Advance Preparation**

2 Ongoing Learning & Practice

Children practice and maintain skills through Math Boxes and Home Link activities.

- ☐ *Math Journal 2*, p. 248
- ☐ Home Link Master (*Math Masters*, p. 376)

3 Options for Individualizing

Enrichment Children use mental arithmetic and a calculator to play *Pick-a-Coin*. [Measurement and Reference Frames; Operations and Computation]

Enrichment Children play variations of *Pick-a-Coin*. [Measurement and Reference Frames; Operations and Computation]

Extra Practice Children identify the total value of a group of coins. [Measurement and Reference Frames]

- ☐ Teaching Master (*Math Masters*, p. 168; optional)
- ☐ Teaching Master transparency (*Math Masters*, p. 168; optional)
- ☐ calculator
- ☐ 1 die per group
- ☐ *Minute Math*®, p. 22

***See* Advance Preparation**

Additional Information

Advance Preparation You may want to use an overhead calculator for demonstration purposes throughout this lesson.

For the game *Pick-a-Coin* in Parts 1 and 3, you may want to make copies of *Math Masters*, page 168 for children to use as additional record tables. You may also want to make an overhead transparency of that page.

Getting Started

 on slates ↓ ②

<table>
<tr><td>

Mental Math and Reflexes

Dictate amounts like the following. Children write them in dollars-and-cents notation on their slates.

- 2 dollars and 71 cents $2.71
- 45 cents $0.45
- 9 cents $0.09

</td><td>

Math Message

4 quarters = $____ $1.00
7 quarters = $____ $1.75
8 quarters = $____ $2.00
15 quarters = $____ $3.75

</td><td>

Home Link 10.2 Follow-Up

Review answers.

</td></tr>
</table>

1 Teaching the Lesson

5-11-05

◆ Math Message Follow-Up

WHOLE-CLASS DISCUSSION

Briefly discuss solution strategies. Some possibilities for 15 quarters:

▷ Double the value of 8 quarters ($4.00) and subtract 1 quarter ($3.75).

▷ Add the values of 7 quarters ($1.75) and 8 quarters ($2.00).

◆ Entering Amounts Greater Than $1.00 into a Calculator (*Math Journal 2,* p. 244)

WHOLE-CLASS ACTIVITY

Ask children to describe how they would enter $3.58 into a calculator. Press ③ ⊙ ⑤ ⑧ Point out that since the calculator does not have a key for the dollar sign, you enter the amount without a dollar sign.

Problems 1 and 2 on journal page 244 provide practice with entering amounts more than $1.00. Work with children on these problems; provide additional practice if needed.

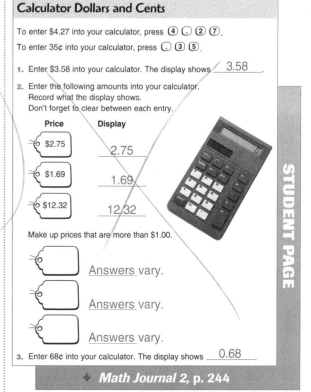

Calculator Dollars and Cents

To enter $4.27 into your calculator, press ④ ⊙ ② ⑦.
To enter 35¢ into your calculator, press ⊙ ③ ⑤.

1. Enter $3.58 into your calculator. The display shows __3.58__.

2. Enter the following amounts into your calculator. Record what the display shows. Don't forget to clear between each entry.

Price	Display
$2.75	2.75
$1.69	1.69
$12.32	12.32

Make up prices that are more than $1.00.

Answers vary.

Answers vary.

Answers vary.

3. Enter 68¢ into your calculator. The display shows __0.68__

◆ *Math Journal 2,* p. 244

STUDENT PAGE

Calculator Dollars and Cents (cont.)

4. Enter the following amounts into your calculator. Record what you see in the display.

Price	Display
$0.10	0.1
$0.26	0.26
$0.09	0.09

Make up prices that are less than $1.00.

	<u>Answers</u> vary.
	<u>Answers</u> vary.
	<u>Answers</u> vary.

5. Use your calculator to add $1.55 and $0.25.
What does the display show? <u>1.8</u>

Explain what happened. _____ Sample answer: Since
$1.55 + $0.25 = $1.80, the calculator doesn't show a zero for
the cents. It shows the number of dollars and dimes only.

◆ *Math Journal 2, p. 245*

Pick-a-Coin

Materials ☐ 1 die ☐ calculator for each player
☐ *Pick-a-Coin* record table for each player
(*Math Journal 2*, p. 247)

Players 2 to 4

Summary
Players roll a die. The numbers that come up are used as numbers of coins and dollar bills. Players try to make collections of coins and bills with the largest value.

Directions
Take turns. When it is your turn, roll the die five times. After each roll, record the number that comes up on the die in any one of the empty cells in the row for that turn on your record table. Then use a calculator to find the total amount for that turn. Record the total in the table.

After four turns, use your calculator to add the four totals. The player with the largest Grand Total wins.

Example: On his first turn, Brian rolled 4, 2, 4, 1, and 6. He filled in his record table like this:

***Pick-a-Coin* Record Table**

	Ⓟ	Ⓝ	Ⓓ	Ⓠ	$1	Total
1st turn	2	1	4	4	6	$ 7 . 47
2nd turn						$__.__
3rd turn						$__.__
4th turn						$__.__
					Grand Total	$__.__

◆ *Math Journal 2, p. 246*

◆ Entering Amounts Less Than $1.00 into a Calculator (*Math Journal 2*, pp. 244 and 245)

WHOLE-CLASS ACTIVITY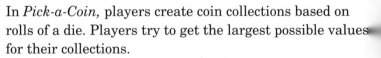

Ask children to do Problem 3 on journal page 244. Ask:

• How did you enter 68 cents into the calculator? Press
Ⓧ ⑥ ⑧. On most calculators, the display shows 0.68.

• What does the zero in front of the decimal point tell you?
The amount is less than 1 dollar.

NOTE: Some children might comment that entering
⓪ before Ⓧ ⑥ ⑧ does not affect the number in the display.

Complete Problem 4 on journal page 245 with children. Watch for children who press Ⓧ ⑨ instead of Ⓧ ⓪ ⑨ to enter 9 cents. Provide additional practice, if needed.

◆ Examining Variations in Decimals Displayed on Calculators (*Math Journal 2*, pp. 244 and 245)

WHOLE-CLASS ACTIVITY

At times, a calculator displays numbers that do not look exactly like what children might write on their papers. It is a good idea to point out such discrepancies in order to avoid confusion.

Have children add 65 cents and 35 cents on their calculators, using decimal notation. The display shows "1."—note the decimal point. This stands for $1.00. Since there are no cents in the sum, the calculator automatically omits the zeros after the decimal point.

Ask children to add 30 cents and 20 cents on their calculators, using decimal notation. The display shows "0.5"—the zero after the 5 in "0.50" is omitted. The calculator display stands for $0.50; one can also think of $0.50 as 5 dimes.

Have children do Problem 5 on journal page 245.

◆ Playing *Pick-a-Coin* (*Math Journal 2*, pp. 246 and 247; *Math Masters*, p. 168)

SMALL-GROUP ACTIVITY

In *Pick-a-Coin*, players create coin collections based on rolls of a die. Players try to get the largest possible values for their collections.

Pick-a-Coin may look complicated, but it isn't. Children should catch on quickly if you demonstrate one or two turns.

1. Draw a *Pick-a-Coin* record table on the board or display an overhead transparency of *Math Masters,* page 168.

2. Roll a die to demonstrate one turn. Write the number that comes up in one of the empty boxes in the "1st turn" row. The number represents that number of pennies, nickels, dimes, quarters, or $1 bills. Roll the die 4 more times to complete the turn. Write the numbers in the same row. *Example:*

	ⓟ	ⓝ	ⓓ	ⓠ	＄1	Total
1st turn	1	3	2	2	5	$___.____
2nd turn						$___.____
3rd turn						$___.____
4th turn						$___.____
Grand Total (total for all 4 turns)						$___.____

Say that once a number has been written in a box, it cannot be erased and moved somewhere else.

3. Show how to use a calculator to find the total amount for that turn. *For example:*

1 penny + 3 nickels + 2 dimes + 2 quarters + 5 dollars

$$\left[\begin{array}{ccccc} 0.01 & + & 0.05 & + & 0.1 & + & 0.25 & + & 5 \\ & + & 0.05 & + & 0.1 & + & 0.25 \\ & + & 0.05 \end{array} \right] = 5.86$$

4. Point out that the winner is the player who gets the largest possible Grand Total (the total for all 4 turns), so it is important to try to get the largest possible total on each turn.

When most children understand what to do, divide the class into groups of 2, 3, or 4. Then lead children through the steps for the first turn. They can complete the next 3 turns on their own.

There are 3 record tables on journal page 247. If children continue to play, they can use copies of *Math Masters,* page 168 or draw their own record tables.

Pick-a-Coin **Record Tables**

	ⓟ	ⓝ	ⓓ	ⓠ	＄1	Total
1st turn						$___.____
2nd turn						$___.____
3rd turn						$___.____
4th turn						$___.____
Grand Total						$___.____

	ⓟ	ⓝ	ⓓ	ⓠ	＄1	Total
1st turn						$___.____
2nd turn						$___.____
3rd turn						$___.____
4th turn						$___.____
Grand Total						$___.____

	ⓟ	ⓝ	ⓓ	ⓠ	＄1	Total
1st turn						$___.____
2nd turn						$___.____
3rd turn						$___.____
4th turn						$___.____
Grand Total						$___.____

◆ *Math Journal 2,* p. 247

STUDENT PAGE

Copies of *Pick-a-Coin* record tables are found on *Math Masters,* page 168.

STUDENT PAGE

1. If $1.00 is ONE, then

$1¢ = \dfrac{1}{100}$

$25¢ = \dfrac{25}{100}$, or $\dfrac{1}{4}$

$32¢ = \dfrac{32}{100}$, $\dfrac{16}{50}$, or $\dfrac{8}{25}$

$50¢ = \dfrac{50}{100}$, or $\dfrac{1}{2}$

$99¢ = \dfrac{99}{100}$

2. Draw 12 Ⓠs. Circle $\frac{1}{3}$ of them. What is the value of the circled coins?

$ __1.00__

Ⓠ Ⓠ Ⓠ Ⓠ Ⓠ Ⓠ
Ⓠ Ⓠ Ⓠ Ⓠ Ⓠ Ⓠ

3. Rosita had $0.39 and found $0.57 more. How much does she have now? Estimate your answer and then use partial sums to solve.

Estimate:

$0.40 + $0.60 = $1.00

Answer: 96¢, or $0.96

4. Solve.

Unit

$50 + 30 = \underline{80}$

$40 + 80 = \underline{120}$

$\underline{140} = 70 + 70$

$\underline{110} = 20 + 90$

5. Use Ⓟ, Ⓝ, Ⓓ, and Ⓠ. Show $1.79 two different ways.

Sample answers:

Ⓠ Ⓠ Ⓠ Ⓠ Ⓠ　　Ⓠ Ⓠ Ⓠ Ⓠ
Ⓠ Ⓠ Ⓟ Ⓟ　　Ⓠ Ⓠ
Ⓟ Ⓟ　　Ⓓ Ⓓ Ⓝ
　　Ⓟ Ⓟ Ⓟ Ⓟ

6. 17 magazines are shared equally among 5 children. Draw a picture to help you.

Each child gets __3__ magazines.

There are __2__ magazines left.

□ □ □ □ □ 　□
□ □ □ □ □ 　□
□ □ □ □ □

◆ *Math Journal 2,* p. 248

HOME LINK MASTER

Coin Values

Family Note

In today's lesson, your child used a calculator to enter amounts of money and find totals. For Problem 2, help your child collect and find the total value of each type of coin. Then find the grand total. If you wish to use a calculator, help your child enter the amounts. Remind your child that amounts like $1.00 and $0.50 will be displayed on the calculator as "1." and "0.5" because the calculator doesn't display ending zeros.

Please return this Home Link to school tomorrow.

1. Complete the table.

Coins	Number of Coins	Total Value
Ⓟ	6	$ 0 . 06
Ⓝ	10	$ 0 . 50
Ⓓ	13	$ 1 . 30
Ⓠ	6	$ 1 . 50
Grand total		$ 3 . 36

2. Ask someone at home to help you collect pennies, nickels, dimes, quarters, and, if possible, half-dollars. Use the coins in your collection to complete the table below.

Coins	Number of Coins	Total Value
Ⓟ		
Ⓝ		
Ⓓ		
Ⓠ		
Half-dollar		
Grand total		

Answers vary.

◇ *Math Masters,* p. 376

ONGOING ASSESSMENT

While children play *Pick-a-Coin,* observe how they enter amounts of money into their calculators. Watch for children having difficulty entering amounts less than $0.10. When appropriate, ask children to explain why the calculator displays numbers that do not look exactly like what was entered. For example, a child enters 1.50 and the calculator displays 1.5.

Adjusting the Activity Once children have some experience playing the game, discuss strategies with them. Ask where they would write 1 and why. Then ask where they would write 6 and other numbers.

2 Ongoing Learning & Practice

◆ Math Boxes 10.3 (*Math Journal 2,* p. 248)

INDEPENDENT ACTIVITY

Mixed Review This journal page provides opportunities for cumulative review or assessment of concepts and skills.

◆ Home Link 10.3 (*Math Masters,* p. 376)

Home Connection Children complete a table showing the total value of a coin collection. Children also ask someone at home to help them collect pennies, nickels, dimes, quarters, and half-dollars (if available). They find the total value of each kind of coin and the total value of all the coins in the collection.

Options for Individualizing

♦ ENRICHMENT **Using Mental Arithmetic and a Calculator to Find *Pick-a-Coin* Totals**
(*Math Masters*, p. 168)

SMALL-GROUP ACTIVITY 5–15 min

One way to find the totals in *Pick-a-Coin* is to enter each money amount into a calculator as a number of cents. A player would complete the following steps to find the total of 2 pennies, 1 nickel, 4 dimes, 5 quarters, and 3 dollars.

1. 2 pennies make 2¢; enter 2 into the calculator.

2. 1 nickel is 5¢; add 5 to 2.

3. 4 dimes make 40¢; add 40 to the total.

4. 5 quarters make $1.25, or 125¢; add 125 to the total.

5. 3 dollars make $3.00, or 300¢; add 300 to the total.

6. The calculator shows 472, which stands for 472 cents. 472 cents = $4.72.

Play one or two rounds of *Pick-a-Coin* in which children use mental and calculator arithmetic to find the totals.

♦ ENRICHMENT **Variations of *Pick-a-Coin***
(*Math Masters*, p. 168)

SMALL-GROUP ACTIVITY 15–30 min

The following are some possible variations of *Pick-a-Coin:*

▷ Try to get the smallest Grand Total rather than the largest.

▷ Aim for a specific Grand Total, such as $10.00. Whoever gets closest to the total without going over is the winner.

▷ Play with fewer than 5 rolls per turn so that some boxes are blank in each row. This variation could be combined with the second variation.

♦ EXTRA PRACTICE **Minute Math**

SMALL-GROUP ACTIVITY 5–15 min

To offer children more experience with finding the total amount of money in coin collections, see the following page in *Minute Math:*

Basic Routines: p. 22

10.4 Using a Calculator to Solve Problems with Money

OBJECTIVES To compare prices; and to solve problems about price differences.

summaries	materials

1 Teaching the Lesson

Children discuss the prices of common items in 1897 and today. They make up and solve problems based on the Then-and-Now Poster. [Numeration; Operations and Computation]

☐ *Math Journal 2*, pp. 250 and 251; and p. 322 (optional)
☐ Home Link 10.3
☐ Teaching Master transparency (*Math Masters*, p. †69)
☐ calculator
***See* Advance Preparation**

2 Ongoing Learning & Practice

Children practice entering money amounts and finding totals using a calculator by playing *Pick-a-Coin*. [Measurement and Reference Frames; Operations and Computation]

Children practice and maintain skills through Math Boxes and Home Link activities.

☐ *Math Journal 2*, pp. 246, 247, and 249
☐ Teaching Master (*Math Masters*, p. 168; optional)
☐ Home Link Master (*Math Masters*, p. 377)
☐ 1 die per group; calculator
***See* Advance Preparation**

3 Options for Individualizing

Language Diversity Children make up and solve ratio and comparison problems. [Operations and Computation]

☐ calculator

Additional Information

Advance Preparation For the game *Pick-a-Coin* in Part 2, you may want to make copies of *Math Masters*, page 168 for additional record tables.

Getting Started

Mental Math and Reflexes

Ask questions about equivalent measures. Children can refer to the Table of Equivalencies on journal page 322 as necessary. *For example:*

- How many quarts are in 1 gallon? 4 quarts
  In a half-gallon? 2 quarts
- How many pints are in a quart? 2 pints
  In 3 quarts? 6 pints
- How many cups are in 1 pint? 2 cups
  In a half-pint? 1 cup

Math Message

Write these amounts in dollars-and-cents notation.

35¢ = \$__.___ \$0.35   6¢ = \$__.___ \$0.06
80¢ = \$__.___ \$0.80   152¢ = \$__.___ \$1.52

Home Link 10.3 Follow-Up

Briefly review answers for Problem 1.

Teaching the Lesson

✦ Math Message Follow-Up

WHOLE-CLASS DISCUSSION

Briefly go over the answers.

✦ Discussing the Then-and-Now Poster
(*Math Journal 2*, p. 250; *Math Masters*, p. 169)

WHOLE-CLASS DISCUSSION

Display an overhead transparency of *Math Masters*, page 169, the Then-and-Now Poster, and ask the class to study the poster on journal page 250. Tell children that the "then" prices come from a mail-order catalog published in 1897. As children share their observations about the poster, ask them to discuss similarities and differences between the "then" and "now" items.

A comparison of the items and prices on the poster also lends itself to an interesting discussion of such questions as the following:

• Why did most things cost so much less then?

• Since most things cost less then, were people more able to afford them?

• Can you think of things that cost less now than they did 5 or 10 years ago? Why might they cost less now?

Although these are complex issues with no simple (or unique) correct answers, it is not too early for children to start thinking about them. Encourage children to debate these questions, but refrain from placing value judgments on their arguments.

 Adjusting the Activity The pictures of the food items on the Then-and-Now Poster will be more meaningful to children with language difficulties if the actual items are displayed in the classroom.

Then-and-Now Poster

✦ *Math Journal 2, p. 250*

STUDENT PAGE

Adjusting the Activity Help children make difference and ratio comparisons by first asking about the items being considered. *For example:*

- What was the price of the bicycle in 1897? $29.00

- Is $29.00 closer to $20.00 or $30.00? $30.00

- What is the price of the bicycle now? $119.99

- $119.99 is about how much? $120.00

Once children have organized their information, proceed with the difference or ratio comparison.

NOTE: Question 4 on journal page 251 asks which item had the biggest price increase. The biggest difference in price is for the bicycle: $119.99 − $29.00 = $90.99. This is the answer most children will find, and it is correct. The biggest relative price increase, however, was for the cheese, which now costs almost 40 times as much as in 1897. This increase is more than any other; compare it with the bicycle, for example, which increased about 4 times in price.

STUDENT PAGE

Then-and-Now Prices

Use your calculator.

1. How much did a 20-inch bicycle cost in 1897? $29.00
   How much does it cost now? $119.99
   How much more does it cost now? $90.99

2. How much more does a pound of cheese cost now than it did in 1897? $4.66

3. In 1897, raisins were packed in cartons. Each carton contained 24 one-pound boxes. How much did a 24-pound carton cost then? $2.40
   How much would it cost now? $54.96

4. Which item had the biggest price increase from "then" to "now"?
   The 20-inch girl's bicycle had the biggest price increase.
   How much more does it cost now? $90.99

5. Our Own Problems about Then-and-Now: Answers vary.

_____
_____
_____
_____
_____
_____

✦ *Math Journal 2,* p. 251

✦ Making Rough Comparisons between Then-and-Now Prices (*Math Journal 2,* p. 250)

WHOLE-CLASS DISCUSSION

Pose problems like the following:

- Difference comparisons: About how much more does a bicycle cost now than it cost in 1897? About $90.99 more

- Ratio comparisons: Is the price of a bicycle now more than twice its price in 1897? yes About how many times more? 4 Is the price of a harmonica today more or less than 10 times its price in 1897? more

✦ Using a Calculator to Solve Then-and-Now Problems (*Math Journal 2,* pp. 250 and 251)

INDEPENDENT ACTIVITY

Children use their calculators to solve Problems 1–4 on journal page 251. As you circulate, check children's calculator displays of dollars-and-cents amounts. Bring the class together to share thinking and strategies for solving the problems. In Problem 2, for example, the information requested is for a pound of cheese. The poster gives the price for $\frac{1}{2}$ pound of cheese. One possible strategy is to find the difference for $\frac{1}{2}$ pound and then multiply by 2.

✦ Making Up and Solving Then-and-Now Problems (*Math Journal 2,* pp. 250 and 251)

PARTNER ACTIVITY

Partners do Problem 5 by using the information on the Then-and-Now Poster to make up their own problems. They record some of their problems and solutions at the bottom of the page.

Ask several volunteers to share their problems. Try to clarify any problems that are hard to understand or that have no answer. If you want, you can make up one or more ill-formed problems and ask children what's wrong with them. For example, in the problem *"How much more does it cost now than it did in 1897?"* it is not clear which object's prices are being compared.

Ongoing Learning & Practice

♦ Playing *Pick-a-Coin*
(*Math Journal 2*, pp. 246 and 247;
Math Masters, p. 168)

SMALL-GROUP ACTIVITY

Challenge children to play one of the possible variations of
Pick-a-Coin described on page 713 of this book.

♦ Math Boxes 10.4 (*Math Journal 2*, p. 249)

INDEPENDENT ACTIVITY

Mixed Review This journal page provides
opportunities for cumulative review or
assessment of concepts and skills.

♦ Home Link 10.4 (*Math Masters*, p. 377)

Home Connection Children enter amounts
into the calculator and record the displays.
Children also ask an adult to compare the
price of an item now to the price of that same
item when he or she was a child.

Options for Individualizing

♦ LANGUAGE DIVERSITY Comparing Prices

INDEPENDENT ACTIVITY   5–15 min

Encourage children to tell the class about food items that
are unique to their culture and the prices of those items.
Make up ratio and difference problems about the items
that require rough comparisons, as well as number stories
that require the use of a calculator.

For this activity, it might not be possible to do
then-and-now comparisons as described in the lesson.
Instead, compare prices of individual items.

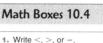

Math Boxes 10.4

1. Write <, >, or =.

   $0.73 \;>\; $0.07

   $0.46 \;<\; $1.46

   $3.29 \;>\; $2.93

2. Draw 16 ⓠs. Circle $\frac{1}{4}$ of them.
   What is the value of the circled
   coins?

   $ __1.00__

   ⓠ ⓠ ⓠ ⓠ ⓠ ⓠ
   ⓠ ⓠ ⓠ ⓠ ⓠ ⓠ
   ⓠ ⓠ ⓠ ⓠ

3. Write the money amounts in
   dollars-and-cents notation.

    = $__0.01__   = $__0.25__

   = $__0.05__   = $__0.10__

    = $__1.00__

4. I have $2.00. Can I buy 4 bags
   of chips for $0.55 each?

   __no__

5. Fill in the diagram and write
   a number model.

Start	Change	End
27	+27	54

   27 + 27 = 54

6. Estimate the height of your
   desk. Then measure it.
   Sample answers:
   Estimate: about ___25 in.___
                      (unit)

   Measurement: ___25 in.___
                     (unit)

♦ *Math Journal 2*, p. 249

Calculators and Money   Home Link 10.4

Family Note In today's lesson, your child used a calculator to solve problems with money. In
Problem 2, your child will ask you or another adult to compare the cost of an
item when you were a child to its current cost. There are two ways to make this
type of comparison. You might describe a *difference comparison*. For example: "A
bicycle costs about $90.00 more now than it did then." You might also use a *ratio
comparison*. For example, "A bicycle costs about 4 times as much now as it did
then." You do not need to share the terms "difference comparison" and "ratio
comparison" with your child, but it is important that your child be exposed to
both types of comparisons.

Please return this Home Link to school tomorrow.

1. Enter the following amounts into your calculator.
   What does your calculator show?

Enter	Calculator Shows
$1.09	1.09
$2.50	2.5
98¢	0.98
$3.18	3.18
6¢	0.06

2. Ask an adult to think about an item that he or she remembers
   from when he or she was a child. Ask the adult to compare how
   much the item cost then and now. Make a record below of what
   you find out. Answers vary.

   _____

   _____

♦ *Math Masters*, p. 377

10.5

Estimating and Finding Exact Costs

OBJECTIVES To estimate costs; and to calculate exact costs.

5-8-02

summaries	materials

1 Teaching the Lesson

Children estimate the total cost of grocery items and use a calculator to find the exact total cost. [Operations and Computation]

☐ *Math Journal 2*, pp. 240 and 252
☐ Home Link 10.4
☐ Teaching Master (*Math Masters*, p. 163)·
☐ Teaching Master transparency (*Math Masters*, p. 163; optional)
☐ slate; calculator
See **Advance Preparation**

2 Ongoing Learning & Practice

Children practice and maintain skills through Math Boxes and Home Link activities.

☐ *Math Journal 2*, p. 253
☐ Home Link Master (*Math Masters*, p. 378)

3 Options for Individualizing

Extra Practice Children estimate the total cost of items from a classroom store and use a calculator to find the exact total cost. [Operations and Computation]

Extra Practice Children solve number stories about the cost of candy bars. [Operations and Computation]

☐ Teaching Master (*Math Masters*, p. 170)
☐ calculator
☐ *Minute Math*®, p. 141

Additional Information

Advance Preparation For the Part 1 activities that involve the Good Buys Poster, you may want to make copies or use an overhead transparency of *Math Masters*, page 163. By doing this, children won't have to flip back to the journal page to see the poster.

Getting Started

Mental Math and Reflexes

Write a money amount on the board. Ask a volunteer to read it aloud. Have the class draw coin and bill symbols (Ⓟ, Ⓝ, Ⓓ, Ⓠ, $1) on their slates to represent the amount. *Suggestions:*

• $4.59 $1 $1 $1 $1 Ⓠ Ⓠ Ⓝ Ⓟ Ⓟ Ⓟ Ⓟ
• $0.67 Ⓠ Ⓠ Ⓓ Ⓝ Ⓟ Ⓟ   • $0.08 Ⓝ Ⓟ Ⓟ Ⓟ

Answers vary. Sample answers show amounts using the least number of bills and coins.

Math Message

90 + 110 = ____ 200   ____ = 140 + 90 230
____ = 180 + 60 240   30 + 100 + 70 = ____ 200

Home Link 10.4 Follow-Up

Children share then-and-now stories from home.

Teaching the Lesson

✦ Math Message Follow-Up

WHOLE-CLASS DISCUSSION

Check responses to assess children's ability to add multiples of 10 up to 200. This skill will aid children in making estimates.

✦ Estimating Costs
(*Math Journal 2,* p. 240; *Math Masters,* p. 163)

WHOLE-CLASS DISCUSSION

If possible, display an overhead transparency of *Math Masters,* page 163, the Good Buys Poster. Ask children to describe what they notice about the items and their prices on the Good Buys Poster. Sample answers: The items are grouped according to kinds of foods. Both the price and the quantity of an item that can be bought at that price are shown. All but one of the prices end in 9. Ask why advertised prices often end in 9. Sample answer: If people look at the dollars, or the large number, first, they may think that the item costs less than it actually does.

Pose the following problem: *If you had two $1 bills, would you have enough money to buy 1 pound of grapes (99¢) and 1 jar of peanut butter ($1.29)?* (Pretend that there is no sales tax on grocery items.) no *What if you had $3.00?* yes

As children share strategies, emphasize that it is not necessary to find the exact total cost to answer such questions; an estimate is good enough to tell whether you have enough money.

Many different estimates are acceptable, depending on the situation. For example, $2.00 might be as good an estimate as $2.30 if you have $5.00.

When estimating the cost of several items, it helps to think of prices to the nearest 10 cents. (While you need not mention it at this time, keep in mind that for larger prices, one would estimate with amounts to the nearest dollar, 10 dollars, 100 dollars, or whatever other amounts are appropriate.) Using the problem above about the grapes and peanut butter: 99 cents is closer to $1.00 than to 90 cents, and $1.29 is closer to $1.30 than to $1.20, so one can think 100 + 130 = 230 or $1.00 + $1.30 = $2.30. Most children will become adept at this kind of thinking, given time and experience.

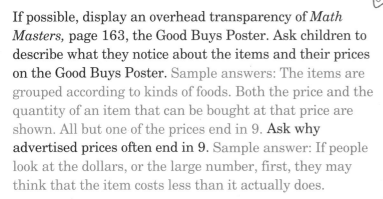

Adjusting the Activity If children need to review this skill, take a few minutes to share strategies for solving these problems. For 90 + 110, encourage children to think about 9 + 11; for 180 + 60, think 18 + 6 or 8 + 6 if necessary. You might want to begin with numbers less than 100.

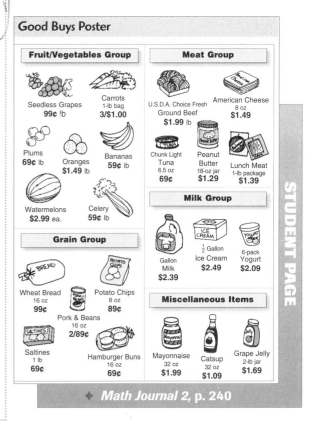

✦ *Math Journal 2,* p. 240

Buying Food

Choose items to buy from the Good Buys Poster on journal page 240.
For each purchase:

- Record the items on the sales slip.
- Write the price of each item on the sales slip.
- Estimate the total cost and record it.
- Find the total cost and write it on the sales slip.

Purchase 1	Store	
Items:		
bananas	$ 0 . 59	
wheat bread	$ 0 . 99	Estimated cost:
Total:	$ 1 . 58	about $ 1 . 60

Purchase 2	Store	
Items:		
_____	$__ . ____	
_____	$__ . ____	Estimated cost:
Total:	$__ . ____	about $__ . ____

Purchase 3	Store	
Items:		
_____	$__ . ____	
_____	$__ . ____	Estimated cost:
Total:	$__ . ____	about $__ . ____

Math Journal 2, p. 252

Adjusting the Activity To extend the
estimating costs activity, challenge
children to purchase multiple pounds of
fruit and vegetables. For example,
3 pounds of oranges at $1.49 a pound is
about $4.50.

Math Boxes 10.5

1. Estimate. Then use partial
sums to solve.

Estimate:

60 + 50 = 110

$$\begin{array}{r} 57 \\ + 48 \\ \hline 105 \end{array}$$

2. Solve.

Area: __8__ sq cm

Perimeter: __12__ cm

3. There are __10__ pennies in
1 dime. What fraction
of a dime is 1 penny? $\frac{1}{10}$

There are __25__ pennies in
1 quarter. What fraction
of a quarter is 1 penny? $\frac{1}{25}$

4. The pet store sold 12 fish.
$\frac{1}{2}$ were guppies and $\frac{1}{4}$ were
neons. The rest were angelfish.
How many of each?

There were __6__ guppies.

There were __3__ neons.

There were __3__ angelfish.

5. __300__ pennies = $3.00

__60__ nickels = $3.00

__30__ dimes = $3.00

__12__ quarters = $3.00

6. Circle the answer.

$2.88 is closer to:
$2.80 or ($2.90)

$5.61 is closer to:
($5.60) or $5.70

$1.97 is closer to:
$1.90 or ($2.00)

Math Journal 2, p. 253

Ask: *Why is it useful to estimate total costs when shopping
in the store?* It helps in deciding if you have enough money
to pay for the items. An estimate can also be used to check
if the cashier has made a mistake.

Ask a volunteer to choose two or more items from the
poster. Record the items and children's estimates of their
total cost on the board. These will be compared to exact
costs later on.

Repeat this activity with several sets of items. Do not
erase the board.

◆ Calculating Exact Costs with a Calculator

INDEPENDENT ACTIVITY

When it's time to pay for purchases, the exact cost is
required. Costs are entered into the cash register much as
they are entered into a calculator.

Have children find the exact total cost for each set of items
on the board. They may use their calculators. If necessary,
review how to enter dollars-and-cents amounts into the
calculator using the decimal point. Record the totals and
compare them to the estimates.

Remind children that it is also appropriate to estimate
after finding an exact answer in order to check for possible
errors in computation.

◆ Estimating Costs and Finding Exact Costs
(*Math Journal 2,* pp. 240 and 252)

WHOLE-CLASS ACTIVITY

Work with children to complete the first sales slip on
journal page 252 by completing the steps listed on the
journal page.

1. Choose two items from the Good Buys Poster and
   record them.

2. Write the cost of each item on the sales slip. Point out
   that all decimal points line up one under the other.

3. Estimate the total cost of the items and record it.
   Children may use the blank space to make notes to
   help them keep track of the amounts.

4. Find the total cost of the items, with or without a
   calculator.

Children complete the other two sales slips.

NOTE: Many children are hesitant to make estimates.
Some children find the exact answer and then give an
estimate that is close to the exact answer. Other children

make an estimate, but then erase it and record a "better" one once they determine the exact answer. Consider asking children to record all estimates on journal page 252 in pen before they calculate the exact costs.

Ongoing Learning & Practice

◆ Math Boxes 10.5 (*Math Journal 2*, p. 253)

INDEPENDENT ACTIVITY

Mixed Review This journal page provides opportunities for cumulative review or assessment of concepts and skills.

◆ Home Link 10.5 (*Math Masters*, p. 378)

Home Connection Children select the closest multiple of ten cents for different money amounts. Then children estimate totals by adding multiples of ten cents.

Options for Individualizing

◆ EXTRA PRACTICE Purchasing Items from a Classroom Store (*Math Masters*, p. 170)

SMALL-GROUP ACTIVITY **30+ min**

Children gather items from the classroom and label each with a price tag to create a pretend Classroom Store. Shoppers "purchase" items from the store by completing *Math Masters*, page 170.

◆ EXTRA PRACTICE Minute Math

SMALL-GROUP ACTIVITY **5–15 min**

To offer children more experience with solving problems about food items, see the following page in *Minute Math:*

Number Stories: p. 141

Estimation to the Nearest 10¢ — Home Link 10.5

Family Note In today's lesson, your child estimated sums by first finding the nearest ten cents for each amount of money being added and then adding the amounts for the nearest ten cents together. For Problems 1–7, ask your child how she or he arrived at each answer. If needed, use coins to show which amount is actually closer. For Problems 8–11, help your child find the totals by thinking of a problem like $1.20 + $0.60 as 12 + 6 or as 120 cents + 60 cents.

Please return this Home Link to school tomorrow.

Write the correct answer to each question.
Talk with someone at home about your answers.

1. Is $0.69 closer to $0.60 or $0.70? $0.70
2. Is $2.59 closer to $2.50 or $2.60? $2.60
3. Is $0.99 closer to $0.90 or $1.00? $1.00
4. Is $1.31 closer to $1.30 or $1.40? $1.30
5. Is $3.99 closer to $3.90 or $4.00? $4.00
6. Is $1.17 closer to $1.10 or $1.20? $1.20
7. Is $2.34 closer to $2.30 or $2.40? $2.30

Fill in the blanks and estimate the total cost in each problem.

Example
$1.19 + $0.59 is about $1.20 + $0.60 = $1.80 .

8. $1.29 + $0.48 is about $1.30 + $0.50 = $1.80 .
9. $0.79 + $0.39 is about $0.80 + $0.40 = $1.20 .
10. $0.69 + $0.89 is about $0.70 + $0.90 = $1.60 .
11. $1.41 + $0.77 is about $1.40 + $0.80 = $2.20 .

Math Masters, p. 378

Shopping at the Classroom Store

Choose items to buy from the Classroom Store. For each purchase:
- Record the items on the sales slip.
- Write the price of each item on the sales slip.
- Estimate the total cost and record it.
- Find the total cost and write it on the sales slip.

Purchase 1   Classroom Store
Items:
_____ $___ . _____
_____ $___ . _____   Estimated cost:
                        Total: $___ . _____   about $_____

Purchase 2   Classroom Store
Items:
_____ $___ . _____
_____ $___ . _____   Estimated cost:
                        Total: $___ . _____   about $_____

Purchase 3   Classroom Store
Items:
_____ $___ . _____
_____ $___ . _____   Estimated cost:
                        Total: $___ . _____   about $_____

Math Masters, p. 170

10.6

Making Change

OBJECTIVES To make change by counting up; and to estimate totals by rounding to the nearest 10 cents.

	summaries	materials

1 Teaching the Lesson

Children estimate and find the exact total cost of several grocery items. They estimate and find the exact change from a $10 bill. [Operations and Computation; Numeration]

- ☐ *Math Journal 2,* pp. 240, 254, and 255
- ☐ Home Link 10.5
- ☐ Teaching Masters (*Math Masters,* pp. 163 and 171; optional)
- ☐ Teaching Master transparency (*Math Masters,* p. 163; optional)
- ☐ slate; coins and bills; calculator

***See* Advance Preparation**

2 Ongoing Learning & Practice

Children identify equivalent fractions by playing the *Equivalent Fractions Game* or compare fractions by playing *Fraction Top-It.* [Numeration]

Children practice and maintain skills through Math Boxes and Home Link activities.

- ☐ *Math Journal 2,* pp. 202, 203, 208, 209, and 256
- ☐ Home Link Master (*Math Masters,* p. 379)
- ☐ Fraction Cards cut from *Math Journal 2,* Activity Sheet 5

3 Options for Individualizing

Enrichment Children read literature selections involving computation with amounts of money. [Operations and Computation]

Reteaching Children use the Class Number Grid Poster to find differences between pairs of numbers. [Patterns, Functions, and Algebra; Numeration]

- ☐ *Pigs Will Be Pigs: Fun with Math and Money*
- ☐ *Alexander, Who Used to Be Rich Last Sunday*
- ☐ Class Number Grid Poster

***See* Advance Preparation**

Additional Information

Advance Preparation The Math Message problems are also provided on *Math Masters,* page 171. If you want to use the Teaching Master, make 1 copy for every 2 children. Cut the copies apart and put them near the Math Message. Change the directions to: *Take a slip of paper. Complete the problems.*

For the Part 1 activities that involve the Good Buys Poster, you may want to make copies or use an overhead transparency of *Math Masters,* page 163. By doing this, children won't have to flip back to the journal page to see the poster.

Before beginning the optional Enrichment activity in Part 3, obtain the following books: *Pigs Will Be Pigs: Fun with Math and Money* by Amy Axelrod (Simon & Schuster, 1994) and *Alexander, Who Used to Be Rich Last Sunday* by Judith Viorst (Atheneum, 1979).

Vocabulary • **counting up to make change**

Getting Started

✓ on slates from desks

Mental Math and Reflexes

Write problems like the following on the board. Children record estimates on their slates. For each problem, have children tell how they arrived at their estimates. *Suggestions:*

- $0.32 + $1.61 = ? $0.30 + $1.60 = $1.90
- $0.49 + $0.78 = ? $0.50 + $0.80 = $1.30
- $3.42 + $2.29 = ? $3.40 + $2.30 = $5.70

Home Link 10.5 Follow-Up
Review answers.

Math Message

Write in decimal notation:

1. *29 cents* = $__ 0.29

2. *59¢* = $__ 0.59

3. *9 cents* = $__ 0.09

4. *a dollar forty-seven* = $__ 1.47

5. *10 dollars and 2 cents* = $__ 10.02

6. *nine hundred thirty-three dollars and thirty cents* =
$__ 933.30

Challenge

7. *three thousand five hundred forty-six dollars and sixteen cents* = $__ 3,546.16

---

1 Teaching the Lesson

◆ Math Message Follow-Up
(*Math Masters,* p. 171)

WHOLE-CLASS DISCUSSION

Assess children's responses and review concepts as needed.

◆ Using Coins and Bills to Make Change from $10.00

✓ partner slate

PARTNER ACTIVITY

Pose the following problem:

- I bought soup and a sandwich for $6.32 (including tax). I gave the cashier a $10 bill. About how much change should I get? $3.70 Exactly how much? $3.68

Ask children to estimate the amount of change. Record several of their estimates on the board.

Then use coins and bills to demonstrate the process of **counting up to make change:** Begin with the amount owed, and count up to the amount given to the cashier. One way to count up from $6.32 to $10.00 would be as follows:

$6.33 (1¢), $6.34 (2¢), $6.35 (3¢), $6.45 (13¢),
$6.50 (18¢), $6.75 (18¢ + 25¢ = 43¢),
$7.00 (43¢ + 25¢ = 68¢), $8.00 ($1.68),
$9.00 ($2.68), $10.00 ($3.68).   The change is $3.68.

 Adjusting the Activity If children are having difficulty making an estimate, ask such questions as the following to help children "close in" on an estimate. For each question, ask children to explain how they know the answer.

- Should I get more or less than $10.00 in change? less
- Should I get more or less than $1.00 in change? more
- Should I get more or less than $3.00 in change? more
- Should I get more or less than $4.00 in change? less

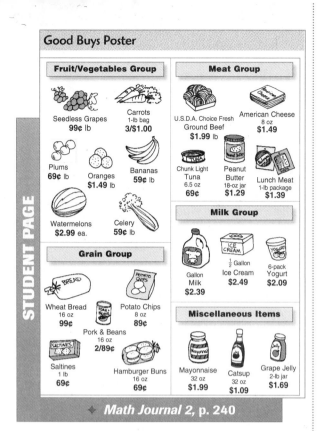

Good Buys Poster

Fruit/Vegetables Group

Seedless Grapes
99¢ lb

Carrots
1-lb bag
3/$1.00

Plums
69¢ lb

Oranges
$1.49 lb

Bananas
59¢ lb

Watermelons
$2.99 ea.

Celery
59¢ lb

Grain Group

Wheat Bread
16 oz
99¢

Potato Chips
8 oz
89¢

Pork & Beans
16 oz
2/89¢

Saltines
1 lb
69¢

Hamburger Buns
16 oz
69¢

Meat Group

U.S.D.A. Choice Fresh
Ground Beef
$1.99 lb

American Cheese
8 oz
$1.49

Chunk Light
Tuna
6.5 oz
69¢

Peanut
Butter
18-oz jar
$1.29

Lunch Meat
1-lb package
$1.39

Milk Group

Gallon
Milk
$2.39

½ Gallon
Ice Cream
$2.49

6-pack
Yogurt
$2.09

Miscellaneous Items

Mayonnaise
32 oz
$1.99

Catsup
32 oz
$1.09

Grape Jelly
2-lb jar
$1.69

Math Journal 2, p. 240

There are many other ways to count up to make change; for example, by adding dimes ($6.42, $6.52, and so on).

Have children use their calculators to check the answer by subtracting the amount owed from $10.00.

Demonstrate this routine for one or two other purchases. Then have partners practice this procedure (estimate, count out change, use a calculator to check) with several other amounts.

NOTE: Although most cash registers display the amount of change, it is useful to learn to make change without the help of a cash register or calculator. It takes time and experience to develop this skill.

◆ Shopping for Groceries
(*Math Journal 2*, pp. 240, 254, and 255; *Math Masters*, p. 163)

PARTNER ACTIVITY

One partner is the Shopper, the other is the Clerk. Lead the class through the steps listed on journal page 254.

Partners switch roles and repeat the activity with different purchases. Have the class come together to share estimation strategies and ways of finding change.

Making Change

Work with a partner. Use your tool-kit coins and bills. One of you is the Shopper. The other is the Clerk.

The Shopper does the following:

- Chooses one item from each food group on the Good Buys Poster on journal page 240.
- Lists these items on the Good Buys sales slip in the Shopper's journal on page 255.
- Writes the cost of each item on the sales slip.
- Estimates the total cost of all the items and writes it on the sales slip.
- Pays with a $10 bill.
- Estimates the change and writes it on the sales slip.

The Clerk does the following:

- Uses a calculator to find the exact total cost.
- Writes the exact total cost on the sales slip.
- Gives the Shopper change by counting up.
- Writes the exact change from $10.00 on the sales slip.

The Shopper uses a calculator to check the Clerk's change.

Change roles and repeat.

Math Journal 2, p. 254

Making Change (cont.)

The Good Buys Store Sales Slip

	Item	Cost
Fruit/vegetables group	_____	$ __ . ____
Grain group	_____	$ __ . ____
Meat group	_____	$ __ . ____
Milk group	_____	$ __ . ____
Miscellaneous items	_____	$ __ . ____
Estimated total cost		$ __ . ____
Estimated change from $10.00		$ __ . ____
Exact total cost		$ __ . ____
Exact change from $10.00		$ __ . ____

Math Journal 2, p. 255

ONGOING ASSESSMENT

As children complete journal page 255, ask them to explain how they arrived at their estimates. Watch for children rounding to the nearest 10 cents as they estimate.

1. Cross out the names that don't belong.

10¢

ten cents, $\frac{1}{10}$ of a dollar,

~~$10.00~~; ⓓ, ⓝⓝ, ~~$0.01~~;

~~$\frac{1}{100}$ of a dollar~~;

~~$\frac{1}{2}$ of a dollar~~

2. A $\frac{1}{2}$ pint of berries costs $0.99. I have $2.00. Can I buy 1 pint of berries?

__yes__

3. Solve.

Unit

$180 - 60 = \underline{120}$

$150 + 60 + 40 = \underline{250}$

$240 - 120 = \underline{120}$

$170 + 30 + 80 = \underline{280}$

4. Trade first. Then subtract.

$$\begin{array}{r} \$0.81 \\ - \$0.35 \\ \hline \end{array}$$
46¢, or $0.46

5. If $1.00 is ONE, then

$10¢ = \frac{1}{10}$

$30¢ = \frac{30}{100}$, or $\frac{3}{10}$

$50¢ = \frac{50}{100}$, or $\frac{1}{2}$

$80¢ = \frac{80}{100}$, $\frac{8}{10}$, or $\frac{4}{5}$

$2.00 = \underline{2}$

6. Write >, <, or =.

1 qt $>$ 1 pt

3 c $<$ 1 gal

1 qt $=$ 4 c

1 gal $>$ 5 pt

✦ *Math Journal 2, p. 256*

2 Ongoing Learning & Practice

✦ Playing the *Equivalent Fractions Game* or *Fraction Top-It*
(*Math Journal 2,* pp. 202, 203, 208, and 209)

PARTNER ACTIVITY

Children practice identifying equivalent fractions in the *Equivalent Fractions Game.* Children practice comparing fractions in *Fraction Top-It.* For detailed instructions, see Lessons 8.5 and 8.6. An advanced version of each game is provided.

✦ Math Boxes 10.6 (*Math Journal 2,* p. 256)

INDEPENDENT ACTIVITY

Mixed Review This journal page provides opportunities for cumulative review or assessment of concepts and skills.

✦ Home Link 10.6 (*Math Masters,* p. 379)

Home Connection Children pretend that they are Clerks in a store and ask someone at home to be the Customer. The Customer pretends to buy several items (groceries or other things). Children practice counting out the change for each item. If possible, they go to a store, buy something, and get change.

Making Change

Home Link 10.6

Family Note

In today's lesson, your child made change by counting up. When counting out change, encourage your child to begin with the cost of the item and count up to the amount of money that the customer has given to the clerk. For the example listed in the table below, your child could do the following:

1. Say, "89 cents"—the price of the item.

2. Put a penny on the table and say, "90 cents."

3. Put a dime on the table and say, "$1.00."

4. Count the coins on the table. 1¢ + 10¢ = 11¢. The change is 11¢.

Please return this Home Link to school tomorrow.

Materials ☐ coins and bills (You can make bills out of paper.)

☐ items with prices marked

Practice making change with someone at home. Pretend you are the Clerk at a store and the other person is a Customer. The Customer buys one of the items and pays with a bill. You count out the change.

Record some purchases here.

Item	Price	Amount Used to Pay	Change
can of black beans	$0.89	$1.00	$0.11

If possible, go to the store with someone. Buy something and get change. Count the change. Is it correct?

✦ *Math Masters, p. 379*

◆ **ENRICHMENT** **Using Money in Literature**

SMALL-GROUP ACTIVITY   5–15 min

Literature Link Read the following books to the children, or have children read the books themselves.

Pigs Will Be Pigs: Fun with Math and Money

Summary: The Pig family searches its home for enough money to buy dinner at its favorite restaurant, the Enchanted Enchilada. Questions at the end of the book involve how much money the Pigs found, spent, and had left. Children are encouraged to choose other items on the menu that cost the same amount of money.

Alexander, Who Used to Be Rich Last Sunday

Summary: Alexander receives a dollar from his grandparents on Sunday. His money soon disappears for a variety of reasons, such as paying a ten-cent fine for using bad language. By accounting for his expenses, children must determine whether Alexander has lost all his money.

◆ **RETEACHING** **Finding Differences between Pairs of Numbers on the Number Grid**

INDEPENDENT ACTIVITY   5–15 min

If children are having difficulty using a counting-up procedure to count out change, they may benefit from using a similar procedure to find differences between pairs of numbers on the Class Number Grid Poster.

Pose such problems as the following: *Start at 30. How many spaces on the number grid is it to 57?* Sample response: I put my finger on 30. I moved one row down, to 40. That's 10 spaces. Then I moved down one more row to 50. That's 10 more, so I've moved 20 spaces. Then I moved one space at a time and counted, until I got to 57—that's 21, 22, 23, 24, 25, 26, 27. So it is 27 spaces from 30 to 57.

Class Number Grid

1	2	3	4	5	6	7	8	9	10
11	12	13	14	15	16	17	18	19	20
21	22	23	24	25	26	27	28	29	30
31	32	33	34	35	36	37	38	39	40
41	42	43	44	45	46	47	48	49	50
51	52	53	54	55	56	57	58	59	60
61	62	63	64	65	66	67	68	69	70
71	72	73	74	75	76	77	78	79	80
81	82	83	84	85	86	87	88	89	90
91	92	93	94	95	96	97	98	99	100
101	102	103	104	105	106	107	108	109	110

Count: 10, 20, 21, 22, 23, 24, 25, 26, 27

10.7

EXPLORATIONS

Exploring Area, Polygons, and Geoboard Fractions

Lesson 10.7 (N.ME.02.18)

Part 1, Exploration C (teacher involvement): Instead of using geo-boards, give students 6 strips (11" x 2"). Direct students to fold strips so they have one of each of the following: halves, fourths, eighths, thirds, sixths, & twelfths. Label each fractional section correctly; trace each folded line.

OBJECTIVES To explore finding areas of irregular shapes; to make polygons with trapezoids; and to form fractions on a geoboard.

materials

1 Teaching the Lesson

Exploration A: Children trace their hands and feet on centimeter grid paper, and determine the area of their handprints and footprints. [Measurement and Reference Frames; Geometry]

Exploration B: Children build polygons and other shapes with trapezoids and use Pattern-Block Templates to record their work. [Geometry]

Exploration C: Children divide shapes made on a geoboard into fractional parts. [Measurement and Reference Frames; Geometry]

- ☐ Teaching Master (*Math Masters,* p. 172; optional)
- ☐ Home Link 10.6
- ☐ slate

Exploration A: Per partnership:
- ☐ *Math Journal 2,* pp. 257 and 258
- ☐ Teaching Master (*Math Masters,* p. 173)

Exploration B: Per small group:
- ☐ *Math Journal 2,* p. 259
- ☐ Teaching Master (*Math Masters,* p. 174)
- ☐ trapezoid pattern blocks; Pattern-Block Template
- ☐ triangle and rhombus blocks (optional)

Exploration C: Per partnership:
- ☐ *Math Journal 2,* p. 260
- ☐ Teaching Master (*Math Masters,* p. 175)
- ☐ geoboard; rubber bands

***See* Advance Preparation**

2 Ongoing Learning & Practice

Children practice entering money amounts and finding totals using a calculator by playing *Pick-a-Coin.* [Measurement and Reference Frames; Operations and Computation]

Children practice and maintain skills through Math Boxes and Home Link activities.

- ☐ *Math Journal 2,* pp. 246, 247, and 261
- ☐ Teaching Master (*Math Masters,* p. 168)
- ☐ Home Link Master (*Math Masters,* p. 380)
- ☐ calculator
- ☐ 1 six-sided die per group

3 Options for Individualizing

Extra Practice Children review 2-dimensional shapes by making them with parts of their bodies. [Geometry]

- ☐ *Minute Math*®, p. 56

Additional Information

Advance Preparation The Math Message problems are also provided on *Math Masters,* page 172. If you want to use the Teaching Master, make 1 copy for every 4 children. Cut the copies apart and place them near the Math Message. Change the directions to: *Take a slip of paper. Complete the problems.*

Have children's socks on hand for Exploration A.

Getting Started

Mental Math and Reflexes

Write sets of numbers on the board. Volunteers read the numbers aloud. Have children record the median of each set on their slates. *Suggestions:*

- 349, 487, 204, 981, 500 487
- 2,581; 2,005; 3,096; 8,888; 5,210 3,096

Math Message

Count squares to find the area of each shaded figure.

1. __ square centimeters 7

2. __ sq cm 7

Home Link 10.6 Follow-Up

Ask children to share some of the making change problems that they made up and solved.

NOTE: Point out that there are two other ways to write *square centimeter: sq cm* and *cm²*. Do not expect children to use the cm² notation, but be sure to expose them to it.

My Handprint and Footprint Areas

Work with a partner.

1. Trace your partner's hand onto his or her journal page 257. When your hand is traced, keep your fingers close together.

2. Count the number of whole square centimeters inside your handprint.

   • If more than half of a square centimeter is inside your handprint, count the whole square.

   • If less than half of a square centimeter is inside your handprint, do not count the square.

3. Record the area of your handprint at the bottom of that page.

4. Trace your partner's foot onto his or her journal page 258. (Keep your sock on your foot.)

5. Count to find the area of your footprint. Record the area of your footprint at the bottom of that page.

6. Exchange journals and check each other's counts. Count again if you don't agree with your partner.

Follow-Up

Work in a small group. Compare your hand to other group members'. Then compare your foot to others'. Predict the following:

   • Whose hand areas are about the same? Whose are larger? Smaller?

   • Whose foot areas are about the same? Larger? Smaller?

Compare your predictions to the areas you recorded.

Math Masters, p. 173

TEACHING MASTER

---

1 Teaching the Lesson

◆ Math Message Follow-Up
(*Math Masters*, p. 172)

WHOLE-CLASS DISCUSSION

Review answers. Ask children to explain how they determined the area for Problem 2. Some children may remember from Unit 9 that if more than $\frac{1}{2}$ of a square centimeter is shaded, it is counted as 1 square centimeter; if less than $\frac{1}{2}$ of a square centimeter is shaded, it is ignored. Children continue to use this rule in Exploration A.

ONGOING ASSESSMENT

Collect the Math Message slips to assess children's progress with counting squares to find area. Exploration A provides children with additional practice, but it will be more difficult to quickly assess children's skill level there.

◆ Exploration A: Tracing Areas of Handprints and Footprints
(*Math Journal 2*, pp. 257 and 258; *Math Masters*, p. 173)

PARTNER ACTIVITY

Partners help each other carefully trace one hand and one foot (that is wearing a sock) on the centimeter grid pages. For the hand tracings, children should keep their fingers close together. They count all the whole square centimeters. If more than $\frac{1}{2}$ of a square centimeter is inside a tracing, it is counted as 1 square centimeter; less than $\frac{1}{2}$ of a square centimeter is ignored. Children trade papers and check each other's counts.

As a follow-up, children can compare their actual hand and feet sizes to those of other class members. As they make these visual comparisons, ask them to predict which areas are about the same and which are larger or smaller. If there is time, children can try to predict areas of other small objects.

 Adjusting the Activity Challenge children to find the median values for all of the areas of the hands in the class. Repeat for all of the areas of the feet in the class.

◆ Exploration B: Making Pattern-Block Worktables
(*Math Journal 2*, p. 259; *Math Masters*, p. 174)

SMALL-GROUP ACTIVITY

Children pretend that the trapezoid pattern blocks are small worktables and that you, their teacher, want to make larger tables by fitting the small trapezoid tables together. Children first make some polygons and then try to make as many different-shape and different-size tables as possible.

Using Pattern-Block Templates, children record their "worktable" shapes on journal page 259. Group members compare reports to try to find as many different worktable sizes and shapes as possible.

Children use trapezoids to build multiple shapes.

 Adjusting the Activity Challenge children to use small triangle or rhombus pattern blocks to make even more worktables.

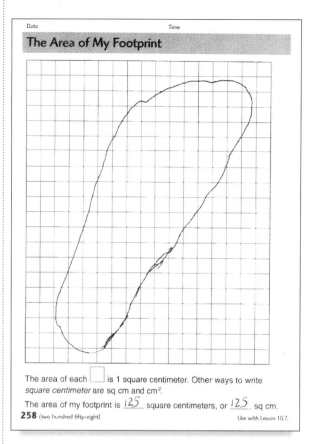

The Area of My Footprint

The area of each ☐ is 1 square centimeter. Other ways to write *square centimeter* are sq cm and cm².

The area of my footprint is _125_ square centimeters, or _125_ sq cm.

258 (two hundred fifty-eight)   Use with Lesson 10.7.

Children find their foot areas by counting whole square units.

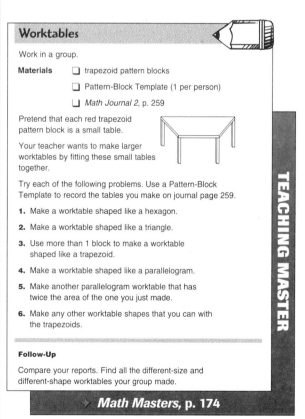

Worktables

Work in a group.

Materials   ☐ trapezoid pattern blocks
                ☐ Pattern-Block Template (1 per person)
                ☐ *Math Journal 2*, p. 259

Pretend that each red trapezoid pattern block is a small table.

Your teacher wants to make larger worktables by fitting these small tables together.

Try each of the following problems. Use a Pattern-Block Template to record the tables you make on journal page 259.

1. Make a worktable shaped like a hexagon.
2. Make a worktable shaped like a triangle.
3. Use more than 1 block to make a worktable shaped like a trapezoid.
4. Make a worktable shaped like a parallelogram.
5. Make another parallelogram worktable that has twice the area of the one you just made.
6. Make any other worktable shapes that you can with the trapezoids.

Follow-Up

Compare your reports. Find all the different-size and different-shape worktables your group made.

Math Masters, p. 174

TEACHING MASTER

Geoboard Fractions

Materials ☐ geoboard ☐ rubber bands
☐ *Math Journal 2*, p. 260

Work with a partner.

1. One partner makes a shape on the geoboard with one rubber band.

2. The other partner tries to divide the shape into equal parts using other rubber bands. The equal parts should be the same size and shape.

3. Take turns until each partner has made 3 shapes.

4. Record some of the shapes you divided on journal page 260. Show the equal parts.

5. Record some shapes on the journal page you could not divide into equal parts.

Work in a group.

6. Check one another's work.

7. Discuss these questions:

   • Are shapes that can be divided equally special in some way?

   • What about the shapes that cannot be divided equally?

Example

◆ Math Masters, p. 175

◆ Exploration C: Forming Fractions on the Geoboard
(*Math Journal 2,* p. 260; *Math Masters,* p. 175)

PARTNER ACTIVITY

Partners take turns. After one partner forms a shape on the geoboard with one rubber band, the other partner tries to divide the shape into 2 (or 3 or more) equal parts using other rubber bands.

Children record results on journal page 260. The geoboard dot paper on the journal page is for a 7 × 7 geoboard. If your children are working with a 5 × 5 geoboard, have them outline a 5 × 5 dot array.

Children divide shapes into fractional parts on the geoboards.

> **Adjusting the Activity** Prepare several geoboard shapes ahead of time. Make most of the shapes so that they can be divided into equal parts, but include a few that can't. Have partners try to divide your shapes into equal parts before they make their own.

2 Ongoing Learning & Practice

◆ Playing *Pick-a-Coin*
(*Math Journal 2,* pp. 246 and 247; *Math Masters,* p. 168)

SMALL-GROUP ACTIVITY

Children practice addition and calculator skills by playing *Pick-a-Coin*. For detailed instructions, see Lesson 10.3.

◆ Math Boxes 10.7 (*Math Journal 2*, p. 261)

INDEPENDENT ACTIVITY

Mixed Review This journal page provides opportunities for cumulative review or assessment of concepts and skills.

◆ Home Link 10.7 (*Math Masters*, p. 380)

Home Connection Children count squares to find the areas of figures.

 Options for Individualizing

◆ EXTRA PRACTICE Minute Math

SMALL-GROUP ACTIVITY   **5–15 min**

To offer children more experience with identifying 2-dimensional shapes, see the following page in *Minute Math*:

Geometry: p. 56

PLANNING AHEAD

If you want to use a demonstration Place-Value Book in Lesson 10.9, use *Math Masters*, pages 184–190. You can staple the pages of your book together or, to allow for flipping of the pages, bind them with an inexpensive spiral binding. (Most quick-copy stores can provide this service.) You can also glue the digit pages to the pages of a spiral notebook.

For children's Place-Value Books, you may want children to make sturdy back covers out of poster board, cardboard, or file-folder stock. If so, you will need to prepare these covers before beginning the lesson. Each child will also need 5 paper clips to hold pages back when numbers are displayed.

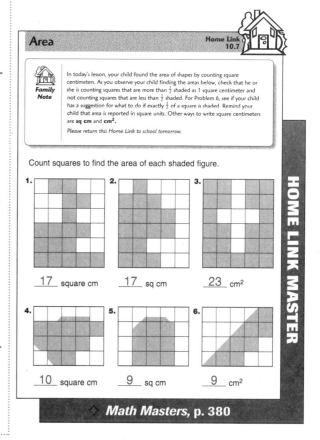

Math Boxes 10.7

1. Fill in the blanks to estimate the total cost. **Sample answers:**

   $2.43 + $0.39 is about

   $2.40 + $0.40 = $2.80

   $0.88 + $0.67 is about

   $0.90 + $0.70 = $1.60

2. I have a 5-dollar bill. I spend $4.38. How much change do I get?

   $0.62

3. Write as dollars and cents.

   eight dollars and forty-three cents: $8.43

   fifteen dollars and 6 cents: $15.06

   fifty dollars and seventeen cents: $50.17

4. Use a straightedge. Draw a rectangle. Measure the sides to the nearest inch.
   Sample answers:
   about 2 in.
   about 1 in.
   about 2 in.
   about 1 in.

3. A cube is the ONE. What number is shown by the blocks?

   347

6. Color $\frac{3}{4}$ of the circle.

   What fraction of the circle is not colored? $\frac{1}{4}$

◆ *Math Journal 2*, p. 261

Area Home Link 10.7

Family Note In today's lesson, your child found the area of shapes by counting square centimeters. As you observe your child finding the areas below, check that he or she is counting squares that are more than $\frac{1}{2}$ shaded as 1 square centimeter and not counting squares that are less than $\frac{1}{2}$ shaded. For Problem 6, see if your child has a suggestion for what to do if exactly $\frac{1}{2}$ of a square is shaded. Remind your child that area is reported in square units. Other ways to write square centimeters are **sq cm** and **cm²**.

Please return this Home Link to school tomorrow.

Count squares to find the area of each shaded figure.

1. _17_ square cm

2. _17_ sq cm

3. _23_ cm²

4. _10_ square cm

5. _9_ sq cm

6. _9_ cm²

◆ *Math Masters*, p. 380

10.8

Place Value

OBJECTIVES To develop place-value concepts; and to connect place value in money with place value in base-10 blocks.

Lesson 10.8 (N.ME.02.02)
Part 1, "Representing 3- & 4-digit #s with Base-10 Blocks": Include writing in words the # represented by the base-10-blocks on their boards or in their math log/paper and pencil, eg. 352, three hundred fifty-two.

materials

1 Teaching the Lesson

Children identify and represent place value and numbers using base-10 blocks. They compare the use of base-10 blocks to the use of money to represent place value. [Numeration; Measurement and Reference Frames]

Children practice place-value exchanges by playing the *Money Exchange Game.* [Numeration]

☐ *Math Journal 2*, pp. 262 and 263
☐ Home Link 10.7
☐ Teaching Master (*Math Masters*, p. 176; optional)
☐ Teaching Master transparency (*Math Masters*, p. 176; optional)
☐ slate
☐ base-10 blocks per class: 1 big cube, 9 flats, 9 longs, 9 cubes
☐ 24 pennies, 39 dimes, thirty-nine $1 bills, and one $10 bill
☐ 1 six-sided die per group
☐ 1 ten- or twelve-sided die per group

***See* Advance Preparation**

2 Ongoing Learning & Practice

Children practice and maintain skills through Math Boxes and Home Link activities.

☐ *Math Journal 2*, p. 264
☐ Home Link Master (*Math Masters*, p. 381)

3 Options for Individualizing

Extra Practice Children build base-10 structures and identify their values as numbers. [Numeration]

☐ base-10 blocks
☐ quarter-sheets of paper

Additional Information

Advance Preparation For the Math Message, label and display a centimeter cube, a long, a flat, and a big cube. Children can refer to the base-10 blocks as they complete the problems.

For the activity about 3- and 4-digit numbers in Part 1, you may want to make an overhead transparency of *Math Masters*, page 176.

Vocabulary • flat • long • cube • place value • big cube

Getting Started

Mental Math and Reflexes

Pose number stories involving estimation.
Suggestions:

About how much change should I get?

- I bought a bag of potato chips for $2.39. I gave the cashier $3.00. About 60¢

- I bought a 6-pack of soda for $1.99. I gave the cashier a $5 bill. About $3.00

- I bought a bag of grapes for $3.23. I gave the cashier a $10 bill. About $6.80, or about $7.00

Math Message

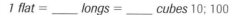

1 *long* = ____ cubes 10

1 *flat* = ____ longs = ____ cubes 10; 100

1 *big cube* = ____ flats = ____ longs = ____ cubes 10; 100; 1,000

Home Link 10.7 Follow-Up

Review answers.

---

1 Teaching the Lesson

◆ Math Message Follow-Up

WHOLE-CLASS DISCUSSION

Quickly review Math Message responses. Discuss relationships among base-10 blocks: each is 10 times larger than the next smaller one, and $\frac{1}{10}$ the size of the next larger one.

◆ Representing 3- and 4-Digit Numbers with Base-10 Blocks (*Math Masters,* p. 176)

WHOLE-CLASS ACTIVITY

Ask three volunteers to form a line at the front of the room. The first child on the left, as viewed by the class, holds up 3 **flats** for all to see, the one in the middle holds up 5 **longs,** and the one on the right, 2 cubes. Tell children to assume that the **cube** is ONE. What is the **place value** of each digit? 3 hundreds, 5 tens, and 2 ones Have children write the number represented by these base-10 blocks on their slates. They should also say the number aloud. 352

Choose a fourth child to stand first in line on the left and hold up a **big cube.** Children write the new number and say it aloud. 1,352 Discuss the change that results from adding the big cube to the collection. The number increases by 1,000.

NOTE: There are many names for base-10 blocks. The following names are used in *Everyday Mathematics: cube* (centimeter cube) for the smallest cube, *long* for the strip of 10 cm cubes, *flat* for the block consisting of 100 cm cubes, and *big cube* for the cube consisting of 1,000 cm cubes. This leaves open the possibility of using the cube, the long, or the flat as the unit (ONE) for decimal and fraction work.

| Place-Value Chart | | | | |
Ten-Thousands	Thousands	Hundreds	Tens	Ones

TEACHING MASTER

◇ *Math Masters,* p. 176

Money Exchange Game

Materials
- ☐ 1 six-sided die
- ☐ 1 ten- or twelve-sided die
- ☐ 24 pennies, 39 dimes, thirty-nine $1 bills, and one $10 bill per player

Players   2 or 3

Directions

1. Each player puts 12 pennies, 12 dimes, twelve $1 bills, and one $10 bill in the bank.

2. Players take turns. Players use a six-sided die to represent pennies. Players use a ten- or twelve-sided die to represent dimes.

3. Each player
   - rolls the dice.
   - takes from the bank the number of pennies and dimes shown on the faces of the dice.
   - puts the coins in the correct columns on his or her Place-Value Mat on journal page 263.

4. Whenever possible, a player replaces 10 coins or bills of a lower denomination with a coin or bill of the next higher denomination.

5. The first player to trade for a $10 bill wins.

If there is a time limit, the winner is the player with the largest number on the mat when time is up.

◆ *Math Journal 2, p. 262*

Place-Value Mat

ⓟ pennies 1s

Ⓓ dimes 10s

$1 dollars 100s

$10 1,000s

◆ *Math Journal 2, p. 263*

Repeat the activity with other 3- and 4-digit numbers less than 2,000. Then reverse the procedure: Write a 3- or 4-digit number on the board and ask children in the line to represent the number with base-10 blocks. Repeat with several other numbers as needed.

Adjusting the Activity If children are having difficulty recording numbers on their slates, have them write the numbers on a place-value chart (*Math Masters,* page 176). It may also be helpful if you write numbers on an overhead transparency of the place-value chart.

To challenge children, ask the following questions:
- What is the smallest 3-digit number? 100
- What is the largest 3-digit number? 999
- What are the largest and smallest 4-digit numbers? 9,999; 1,000

◆ Reviewing the Role of 0 as a Placeholder

WHOLE-CLASS ACTIVITY

Continue the routines from the previous activity, but have one or more children in the line empty-handed to represent the digit 0 in those places. Children write the numbers on their slates with zeros in the appropriate places.

Reverse the procedure: Write 3- or 4-digit numbers containing one or more zeros on the board and ask children to represent those numbers with base-10 blocks.

◆ Comparing Place Value with Base-10 Blocks and Money

WHOLE-CLASS DISCUSSION

Point out the similarities between base-10 blocks and money, comparing cubes and pennies, longs and dimes, flats and dollars, and so on. Discuss how both groups of materials make trades using a 10-for-1 rule, how both groups represent larger numbers the same way, and how both groups have the ability to represent numbers in more than one way. Also discuss differences between base-10 blocks and money: Relationships among base-10 blocks are reflected in the size of the blocks, but relationships among denominations of coins and bills are not reflected in size; money is used inside and outside of school, but base-10 blocks are used primarily just at school.

◆ Playing the *Money Exchange Game*
(*Math Journal 2*, pp. 262 and 263)

SMALL-GROUP ACTIVITY

Explain the rules of the *Money Exchange Game*. Then divide the class into groups of 2 or 3 players and have children play a practice game.

2 Ongoing Learning & Practice

◆ Math Boxes 10.8 (*Math Journal 2*, p. 264)

INDEPENDENT ACTIVITY

Mixed Review This journal page provides opportunities for cumulative review or assessment of concepts and skills.

◆ Home Link 10.8 (*Math Masters*, p. 381)

Home Connection Children identify digits in specified places in 3- and 4-digit numbers, read the numbers to someone at home, and write 3- and 4-digit numbers represented by sets of base-10 blocks.

3 Options for Individualizing

◆ EXTRA PRACTICE Building Base-10 Structures

SMALL-GROUP ACTIVITY 5–15 min

Each child in the group builds a base-10 structure with flats, longs, and cubes. The cube is the ONE. Children work together to count the "value" of each structure and record it on a quarter-sheet of paper. Then children arrange the sheets in order from least to greatest value.

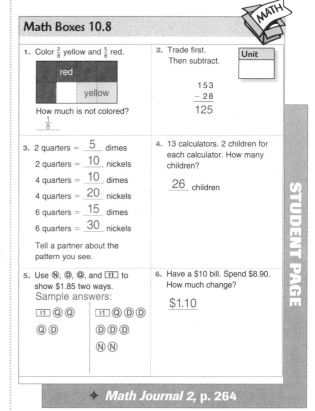

Math Boxes 10.8

1. Color $\frac{2}{8}$ yellow and $\frac{5}{8}$ red.

red

yellow

How much is not colored? $\frac{1}{8}$

2. Trade first. Then subtract.

Unit

$$\begin{array}{r} 153 \\ -\ 28 \\ \hline 125 \end{array}$$

3. 2 quarters = 5 dimes
2 quarters = 10 nickels
4 quarters = 10 dimes
4 quarters = 20 nickels
6 quarters = 15 dimes
6 quarters = 30 nickels

Tell a partner about the pattern you see.

4. 13 calculators. 2 children for each calculator. How many children?

26 children

5. Use Ⓝ, Ⓓ, Ⓠ, and $1 to show $1.85 two ways.
Sample answers:

$1 Ⓠ Ⓠ $1 Ⓠ Ⓓ Ⓓ
Ⓠ Ⓓ   Ⓓ Ⓓ Ⓓ
             Ⓝ Ⓝ

6. Have a $10 bill. Spend $8.90. How much change?

$1.10

◆ *Math Journal 2, p. 264*

STUDENT PAGE

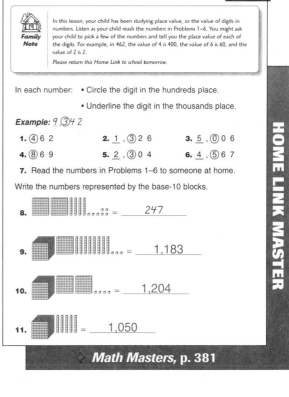

Place Value

Home Link 10.8

Family Note In this lesson, your child has been studying place value, or the value of digits in numbers. Listen as your child reads the numbers in Problems 1–6. You might ask your child to pick a few of the numbers and tell you the place value of each of the digits. For example, in 462, the value of 4 is 400, the value of 6 is 60, and the value of 2 is 2.

Please return this Home Link to school tomorrow.

In each number: • Circle the digit in the hundreds place.
• Underline the digit in the thousands place.

Example: 9 ③ 4 2

1. ④ 6 2   2. 1 , ③ 2 6   3. 5 , ⓪ 0 6
4. ⑧ 6 9   5. 2 , ③ 0 4   6. 4 , ⑤ 6 7

7. Read the numbers in Problems 1–6 to someone at home.

Write the numbers represented by the base-10 blocks.

8. = 247

9. = 1,183

10. = 1,204

11. = 1,050

◆ *Math Masters, p. 381*

HOME LINK MASTER

10.9

Place-Value Tools

OBJECTIVE To develop place-value concepts by using place-value tools that display numbers.

Lesson 10.9 (N.ME.02.02)
Part 1, " Displaying & Reading #s w/ Place-Value Tools": Extend to include writing in words some of the 3-& 4-digit #s displayed on their white boards. Ask, "How much until the next ten/hundred/thousand?" for each number students display.

summaries

materials

1 Teaching the Lesson

Children make a place-value tool and use that tool to read and display 3- and 4-digit numbers. [Numeration]

- ☐ Teaching Masters (*Math Masters*, pp. 177–180, or 181 and 182, or 181 and 183; and pp. 184–190, optional)
- ☐ Home Link 10.8
- ☐ scissors
- ☐ 5 paper clips; stapler; box for plastic wrap or similar box (optional)
- ☐ calculator (optional)

See **Advance Preparation**

2 Ongoing Learning & Practice

Children count money amounts represented by pictures of bills. [Numeration; Measurement and Reference Frames]

Children practice and maintain skills through Math Boxes and Home Link activities.

- ☐ *Math Journal 2*, pp. 265 and 266
- ☐ Home Link Master (*Math Masters*, p. 382)

3 Options for Individualizing

Extra Practice Children use place-value routines and tools to further develop place-value concepts. [Numeration]

- ☐ place-value tools
- ☐ overhead base-10 blocks (optional)

Additional Information

Advance Preparation For the activities involving the place-value tools in Part 1, you may want to make a larger version of the tool for demonstration purposes. For a demonstration Place-Value Book, use *Math Masters,* pages 184–190. You can staple the pages of your book together or, to allow for flipping of the pages, bind them with an inexpensive spiral binding. You can also glue the digit pages to the pages of a spiral notebook.

For the box card holder and the paper card holder, 5 copies of *Math Masters,* page 181 are needed to show repeated digits within a number.

Vocabulary • ones, 1s • tens, 10s • hundreds, 100s • thousands, 1,000s • ten-thousands, 10,000s

Getting Started

Mental Math and Reflexes

For each problem, ask: *About how much change should I get?*

- I bought doughnuts for $3.59. I gave the cashier $4.00. About 40¢
- I bought bananas for $0.48. I gave the cashier $5.00. About $4.50
- I bought oranges for $1.32. I gave the cashier a $10 bill. About $8.70 or $9.00

Math Message

Write the smallest and largest 4-digit numbers that use the digits 1, 6, 8, and 9. 1,689; 9,861

Home Link 10.8 Follow-Up

Review answers.

---

1 Teaching the Lesson

◆ Math Message Follow-Up

WHOLE-CLASS DISCUSSION

Quickly review responses and discuss as needed.

◆ Making a Place-Value Tool
(*Math Masters,* pp. 177–190)

WHOLE-CLASS ACTIVITY

Have children use the following directions to make one of the three place-value tools. Be sure to have a sample of the completed tool available for children to imitate.

Place-Value Book *Math Masters,* pp. 177–180

1. Cut out the cover and 12 pages of the Place-Value Book from *Math Masters,* pages 177–180. Cut along the outside dashed lines.

2. Cut along the dashed lines on pages 1–11. Cut only up to the solid line to separate the digits on each page.

3. Assemble the book with the cover on top, followed by page 1 (the page of blanks), pages 2–11 (the pages for the digits 0, 1, 2, 3, 4, 5, 6, 7, 8, 9), and page 12 (the place-value page).

4. Staple the assembled book. (Help children, if needed.)

5. Fold the digits on pages 1–11 back and forth along the solid line to produce a crease.

6. Write your tool-kit number on the cover.

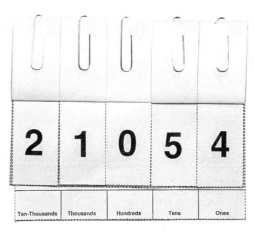

A Place-Value Book

NOTE: A demonstration Place-Value Book can be made from *Math Masters,* pages 184–190.

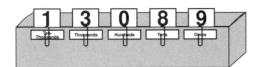

A box card holder

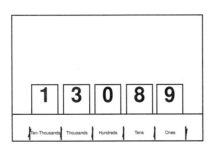

A paper card holder

Box Card Holder *Math Masters,* pp. 181 and 182

1. Remove the metal cutting strip from a box for plastic wrap or a similar box. (You may want to carry out this step yourself or have a parent help.)

2. Fold the lid into the box so that digit cards will fit into the space between the lid and the box. This also allows the cards to stand up vertically.

3. Cut out the digit cards from 5 copies of *Math Masters,* page 181.

4. Put five digit cards side by side into the box. Be sure the cards are evenly spaced.

5. Attach place-value labels (ones, tens, hundreds, thousands, and ten-thousands) with paper clips onto the front of the box under the cards. These labels are found on *Math Masters,* page 182.

Paper Card Holder *Math Masters,* pp. 181 and 183

1. Cut along the dashed line and then fold along the dotted line on *Math Masters,* page 183.

2. Staple on the heavy lines between the place values to make small pockets to hold the digit cards.

3. Cut out the digit cards from 5 copies of *Math Masters,* page 181 and place one card in each pocket.

◆ Establishing a Routine for Place-Value Tools

WHOLE-CLASS DISCUSSION

Discuss the care and storage of the place-value tools. The books are small enough to fit inside the tool kits, but they should be put away carefully to avoid unnecessary page bending. The other tools are bulkier and will not fit in the tool kits.

The routine for using the place-value tools can be similar to that for slates. You can use signals such as Listen, Think, Fix digits, and Show.

◆ Displaying Counts with Place-Value Tools

WHOLE-CLASS ACTIVITY

Review place-value names (**ones or 1s; tens or 10s; hundreds or 100s; thousands or 1,000s; and ten-thousands or 10,000s**), calling children's attention to the labels on their place-value tools. Discuss the relationships between the values of the places: 1 ten is 10 ones (or 1 is $\frac{1}{10}$ of 10), 1 hundred is 10 tens (or 10 is $\frac{1}{10}$ of 100), and so on. This "ten-for-one" relationship is fundamental to the base-ten place-value system.

Direct children to display the digit zero in the ones and the tens place. You and children count aloud by tens while changing the digits in the tens place. When you reach 90, ask someone to tell which digits must be changed when 10 more is added. Children show this while you check that their displays read 100.

Continue counting aloud by 100s while changing digits in the hundreds place until you reach 900. Follow the same procedure as for the tens while children show 1,000.

Repeat, counting by thousands to 10,000.

 Adjusting the Activity If children have trouble with these transitions, let them count using their calculators. For example, enter 100 ⊕ ⊜ ⊜ … while matching the calculator display to the place-value tool display.

NOTE: Begin the activity with numbers of whatever size you think will work in your class. Tens are a good place to start, but you may want to start with ones or hundreds. Demonstrate the routines while children follow along.

Once children have learned to display numbers with their place-value tools, you may find it convenient to write numbers in a place-value chart on the board instead of displaying them with your demonstration tool. Children, however, should continue to use their own place-value tools to display numbers.

◆ Displaying and Reading Numbers with Place-Value Tools

WHOLE-CLASS ACTIVITY

Call out a 3-digit number. Children display the number on their place-value tools. *Which digit shows ones? Tens? Hundreds?* Repeat the activity with other 3- and 4-digit numbers. Then reverse the procedure: Display 3- and 4-digit numbers with your place-value tool, and have children say the numbers aloud.

◆ Practicing Displaying and Reading Numbers with Place-Value Tools

PARTNER ACTIVITY

Partners take turns. One partner displays a number with a place-value tool; the other reads the number. Then they reverse the procedure. One partner calls out a number; the other displays it with the tool.

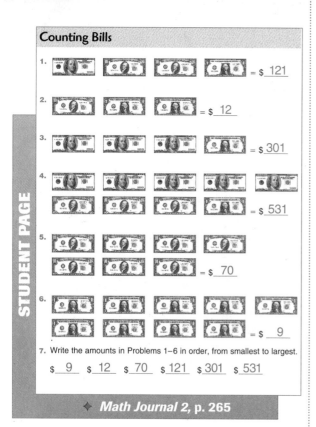

Counting Bills

1. = $ 121

2. = $ 12

3. = $ 301

4. = $ 531

5. = $ 70

6. = $ 9

7. Write the amounts in Problems 1–6 in order, from smallest to largest.

$ 9 $ 12 $ 70 $ 121 $ 301 $ 531

Math Journal 2, p. 265

◆ Counting $100, $10, and $1 Bills
(*Math Journal 2,* p. 265)

INDEPENDENT ACTIVITY

Children count money amounts represented by pictures of bills.

◆ Math Boxes 10.9 (*Math Journal 2,* p. 266)

INDEPENDENT ACTIVITY

Mixed Review This journal page provides opportunities for cumulative review or assessment of concepts and skills.

◆ Home Link 10.9 (*Math Masters,* p. 382)

Home Connection Children complete a table in which numbers are increased by 10, 100, and 1,000 and describe any patterns they see in the rows of the table.

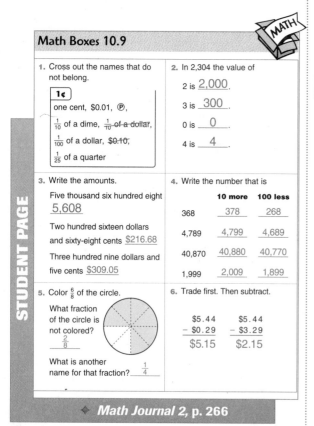

Math Boxes 10.9

1. Cross out the names that do not belong.

   1¢

   one cent, $0.01, ℗,

   $\frac{1}{10}$ of a dime, ~~$\frac{1}{10}$ of a dollar,~~

   $\frac{1}{100}$ of a dollar, ~~$0.10,~~

   $\frac{1}{25}$ of a quarter

2. In 2,304 the value of

   2 is 2,000.

   3 is 300.

   0 is 0.

   4 is 4.

3. Write the amounts.

   Five thousand six hundred eight
   5,608

   Two hundred sixteen dollars and sixty-eight cents $216.68

   Three hundred nine dollars and five cents $309.05

4. Write the number that is

	10 more	100 less
368	378	268
4,789	4,799	4,689
40,870	40,880	40,770
1,999	2,009	1,899

5. Color $\frac{6}{8}$ of the circle.

   What fraction of the circle is not colored?
   $\frac{2}{8}$

   What is another name for that fraction? $\frac{1}{4}$

6. Trade first. Then subtract.

   $$\begin{array}{r} \$5.44 \\ - \$0.29 \\ \hline \$5.15 \end{array} \qquad \begin{array}{r} \$5.44 \\ - \$3.29 \\ \hline \$2.15 \end{array}$$

Math Journal 2, p. 266

◆ EXTRA PRACTICE Practicing Routines with Place-Value Tools

SMALL-GROUP ACTIVITY   **5–15 min**

The following are suggestions for activities that can be done with place-value tools. Keep these routines brief and maintain a brisk pace. Revisit the routines over the next few weeks and throughout the year. (In future lessons, the Mental Math and Reflexes exercises will make use of place-value tools.)

Counting: Children count in unison as they change the digits in their place-value tools. They count by 1s starting at 1; by 10s starting at 10; and so on.

Counting through transitions: Pay special attention to transitions. *Start at 7 and count to 14. What happens when you go from 9 to 10? Start at 97 and count to 105. What happens when you go from 99 to 100?* Repeat the process for the transition from 999 to 1,000, and so on.

Counting with base-10 blocks: Tell children that the cube is ONE. Repeat the counting exercises above, but illustrate them with blocks on the overhead projector.

Numbers for base-10 block displays: Display a group of blocks on the overhead (for example, 2 flats, 3 longs, and 5 cubes). Ask children to use their place-value tools to show the corresponding number. 235

Numbers for simple pictures of base-10 blocks: Draw simple pictures of base-10 blocks and have children show the number with their place-value tools.

Dictation: Dictate a number or have a child dictate one. Children display the number with their place-value tools. Include numbers containing zeros, such as 1,508; 10,905; and 406.

Reading numbers: One partner displays a number with a place-value tool; the other partner reads it.

Putting digits in specified places: Ask children to display digits in places you specify and to read the resulting number. For example, ask children to display 5 in the hundreds place, 3 in the tens place, 8 in the thousands place, and 4 in the ones place. Children display 8,534 and read *eight thousand five hundred thirty-four.* Sometimes specify only one place and digit. For example, *Make a number with 5 in the tens place.* Then discuss the various possible answers.

10 more (less), 100 more (less): Give children a number to display. Then ask them to display and read the number that is 1 more (less), 10 more (less), 100 more (less), and so on.

Which is more (less)? Divide the class into partnerships. Dictate pairs of numbers. One partner displays one number, the other partner the other number. Partners determine which number is more (less).

Trading rules: Review the relationships between adjacent places: 1 ten is the same as 10 ones; 1 hundred is the same as 10 tens; 1,000 is the same as 10 hundreds; and so on. Similarly, 1 one is $\frac{1}{10}$ of 1 ten; 10 is $\frac{1}{10}$ of 1 hundred; 100 is $\frac{1}{10}$ of 1 thousand; and so on.

Counting by 10s, 100s, and 1,000s — Home Link 10.9

Family Note

In this lesson, your child used place value to count by 10s, 100s, and 1,000s. For Problems 1 and 2, listen carefully to find out if your child counts quickly and accurately. Help your child complete the table in Problem 3. If necessary, have your child use a calculator to find the answers. Ask your child to describe any patterns he or she sees in the completed table.

Please return this Home Link to school tomorrow.

1. Show someone at home how to count by 100s from 0 to 1,000. Record your counts.

0; 100; 200; 300; 400; 500; 600; 700; 800; 900; 1,000

2. Now count by 1,000s from 0 to 10,000. Record your counts.

0; 1,000; 2,000; 3,000; 4,000; 5,000; 6,000; 7,000; 8,000; 9,000; 10,000

3. Complete the table.

Number	10 More	100 More	1,000 More
32	42	132	1,032
146	156	246	1,146
309	319	409	1,309
1,468	1,478	1,568	2,468
10,037	10,047	10,137	11,037

◆ *Math Masters, p. 382*

NOTE: Consider placing a stick-on note on this page so that you can quickly refer to the list of place-value tool routines when you have a few spare minutes for a short activity.

10.10

Place-Value Notation for Ten-Thousands

OBJECTIVE To extend place-value concepts to ten-thousands.

Lesson 10.10 (N.ME.02.02, N.ME.02.05)
Part 1, J367: Extend to include one # from problems 7, 8, & 9 to be written in # words, eg. 1,800 = one thousand eight hundred.
Model each number in **expanded notation**.

summaries *materials*

1 Teaching the Lesson

Children count aloud by thousands and ten-thousands. They display and read 5-digit numbers, identify digits in specified places, and review the relationships among place values. [Numeration]

☐ *Math Journal 2,* p. 267
☐ Home Link 10.9
☐ place-value tool
☐ demonstration place-value tool (optional)

2 Ongoing Learning & Practice

Children practice place-value exchanges by playing the *Money Exchange Game.* [Numeration]

Children practice and maintain skills through Math Boxes and Home Link activities.

☐ *Math Journal 2,* pp. 262, 263, and 268
☐ Home Link Master (*Math Masters,* p. 383)
☐ 1 six-sided die
☐ 1 ten- or twelve-sided die
☐ 12 pennies, 12 dimes, twelve $1 bills, and one $10 bill

3 Options for Individualizing

Enrichment Children order 5-digit numbers. [Numeration]

Reteaching Children count through transitions on a calculator. [Numeration]

Extra Practice Children practice forming and comparing numbers by playing the *Digit Game.* [Numeration]

☐ *Math Journal 1,* p. 56
☐ Teaching Master (*Math Masters,* p. 191)
☐ calculator
☐ 4 each of the number cards 0–9 per partnership (from the Everything Math Deck, if available)

Additional Information

Vocabulary • **ten-thousands, 10,000s**

Getting Started

Mental Math and Reflexes

Say 3-digit and 4-digit numbers. Children display each number using their place-value tools. *Which digit shows ones? Tens? Hundreds? Thousands?*

Write 3- and 4-digit numbers on the board and have children say the numbers aloud.

Math Message

What is a digit? How many digits are there? Name them.

Home Link 10.9 Follow-Up

Review answers.

✦ Math Message Follow-Up

WHOLE-CLASS DISCUSSION

List the digits 0 to 9 on the board, and review the fact that any counting number can be written with these 10 digits. With the addition of a few more symbols, the digits can express many other numbers—0.50, $\frac{3}{4}$, $2\frac{1}{2}$, and -10, to name a few. Invite children to give examples of such numbers.

5-15-07

✦ Extending Place-Value Concepts to Ten-Thousands

WHOLE-CLASS ACTIVITY

Children work with their place-value tools as you demonstrate each step.

Start by displaying 1,000 with your place-value tool. Count aloud by 1,000s as you and children change the digits in the thousands place. When you reach 9,000, ask which digits must be changed when 1,000 more is added. The digit in the thousands place must change to 0, and the digit in the **ten-thousands** place must change to 1.

Next, have children count aloud by **10,000s** as they change the digits in the ten-thousands place. *When you count by 10,000s, what number comes after 90,000?* 100,000 *How do you write this number?*

Ask children to display the largest number they can with their place-value tools. 99,999 Ask them to read this number.

Say 5-digit numbers. Children show each number with their place-value tools. For each number, ask: *Which digit shows ones? Tens? Hundreds? Thousands? Ten-thousands?*

Display 4- and 5-digit numbers with your demonstration tool (or write them on the board). Ask children to read the numbers.

Place Value

1. Match names.

A.	5 ones	_B_	50
B.	5 tens	_C_	500
C.	5 hundreds	_E_	50,000
D.	5 thousands	_A_	5
E.	5 ten-thousands	_D_	5,000

Fill in the blanks. Write ones, tens, hundreds, thousands, or ten-thousands.

2. The 8 in 74,863 stands for 8 ___hundreds___.

3. The 6 in 35,926 stands for 6 ___ones___.

4. The 2 in 2,785 stands for 2 ___thousands___.

5. The 5 in 58,047 stands for 5 ___ten-thousands___.

6. The 0 in 13,409 stands for 0 ___tens___.

Continue.

7. 364; 365; 366; __367__ ; __368__ ; __369__

8. 1,796; 1,797; 1,798; __1,799__ ; __1,800__ ; __1,801__

9. 996; 997; 998; __999__ ; __1,000__ ; __1,001__

10. 1,996; 1,997; 1,998; __1,999__ ; __2,000__ ; __2,001__

11. 9,996; 9,997; 9,998; __9,999__ ; __10,000__ ; __10,001__

✦ *Math Journal 2,* p. 267

STUDENT PAGE

✦ Reviewing 0 as a Placeholder

WHOLE-CLASS DISCUSSION

Write 1,001 on the board and ask someone to read the number. *One thousand one* Ask:

• If a cent is ONE, how would you show 1,001 with the fewest number of bills and coins? *A $10 bill and a penny*

• If a cube is ONE, how would you show 1,001 with the fewest number of base-10 blocks? *A big cube and a cube*

• Why is it necessary to write zeros to show 1,001? Discuss what would happen if the zeros were not there.

Call out several 4- and 5-digit numbers containing zeros. Check children's work as they show the numbers with their place-value tools.

Display several such numbers with your demonstration tool (or write them on the board) and ask children to read the numbers.

✦ Reviewing Relationships among Place Values

WHOLE-CLASS DISCUSSION

Write 22,222 on the board. Ask children to give the value of each digit. *2 ones = 2; 2 tens = 20; 2 hundreds = 200; 2 thousands = 2,000; and 2 ten-thousands = 20,000*

Observe that 20 is ten times as much as 2; 200 is ten times as much as 20; 2,000 is ten times as much as 200; and so on. Similarly, 2 is one-tenth of 20; 20 is one-tenth of 200; 200 is one-tenth of 2,000; and so on.

Summary: Remind children that each place has a value ten times that of the place to its right and one-tenth of the value of the place to its left.

✦ Solving 4- and 5-Digit Place-Value Problems
(*Math Journal 2,* p. 267)

INDEPENDENT ACTIVITY

These problems involve matching equivalent names for numbers and finding the values of digits in numerals.

ONGOING ASSESSMENT
Use Problems 7–11 on journal page 267 to assess children's ability to count through transitions.

2 Ongoing Learning & Practice

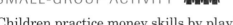

◆ Playing the *Money Exchange Game*
(*Math Journal 2*, pp. 262 and 263)

SMALL-GROUP ACTIVITY

Children practice money skills by playing the *Money Exchange Game*. For detailed instructions, see Lesson 10.8.

◆ Math Boxes 10.10 (*Math Journal 2*, p. 268)

INDEPENDENT ACTIVITY

Mixed Review This journal page provides opportunities for cumulative review or assessment of concepts and skills.

◆ Home Link 10.10 (*Math Masters*, p. 383)

Home Connection Children read numbers to someone at home, write a number given the digits of each place value, and identify numbers that are more or less than a given number.

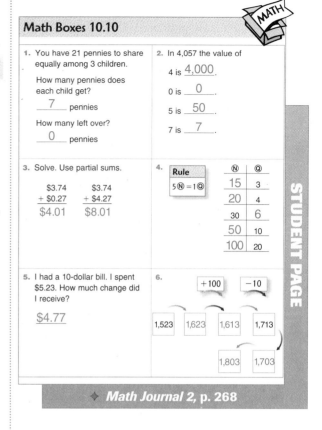

Math Boxes 10.10

1. You have 21 pennies to share equally among 3 children.

   How many pennies does each child get?

   _7_ pennies

   How many left over?

   _0_ pennies

2. In 4,057 the value of

   4 is _4,000_.

   0 is _0_.

   5 is _50_.

   7 is _7_.

3. Solve. Use partial sums.

$3.74	$3.74
+ $0.27	+ $4.27
$4.01	$8.01

4. Rule: 5 Ⓝ = 1 Ⓠ

Ⓝ	Ⓠ
15	3
20	4
30	6
50	10
100	20

5. I had a 10-dollar bill. I spent $5.23. How much change did I receive?

   $4.77

6. +100 / −10

   1,523 → 1,623 → 1,613 → 1,713

   1,803 → 1,703

◆ Math Journal 2, p. 268

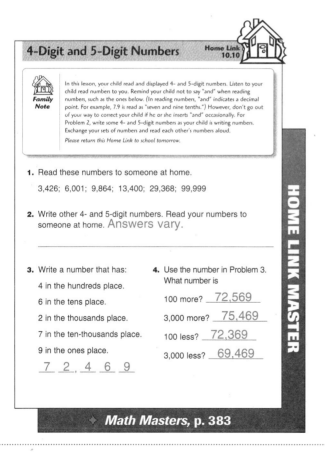

4-Digit and 5-Digit Numbers Home Link 10.10

Family Note

In this lesson, your child read and displayed 4- and 5-digit numbers. Listen to your child read numbers to you. Remind your child not to say "and" when reading numbers, such as the ones below. (In reading numbers, "and" indicates a decimal point. For example, 7.9 is read as "seven and nine tenths.") However, don't go out of your way to correct your child if he or she inserts "and" occasionally. For Problem 2, write some 4- and 5-digit numbers as your child is writing numbers. Exchange your sets of numbers and read each other's numbers aloud.

Please return this Home Link to school tomorrow.

1. Read these numbers to someone at home.

   3,426; 6,001; 9,864; 13,400; 29,368; 99,999

2. Write other 4- and 5-digit numbers. Read your numbers to someone at home. Answers vary.

_____

3. Write a number that has:

   4 in the hundreds place.

   6 in the tens place.

   2 in the thousands place.

   7 in the ten-thousands place.

   9 in the ones place.

   _7_ _2_ , _4_ _6_ _9_

4. Use the number in Problem 3. What number is

   100 more? _72,569_

   3,000 more? _75,469_

   100 less? _72,369_

   3,000 less? _69,469_

◆ Math Masters, p. 383

Areas of States

List the states in the table from largest area to smallest area.

State	Area (sq miles)	State	Area (sq miles)
Arkansas	53,182	largest: Florida	59,928
Florida	59,928	Georgia	58,977
Georgia	58,977	Illinois	57,918
Illinois	57,918	Iowa	56,276
Iowa	56,276	New York	53,989
New York	53,989	smallest: Arkansas	53,182

Name _____ Date _____ Time _____

Areas of States

List the states in the table from largest area to smallest area.

State	Area (sq miles)	State	Area (sq miles)
Arkansas	53,182	largest:	
Florida	59,928		
Georgia	58,977		
Illinois	57,918		
Iowa	56,276		
New York	53,989	smallest:	

◆ Math Masters, p. 191

The *Digit Game*

Materials ❑ 4 cards each of numbers 0–9
(from the Everything Math Deck, if available)

Players 2

Directions

1. Shuffle the deck. Place it facedown between the players.
2. Each player draws 2 cards from the deck and uses them to make the largest number possible.
3. The player who makes the larger number takes all of the cards.
4. The game is over when all of the cards have been used.
5. The player with more cards wins.

Other Ways to Play

A. Players draw 3 cards instead of 2 cards each time. Each player makes the largest 3-digit number possible.

B. Players try to make the smallest number possible each time. The person who makes the greatest number takes all of the cards. The player with fewer cards at the end wins.

◆ Math Journal 1, p. 56

---

3 Options for Individualizing

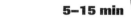

◆ ENRICHMENT Ordering 5-Digit Numbers
(*Math Masters*, p. 191)

INDIVIDUAL ACTIVITY   **5–15 min**

Social Studies Link Children are given an alphabetical list of 6 states and their areas in square miles. They list the states in order from largest to smallest.

◆ RETEACHING Counting through Transitions Using a Calculator

SMALL-GROUP ACTIVITY   **5–15 min**

Some children may find it easier to understand transitions if they are done using a calculator. *Suggestions:*

▷ Start at 0 and count by 1,000s. Pause at 9,000 and ask what happens next. The display shows 10,000; the digit in the thousands place changes to 0, and a 1 appears in the ten-thousands place.

▷ Start at 9,900 and count by 10s. Pause at 9,990 and ask what happens next. The display shows 10,000; the digits in the tens, hundreds, and thousands places change to 0, and a 1 appears in the ten-thousands place.

▷ Start at 9,990 and count by 1s. Pause at 9,999 and ask what happens next. The display shows 10,000; the digits in the ones, tens, hundreds, and thousands places change to 0, and a 1 appears in the ten-thousands place.

◆ EXTRA PRACTICE Playing a Variation of the *Digit Game* (*Math Journal 1*, p. 56)

PARTNER ACTIVITY   **5–15 min**

Children practice forming and comparing numbers by playing the *Digit Game*. For detailed instructions, see Lesson 3.2.

NOTE: In Lesson 3.2, the game was played with 2 or 3 cards. This variation uses 5 cards.

10.11

Grouping with Parentheses

OBJECTIVE To introduce the use of parentheses in number models.

summaries	materials

1 Teaching the Lesson

Children are introduced to parentheses in number models and solve problems involving parentheses. [Patterns, Functions, and Algebra; Operations and Computation]

☐ *Math Journal 2*, p. 269
☐ Home Link 10.10
☐ place-value tool

2 Ongoing Learning & Practice

Children display and read numbers using place-value tools. [Numeration]

Children practice and maintain skills through Math Boxes and Home Link activities.

☐ *Math Journal 2*, p. 270
☐ Home Link Master (*Math Masters*, p. 384)
☐ place-value tool

3 Options for Individualizing

Enrichment Children make up and solve problems involving parentheses. [Patterns, Functions, and Algebra; Operations and Computation]

Language Diversity Children compare parentheses in number models to punctuation in word sentences. [Patterns, Functions, and Algebra]

☐ blank sheets of paper

Additional Information

Vocabulary • **parentheses, parenthesis**

Getting Started

Mental Math and Reflexes

Ask children to use their place-value tools to display certain digits in the places you specify. Then ask children to read the resulting number. For example: *Display 5 in the hundreds place, 3 in the tens place, 8 in the thousands place, 7 in the ten-thousands place, and 4 in the ones place.* Children display and read 78,534. Sometimes specify only one place and digit. For example: *Make a number with 5 in the tens place.* Then discuss the various possible answers.

Math Message

Solve: $8 - 5 + 3 =$ ____ 6

Home Link 10.10 Follow-Up

Review answers. Encourage children to use their place-value tools if they have difficulty with Problems 3 and 4.

◆ Math Message Follow-Up

WHOLE-CLASS DISCUSSION

Ask children to explain how they found the answer. Most likely, children will reason that $8 - 5 = 3$ and $3 + 3 = 6$. Ask if they can figure out how to get zero as the answer. Add 5 and 3 first and subtract the result from 8.

Draw **parentheses** around $5 + 3$, so that the problem reads $8 - (5 + 3) = \_\_\_\_$. Explain that parentheses (singular **parenthesis**) are used when several calculations are to be done. The calculation or calculations inside the parentheses are always the ones that should be done first.

◆ Introducing the Use of Parentheses in Number Models

WHOLE-CLASS ACTIVITY

Work together with children to solve several other problems containing parentheses. Children may observe that some problems have the same answer no matter which part is done first, as in the pair of problems in the lower right below. *Suggestions:*

$(10 - 4) + 3 = ?\ 9$	$(12 - 6) - 3 = ?\ 3$
$10 - (4 + 3) = ?\ 3$	$12 - (6 - 3) = ?\ 9$

$(2 \times 4) + 3 = ?\ 11$	$(9 + 8) - 5 = ?\ 12$
$2 \times (4 + 3) = ?\ 14$	$9 + (8 - 5) = ?\ 12$

✦ Solving Parentheses Puzzles and Problems
(*Math Journal 2*, p. 269)

WHOLE-CLASS ACTIVITY

Write $20 - 8 + 6 = 6$ on the board. Ask someone to put parentheses around the part of the problem that was done first so that the result is equal to 6. $20 - (8 + 6) = 6$

Write $20 - 8 + 6 = 18$. *Where do the parentheses go this time?* $(20 - 8) + 6 = 18$ Pose a few more problems until children show that they understand what to do to solve them. *Suggestions:*

$16 - 10 + 2 = 4$ $16 - (10 + 2) = 4$

$16 - 10 + 2 = 8$ $(16 - 10) + 2 = 8$

$25 - 5 \times 2 = 15$ $25 - (5 \times 2) = 15$

$25 - 5 \times 2 = 40$ $(25 - 5) \times 2 = 40$

Children turn to journal page 269 and solve problems and puzzles involving parentheses.

> **Adjusting the Activity** For Problems 7–12, suggest that children insert the parentheses in pencil. If they insert a parenthesis incorrectly, they can easily change its location.

Parentheses Puzzles

Parentheses can make a big difference in a problem.

Example

$15 - 5 + 3 = ?$

$(15 - 5) + 3 = (10) + 3 = 13$; but

$15 - (5 + 3) = 15 - (8) = 7$

Solve problems containing parentheses.

1. $7 + (8 - 3) = \underline{12}$

2. $(4 + 11) - 6 = \underline{9}$

3. $8 + (13 - 9) = \underline{12}$

4. $\underline{4} = (12 + 8) - 16$

5. $140 - (20 + 80) = \underline{40}$

6. $\underline{0} = (30 + 40) - 70$

Put in parentheses to solve the puzzles.

7. $(12 - 4) + 6 = 14$ 8. $15 - (9 - 4) = 10$

9. $(140 - 60) + 30 = 110$ 10. $500 = (400 - 100) + 200$

11. $(3 \times 2) + 5 = 11$ 12. $2 \times (5 - 5) = 0$

✦ *Math Journal 2*, p. 269

---

② Ongoing Learning & Practice

✦ Displaying and Reading 4- and 5-Digit Numbers

PARTNER ACTIVITY

Partners take turns. One partner uses a place-value tool to display a number with up to 5 digits; the other reads the number. Then partners reverse the procedure. One partner calls out a number; the other displays it using the place-value tool.

Math Boxes 10.11

1. Circle $\frac{3}{18}$.

What fraction of dots is not circled?

$\frac{15}{18}$, or $\frac{5}{6}$

2. Jordan spent $6.37 on a book and $1.23 on a magazine. How much did he spend altogether? First, estimate the costs and total. *Sample answer:*

$6.50 + $1.25 = $7.75

Then use partial sums and solve. $7.60

3. Write 5 names for $0.75.

Sample answers:

$1.00 − $0.25

50¢ + 25¢

$2.75 − 200¢

85¢ − 10¢

seventy-five cents

4. You have 17 pieces of gum to share equally. If each child gets 4 pieces, how many children are sharing?

_4_ children

How many pieces of gum are left over?

_1_ pieces of gum

5. Write the number that is 100 more than

542 _642_

837 _937_

5,641 _5,741_

9,863 _9,963_

6. Use each digit once. Write the largest and smallest numbers.

3 1 4 6

Largest number: _6,431_

Smallest number: _1,346_

Read each of your numbers to a partner.

Grouping with Parentheses

Home Link 10.11

Family Note

In this lesson, your child has solved problems and puzzles involving parentheses. For Problems 1–4, 9, and 10, remind your child that the calculations inside of the parentheses need to be done first. In Problem 1, for example, your child should first find 7 − 2 and then add that answer (5) to 4. For Problems 5–8, observe as your child adds parentheses. Ask your child to explain what to do first in order to obtain the number on the right side of the equals sign.

Please return this Home Link to school tomorrow.

Solve problems containing parentheses.

1. 4 + (7 − 2) = _9_

2. (9 + 21) − 15 = _15_

3. 6 + (12 − 5) = _13_

4. (15 + 5) − 14 = _6_

Put in parentheses to solve the puzzles.

5. 13 − (9 + 2) = 2

6. (28 − 8) − 4 = 16

7. (150 − 70) − 40 = 40

8. 800 − (200 + 300) = 300

Cross out the names that don't belong in the name-collection boxes.

9. | 15 |

~~25 − (15 + 5)~~

(25 − 15) + 5

(17 − 9) + 7

~~17 − (9 + 7)~~

(3 + 6) + 6

3 + (6 + 6)

10. | 100 |

(50 + 150) − 100

50 + (150 − 100)

~~400 − (300 − 200)~~

~~(400 − 300) + 200~~

◆ Math Boxes 10.11 (*Math Journal 2*, p. 270)

INDEPENDENT ACTIVITY

Mixed Review This journal page provides opportunities for cumulative review or assessment of concepts and skills.

◆ Home Link 10.11 (*Math Masters*, p. 384)

Home Connection Children solve parentheses problems and puzzles involving parentheses. They determine which names do not belong in name-collection boxes.

3 Options for Individualizing

◆ ENRICHMENT Making up and Solving Parentheses Puzzles

PARTNER ACTIVITY **15–30 min**

Model a way to make up a parentheses puzzle:

1. Write the left side of a number model, including parentheses. *For example:*
(8 − 5) + 4 =

2. Work out what the right side should be:
(8 − 5) + 4 = (3) + 4 = 7

3. Copy the number model, but leave out the parentheses:
8 − 5 + 4 = 7

Distribute blank sheets of paper. Children make up parentheses puzzles for partners to solve.

◆ LANGUAGE DIVERSITY Comparing Number Models to Word Sentences

SMALL-GROUP ACTIVITY   5–15 min

Language Arts Link Using parentheses with number models can change their meanings. In the same manner, using commas with word sentences can change the meaning of sentences. Ask children to compare the meanings of the sentences below:

Jennifer fed Alex the big black dog.

Jennifer fed Alex, the big black dog.

Without commas, this sentence means than Jennifer gave Alex a big black dog to eat. With the comma, this sentence means that the dog's name is Alex and Jennifer gave Alex something to eat.

Ask children to compare these two sentences:

My brother Marcus and Jasmine are going to the museum.

My brother, Marcus, and Jasmine are going to the museum.

Without commas, this sentence means that two people are going to the museum. With the commas, this sentence means that three people are going.

Work with children to make up sentences that have different meanings depending on the use of commas.

10.12

Unit 10 Review and Assessment

OBJECTIVE To review and assess children's progress on the material covered in Unit 10.

1 Assess Progress

learning goals	activities
10a **Beginning Goal** Use parentheses in number models. **(Lesson 10.11)**	❑ Slate Assessment, Problems 5 and 6
10b **Developing Goal** Solve money stories involving change. **(Lessons 10.6 and 10.8)**	❑ Written Assessment, Problem 9
10c **Developing Goal** Estimate totals for "ballpark" check of exact answers. **(Lessons 10.5, 10.6, 10.8, and 10.9)**	❑ Written Assessment, Problems 8 and 9
10d **Developing Goal** Know and express automatically the values of digits in 5-digit numbers. **(Lessons 10.10–10.11)**	❑ Written Assessment, Problems 11–14
10e **Secure Goal** Read and write money amounts in decimal notation. **(Lessons 10.2–10.4 and 10.6)**	❑ Oral Assessment, Problem 2; Slate Assessment, Problems 1 and 3; ❑ Written Assessment, Problem 1
10f **Secure Goal** Use equivalent coins to show money amounts in different ways. **(Lesson 10.1)**	❑ Written Assessment, Problem 2
10g **Secure Goal** Use a calculator to compute money amounts. **(Lessons 10.3, 10.4, and 10.7)**	❑ Slate Assessment, Problem 4 ❑ Written Assessment, Problems 8 and 9
10h **Secure Goal** Know exchange values of U.S. coins. **(Lessons 10.2, 10.8, and 10.10)**	❑ Written Assessment, Problems 3–7
10i **Secure Goal** Know and express automatically the values of digits in 2-, 3-, and 4-digit numbers. **(Lessons 10.8–10.11)**	❑ Oral Assessment, Problem 1; Slate Assessment, Problem 2 ❑ Written Assessment, Problems 10 and 12

materials

- ❑ *Math Journal 2,* pp. 246 and 247
- ❑ Home Link 10.11
- ❑ Assessment Masters (*Math Masters,* pp. 433 and 434)
- ❑ Teaching Masters (*Math Masters,* pp. 22, 38, and 168)
- ❑ slate; calculator; 1 six-sided die
- ❑ 7 pennies, 5 nickels, 5 dimes, 4 quarters, and one $1 bill
- ❑ Money-Game Spinner (made from *Math Masters,* p. 37)

2 Build Background for Unit 11

summaries

Children practice and maintain skills through Math Boxes and Home Link activities.

materials

- ❑ *Math Journal 2,* p. 271
- ❑ Home Link Masters (*Math Masters,* pp. 385–388)

Each **learning goal** listed above indicates a level of performance that might be expected at this point in the *Everyday Mathematics* K–6 curriculum. For a variety of reasons, the levels indicated may not accurately portray your class's performance.

Getting Started

all five (in desks)

on plates

Math Message

Continue.

596, 597, 598, __, __, __ 599, 600, 601

1,003; 1,002; 1,001; __; __; __ 1,000; 999; 998

7,007; 7,008; 7,009; __; __; __ 7,010; 7,011; 7,012

9,996; 9,997; 9,998; __; __; __ 9,999; 10,000; 10,001

Home Link 10.11 Follow-Up

Review answers.

---

1 Assess Progress

✦ Math Message Follow-Up

WHOLE-CLASS DISCUSSION

Discuss the answers. If necessary, use a place-value tool to demonstrate the transitions.

✦ Oral and Slate Assessments

SMALL-GROUP ACTIVITY

If the list of suggested problems below is not appropriate for your class's level of performance, adjust the numbers in the problems or adjust the problems themselves to better assess your children's abilities.

Oral Assessment Suggestions

1. Write a 4-digit number on the board. Children read the number aloud. Repeat with several other numbers. Progress to 5-digit numbers. Ask such questions as *Which digit is in the hundreds place?* or *What is the value of the 7?* **Goal 10i**

2. Write amounts of money in dollars-and-cents notation on the board. Children read the amounts aloud. **Goal 10e**

1. Write the following, one at a time, on the board. Children write *penny* or *dime* on their slates to indicate an equivalent value. **Goal 10e**

    • $0.10 dime

    • $\frac{1}{10}$ of a dollar dime

    • $0.01 penny

    • $\frac{1}{100}$ of a dollar penny

    • $\frac{10}{100}$ of a dollar dime

2. Dictate a 4-digit number. Children write the number. Dictate several other numbers. Progress to 5-digit numbers. Ask such questions as *Which digit is in the hundreds place?* or *What is the value of the 7?* **Goal 10i**

3. Dictate the following. Children write the dollars-and-cents notation for each money amount. **Goal 10e**

    • 1 dollar and 47 cents $1.47

    • 56 cents $0.56

    • 70 cents $0.70

    • 7 cents $0.07

    • 4 dollars and 8 cents $4.08

4. Dictate the following. Children enter each amount into their calculators. They record the calculator displays on their slates. **Goal 10g**

    • $1.38 1.38

    • 60 cents 0.6

    • 9 cents 0.09

    • $78.50 78.5

5. Write the following on the board. Children record the answers on their slates. **Goal 10a**

    • $(10 - 7) + 5 =$ _____ 8

    • $16 - (9 + 2) =$ _____ 5

6. Write the following on the board. Children write the problems with parentheses. **Goal 10a**

    • $10 - 6 + 8 = 12$ $(10 - 6) + 8 = 12$

    • $14 - 7 - 4 = 11$ $14 - (7 - 4) = 11$

✦ Written Assessment
(*Math Masters*, pp. 433 and 434)

INDEPENDENT ACTIVITY

Read the instructions aloud, repeating as needed.
Children respond on the masters.

- Write the amount. (Problem 1) Goal 10e
- Use 💲1, Ⓠ, Ⓓ, Ⓝ, and Ⓟ. Show $1.83 in two different ways. (Problem 2) Goal 10f
- Complete. (Problems 3–7) Goal 10h
- You buy oranges and yogurt. Estimate the total cost. Find the exact cost, with or without a calculator. (Problem 8) Goals 10c, 10g
- You have $5.00. You buy cheese, bananas, and bread. Estimate the total cost. Find the exact cost, with or without a calculator. Find the amount of change you will get back from $5.00. You may use your calculator. (Problem 9) Goals 10b, 10c, 10g
- Fill in the blanks. Write ones, tens, hundreds, thousands, or ten-thousands. (Problems 10–14) Goal 10d, 10i

✦ ALTERNATIVE ASSESSMENT OPTION
Write about Mathematics

INDEPENDENT ACTIVITY

Have children use their Math Logs or blank pieces of paper to respond to the statement below.

Someone said that a 5 is a 5, no matter what. Is that always true? Give examples.

Look for children to focus on the importance of a unit or place value; for example, 5 pennies, 5 quarters, or five $1 bills; 5 ones, 5 hundreds, or 5 ten-thousands.

Unit 10 Checking Progress

1. Write the amount.

💲1 Ⓠ Ⓠ Ⓓ Ⓓ Ⓝ Ⓟ Ⓟ Ⓟ = $ __1.89__

2. Use 💲1, Ⓠ, Ⓓ, Ⓝ, and Ⓟ. Show $1.83 in two different ways.
Sample answers:

Complete.

3. 1 quarter = __5__ nickels　　**4.** 1 dollar = __10__ dimes

5. 1 dime = __10__ pennies　　**6.** 1 dollar = __100__ pennies

7. 1 dime = __2__ nickels

8. You buy:

Oranges
1 lb at $1.49 lb

and Yogurt
6-pack at $2.09

a. Estimate the total cost.

Estimated cost: $ __1.50__ + $ __2.10__ = $ __3.60__

b. Find the exact cost, with or without a calculator.

Exact cost: $ __3.58__

✦ *Math Masters, p. 433*

Unit 10 Checking Progress (cont.)

9. You have $5.00. You buy:

Cheese
8 oz. for $1.49

and Bananas
1 lb at 59¢ lb

and Bread
16 oz for 99¢

a. Estimate the total cost.

Estimated cost: $ __1.50__ + $ __0.60__ + $ __1.00__ = $ __3.10__

b. Find the exact cost, with or without a calculator.

Exact cost: $ __3.07__

c. Find the amount of change you will get back from $5.00. You may use your calculator.

Change: $ __1.93__

Fill in the blanks. Write ones, tens, hundreds, thousands, or ten-thousands.

10. The 7 in 3,745 stands for 7 __hundreds__ .

11. The 3 in 36,051 stands for 3 __ten-thousands__ .

12. The 6 in 465 stands for 6 __tens__ .

13. The 8 in 21,938 stands for 8 __ones__ .

14. The 2 in 92,645 stands for 2 __thousands__ .

✦ *Math Masters, p. 434*

Write Number Stories
(*Math Masters*, p. 22)

INDEPENDENT ACTIVITY

Children write and illustrate number stories that involve finding the total cost of several items and/or the amount of change owed after a purchase.

Portfolio Ideas

Play *Pick-a-Coin*
(*Math Journal 2*, pp. 246 and 247;
Math Masters, p. 168)

SMALL-GROUP ACTIVITY

Children practice addition and calculator skills by playing *Pick-a-Coin*. For detailed instructions, see Lesson 10.3.

As children play, circulate and assess their ability to use a calculator to enter and compute money amounts.

Play *Spinning for Money*
(*Math Masters*, pp. 37 and 38)

SMALL-GROUP ACTIVITY

Children practice money-counting and money-exchange skills by playing *Spinning for Money*. For detailed instructions, see Lessons 3.2 and 10.1.

As children play, circulate and assess their knowledge of exchange values among U.S. coins.

2 Build Background for Unit 11

◆ Math Boxes 10.12 (*Math Journal 2*, p. 271)

INDEPENDENT ACTIVITY

Mixed Review This journal page provides opportunities for cumulative review or assessment of concepts and skills. The skill in Problem 6 is a prerequisite for Unit 11.

◆ Home Link 10.12: Unit 11 Family Letter
(*Math Masters,* pp. 385–388)

Home Connection This Home Link is a four-page newsletter that introduces parents and guardians to Unit 11's topics and terms. The letter also offers ideas for home-based mathematics activities that are supportive of classroom work.

Math Boxes 10.12

1. There are 3 drink boxes per pack. How many packs are needed to serve 25 second graders and 2 teachers one drink box each? Draw an array.

   __9__ packs are needed.

   × × × × × × × × ×
   × × × × × × × × ×
   × × × × × × × × ×

2. Count by 100s.

   3,229; __3,329__; __3,429__;

   __3,529__; 3,629; __3,729__;

   __3,829__; __3,929__; __4,029__

3. How many dimes in $1.00? __10__

   1 dime = __$\frac{1}{10}$__ of $1.00.

   How many cm in 1 meter? __100__

   1 cm = __$\frac{1}{100}$__ of a meter.

   How many inches in 2 feet?
   __24__

   1 in. = __$\frac{1}{24}$__ of 2 ft

4. Use each digit once. Write the largest and smallest numbers.

   7   9   5   2

   Largest number: __9,752__

   Smallest number: __2,579__

   Read each of your numbers to a partner.

5. Draw the hour and minute hands to show the time 20 minutes later than 6:15.

   What time does the clock show now?

   __6__ : __35__

6. If 25¢ is ONE,

   what is 5¢? __$\frac{1}{5}$__

   what is 50¢? __2__

   If $2.00 is ONE,

   what is 50¢? __$\frac{1}{4}$__

   what is $4.00? __2__

◆ *Math Journal 2, p. 271*

STUDENT PAGE

Family Letter

Home Link 10.12

Unit 11:
Whole-Number Operations Revisited

In the beginning of Unit 11, children will solve addition and subtraction stories with dollars and cents. Children will use estimation to examine their answers and determine whether the answers make sense.

Children will also review the uses of multiplication and division and begin to develop multiplication and division fact power, or the ability to automatically recall the basic multiplication and division facts.

Children will work with shortcuts, which will help them extend known facts to related facts. For example, the **turn-around rule for multiplication** shows that the order of the numbers being multiplied (the factors) does not affect the product; 3×4 is the same as 4×3. Children will also learn what it means to multiply a number by 0 and by 1. Patterns in a Facts Table and in fact families will also help children explore ways of learning multiplication and division facts.

×, ÷	1	2	3	4	5	6	7	8	9	10
1	1	2	3	4	5	6	7	8	9	10
2	2	4	6	8	10	12	14	16	18	20
3	3	6	9	12	15	18	21	24	27	30
4	4	8	12	16	20	24	28	32	36	40
5	5	10	15	20	25	30	35	40	45	50
6	6	12	18	24	30	36	42	48	54	60
7	7	14	21	28	35	42	49	56	63	70
8	8	16	24	32	40	48	56	64	72	80
9	9	18	27	36	45	54	63	72	81	90
10	10	20	30	40	50	60	70	80	90	100

Multiplication/Division Facts Table

Finally, children will apply and extend their knowledge as they analyze and compare precipitation data obtained from a map.

Please keep this Family Letter for reference as your child works through Unit 11.

© 2001 Everyday Learning Corporation

◆ *Math Masters, pp. 385–388*

HOME LINK MASTERS

Unit 11
Whole-Number Operations Revisited

overview

The first two lessons of this unit extend addition and subtraction operations by applying them to amounts of money expressed in decimal notation. The rest of the unit focuses on extending multiplication and division operations to a more symbolic and formal level. Past work with multiplication and division is reviewed.

In the penultimate lesson, children work with a set of data and make difference and ratio comparisons. Comparisons will be covered more extensively in *Third Grade Everyday Mathematics.*

contents

UNIT 11

learning goals in perspective

learning goals	links to the past	links to the future
11a **Developing Goal** Estimate and solve addition and subtraction number stories with dollars and cents. **(Lessons 11.1 and 11.2)**	Children began telling and solving number stories in Kindergarten and continued throughout first grade. In Kindergarten, children were introduced to the idea of estimation and to coins and bills. In first grade, estimation was extended to include money, and children counted combinations of coins. *(Related Grade 2 lessons: 1.2, 2.1, 3.2, 3.7, 4.1–4.3, 4.5, 4.6, 5.3, 6.4)*	Children will continue to work with coins and bills in a variety of problem-solving situations in third grade. Throughout the grades, children will continue to create and solve number stories and to use estimation and mental arithmetic.
11b **Developing Goal** Solve 1-digit multiplication stories (multiples of equal groups.) **(Lessons 11.3 and 11.7)**	Children have previously explored multiples of equal groups informally and by skip counting. *(Related Grade 2 lessons: 5.3, 6.8, 6.9, 8.2)*	In third grade, children will extend multiplication stories to include more difficult multiplication facts and fact extensions. *(Related Grade 2 lesson: 12.4)*
11c **Developing Goal** Solve simple division stories (equal sharing and equal grouping). **(Lessons 11.4 and 11.7)**	Through the use of manipulatives, such as money and counters, children modeled equal-sharing and equal-grouping stories. *(Related Grade 2 lessons: 5.2, 6.11, 7.6, 8.2)*	*Third Grade Everyday Mathematics* will continue to focus on number models and diagrams for division stories. *(Related Grade 2 lesson: 12.5)*
11d **Developing Goal** Multiply numbers with 2, 5, or 10 as a factor. **(Lessons 11.5–11.9)**	In Kindergarten and first grade, children skip counted and marked counting patterns on number lines and number grids, which helped prepare them to learn these multiplication facts. *(Related Grade 2 lessons: 6.7–6.11)*	Through fifth grade, children will continue to work on all multiplication facts, utilizing Fact Triangles and the Multiplication/Division Facts Table. *(Related Grade 2 lessons: 12.4, 12.5)*
11e **Developing Goal** Construct multiplication/division fact families. **(Lessons 11.7 and 11.8)**	Children related division to multiplication through equal-grouping and equal-sharing number stories and patterns of doubling and halving. *(Related Grade 2 lessons: 5.3, 6.7–6.11, 7.5, 7.6, 8.2)*	Children will continue to use Fact Triangles in *Third Grade Everyday Mathematics*. *(Related Grade 2 lessons: 12.4, 12.5)*
11f **Developing Goal** Make difference and ratio comparisons. **(Lessons 11.2 and 11.9)**	Children used data sets to make up and solve difference comparison and ratio comparsion number stories. *(Related Grade 2 lessons: 6.2, 6.8, 10.4)*	Through sixth grade, as they develop automaticity with multiplication/division facts. Difference comparison and ratio comparison problems will be extended to fractions and rate tables. *(Related Grade 2 lessons: 12.1, 12.3, 12.6)*
11g **Secure Goal** Multiply numbers with 0 or 1 as a factor. **(Lesson 11.6)**	Children learned the value of shortcuts to help them develop fact power with addition and subtraction facts. *(Related Grade 2 lessons: 6.8, 6.10, 8.2)*	In Grade 3, children will learn other shortcuts and strategies to help them recall harder multiplication facts. *(Related Grade 2 lessons: 12.4, 12.5)*

assessment
ongoing • product • periodic

☑ Informal Assessment

Math Boxes These *Math Journal* pages provide opportunities for cumulative review or assessment of concepts and skills.

Ongoing Assessment: Kid Watching Use the Ongoing Assessment suggestions in the following lessons to make quick, on-the-spot observations about children's understanding of:
• Operations and Computation **(Lessons 11.7 and 11.8)**

Portfolio Ideas Samples of children's work may be obtained from the following assignments:
• Making Up and Solving Number Stories about Purchases **(Lesson 11.1)**
• Making Up and Solving Number Stories **(Lesson 11.2)**
• Making Up and Solving Multiplication and Division Number Stories **(Lesson 11.7)**
• Write about Mathematics **(Lesson 11.10)**
• Make Up and Solve Addition, Subtraction, Multiplication, and Division Number Stories **(Lesson 11.10)**

☑ Unit 11 Review and Assessment

Math Message Use the question in Lesson 11.10 to assess children's progress toward the following learning goal: Goal 11d

Oral and Slate Assessments Use oral or slate assessments during Lesson 11.10 to assess children's progress toward the following learning goals: Goals 11a, 11b, 11c, 11d, 11f, and 11g

Written Assessment Use a written review during Lesson 11.10 to assess children's progress toward the following learning goals: Goals 11a, 11b, 11c, and 11e

Performance/Group Assessment Use small-group activities in Lesson 11.10 to assess children's progress toward the following learning goals: Goals 11a, 11b, 11d, 11e, 11f, and 11g

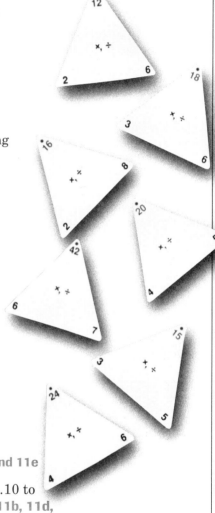

assessment handbook

For more information on how to use different types of assessment in Unit 11, see the Assessment Overview on pages 73–76 in the *Assessment Handbook*. The following Assessment Masters can be found in the *Math Masters* book:

• Unit 11 Checking Progress, p. 435
• Unit 11 Class Checklist, p. 468
• Unit 11 Individual Profile of Progress, p. 469
• Class Progress Indicator, p. 488
• Math Logs, pp. 493–495
• Self-Assessment Forms, pp. 496 and 497
• Interest Inventory, pp. 491 and 492

problemsolving

A process of modeling everyday situations using tools from mathematics

Encourage children to use a variety of strategies when attacking a given problem—and to explain those strategies. *Strategies children might use in this unit:*

- Using estimation
- Identifying needed information
- Using a situation diagram to record information
- Writing a number model
- Using counters and drawing pictures to model problems
- Using information from a picture or a map

Four Problem-Solving REPRESENTATIONS

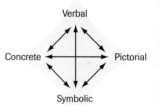

Lessons that teach *through* problem solving, not just *about* problem solving

Lesson	Activity	Lesson	Activity
11.1	Finding the total cost of two items	11.2	Comparing costs
11.1	Is $3.00 enough money to buy two items?	11.3	Making up and solving number stories involving multiples of equal groups
11.1	Writing number stories about purchases	11.7	Making up and solving number stories involving equal sharing and equal groups
11.2	Finding the change received from a purchase	11.9	Solving difference comparison and ratio comparison problems

For more information about problem solving in *Everyday Mathematics,* see the *Teacher's Reference Manual,* pp. 197–208.

cross-curricularlinks

literature

- Read the following books and connect them to equal groups: *Each Orange Had Eight Slices: A Counting Book, Sea Squares,* and *One Hundred Hungry Ants.* **(Lesson 11.3)**
- Use the book *A Remainder of One* to model division with remainders. **(Lesson 11.4)**
- Read *Sea Squares,* a book that introduces square numbers. **(Lesson 11.6)**

language arts

- Discuss the term *per* and the prefix *uni-*. **(Lesson 11.3)**

science

- Discuss a map of rainy or snowy days. **(Lesson 11.9)**

meeting INDIVIDUAL needs

UNIVERSAL ACCESS

◆ RETEACHING

The following features provide additional instructional support:

Adjusting the Activity

- **Lesson 11.1, Parts 1, 2**
- **Lesson 11.2, Part 1**
- **Lesson 11.8, Part 1**

Options for Individualizing

- **Lesson 11.2** Finding Differences between Pairs of Numbers on the Number Grid
- **Lesson 11.3** Making Equal Groups and Building Arrays
- **Lesson 11.4** Acting out Equal Sharing and Equal Grouping
- **Lesson 11.4** Modeling Equal Sharing and Equal Grouping on a Number Line
- **Lesson 11.5** Introducing 5s Facts as the "Clock Facts"

◆ ENRICHMENT

The following features suggest enrichment and extension activities:

Adjusting the Activity

- **Lesson 11.1, Part 1**
- **Lesson 11.3, Part 1**
- **Lesson 11.4, Part 1**
- **Lesson 11.6, Part 1**

Options for Individualizing

- **Lesson 11.1** Making Up and Solving Number Stories about Purchases
- **Lesson 11.2** Making Up and Solving Number Stories
- **Lesson 11.3** Connecting Equal Groups to Literature
- **Lesson 11.4** Connecting Division with Remainders to Literature
- **Lesson 11.6** Investigating Square Numbers
- **Lesson 11.7** Making Up and Solving Multiplication and Division Number Stories

◆ LANGUAGE DIVERSITY

The following features suggest ways to support children who are acquiring proficiency in English:

Adjusting the Activity

- **Lesson 11.5, Part 1**

Options for Individualizing

- **Lesson 11.9** Recognizing Key Words in Difference and Ratio Comparisons

◆ MULTIAGE CLASSROOM

The following chart lists related lessons from Grades 1 and 3 that can help you meet your instructional needs:

Grade 1	8.4 9.2 10.3	8.4 9.4 10.4		8.6 8.8		6.1 6.5	6.3 6.4	6.8	3.13 6.12 10.1
Grade 2	11.1	11.2	11.3	11.4	11.5	11.6	11.7	11.8	11.9
Grade 3	1.10 2.4– 2.6	1.10 2.4– 2.6	4.1– 4.3 4.8	4.4 7.6 9.8	4.5– 4.8 7.3	4.5 4.6 7.2	4.5 4.6 7.2	4.7 7.5 9.2	4.9 5.10

materials

lesson	math masters pages	manipulative kit items	other items
11.1	Home Link Master, p. 389 Teaching Masters, pp. 22, 128, and 192	slate	Class Data Pad (optional) calculator store catalogs or sales flyers
11.2	Home Link Master, p. 390 Teaching Masters, p. 22; and p. 128 (optional)		place-value tool Class Data Pad (optional) calculator store catalogs or sales flyers number grid
11.3	Home Link Masters, pp. 391 and 392 Teaching Masters, pp. 85, 86, 110, and 111 or 112 transparency of Teaching Master, p. 193 *See* **Advance Preparation, p. 782**	slate	counters (optional) various literature selections
11.4	Home Link Master, p. 393 Teaching Masters, pp. 80, 82, 83, 114, and 132 transparency of Teaching Master, p. 193 *See* **Advance Preparation, p. 788**	slate	crayons *A Remainder of One* by Elinor Pinczes
11.5	Home Link Master, p. 394 Teaching Masters, pp. 194 and 195	slate number cards	calculator (optional) analog clock or picture of a clock
11.6	Home Link Master, p. 395 Teaching Masters, pp. 86, 197, 198 transparency of Teaching Master, p. 196 *See* **Advance Preparation, p. 800**	centimeter cubes	*Sea Squares* by Joy Hulme pennies tape
11.7	Home Link Masters, pp. 396 and 397 Teaching Master, p. 22 transparencies of Teaching Masters, pp. 193 and 199 *See* **Advance Preparation, p. 806**		paper clip
11.8	Home Link Master, p. 398		calculator Fact Triangles
11.9	Home Link Master, p. 399 Teaching Master, p. 200		calculator Fact Triangles
11.10	Home Link Masters, pp. 400–403 Teaching Master, p. 201 Assessment Master, p. 435	slate	calculator Fact Triangles Cards

planningtips

Pacing

Pacing depends on a number of factors, such as children's individual needs and how long your school has been using *Everyday Mathematics*. At the beginning of Unit 11, review your Content by Strand Poster to help you set a monthly pace.

◄——MOST CLASSROOMS——►		
A P R I L	M A Y	J U N E

Using the Projects

If you did not use Project 7 earlier in the year, have children describe a collection during Unit 11. Children prepare an information sheet including such attributes as number, size, and age about a collection of their own or of someone they know well. They may bring a selection from the collection to display. The Projects can be found at the back of this book.

Home Communication

Share Home Links 11.1–11.9 with families to help them understand the content and procedures in this unit. At the end of the unit, use Home Link 11.10 to introduce Unit 12. Supplemental information can be found in the *Home Connection Handbook*.

NCTM Standards

Standard	1	2	3	4	5	6	7	8	9	10
Unit 11 Lessons	1–9	3, 6–8	2, 5, 6, 9	5, 6, 9	9	1–9	1–9	1–9	1–9	1–9

Content Standards
1 Number and Operation
2 Patterns, Functions, and Algebra
3 Geometry and Spatial Sense
4 Measurement
5 Data Analysis, Statistics, and Probability

Process Standards
6 Problem Solving
7 Reasoning and Proof
8 Communication
9 Connections
10 Representations

PRACTICE *through* Games

Everyday Mathematics uses games to help children develop good fact power and other math skills.

- Practice counting up mentally and practice using a calculator with *Hit the Target* **(Lessons 11.1 and 11.2)**
- Find the total number of dots in array in *Array Bingo* **(Lesson 11.3)**
- Multiply 2, 5, and 10 and the numbers 1 through 5 and 10 in *Multiplication Draw* **(Lesson 11.5)**
- Practice multiplication facts with *Beat the Calculator* **(Lessons 11.8, 11.9, and 11.10)**

The notes below highlight the major content ideas presented in Unit 11. These notes may help you establish instructional priorities.

Estimates as a Safeguard Against Errors
(Lessons 11.1 and 11.2)

Whenever children obtain an answer to a number story or arithmetic problem, whether by using a calculator, computing mentally, or making a paper-and-pencil calculation, they should examine the answer and ask themselves if it makes sense. By rounding the numbers in the problem up or down to "close-but-easier" numbers and then performing the operation using these numbers, children can obtain ballpark estimates. The goal is for children to be able to recognize when an answer is reasonable; this ability will then serve as a safeguard against answers that are completely off the mark.

Units in Multiplication and Division
(Lessons 11.3, 11.4, and 11.7)

A candy bar costs 50¢. How many can I buy with $2.00?

Throughout, *Everyday Mathematics* has emphasized that a number is not meaningful unless one thinks of it in the context of a unit. For the most part, addition and subtraction stories are concerned with counts or measures that have the same unit.

This is usually not the case in multiplication and division stories. More likely than not, the two factors have different units, and the product has a third unit.

Early in second grade, children were introduced to the unit box as a device to help them focus on the unit. By now, they should also be familiar and comfortable with the diagrams that are used to identify known and unknown quantities in addition and subtraction number stories.

The diagrams introduced for multiplication and division situations in Unit 6 combine the functions of the unit box and the diagrams; that is, they call attention to the different units in the problem and, at the same time, identify what information is known and what information is missing. Although you should not expect children to be able to produce their own diagrams at this time, repeated exposure to these diagrams over time will help them refine their problem-solving skills. Thus, it is important that you display the diagrams on the board whenever you discuss strategies for solving multiplication and division number stories.

triangles	corners per triangle	corners in all
4	3	?

Display multiplication and division diagrams on the board or overhead as needed.

Arrays as Representations of Multiplication and Division Facts (Lesson 11.5)

Through informal exercises in Math Boxes and "Array-of-the-Day" routines, children should, by now, have made arrays for most of the multiplication facts. Arrays can play the same role in making products and quotients more concrete as counting on or counting back—perhaps using one's fingers—does for simple sums and differences.

Multiplication and Division Facts (Lessons 11.3–11.8)

Beginning in Lesson 11.3, the focus is on multiplication and division fact power. The lesson sequence presented is similar to that used for developing addition and subtraction fact power.

Consideration of shortcuts: These are properties of multiplication and division that help children extend known facts to related facts. The shortcuts include the commutative property of multiplication (the turn-around rule), patterns in multiplying by 1 and by 0, and links between multiplication and division facts.

Patterns in a fact table: By examining the facts table, children discover how much fact power they already have. Examples include children's knowledge of multiplication by 1, by 0, and with doubles. In Lesson 11.6, children use a multiplication facts table to generate division facts.

Fact families (Lesson 11.7): children explore fact families to discover links between multiplication and division.

Multiplication and division Fact Triangles: Fact Triangles and games like *Beat the Calculator* provide fact practice without a lot of paper-and-pencil exercises. Parents should be encouraged to do Fact Triangle exercises with their children during this unit and throughout summer vacation.

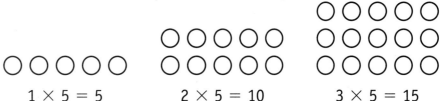

$1 \times 5 = 5$ $2 \times 5 = 10$ $3 \times 5 = 15$

Although mastery of all the multiplication and division facts is not expected by the end of the year, most children should master many of the simpler multiplication and division facts, along with all of the basic addition and subtraction facts.

Comparisons with Differences and Ratios (Lesson 11.9)

In Lesson 11.9, children compare the amounts of yearly precipitation in several large cities. Children answer the questions *How much more …?* or *How much less …?* (differences) and *How many times as much …?* or *What fraction of …?* (ratios). These informal exposures to differences and ratios will be extended in coming years. As a result, it is expected that today's children will eventually do better than many adults, who, while able to answer such questions, do not always understand what the answers mean or under what circumstances one kind of comparison is more appropriate than another.

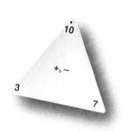

"Units Analysis" as a Link to Science Teaching

words/min
hits/misses
mi/h
mi/g

A more detailed study of rates and ratios is reserved for Grade 3.

One of the main complaints of science teachers is that work in arithmetic has tended to focus on pure numbers, without taking into account the units that give the numbers real-life contexts. At the second grade level, *Everyday Mathematics* has addressed this complaint by making sure that units for counts and measures are always kept in the picture.

Starting in third grade, this concern with units will be extended through an extensive analysis of how the units are affected by the operations performed on the numbers. For example, the unit "miles per hour" which, in fraction form, is expressed as mi/h, reflects the fact that this rate is obtained by dividing distance by time.

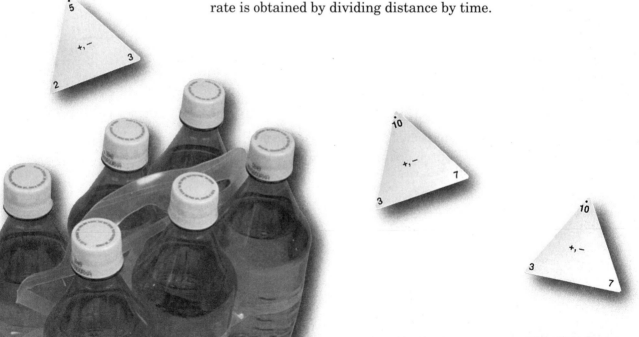

Review and Assessment (Lesson 11.10)

Since you are nearing the end of the school year, you will want to assess children's progress on the most important topics, as well as those in this unit. Pay attention to addition and subtraction facts; addition and subtraction of multidigit numbers; money and time-telling skills; whole-number notation and place value for numbers less than 100,000; and basic fraction concepts.

Unit 12 is a review unit. If you will not have enough time to do all of the lessons in that unit, you may want to select lessons on those topics that are in greatest need of review.

For **additional information** on the following topics, see the *Teacher's Reference Manual:*

- basic facts
- data collection, organization, and analysis
- estimates in calculations
- number models and number sentences
- operations and use classes

11.1 Addition Number Stories with Dollars and Cents

OBJECTIVES To estimate sums for amounts of money; and to add 2- and 3-digit amounts of money.

summaries	materials
1 **Teaching the Lesson**	
Children estimate, and then calculate, the cost of two items. They discuss addition strategies. [Operations and Computation; Measurement and Reference Frames]	☐ *Math Journal 2*, pp. 272 and 273 ☐ slate ☐ Class Data Pad (optional)
2 **Ongoing Learning & Practice**	
Children practice finding differences between 2-digit numbers and higher multiples of ten by playing *Hit the Target.* [Operations and Computation] Children practice and maintain skills through Math Boxes and Home Link activities.	☐ *Math Journal 2*, p. 274 ☐ Teaching Master (*Math Masters*, p. 128; optional) ☐ Home Link Master (*Math Masters*, p. 389) ☐ calculator
3 **Options for Individualizing**	
Enrichment Children make up and solve number stories about purchases. [Operations and Computation; Measurement and Reference Frames] **Extra Practice** Children estimate the costs of grocery items. [Operations and Computation; Measurement and Reference Frames] **Extra Practice** Children solve addition number stories with 2- and 3-digit amounts of money. [Operations and Computation; Measurement and Reference Frames]	☐ Teaching Masters (*Math Masters*, pp. 22 and 192) ☐ store catalogs or sales flyers ☐ supermarket sales flyers (optional) ☐ *Minute Math®*, p. 16 ***See* Advance Preparation**

Additional Information

Advance Preparation Before starting the first optional Extra Practice activity in Part 3, make 1 copy of *Math Masters*, page 192 for every 2 children. Cut the *Math Masters* page on the dashed line.

Getting Started

Mental Math and Reflexes

Review dollars-and-cents (decimal) notation, particularly for amounts less than $1.00. Children give both oral and slate responses. *Suggestions:*

- Say: *Write 75 cents in dollars-and-cents notation.* $0.75
- *Write $0.07 on the board. How much is that?* 7 cents
- *Write 140 cents in dollars-and-cents notation.* $1.40

Math Message

Use the Art Supply Poster on journal page 272 to answer these questions:

- I have $3.00. Is that enough to buy markers and pipe cleaners?
- Is $3.00 enough to buy scissors and glue?
- Is $3.00 enough to buy 2 paintbrushes?

Teaching the Lesson

◆ Math Message Follow-Up
(*Math Journal 2*, p. 272)

WHOLE-CLASS DISCUSSION

As children share their solution strategies, remind them that it is not necessary to find the exact total costs to answer the questions. Encourage estimation strategies, such as the following:

- For markers and pipe cleaners: $1.37 is less than $2.00, and $0.76 is less than $1.00, so the total cost is less than $3.00.

- For scissors and glue: $2.20 and $0.80 add up to $3.00, so $2.23 plus $0.84 is more than $3.00.

- For 2 paintbrushes: $0.54 is more than half a dollar, so 2 times $0.54 is more than $1.00, and 2 times $1.54 is more than $3.00.

Working with children, make up similar stories based on the data from the Art Supply Poster. Use different amounts of available spending money.

Adjusting the Activity Challenge children by making up stories for purchases of more than two items.

◆ Solving Problems with 2- and 3-Digit Addends (*Math Journal 2*, pp. 272 and 273)

SMALL-GROUP ACTIVITY

Have group members work together to solve the problems on journal page 273. Remind children to estimate the cost before calculating the total cost. Children are required to calculate the total cost when the estimate is $3.00 or greater. Once children realize this, they should be much more eager to "estimate first and calculate later."

Adjusting the Activity Suggest that children first write the prices from the Art Supply Poster next to the names of the items on the journal page. Having the prices written close to the workspace should make it easier for some children to solve the problems.

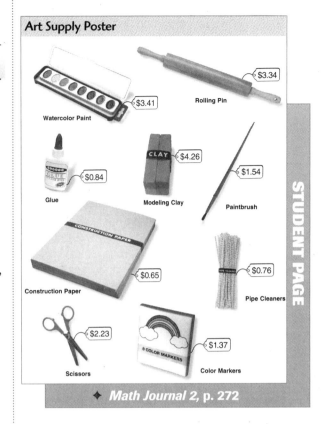

Art Supply Poster

◆ *Math Journal 2,* p. 272

STUDENT PAGE

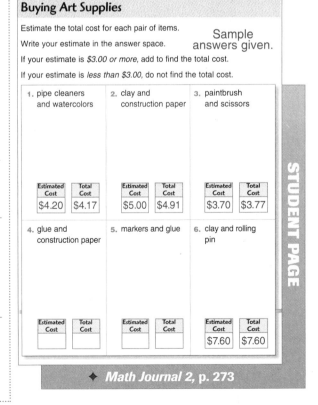

Buying Art Supplies

Estimate the total cost for each pair of items.
Write your estimate in the answer space.

Sample answers given.

If your estimate is *$3.00 or more*, add to find the total cost.

If your estimate is *less than $3.00*, do not find the total cost.

1. pipe cleaners and watercolors	2. clay and construction paper	3. paintbrush and scissors
Estimated Cost $4.20 / Total Cost $4.17	Estimated Cost $5.00 / Total Cost $4.91	Estimated Cost $3.70 / Total Cost $3.77
4. glue and construction paper	5. markers and glue	6. clay and rolling pin
Estimated Cost / Total Cost	Estimated Cost / Total Cost	Estimated Cost $7.60 / Total Cost $7.60

◆ *Math Journal 2,* p. 273

STUDENT PAGE

After children have completed several problems, bring the class together to share solution strategies. Record successful strategies on the board or Class Data Pad. Once most of the class seems to be catching on, let children complete the rest of the problems.

The following illustrates four strategies that children are likely to propose.

Example: Find the cost of watercolors and a paintbrush. ($3.41 + $1.54 = ?)

Typical solutions

- Ignore dollars-and-cents notation and use partial sums. Think of the money amounts as pennies.

$$
\begin{array}{r}
341 \\
+\ 154 \\
\hline
400 \\
90 \\
+\quad 5 \\
\hline
495
\end{array}
$$

  495 pennies is $4.95.

- Combine dollars and cents separately.

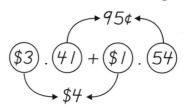

  $4 + 95¢ = $4.95

- Count on.

  I started with $3.41
  I added $1. $4.41
  Then 50¢ $4.91
  Then 4¢ $4.95

- Compensate.

  I took the penny away from $3.41.
  I gave it to $1.54.
  Now the problem is $3.40 + $1.55.
  I added dollars, and then I added cents:
  $3 + $1 = $4   40¢ + 55¢ = 95¢
  The total is $4.95.

NOTE: The first two strategies will work with any addition problem. The third strategy can be tedious and quite difficult with 3- and 4-digit numbers. The fourth strategy works for some combinations of addends, but not all.

Adjusting the Activity It is often convenient to think of 3- and 4-digit addition problems as dollars-and-cents problems. *For example:*

To add: 2,354   Think: $23.54
         + 4,667   + 46.67

Add the dollars: 23   Add the cents: 54
                 + 46   + 67
                   60   110
                    9   11
                   69   121

Combine dollars and cents: $69 + $1.21 = $70.21.

So 2,354 + 4,667 = 7,021.

Ongoing Learning & Practice

◆ Playing *Hit the Target* (*Math Masters*, p. 128)

PARTNER ACTIVITY

This game was introduced in Lesson 7.3. *Hit the Target* provides practice in counting up. Children will use this skill extensively in the next lesson as they make change and solve comparison problems.

 Adjusting the Activity As children continue to play the game, their responses should become essentially automatic. If some children are having difficulty, have them use *Math Masters*, page 128 as a record sheet.

◆ Math Boxes 11.1 (*Math Journal 2*, p. 274)

INDEPENDENT ACTIVITY

 Mixed Review This journal page provides opportunities for cumulative review or assessment of concepts and skills.

◆ Home Link 11.1 (*Math Masters*, p. 389)

 Home Connection Children explain how they solve addition problems. Then they calculate the total cost of pairs of items.

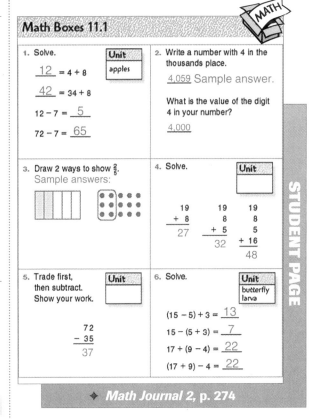

Math Boxes 11.1

1. Solve.

   Unit
   apples

   __12__ = 4 + 8

   __42__ = 34 + 8

   12 − 7 = __5__

   72 − 7 = __65__

2. Write a number with 4 in the thousands place.

   4,059 Sample answer.

   What is the value of the digit 4 in your number?

   __4,000__

3. Draw 2 ways to show $\frac{2}{5}$.
   Sample answers:

4. Solve.

   Unit

   19   19   19
   + 8   8   8
   27   + 5   5
             32   + 16
                        48

5. Trade first, then subtract. Show your work.

   Unit

   72
   − 35
   37

6. Solve.

   Unit
   butterfly
   larva

   (15 − 5) + 3 = __13__

   15 − (5 + 3) = __7__

   17 + (9 − 4) = __22__

   (17 + 9) − 4 = __22__

◆ *Math Journal 2, p. 274*

Buying Art Supplies   Home Link 11.1

Family Note In today's lesson, your child solved number stories involving money amounts. Ask your child to explain to you how he or she solved each of the addition problems below. Challenge your child to find the total cost of 3 or 4 items. Encourage your child to use estimation before solving each problem. Ask such questions as: *Is the total cost of the crayons and glitter more or less than $3.00?* (less)

Please return this Home Link to school tomorrow.

$0.75 $1.47 $2.59 $0.89
Crayons   Glitter   Coloring Pencils Glue Stick

Find the total cost of each pair of items.

1. crayons and glitter	2. glitter and coloring pencils
Total cost: $2.22	Total cost: $4.06
3. crayons and coloring pencils	4. glue stick and crayons
Total cost: $3.34	Total cost: $1.64

✧ *Math Masters, p. 389*

The Great Party Supply Store

Party Balloons
89¢

Party Forks
$1.39

Party Hats
59¢

Party Napkins
79¢

Plastic Cups
$1.29

◆ ENRICHMENT Making up and Solving Number Stories about Purchases
(*Math Masters*, p. 22)

INDEPENDENT ACTIVITY   15–30 min

Children use store catalogs or sales flyers to write and illustrate their own number stories. Stories can be displayed on a bulletin board or assembled in a class booklet.

Portfolio Ideas

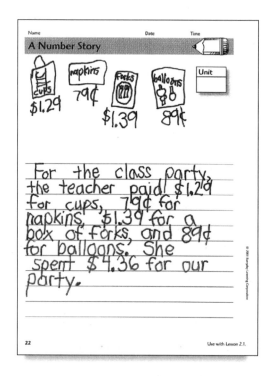

◆ EXTRA PRACTICE Estimating Costs
(*Math Masters*, p. 192)

INDEPENDENT ACTIVITY   5–15 min

Children list 6 supermarket items and the cost of each item. Children estimate how many of each item can be bought with $3.00. You can do this activity at school by providing children with supermarket sales flyers. This activity may also be done with someone at home. There are two copies of the master on each sheet.

TEACHING MASTER

Estimating Costs

Find the costs of 6 items that are sold in a supermarket. You might go to the supermarket, look at an ad in the newspaper, or find the items in your own home.

List the items and their costs. Estimate how many of each item you could buy with $3.00. Continue the chart on the back of this page.

Item	Cost per Item	Number of Items for $3.00
Loaf of Bread	$1.49	2

Name   Date   Time

Estimating Costs

Find the costs of 6 items that are sold in a supermarket. You might go to the supermarket, look at an ad in the newspaper, or find the items in your own home.

List the items and their costs. Estimate how many of each item you could buy with $3.00. Continue the chart on the back of this page.

Item	Cost per Item	Number of Items for $3.00
Loaf of Bread	$1.49	2

✦ *Math Masters*, p. 192

◆ EXTRA PRACTICE Minute Math

SMALL-GROUP ACTIVITY   **5–15 min**

To offer children more experience with solving addition number stories, see the following page in *Minute Math*.

Basic Routines: p. 16

PLANNING AHEAD

The optional Reteaching activity in Lesson 11.3 is a choice of Explorations from previous lessons. Children will need the following materials to perform these Explorations:

Exploration C: Egg Nests (Unit 2, Lesson 2.7)

Materials per partnership:

Teaching Master (*Math Masters,* p. 27)

6 quarter-sheets of paper

36 pennies or other counters

1 six-sided die

Exploration H: Cube Arrays (Unit 5, Lesson 5.3)

Materials per partnership or group:

Teaching Masters (*Math Masters,* pp. 85 and 86)

40 centimeter cubes

2 six-sided dice

Exploration A: Geoboard Arrays (Unit 6, Lesson 6.7)

Materials per individual:

Teaching Masters (*Math Masters,* p. 110 and p. 111 or 112)

geoboard

rubber bands

overhead geoboard (optional)

Materials per group:

scissors

glue or paste (optional)

large sheet of paper (optional)

11.2

Subtraction Number Stories and Cents

Lesson 11.2 (N.FL.02.12)
Mental Math & Reflexes: Extend to include showing 3-digit# & adding hundreds to it, then tens, then ones.

OBJECTIVES To ___ ___ by counting up; and to solve comparison pro___ for 2- and 3-digit money amounts.

1 Teaching the Lesson

Children count up to find the amount of change due; children find the difference between the costs of two items.
[Numeration; Operations and Computation]

- ☐ *Math Jou___ 2* ___ 272 and 276
- ☐ Home Lin___ ___
- ☐ place-value tool; Class Data Pad (optional)

2 Ongoing Learning & Practice

Children calculate the cost of a pair of items. [Operations and Computation; Measurement and Reference Frames]

Children practice and maintain skills through Math Boxes and Home Link activities.

- ☐ *Math Journal 2*, pp. 272, 273, and 276
- ☐ Home Link Master (*Math Masters*, p. 390)

3 Options for Individualizing

Enrichment Children make up and solve number stories about purchases. [Operations and Computation; Measurement and Reference Frames]

Reteaching Children find the difference between number pairs on a number grid. [Numeration; Operations and Computation]

Extra Practice Children practice finding differences between 2-digit numbers and higher multiples of 10 by playing *Hit the Target*. [Operations and Computation]

- ☐ Teaching Masters (*Math Masters*, p. 22; and p. 128, optional)
- ☐ calculator
- ☐ store catalogs or sales flyers
- ☐ number grid

Getting Started

Mental Math and Reflexes

Dictate 4- and 5-digit numbers. Children display each number using their place-value tools. Ask: *Which digit shows ones? Tens? Hundreds? Thousands? Ten-thousands?*

Write 4- and 5-digit numbers on the board and have children say the numbers aloud.

Math Message

You buy a pair of scissors for $2.23. You pay with a $5 bill. Should you get more or less than $3.00 in change?

Home Link 11.1 Follow-Up

Review answers. Give children practice with estimation skills by asking questions like the following:

- Is the total cost of the coloring pencils and the glitter more or less than $5.00? less
- Is the total cost of the glue stick and the coloring pencils more or less than $3.00? more

Teaching the Lesson

✦ Math Message Follow-Up

WHOLE-CLASS DISCUSSION

Ask children to share their solution strategies. Remind them that it is not necessary to find the exact amount of change in order to solve such problems. Encourage strategies, such as the following:

▷ Use a number close to the price of the scissors that is easier to work with. $2.23 is close to $2.25. If you paid with 3 dollar bills, your change would be about 75 cents. Since you paid with $5.00, your change will be about $2.75.

▷ Use another number close to the price of the scissors that is easier to work with. $2.23 is close to $2.00. If the scissors cost $2.00, your change would be $3.00. But the scissors cost more than $2.00, so your change will be less than $3.00.

▷ Count up to make change. Start at a close, easier number for the price of the scissors. $2.23 is about $2.20. Count up 80 cents to $3.00. Count up $2.00 more to $5.00. Add the amounts you counted up. $0.80 + $2.00 = $2.80, so your change is less than $3.00.

✦ Counting up to the Next Dollar
(*Math Journal 2,* p. 272)

WHOLE-CLASS DISCUSSION

Pose problems about making change based on the Art Supply Poster on journal page 272. Pay for purchases with the next dollar amount and find the change.

Example: You buy a bunch of pipe cleaners for $0.76. How much change should you get from a $1 bill?

1. Count up to the next 10 (dime):
76 cents + 4 cents = 80 cents.

2. Count by 10s (dimes) to the next dollar:
80 cents + 20 cents = $1.00.

3. Add the counts: 4 + 20 = 24. Your change is 24 cents, or $0.24.

> NOTE: Finding the change from a dollar is like playing *Hit the Target,* with 100 as the target number.

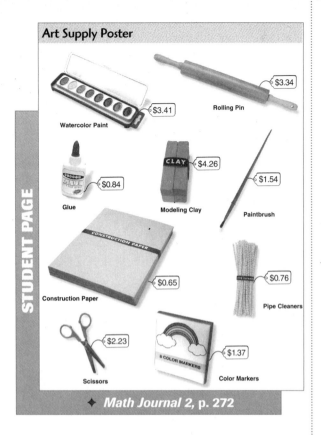

Art Supply Poster

Watercolor Paint $3.41

Rolling Pin $3.34

Glue $0.84

Modeling Clay CLAY $4.26

Paintbrush $1.54

Construction Paper $0.65

Pipe Cleaners $0.76

Scissors $2.23

Color Markers 8 COLOR MARKERS $1.37

◆ *Math Journal 2*, p. 272

Move on to problems about making change where the items cost more than a dollar.

Example: You buy a pair of scissors for $2.23 and pay with three $1 bills. How much change should you get?

1. Count up to the next 10 (dime): $2.23 + 7$ cents $= \$2.30$.

2. Count by 10s (dimes) to the next dollar: $2.30 + 70$ cents $= \$3.00$.

3. Add the counts: $7 + 70 = 77$. Your change is 77 cents, or $0.77.

◆ Counting up to Larger Dollar Amounts
(*Math Journal 2*, p. 272)

WHOLE-CLASS DISCUSSION

Pose problems about making change based on the Art Supply Poster on journal page 272. Pay for purchases with larger dollar amounts and find the change.

Example: John went to the store with only a $5 bill in his pocket. He bought a set of markers for $1.37. When he got home, he had three $1 bills and some change in his pocket. He wondered if he had lost a dollar bill on the way home. Do you think John did? no

How much change should he have in his pocket?

1. Count up to the next 10 (dime): $1.37 + 3$ cents $= \$1.40$.

2. Count by 10s (dimes) to the next dollar: $1.40 + 60$ cents $= \$2.00$.

3. Count by 100s (dollars) to $5.00: $2.00 + 3$ dollars $= \$5.00$.

4. Add the counts: 3 cents $+$ 60 cents $+$ 3 dollars $= \$3.63$. John's change is $3.63.

◆ Solving Comparison Problems
(*Math Journal 2*, pp. 272 and 275)

SMALL-GROUP ACTIVITY

Divide the class into small groups. Have group members work together to solve the problems on journal page 275. After children have completed several problems, bring them together to share solution strategies. Record successful strategies on the board or the Class Data Pad. Once most of the class seems to be catching on, let children complete the rest of the problems.

NOTE: Rather than having children flip the journal pages between pages 272 and 275, assign one child in each group to leave his or her journal open to page 272 while the others work on page 275. Another option is to write the prices from the Art Supply Poster on the board.

Two solution strategies your children are likely to mention are shown below.

- Work with dollars and cents separately. (Example: items cost $3.41 and $1.37.)

I subtracted.

$$\begin{array}{r} \boxed{3}.\boxed{4\ 1} \\ -\ \boxed{1}.\boxed{3\ 7} \\ \hline \end{array}$$

2 dollars　　4 cents = $2.04

- Count up. (Example: items cost $1.54 and $0.76.)

I counted up.

$$76 + 4 = 80$$

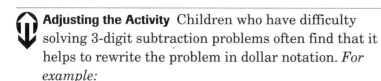

$$80 + 20 = 100$$
$$100 + 54 = 154$$

$$\begin{array}{r} 4 \\ 20 \\ +\ 54 \\ \hline 70 \\ +\ 8 \\ \hline 78 \end{array} \quad \boxed{78¢}$$

 Adjusting the Activity Children who have difficulty solving 3-digit subtraction problems often find that it helps to rewrite the problem in dollar notation. *For example:*

To subtract:　426　Think: $4.26
　　　　　　　− 223　　　　− 2.23

Subtract the dollars: $4 − $2 = $2

Subtract the cents: 26¢ − 23¢ = 3¢ (3¢ = $0.03)

Combine dollars and cents: $2 + $0.03 = $2.03

2 Ongoing Learning & Practice

◆Calculating Sums of Money
(*Math Journal 2*, pp. 272 and 273)

INDEPENDENT ACTIVITY

In the preceding lesson, children were asked to calculate the total cost for a pair of items only if their estimated cost for that pair was $3.00 or greater. Ask them now to calculate the total costs for the remaining pairs of items.

Comparing Costs

Use the Art Supply Poster on journal page 272.
In Problems 1–6, circle the item that costs more.
Then find how much more.

1. glue or (markers)
   How much more? $0.53

2. (rolling pin) or scissors
   How much more? $1.11

3. pipe cleaners or (paintbrush)
   How much more? $0.78

4. construction paper or (paintbrush)
   How much more? $0.89

5. (watercolors) or markers
   How much more? $2.04

6. paintbrush or (watercolors)
   How much more? $1.87

7. You buy a pack of construction paper. You pay with a $1 bill.
   Should you get more or less than 2 quarters in change? less

8. You buy pipe cleaners. You pay with a $1 bill.
   How much change should you get? $0.24

9. You buy a rolling pin. You pay with a $5 bill.
   How much change should you get? $1.66

◆ *Math Journal 2, p. 275*

Buying Art Supplies

Estimate the total cost for each pair of items.
Write your estimate in the answer space.

Sample answers given.

If your estimate is *$3.00 or more*, add to find the total cost.
If your estimate is *less than $3.00*, do not find the total cost.

1. pipe cleaners and watercolors	2. clay and construction paper	3. paintbrush and scissors

Estimated Cost	Total Cost	Estimated Cost	Total Cost	Estimated Cost	Total Cost
$4.20	$4.17	$5.00	$4.91	$3.70	$3.77

4. glue and construction paper	5. markers and glue	6. clay and rolling pin

Estimated Cost	Total Cost	Estimated Cost	Total Cost	Estimated Cost	Total Cost
$1.50	$1.49	$2.20	$2.21	$7.60	$7.60

◆ *Math Journal 2, p. 273*

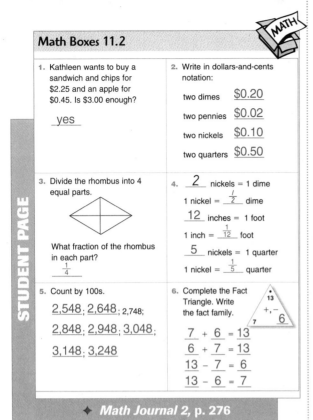

1. Kathleen wants to buy a sandwich and chips for $2.25 and an apple for $0.45. Is $3.00 enough?

yes

2. Write in dollars-and-cents notation:

two dimes $0.20

two pennies $0.02

two nickels $0.10

two quarters $0.50

3. Divide the rhombus into 4 equal parts.

What fraction of the rhombus in each part?

$\frac{1}{4}$

4. _2_ nickels = 1 dime

1 nickel = $\frac{1}{2}$ dime

_12_ inches = 1 foot

1 inch = $\frac{1}{12}$ foot

_5_ nickels = 1 quarter

1 nickel = $\frac{1}{5}$ quarter

5. Count by 100s.

2,548; 2,648; 2,748;

2,848; 2,948; 3,048;

3,148; 3,248

6. Complete the Fact Triangle. Write the fact family.

$7 + 6 = 13$

$6 + 7 = 13$

$13 - 7 = 6$

$13 - 6 = 7$

♦ *Math Journal 2*, p. 276

STUDENT PAGE

♦ **Math Boxes 11.2** (*Math Journal 2*, p. 276)

Mixed Review This journal page provides opportunities for cumulative review or assessment of concepts and skills.

♦ **Home Link 11.2** (*Math Masters*, p. 390)

Home Connection Children determine which item in a pair costs more, and then they calculate how much more. Children also determine the amount of change received following a purchase.

3 Options for Individualizing

♦ ENRICHMENT **Making up and Solving Number Stories** (*Math Masters*, p. 22)

Children use store catalogs or sales flyers to write and illustrate their own number stories. Encourage children to write stories that include making change or comparing the costs of two items. Stories may be displayed on a bulletin board or assembled into a class booklet.

Portfolio Ideas

HOME LINK MASTER

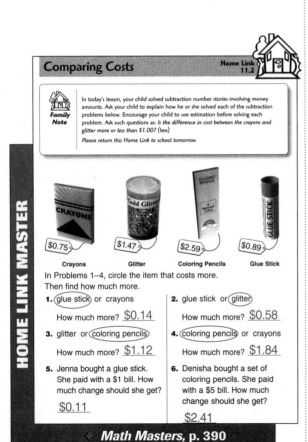

Comparing Costs

Home Link 11.2

Family Note

In today's lesson, your child solved subtraction number stories involving money amounts. Ask your child to explain how he or she solved each of the subtraction problems below. Encourage your child to use estimation before solving each problem. Ask such questions as: *Is the difference in cost between the crayons and glitter more or less than $1.00?* (less)

Please return this Home Link to school tomorrow.

$0.75 Crayons $1.47 Glitter $2.59 Coloring Pencils $0.89 Glue Stick

In Problems 1–4, circle the item that costs more. Then find how much more.

1. (glue stick) or crayons

How much more? $0.14

2. glue stick or (glitter)

How much more? $0.58

3. glitter or (coloring pencils)

How much more? $1.12

4. (coloring pencils) or crayons

How much more? $1.84

5. Jenna bought a glue stick. She paid with a $1 bill. How much change should she get?

$0.11

6. Denisha bought a set of coloring pencils. She paid with a $5 bill. How much change should she get?

$2.41

◄ *Math Masters*, p. 390

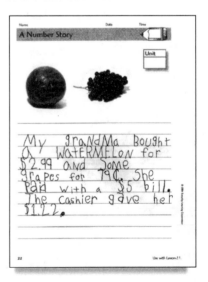

A Number Story

Unit

My GrandMa Bought a WATERMELON for $2.99 and Some GraPes for 79¢. She Paid With a $5 bill. The cashier gave her $1.22.

Children use *Math Masters*, page 22 to write their own number stories.

✦ RETEACHING Finding Differences between Pairs of Numbers on the Number Grid

INDEPENDENT ACTIVITY   5–15 min

If children are having difficulty using a counting-up procedure to count out change, they may benefit from using a similar procedure to find differences between pairs of numbers on a number grid.

Pose such problems such as the following: *Use your number grid. Start at 40. How many spaces on the number grid is it to 76?*

Sample response: I put my finger on 40. I moved one row down, to 50—that's 10. Then I moved down one more row to 60. That's 10 more, so I've got 20 so far. Then I moved down one more row to 70. That's 10 more, so I've got 30 so far. Then I moved one space at a time and counted, until I got to 76—that's 31, 32, 33, 34, 35, 36. So there are 36 spaces from 40 to 76.

✦ EXTRA PRACTICE Playing *Hit the Target* (*Math Masters,* p. 128)

PARTNER ACTIVITY   5–15 min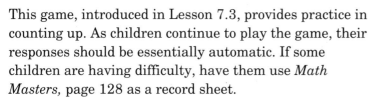

This game, introduced in Lesson 7.3, provides practice in counting up. As children continue to play the game, their responses should be essentially automatic. If some children are having difficulty, have them use *Math Masters,* page 128 as a record sheet.

PLANNING AHEAD

The first optional Reteaching activity in Lesson 11.4 is a choice of Explorations from previous lessons. Children will need the following materials to perform these Explorations:

Exploration F: Equal Sharing (Unit 5, Lesson 5.2)

   Materials per partnership:

   Teaching Masters (*Math Masters,* pp. 80, 82, and 83)

   geoboard

   rubber bands

Exploration C: How Many Children Get *n* Things? (Unit 6, Lesson 6.7)

   Materials per individual:

   Math Journal 1, p. 151

   Teaching Master (*Math Masters,* p. 114)

   Materials per group:

   50 pennies or other counters

   1 regular die

Exploration B: Sharing Money (Unit 7, Lesson 7.6)

   Materials per group:

   Teaching Master (*Math Masters,* p. 132)

   Teaching Aid Assessment Master (*Math Masters,* p. 498)

   one $5 bill, five $1 bills, 4 quarters, 10 dimes, 20 nickels, and 100 pennies

   half-sheet of paper

11.3 Multiples of Equal Groups

5-24-07

OBJECTIVE To find the total number of items in several equal groups by multiplying.

summaries	materials

1 Teaching the Lesson

Children make up and solve number stories about multiples of equal groups, using a multiplication diagram to record known and missing information. [Operations and Computation; Patterns, Functions, and Algebra]

- ☐ *Math Journal 2*, pp. 278 and 279
- ☐ Home Link 11.2
- ☐ Teaching Master transparency (*Math Masters*, p. 193; optional)
- ☐ counters (optional); slate

See **Advance Preparation**

2 Ongoing Learning & Practice

Children practice and maintain skills through Math Boxes and Home Link activities.

- ☐ *Math Journal 2*, p. 277
- ☐ Home Link Masters (*Math Masters*, pp. 391 and 392)

3 Options for Individualizing

Enrichment Children write multiplication number stories about equal groups found in literature selections. [Operations and Computation; Patterns, Functions, and Algebra]

Reteaching Children solve problems involving multiples of equal groups by using manipulatives. [Operations and Computation; Patterns, Functions, and Algebra]

Extra Practice Children find the number of items in an array by playing *Array Bingo*. [Operations and Computation; Patterns, Functions, and Algebra]

- ☐ Teaching Masters (*Math Masters*, p. 27, per partnership; pp. 85 and 86, per group; p. 110 and p. 111 or 112; and pp. 118 and 119)
- ☐ children's literature selections
- ☐ 9 cards labeled "A" cut from *Math Masters*, p. 117
- ☐ 7 cards not labeled "A" cut from *Math Masters*, p. 117 (optional)

See **Advance Preparation**

Additional Information

Advance Preparation For the activities in Part 1, decide how you will display a multiplication diagram. You can make an overhead transparency of *Math Masters*, page 193 or draw the diagram on the board, preferably with semipermanent chalk.

For the optional Enrichment activity in Part 3, you will need the following books: *Each Orange Had Eight Slices: A Counting Book* by Paul Giganti, Jr. (Greenwillow Books, 1992), *Sea Squares* by Joy N. Hulme (Hyperion Books for Children, 1991), and *One Hundred Hungry Ants* by Elinor J. Pinczes (Houghton Mifflin, 1995).

The optional Reteaching activity in Part 3 is a choice of Explorations from previous units. (See Planning Ahead on page 775.)

Vocabulary • **multiplication diagram** • **factor** • **product** • **per** • **in each** • **for each**

Vocabulary (teacher) • **rate multiplication stories**

Getting Started

Skip
Skip no

Mental Math and Reflexes

Write problems about addition with money on the board. Children record estimates on their slates. For each problem, discuss how children arrived at their estimates. *Suggestions:*

- $0.68 + $1.31 $2.00
- $0.17 + $0.58 $0.80
- $2.32 + $5.27 $7.60

Home Link 11.2 Follow-Up

Review answers. Give children practice with estimation skills by asking such questions as the following:

- You buy a bottle of glitter. You pay with a $5 bill. Should you get more or less than $3.00 in change? more
- You buy a box of crayons. You pay with a $1 bill. Should you get more or less than 4 dimes in change? less

Math Message

How many corners does a triangle have?
How many corners do 4 triangles have?

on slates draw + write equation

---

1 Teaching the Lesson

◆ Math Message Follow-Up
(*Math Masters*, p. 193)

WHOLE-CLASS DISCUSSION

Children solved number stories involving multiples of equal groups in Lessons 6.8–6.10. This lesson reviews and extends that earlier work.

Display a **multiplication diagram.** Leave space to draw an array and to write a number model.

As children share strategies for solving the Math Message problem, as well as other problems involving multiples of equal groups, you may want to use a routine like the following:

1. Display a multiplication diagram. Ask children to help you fill it in.

_____	____ per ____	____ in all

NOTE: The multiplication diagram can also be used to represent division problems, and it will appear in subsequent lessons in this unit. The diagram has two important uses:

- To help children organize the information in a problem by showing the quantities that are known and the quantity that is unknown and needs to be found

- To help children understand that multiplication and division are related (inverse) operations, in the same way that addition and subtraction are related operations

Children are not expected to draw diagrams at this time; however, they are expected to use a multiplication diagram to record the known and missing information for a problem.

Language Arts Link

The term **per** means **in each** or **for each.** Practice using these terms by asking children to rephrase information. For example, "6 tickets per family" can be rephrased as "6 tickets for each family," and "3 balls in each package" as "3 balls per package." Ask: *How many days per week?* 7 *How many minutes per hour?* 60 *How many hours per day?* 24 *How many weeks per year?* 52

2. Enter the known quantities; then write a question mark for the unknown quantity.

triangles	corners **per** _triangle_	corners **in all**
4	3	?

3. Have children use whatever means they want to solve the problem—counters, pictures, doodles, arrays, and so on.

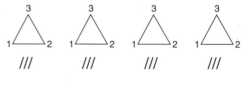

4. Ask a volunteer to write a number model for the problem.

$$4 \times 3 = 12$$

◆ Reviewing Multiplication Ideas and Terms

WHOLE-CLASS DISCUSSION

One use of multiplication is to find the total number of things in several equal groups. Emphasize that each group must contain the same number of things. That is, there are "so many things per group."

Remind children of phrases used to talk about multiplication. Examples include "4 times 3" and "3 multiplied by 4."

In the number model $4 \times 3 = 12$, 4 and 3 are called **factors** and 12 is called the **product.** Try to use the terms *factor* and *product* regularly, but do not expect children to use them.

◆ Making up and Solving Number Stories about Multiples of Equal Groups
(*Math Journal 2*, pp. 278 and 279)

PARTNER ACTIVITY

All of the number stories in this lesson have the same form. The number of groups and the number of objects in

Multiplication Number Stories

1. 3 vans full of people. How many people in all?

Holds 10 people

vans	people per **van**	people in all
3	10	?

Answer: _30_ people

Number model: _3_ × _10_ = _30_

2. 4 insects on the flower. How many legs in all?

Has 6 legs

insects	legs per **insect**	legs in all
4	6	?

Answer: _24_ legs

Number model: _4_ × _6_ = _24_

3. 9 windows. How many panes in all?

Has 4 panes

windows	panes per **window**	panes in all
9	4	?

Answer: _36_ panes

Number model: _9_ × _4_ = _36_

◆ *Math Journal 2*, p. 278

each group are known. The total number of objects is to be found. (These are called **rate multiplication stories.**)

As a warm-up, you and children make up and solve a few number stories about equal groups. Follow the routine described in the Math Message Follow-Up: Fill in a diagram; use counters, pictures, or diagrams to solve the problem; and write a number model. *Suggestions:*

- 6 four-leaf clovers. How many leaves in all? 24

- 3 pizzas, each in 6 pieces. How many pieces in all? 18

- 5-story building, 3 apartments per floor. How many apartments in all? 15

- 2 purses, 0 coins in each purse. How many coins in all? $0, 2 \times 0 = 0$

- 8 three-headed monsters. How many heads in all? 24

- 10 cartons, 8 bottles of juice in each carton. How many bottles in all? 80

 Adjusting the Activity Challenge children with the following problems:

- You saved 9 quarters. How much money is that? $9 \times 25 = 225$, or $2.25

- 56 tricycles. How many wheels in all? Use a calculator. $56 \times 3 = 168$

- 27 unicorns. How many horns in all? $27 \times 1 = 27$

The prefix *uni-* means *one.* For example, a unicorn has one horn and a unicycle has one wheel.

Once children are comfortable with the routine, assign the journal pages. Journal page 279 asks children to make up their own stories. While this may be difficult for some, the problems on journal page 278 furnish examples that children may imitate.

 Ongoing Learning & Practice

◆ Math Boxes 11.3 (*Math Journal 2*, p. 277)

INDEPENDENT ACTIVITY

 Mixed Review This journal page provides opportunities for cumulative review or assessment of concepts and skills.

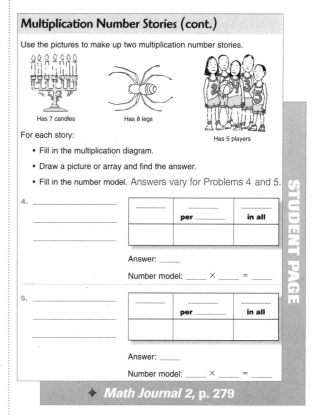

Multiplication Number Stories (cont.)

Use the pictures to make up two multiplication number stories.

Has 7 candles   Has 8 legs   Has 5 players

For each story:
- Fill in the multiplication diagram.
- Draw a picture or array and find the answer.
- Fill in the number model. Answers vary for Problems 4 and 5.

4. _____

	per _____	in all

Answer: _____

Number model: _____ × _____ = _____

5. _____

	per _____	in all

Answer: _____

Number model: _____ × _____ = _____

◆ *Math Journal 2*, p. 279

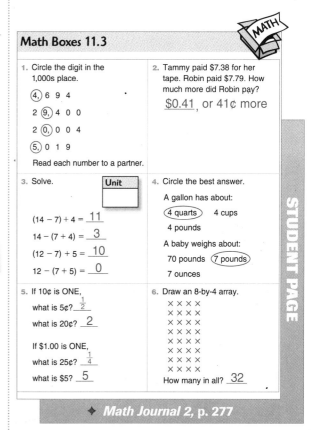

Math Boxes 11.3

1. Circle the digit in the 1,000s place.

   ④, 6 9 4

   2 ⑨, 4 0 0

   2 ⓪, 0 0 4

   ⑤, 0 1 9

   Read each number to a partner.

2. Tammy paid $7.38 for her tape. Robin paid $7.79. How much more did Robin pay?

   $0.41, or 41¢ more

3. Solve. **Unit**

   $(14 - 7) + 4 = $ 11

   $14 - (7 + 4) = $ 3

   $(12 - 7) + 5 = $ 10

   $12 - (7 + 5) = $ 0

4. Circle the best answer.

   A gallon has about:

   ④ quarts   4 cups

   4 pounds

   A baby weighs about:

   70 pounds ⑦ pounds

   7 ounces

5. If 10¢ is ONE,

   what is 5¢? $\frac{1}{2}$

   what is 20¢? 2

   If $1.00 is ONE,

   what is 25¢? $\frac{1}{4}$

   what is $5? 5

6. Draw an 8-by-4 array.

   × × × ×
   × × × ×
   × × × ×
   × × × ×
   × × × ×
   × × × ×
   × × × ×
   × × × ×

   How many in all? 32

◆ *Math Journal 2*, p. 277

Multiplication Number Stories

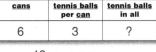

Family Note

In today's lesson, your child solved multiplication number stories in which he or she found the total number of things in several equal groups. Observe the strategies your child uses to solve the problems below. The "multiplication diagram" is a device used to keep track of the information in a problem.

To solve Problem 1, your child would identify the known information by writing a 6 under *cans* and a 3 under *tennis balls per can*. To identify the unknown information, your child would write a ? under *tennis balls in all*.

Please return this Home Link to school tomorrow.

Show someone at home how to solve these multiplication stories. Fill in each multiplication diagram.
Use counters or draw pictures or arrays to help you.

1. The store has 6 cans of tennis balls.
There are 3 balls in each can.
How many tennis balls are there in all?

cans	tennis balls per <u>can</u>	tennis balls in all
6	3	?

Answer: __18__ tennis balls

Number model: __6__ × __3__ = __18__

Math Masters, p. 391

Multiplication Stories (cont.)

2. Hamburger buns come in packages of 8.
You buy 4 packages.
How many buns are there in all?

packages	buns per <u>package</u>	buns in all
4	8	?

Answer: __32__ buns

Number model: __4__ × __8__ = __32__

3. Make up and solve a multiplication number story below.
<u>Number stories vary.</u>
_____
_____

_____	per _____	in all

Answer: _____

Number model: _____ × _____ = _____

Math Masters, p. 392

Home Connection Children show someone at home how to solve multiplication stories. Then they make up and solve a multiplication story of their own.

3 Options for Individualizing

◆ **ENRICHMENT Connecting Equal Groups to Literature**

SMALL-GROUP ACTIVITY 15–30 min

Literature Link Read the following books to children, or have them read the books themselves. Ask children to write and solve a multiplication number story from each book.

Each Orange Had Eight Slices: A Counting Book

Summary: Multiplication concepts are explored. For example, 3 red flowers are seen; each flower has 6 petals, and each petal has 2 black bugs. Questions are posed about the number of flowers, the number of petals, and the number of bugs.

Sea Squares

Summary: The concepts of multiples of equal groups and square numbers are introduced through such text as: "Seven heavy pelicans diving for their dinner. Seven fish in every pouch can never make them thinner."

One Hundred Hungry Ants

Summary: A group of 100 ants arrange themselves in a variety of arrays as they try to determine the most efficient way to get to a picnic.

✦ RETEACHING Making Equal Groups and Building Arrays
(*Math Masters,* p. 27; pp. 85 and 86; and pp. 110 and 111 or 112)

SMALL-GROUP ACTIVITY   **5–15 min**

The following Explorations, completed in previous units, use manipulatives to reinforce the concept of multiplication. Please choose one for student review at this time.

Exploration C: Egg Nests (Unit 2, Lesson 2.7)

Children roll a die twice to determine a number of nests and the number of eggs in each nest. Children draw the nests.

Exploration H: Cube Arrays (Unit 5, Lesson 5.3)

Children use centimeter cubes to make rectangular arrays. Children roll two dice to determine the number of rows and the number of cubes in each row. Children record their arrays on centimeter grid paper.

Exploration A: Geoboard Arrays (Unit 6, Lesson 6.7)

Children use rubber bands to make arrays on geoboards. Then they record these arrays on geoboard dot paper.

✦ EXTRA PRACTICE Playing *Array Bingo*
(*Math Masters,* pp. 117–119)

SMALL-GROUP ACTIVITY   **5–15 min**

This game was introduced in Lesson 6.10 and gives children practice in finding the total number of items in an array.

11.4 Division Number Models

OBJECTIVES To solve division number stories; and to introduce number models for division stories.

summaries	materials

1 Teaching the Lesson

Children make up and solve division stories, modeling them with counters, pictures, and diagrams; they use a diagram to record division story information; children write number models for division stories, including notation for remainders.
[Operations and Computation; Patterns, Functions, and Algebra]

- ☐ *Math Journal 2,* pp. 280 and 281
- ☐ Home Link 11.3
- ☐ Teaching Master transparency (*Math Masters,* p. 193; optional)
- ☐ slate
- ☐ 16 crayons for demonstration purposes

***See* Advance Preparation**

2 Ongoing Learning & Practice

Children practice and maintain skills through Math Boxes and Home Link activities.

- ☐ *Math Journal 2,* p. 282
- ☐ Home Link Master (*Math Masters,* p. 393)

3 Options for Individualizing

Enrichment Children write number models for arrays described in a literature selection. [Operations and Computation; Patterns, Functions, and Algebra]

Reteaching Children solve problems involving equal sharing and equal grouping by using manipulatives. [Operations and Computation; Measurement and Reference Frames; Patterns, Functions, and Algebra]

Reteaching Children model equal sharing and equal grouping on a number line. [Operations and Computation; Patterns, Functions, and Algebra]

- ☐ *Math Journal 1,* p. 151
- ☐ Teaching Masters (*Math Masters,* pp. 80, 82, and 83; p. 114; and p. 132)
- ☐ Teaching Aid Assessment Master (*Math Masters,* p. 486)
- ☐ *A Remainder of One*
- ☐ number line

***See* Advance Preparation**

Additional Information

Advance Preparation For the activities in Part 1, decide how you will display a multiplication/division diagram. You can make an overhead transparency of *Math Masters,* page 193 or draw the diagram on the board, preferably with semipermanent chalk.

For the optional Enrichment activity in Part 3, you will need to obtain the book *A Remainder of One* by Elinor J. Pinczes (Houghton Mifflin, 1995).

The first optional Reteaching activity in Part 3 is a choice of Explorations from previous units. (See Planning Ahead on page 781.)

Vocabulary • multiplication/division diagram • division • quotient • remainder • divided by

Mental Math and Reflexes

Pose problems involving equal groups. *Suggestions:*

- 5 kiddie pools. 3 children playing in each pool. How many children in all? 15 children
- 2 slides. 6 children waiting in line at each slide. What is the total number of children waiting? 12 children
- 7 swings. One child per swing. How many children are swinging? 7 children

Math Message

How can 2 children share 16 crayons equally? How can 3 children share 16 crayons equally? Draw a picture or diagram to solve the problem.

on slate

Home Link 11.3 Follow-Up

Review answers. Ask volunteers to share their multiplication stories. Consider saving the remainder of the stories for use as Mental Math and Reflexes problems in future lessons.

1 Teaching the Lesson

◆Math Message Follow-Up

WHOLE-CLASS DISCUSSION

Children solved division number stories about sharing and grouping in Lesson 6.11. This lesson reviews and extends that earlier work.

Display a multiplication diagram. Children used this diagram in the preceding lesson to help solve multiplication stories. Now they use the same diagram—more properly called a **multiplication/division diagram**—to help solve **division** stories.

1. Start with the story about 2 children sharing crayons. Ask the class to identify the known and unknown quantities as you record them on the diagram.

children	crayons per child	crayons in all
2	?	16

_____	____ per ____	____ in all

Use the same diagram for multiplication and division.

2. Have several volunteers act out the solution with real crayons. For example, one child might hold 16 crayons and "deal" these out to 2 other children in the same way that cards are dealt.

3. Draw an array or other diagram on the board to illustrate the story.

$$\times\times\times\times\times\times\times\times \ \ 8$$

$$\times\times\times\times\times\times\times\times \ \ 8$$

4. Ask children to describe the result. If 16 crayons are shared equally by 2 children, each child gets 8 crayons. No crayons are left over. Tell the class that the number of crayons each child gets (8) is called the **quotient** and that the number left over (0) is called the **remainder.**

Display another multiplication/division diagram. (Keep the one that is already filled in on display.) Follow the procedure described above for the story about 3 children sharing crayons. In this situation, the quotient is 5 and the remainder is 1. (See the margin.)

◆ Introducing Number Models for Division Stories

WHOLE-CLASS DISCUSSION

Tell the class that ÷ is a symbol for division in number models. This symbol is read "**divided by.**" (Other symbols for division are ⌐, the diagonal slash /, the horizontal fraction bar –, and the colon : .)

Write the following number-model format under the "2-children-share" multiplication/division diagram.

$$\underline{\ \ \ } \div \underline{\ \ \ } \rightarrow \underline{\ \ \ } \text{ R} \underline{\ \ \ }$$

Fill in the blanks, pointing out the numbers in the diagram.

$$\underline{16} \div \underline{2} \rightarrow \underline{8} \text{ R} \underline{0}$$

1. The first blank is for the number "in all."

2. The second blank is for the number of children sharing equally.

children	crayons per child	crayons in all
2	?	16

NOTE: Division of whole numbers gives two whole numbers—the quotient and the remainder. Since writing a number model such as 16 ÷ 3 = 5 R1 distorts the usual meaning of the = sign, it is suggested that you use the language and notation shown in this lesson.

3. The first blank to the right of the arrow is for the quotient.

4. The blank after R is for the remainder.

5. The resulting number model is read *16 divided by 2 gives 8, remainder 0.*

Repeat the above steps for the "3-children-share" problem. The number model is $16 \div 3 \rightarrow 5$ R1.

Have children practice writing the division symbol in the air and on their slates. Remind them to be very careful when reading or writing mathematical symbols so that they don't confuse one symbol with another. For example, it is easy to confuse $+$ and $\div$ symbols.

Children can fill in number models for division stories, but do not expect them to write the models from scratch at this time. Do, however, write such number models on the board so that children get used to them.

◆Making up and Solving Division Number Stories

WHOLE-CLASS ACTIVITY 👥👥👥

You and children make up and solve division number stories. In discussing solutions, follow the same procedure used previously: Fill in a diagram; use counters, pictures, or diagrams to help solve the problem; and write a number model. *Suggestions:*

- 12 pounds of meat are shared equally by 4 lions. How many pounds of meat per lion? How many pounds are left over? $12 \div 4 \rightarrow 3$ R0

- 2 trucks have 16 wheels in all. If each truck has the same number of wheels, how many wheels is that per truck? $16 \div 2 \rightarrow 8$ R0

 Adjusting the Activity Challenge children with the following problem: A deck of playing cards has 52 cards. If the cards are shared equally by 10 children, how many does each child get? How many cards are left over? $52 \div 10 \rightarrow 5$ R2

Some division stories involve making equal groups of things. Make up and solve stories of this type as well:

- 18 cans of juice are sold in 6-packs. How many 6-packs of juice? $18 \div 6 \rightarrow 3$ R0

- 28 hot dog buns are packed 8 buns to a package. How many packages? How many leftover buns?
  $28 \div 8 \rightarrow 3$ R4

Picture solution—12 pounds of meat are shared equally by 4 lions. How many pounds for each lion?

Division Number Stories

For each number story:

- Fill in the diagram.
- On a separate sheet of paper, draw a picture or array and find the answer. Complete the sentences.
- Fill in the number model.

1. The pet shop has 12 puppies in pens. There are 4 puppies in each pen. How many pens have puppies in them?

pens	puppies per __pen__	puppies in all
?	4	12

__3__ pens have puppies in them.   __0__ puppies are left over.

Number model: __12__ ÷ __4__ → __3__ R __0__

2. Five children are playing a game with a deck of 30 cards. How many cards can the dealer give each player?

childre	cards per __child__	cards in all
5	?	30

__6__ cards to each player.   __0__ cards are left over.

Number model: __30__ ÷ __5__ → __6__ R __0__

3. Eight children share 18 toys equally. How many toys does each child get?

children	toys per __child__	toys in all
8	?	18

Each child gets __2__ toys.

__2__ toys are left over.

Number model: __18__ ÷ __8__ → __2__ R __2__

◆ *Math Journal 2, p. 280*

Division Number Stories (cont.)

4. Tennis balls are sold 3 to a can. Rebecca buys 15 balls. How many cans is that?

cans	balls per __can__	balls in all
?	3	15

Rebecca buys __5__ cans.

Number model: __15__ ÷ __3__ → __5__ R __0__

5. Seven friends share 24 marbles equally. How many marbles does each friend get?

friends	marbles per __friend__	marbles in all
7	?	24

Each friend gets __3__ marbles.   __3__ marbles are left over.

Number model: __24__ ÷ __7__ → __3__ R __3__

6. Tina is storing 20 packages of seeds in boxes. Each box holds 6 packages. How many boxes does Tina need to store all the packages? (Be careful. Think!)

boxes	packages per __box__	packages in all
?	6	20

Tina needs __4__ boxes.

Number model: __20__ ÷ __6__ → __3__ R __2__

◆ *Math Journal 2, p. 281*

◆ Solving Division Number Stories
(*Math Journal 2*, pp. 280 and 281)

INDEPENDENT ACTIVITY

For Problems 3, 5, and 6, children must fill in the units (top line) in the diagram. Be sure to discuss Problem 6 on journal page 281. Tina will need 4 boxes, not 3.

Examples of student solutions

Problem 3: Eight children share 18 small toys equally. How many toys does each child get?

An array-type solution   A solution using counters

If each kid gets 1, that's 8.
If each kid gets 2, that's 16.
2 are left over.

A mental solution

Problem 6: Tina is storing 20 packages of seeds in boxes. Each box holds 6 packages. How many boxes does Tina need to store all the packages?

6   12   18   20

Tina needs 4 boxes.
1 box is not full.

Picture solution

counted: 1, 2, 3,   7, 8, 9,   13, 14, 15,   19, 20
          4, 5, 6   10, 11, 12   16, 17, 18

A solution using counters

2 Ongoing Learning & Practice

◆ Math Boxes 11.4 (*Math Journal 2*, p. 282)

INDEPENDENT ACTIVITY

 Mixed Review This journal page provides opportunities for cumulative review or assessment of concepts and skills.

◆ Home Link 11.4 (*Math Masters*, p. 393)

 Home Connection Children show someone at home how to solve division number stories. Then they make up and solve a number story of their own.

3 Options for Individualizing

◆ ENRICHMENT Connecting Division with Remainders to Literature

SMALL-GROUP ACTIVITY 5–15 min

 Literature Link Read the following book to children, or have them read the book themselves.

A Remainder of One

Summary: Joe is an ant. When groups of ants are formed into an array, he is always left out—"a remainder of one." He tells the queen ant of an array design in which he won't be left out.

Have children write number models for the different arrays shown in the story.

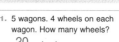

Math Boxes 11.4

1. 5 wagons. 4 wheels on each wagon. How many wheels?

__20__ wheels

Fill in the diagram and write a number model.

wagons	wheels per wagon	wheels in all
5	4	?

__5__ × __4__ = __20__

2. Sue spent $0.88 on glitter stickers and $0.23 on a large teddy bear sticker. How much did she spend?

Estimate: Sample answer:

$0.90 + $0.20 = $1.10

Answer:
$1.11

3. What is the value of the digit 4 in each number?

14 __4__

142 __40__

436 __400__

4,678 __4,000__

4. Count by 10s.

__872__, 882, __892__,

__902__, __912__, __922__,

__932__, __942__

5. You buy some stickers for $1.89. Show 2 ways to pay. Use Ⓟ, Ⓝ, Ⓓ, Ⓠ, and $1.

Sample answers:

$1 Ⓠ Ⓠ   Ⓠ Ⓠ Ⓠ Ⓠ
Ⓠ Ⓓ Ⓟ Ⓟ   Ⓠ Ⓓ Ⓓ Ⓝ
Ⓟ Ⓟ   Ⓟ Ⓟ Ⓟ Ⓟ

6. Solve. | Unit |

300 + 200 + 40 + 18 = __558__

40 + 20 + 19 = __79__

__669__ = 400 + 260 + 9

__657__ = 500 + 130 + 27

 ◆ *Math Journal 2*, p. 282

Division Number Stories
Home Link 11.4

Family Note: Today your child solved division number stories about equal sharing and equal groups. The diagram used for multiplication can also be used for division number stories to identify known and unknown information. Your child will write a number model for each problem below. A number model is the symbolic representation of a number story. For example, in Problem 1, the number model is 18 ÷ 3 → 6 R0. This model is read as *18 divided by 6 gives 3, remainder 0.* An arrow is used instead of an equals (=) sign because the result of a division problem can be two whole numbers: the quotient and remainder.

Please return this Home Link to school tomorrow.

Show someone at home how to solve these division stories. Use counters or draw pictures or diagrams to help you.

1. Our group needs 18 pens. There are 3 pens in each package. How many packages must we buy?

packages	pens per package	pens in all
?	3	18

Answer: __6__ packages

Number model: __18__ ÷ __3__ → 6 R__0__

2. Four children are playing a game with 25 cards. How many cards can the dealer give each player?

children	cards per child	cards in all
4	?	25

Answer: __6__ cards

Number model: __25__ ÷ __4__ → 6 R__1__

3. Make up and solve a division story on the back of this sheet.
Answers vary.

 ◆ *Math Masters*, p. 393

✦ RETEACHING Acting out Equal Sharing and Equal Grouping

(Math Journal 1, p. 151; Math Masters, pp. 81, 83, and 84; p. 114; and pp. 132 and 486)

SMALL-GROUP ACTIVITY 15–30 min

The following Explorations, completed in previous units, use manipulatives to reinforce the concepts of equal sharing and equal grouping. Please choose one for student review at this time.

Exploration F in Unit 5 (Lesson 5.2): Equal Sharing

The setting of eggs in nests is repeated, but this time the activity calls for sharing a certain number of eggs equally among a given number of nests.

Exploration C in Unit 6 (Lesson 6.7): How Many Children Get n Things?

Instead of asking children to equally share a given number of things among a specified number of groups, children are asked to determine how many groups of a certain number can be made from a specified number.

Exploration B in Unit 7 (Lesson 7.6): Sharing Money

Children are given a problem involving equal sharing of money.

✦ RETEACHING Modeling Equal Sharing and Equal Grouping on a Number Line

SMALL-GROUP ACTIVITY 15–30 min

Counters are one device to model equal-sharing and equal-grouping situations. Number lines are another. Some children may find the concepts easier to understand if they are modeled as follows:

Equal sharing

Consider the problem $15 \div 3 \rightarrow ?$ On a number line, the distance from 0 to 15 can be divided into 3 equal parts. The size of each part is the number of "hops" in each part. The total is known, and the number of parts is known. The size of each part needs to be determined.

Equal grouping

Again consider $15 \div 3 \rightarrow ?$ Using a number line, the total distance from 0 to 15 (or from 15 to 0) is measured out in "hops" of 3. The number of "hops" of 3 is the total number of equal groups. The total is known, and the size of each group is known. The number of groups needs to be determined.

11.5 Multiplication Facts

OBJECTIVES To introduce multiplication facts; and to review and practice 2s, 5s, and 10s products.

summaries	materials
1 Teaching the Lesson	
Children use arrays to list multiplication facts and to find products. [Operations and Computation; Patterns, Functions, and Algebra]	☐ *Math Journal 2*, pp. 283 and 284 ☐ Home Link 11.4 ☐ slate
2 Ongoing Learning & Practice	
Children practice and maintain skills through Math Boxes and Home Link activities.	☐ *Math Journal 2*, p. 285 ☐ Home Link Master (*Math Masters*, p. 394)
3 Options for Individualizing	
Reteaching Children connect 5s facts to the "clock facts" by identifying minutes past the hour as multiples of 5. [Numeration; Operations and Computation] **Extra Practice** Children practice multiplication facts by playing *Multiplication Draw*. [Operations and Computation] **Extra Practice** Children practice multiplying by 10. [Operations and Computation]	☐ Teaching Masters (*Math Masters*, pp. 194 and 195) ☐ analog clock or picture of a clock ☐ number cards 1–5 and 10 (from the Everything Math Deck, if available) ☐ calculator (optional) ☐ *Minute Math®*, p. 43

Additional Information

Vocabulary • **multiplication fact** • **fact power**

Getting Started

Mental Math and Reflexes

Have children count in unison …

- by 2s to 30.
- by 5s to 50.
- by 10s to 100.

Math Message

5 rows of tomato plants.
4 plants in each row.
How many plants in all?
Draw an array.

Home Link 11.4 Follow-Up

Review answers. Volunteers share their division stories. Consider saving the remainder of the stories for use as Mental Math and Reflexes problems in future lessons.

◆ Math Message Follow-Up

WHOLE-CLASS DISCUSSION

Ask a volunteer to draw an array for the problem on the board. Review the language of arrays. Examples: "5 rows of plants, 4 plants in each row" or "a 5-by-4 array of plants." Have children describe how they found the total number of plants. Some strategies: count by 4s; add $4 + 4 + 4 + 4 + 4$; double 4, double the result, and add 4 to the total; double 5 and double the result.

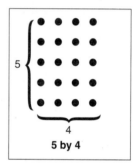

5-by-4 array: 5 rows, 4 in each row

◆ Discussing the Meaning of *Multiplication Fact*

WHOLE-CLASS DISCUSSION

Explain that a **multiplication fact** is the product of two numbers that are either 1-digit numbers, or 10. The multiplication fact for the Math Message problem is $5 \times 4 = 20$.

Pose other "tomato plant" problems. For example, *How many tomato plants are there in 6 rows with 3 plants in each row?* $6 \times 3 = 18$ Have children draw arrays on their slates and write the multiplication fact for the array.

Remind children of the importance of **fact power.** As with addition facts, it is much easier in the long run to know multiplication facts than to have to figure them out.

◆ Multiplying by 2, 5, and 10

WHOLE-CLASS ACTIVITY

Tell children that they already know many multiplication facts. To review these facts, you might try the following routine:

You say	Class answers
double 1	2
double 2	4
double 3	6
and so on	
1 nickel	5 cents
2 nickels	10 cents
3 nickels	15 cents
and so on	
1 dime	10 cents
2 dimes	20 cents
3 dimes	30 cents
and so on	

Provide visual reinforcement by writing the related multiplication facts on the board.

Examples: For "2 nickels is 10 cents," write $2 \times 5 = 10$.
For "3 dimes is 30 cents," write $3 \times 10 = 30$.

This oral review suggests a memory aid that may help many children.

For times-5 facts, suggest that children "think nickels."

Example: $7 \times 5 = ?$ 7 nickels is 35¢, so $7 \times 5 = 35$.

For times-10 facts, suggest that children "think dimes."

Example: $7 \times 10 = ?$ 7 dimes is 70¢, so $7 \times 10 = 70$.

◆ Listing Multiplication Facts from 2s to 10s
(*Math Journal 2,* p. 283)

SMALL-GROUP ACTIVITY

Divide the class into nine groups and ask children to turn to journal page 283. Assign the times-2 facts to one group, the times-3 facts to another group, and so on, through the times-10 facts.

Children complete the facts and their products on the journal page. They draw arrays for the facts they don't know by circling dots or marking them with Xs. Encourage children to look for patterns in their lists. Tell them to be prepared to talk about the patterns they see. For example, the products of the times-4 facts, listed in increasing order, are the same as counts by 4.
8, 12, 16, …, 32, 36, 40

In the following lesson, groups will combine their answers to journal page 283 and complete a Products Table on journal page 286.

Adjusting the Activity Provide additional visual support by drawing an array for each fact that you write. *For example:*

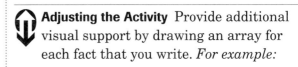

$1 \times 5 = 5$ $2 \times 5 = 10$ $3 \times 5 = 15$ and so on

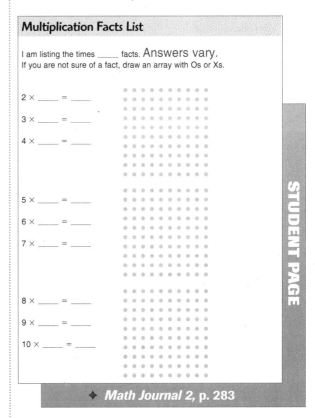

Multiplication Facts List

I am listing the times _____ facts. Answers vary.
If you are not sure of a fact, draw an array with Os or Xs.

$2 \times$ _____ = _____

$3 \times$ _____ = _____

$4 \times$ _____ = _____

$5 \times$ _____ = _____

$6 \times$ _____ = _____

$7 \times$ _____ = _____

$8 \times$ _____ = _____

$9 \times$ _____ = _____

$10 \times$ _____ = _____

STUDENT PAGE

◆ *Math Journal 2,* p. 283

Using Arrays to Find Products

Draw an array to help you find each product.
Use Xs to draw your arrays.

1. $2 \times 4 =$ __8__ x x x x x x x x x x	**2.** $4 \times 2 =$ __8__ x x x x x x x x
3. $6 \times 5 =$ __30__ x x x x x x x x x x x x x x x x x x x x x x x x x x x x x x	**4.** $5 \times 6 =$ __30__ x x x x x x x x x x x x x x x x x x x x x x x x x x x x x x
5. $5 \times 5 =$ __25__ x x x x x x x x x x x x x x x x x x x x x x x x x	**6.** $2 \times 10 =$ __20__ x x x x x x x x x x x x x x x x x x x x

Challenge

7. $4 \times 15 =$ __60__
x x x x x x x x x x x x x x x
x x x x x x x x x x x x x x x
x x x x x x x x x x x x x x x
x x x x x x x x x x x x x x x

Math Journal 2, p. 284

◆ Using Arrays to Find Products
(*Math Journal 2*, p. 284)

INDEPENDENT ACTIVITY

Children draw arrays for multiplication facts.

2 Ongoing Learning & Practice

◆ Math Boxes 11.5 (*Math Journal 2*, p. 285)

INDEPENDENT ACTIVITY

Mixed Review This journal page provides opportunities for cumulative review or assessment of concepts and skills.

◆ Home Link 11.5 (*Math Masters*, p. 394)

Home Connection Children show someone at home how to find products by drawing arrays. Then they find the product without the help of visual aids.

Math Boxes 11.5

1. Each square has 4 corners. 16 corners in all. How many squares? __4__ squares
Fill in the diagram and write a number model.

squares	corners per square	corners in all
?	4	16

$16 \div 4 \rightarrow 4$ R 0

2. 3 insects. 6 legs per insect. How many legs in all?
__18__ legs
Fill in the diagram and write a number model.

insects	legs per insect	legs in all
3	6	?

$3 \times 6 = 18$

3. Write another name for each number.

50 tens = ___500___

32 hundreds = ___3,200___

6,240 = 624 ___tens___

12,000 = 12 ___thousands___

4. A movie ticket costs $2.50. Popcorn costs $1.75. I have $5.00. Is that enough to buy both?

___yes___

5. Write a number or a fraction.

There are __4__ quarters in one dollar.

One quarter = $\frac{1}{4}$ dollar.

There are __10__ dimes in one dollar.

One dime = $\frac{1}{10}$ dollar.

6. Draw a rectangle.
Make 2 sides $4\frac{1}{2}$ cm long.
Make the other 2 sides $2\frac{1}{2}$ cm long.

Math Journal 2, p. 285

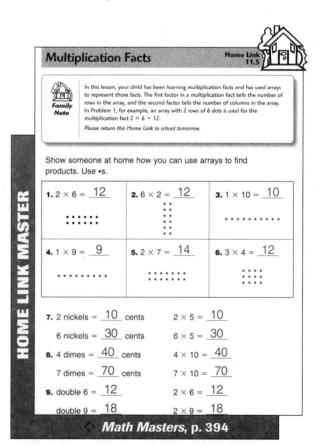

Multiplication Facts

Home Link 11.5

Family Note

In this lesson, your child has been learning multiplication facts and has used arrays to represent those facts. The first factor in a multiplication fact tells the number of rows in the array, and the second factor tells the number of columns in the array. In Problem 1, for example, an array with 2 rows of 6 dots is used for the multiplication fact $2 \times 6 = 12$.

Please return this Home Link to school tomorrow.

Show someone at home how you can use arrays to find products. Use •s.

1. $2 \times 6 =$ __12__	**2.** $6 \times 2 =$ __12__	**3.** $1 \times 10 =$ __10__
4. $1 \times 9 =$ __9__	**5.** $2 \times 7 =$ __14__	**6.** $3 \times 4 =$ __12__

7. 2 nickels = __10__ cents $2 \times 5 =$ __10__

6 nickels = __30__ cents $6 \times 5 =$ __30__

8. 4 dimes = __40__ cents $4 \times 10 =$ __40__

7 dimes = __70__ cents $7 \times 10 =$ __70__

9. double 6 = __12__ $2 \times 6 =$ __12__

double 9 = __18__ $2 \times 9 =$ __18__

Math Masters, p. 394

---

3 Options for Individualizing

✦ RETEACHING Introducing 5s Facts as the "Clock Facts"

SMALL-GROUP ACTIVITY 5–15 min

If some children are having difficulty with the times-5 facts, a clock or picture of a clock may help them remember the products. The "clock facts" focus on the minute hand of the clock. *For example:*

▷ When the minute hand is on the 8, the time is 40 minutes past the hour: $8 \times 5 = 40$.

▷ When the minute hand is on the 2, the time is 10 minutes past the hour: $2 \times 5 = 10$.

✦ EXTRA PRACTICE Playing *Multiplication Draw* (*Math Masters,* pp. 194 and 195)

SMALL-GROUP ACTIVITY 15–30 min

This game gives children practice multiplying 2, 5, and 10 times the numbers 1 through 5 and 10. If children are ready for a challenge, have them use the 1–10 number cards.

✦ EXTRA PRACTICE Minute Math

SMALL-GROUP ACTIVITY 5–15 min

To offer children more experience with multiplying by 10, see the following page in *Minute Math:*

Operations: p. 43

Multiplication Draw

Materials	number cards 1–5 and 10
	calculator (optional)
Players	2 to 4

Directions

1. Mix the cards. Place them facedown between the players.
2. Begin with the 1st Round (times-2 facts).
3. Each player …
   - draws a card. This is a missing factor.
   - writes this factor after "1st draw" in the 1st Round column on the next page.
   - writes the product.

Example: A player …
   - draws a 3.
   - writes 3 in 2 × ____.
   - solves 2 × __3__ = ____.

4. Players return their cards to the pile. Mix the cards and place them facedown.
5. Repeat Steps 3 and 4 for four more draws.

◇ *Math Masters,* p. 194

TEACHING MASTER

Multiplication Draw (cont.)

6. After the 5th draw, players add their five products. They may use calculators.
7. The player with the largest sum wins the round.
8. Repeat the above steps for the 2nd Round (times-5 facts) and 3rd Round (times-10 facts).

	1st Round: 2s	2nd Round: 5s	3rd Round: 10s
1st draw	2 × ___ = ___	5 × ___ = ___	10 × ___ = ___
2nd draw	___ × 2 = ___	___ × 5 = ___	___ × 10 = ___
3rd draw	___ × 2 = ___	___ × 5 = ___	___ × 10 = ___
4th draw	2 × ___ = ___	5 × ___ = ___	10 × ___ = ___
5th draw	___ × 2 = ___	___ × 5 = ___	___ × 10 = ___
Sum of products			

✓ *Math Masters,* p. 195

TEACHING MASTER

11.6

Products Table

OBJECTIVES To learn the 1s and 0s multiplication facts; and to discover patterns in multiplication facts.

summaries	materials
1 Teaching the Lesson	
Children complete a table of multiplication facts up to 10 × 10; children look for patterns in the table, including the turn-around rule. [Operations and Computation; Patterns, Functions, and Algebra]	☐ *Math Journal 2*, pp. 283 and 286 ☐ Home Link 11.5 ☐ Teaching Master transparency (*Math Masters*, p. 196; optional) ☐ *Sea Squares* (optional) ***See* Advance Preparation**
2 Ongoing Learning & Practice	
Children practice multiplication with 2, 5, and 10. [Operations and Computation] Children practice and maintain skills through Math Boxes and Home Link activities.	☐ *Math Journal 2*, pp. 287, 288, and Activity Sheets 6 and 7 ☐ Home Link Master (*Math Masters*, p. 395) ☐ scissors
3 Options for Individualizing	
Enrichment Children investigate square numbers by drawing arrays on grid paper. [Operations and Computation; Patterns, Functions, and Algebra] **Extra Practice** Children practice multiplication facts with "What's My Rule?" exercises. [Operations and Computation]	☐ Teaching Masters (*Math Masters*, pp. 86, 197, and 198) ☐ centimeter cubes and/or pennies; tape ☐ *Minute Math*®, p. 15 ***See* Advance Preparation**

Additional Information

Advance Preparation For the activities in Part 1, you may want to obtain the book *Sea Squares* by Joy N. Hulme (Hyperion Books for Children, 1991). For the *Introducing the Products Table* activity, you may want to create an overhead transparency of *Math Masters*, page 196.

For the optional Enrichment activity in Part 3, provide each group with several copies of *Math Masters*, page 86.

Vocabulary • **factor** • **product** • **square (of a number)** • **turn-around rule for multiplication**

Getting Started

Mental Math and Reflexes

Pose division number stories. *Suggestions:*

• 4 children share 9 chocolate bars equally. How many chocolate bars are there per child? 2 How many are left over? 1

• There are 12 flowers. Each child gets 2 flowers. How many children are there? 6 How many flowers are left over? 0

Math Message

5 children share 3 bags of apples equally.
Each bag contains 6 apples.
How many apples does each child get?
How many apples are left over?

Home Link 11.5
Follow-Up
Review answers.

1 Teaching the Lesson

◆ Math Message Follow-Up

WHOLE-CLASS DISCUSSION

You may want to have children act out the problem to demonstrate the use of both multiplication and division in the solution.

- How many apples are there in all? $3 \times 6 = 18$

- How many apples does each child get? 3 How many apples are left over? 3

- Number model: $18 \div 5 \rightarrow 3$ R3

◆ Introducing the Products Table
(*Math Journal 2*, p. 286; *Math Masters*, p. 196)

WHOLE-CLASS DISCUSSION

Remind children of the phrases and terms used to talk about multiplication. *For example:*

- 4×3 is read "4 times 3" or "3 multiplied by 4."

- In the number model $4 \times 3 = 12$, 4 and 3 are called **factors** and 12 is called the **product.**

Ask the class to look for patterns in the Products Table on journal page 286. The patterns might include the following:

▷ The first factor is the same for all problems in any one row.

▷ The second factor is the same for all problems in any one column.

NOTE: You may want to demonstrate the patterns in the Products Table on *Math Masters*, page 196 on an overhead projector. This master is identical to journal page 286.

▼ For additional practice, you may use *Math Masters*, page 196, which is identical to this page.

Products Table

0×0 =0	0×1 =0	0×2 =0	0×3 =0	0×4 =0	0×5 =0	0×6 =0	0×7 =0	0×8 =0	0×9 =0	0×10 =0
1×0 =0	1×1 =1	1×2 =2	1×3 =3	1×4 =4	1×5 =5	1×6 =6	1×7 =7	1×8 =8	1×9 =9	1×10 =10
2×0 =0	2×1 =2	2×2 =4	2×3 =6	2×4 =8	2×5 =10	2×6 =12	2×7 =14	2×8 =16	2×9 =18	2×10 =20
3×0 =0	3×1 =3	3×2 =6	3×3 =9	3×4 =12	3×5 =15	3×6 =18	3×7 =21	3×8 =24	3×9 =27	3×10 =30
4×0 =0	4×1 =4	4×2 =8	4×3 =12	4×4 =16	4×5 =20	4×6 =24	4×7 =28	4×8 =32	4×9 =36	4×10 =40
5×0 =0	5×1 =5	5×2 =10	5×3 =15	5×4 =20	5×5 =25	5×6 =30	5×7 =35	5×8 =40	5×9 =45	5×10 =50
6×0 =0	6×1 =6	6×2 =12	6×3 =18	6×4 =24	6×5 =30	6×6 =36	6×7 =42	6×8 =48	6×9 =54	6×10 =60
7×0 =0	7×1 =7	7×2 =14	7×3 =21	7×4 =28	7×5 =35	7×6 =42	7×7 =49	7×8 =56	7×9 =63	7×10 =70
8×0 =0	8×1 =8	8×2 =16	8×3 =24	8×4 =32	8×5 =40	8×6 =48	8×7 =56	8×8 =64	8×9 =72	8×10 =80
9×0 =0	9×1 =9	9×2 =18	9×3 =27	9×4 =36	9×5 =45	9×6 =54	9×7 =63	9×8 =72	9×9 =81	9×10 =90
10×0 =0	10×1 =10	10×2 =20	10×3 =30	10×4 =40	10×5 =50	10×6 =60	10×7 =70	10×8 =80	10×9 =90	10×10 =100

STUDENT PAGE

◆ *Math Journal 2*, p. 286

Literature Link

Sea Squares by Joy N. Hulme (Hyperion Books for Children, 1991) introduces square numbers with such text as "Seven heavy pelicans diving for their dinner. Seven fish in every pouch can never make them thinner."

Be sure children notice that each product in the highlighted diagonal has two identical factors. A product of two identical factors is called a **square.** For example, $7 \times 7 = 49$, so 49 is the square of 7.

Adjusting the Activity Challenge children by asking them to find a pattern for the products along the diagonal. Ask children to look for the difference between the products in order, beginning with 0 and 1. Children will most likely notice that the differences between the products increases by 2 as the products become larger.

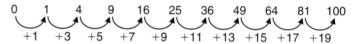

◆ Discussing and Recording 1s and 0s Products (*Math Journal 2*, p. 286)

WHOLE-CLASS DISCUSSION

Point out sets of objects in the room to illustrate the 1s products. For example: *How many pencils in 1 set of 6 pencils?* $1 \times 6 = 6$ *How many chairs at 4 tables with 1 chair at each table?* $4 \times 1 = 4$

Have the class chant the ones products in unison and write them under the problems in the ones rows and ones columns of their tables. Ask if anyone sees a pattern. The product of any number and 1 is always that number. Ask: *What is 1 times 100?* 100 *356 times 1?* 356 And so on.

Tell "zero stories" like the following to illustrate zero products:

• Marla's jacket has 4 pockets. All 4 pockets are empty. How many pennies are there in Marla's pockets? $4 \times 0 = 0$

• There are 10 pieces of chalk in a box. Mrs. Gardner has no boxes of chalk. How many pieces of chalk does she have in boxes? $0 \times 10 = 0$

Ask children to make up other "zero stories."

Ask, *Does anyone see a pattern?* The product of a number and 0 is always 0. *What is 0×273?* 0 *What is 999×0?* 0

Children write the products in the zeros rows and zeros columns of the Products Table.

If I hide my hands, how many fingers can you see?

A child's "zero story" idea

◆ Recording Other Products in the Products Table (*Math Journal 2*, pp. 283 and 286)

Start by asking children who were responsible for listing the 2s products on journal page 283 to report their products. Each child records these products on his or her Products Table on journal page 286. Children discuss any patterns they find in the list.

Follow the same procedure for the other products. Children share patterns after recording each list of products. *For example:*

▷ Products for multiplication facts by *n*, when listed in increasing order, are the same as counts by *n*. For example, the products for times-5 facts are 0, 5, 10, 15, 20, and so on.

▷ The ones digits for products of multiplication facts by *n* have a repeating pattern. For times-5 facts, the ones digits have the simple pattern 0, 5, 0, 5, 0, ... For times-4 facts, the pattern is 0, 4, 8, 2, 6, 0, 4, 8, 2, 6, ...

Ask whether there is a **turn-around rule for multiplication.** Yes. If the order of the factors is reversed, the product remains the same. Have children verify the turn-around rule using examples from the Products Table. Discuss why the turn-around rule helps build fact power. If you know a fact, then you also know the turn-around fact.

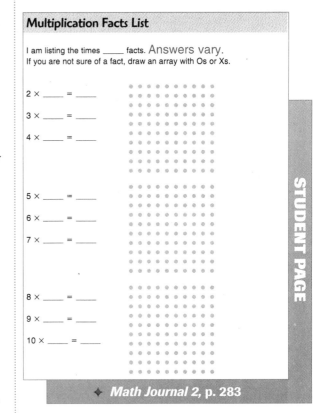

✦ *Math Journal 2, p. 283*

2 Ongoing Learning & Practice

◆ Practicing Multiplication Facts with 2, 5, and 10 (*Math Journal 2*, p. 287)

INDEPENDENT ACTIVITY

Children practice facts by completing number models, finding the total cents for amounts of nickels and dimes, and writing turn-around facts.

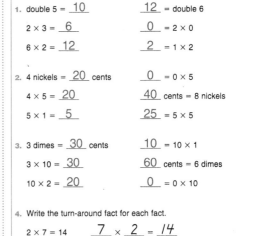

✦ *Math Journal 2, p. 287*

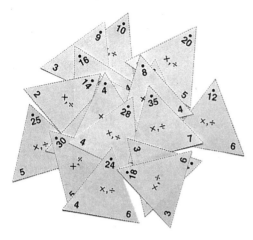

Activity Sheets 6 and 7 contain these Fact Triangles.

◆ Cutting out Fact Triangles
(*Math Journal 2,* Activity Sheets 6 and 7)

INDEPENDENT ACTIVITY

Children cut out the Fact Triangles from Activity Sheets 6 and 7.

There are four pages of Fact Triangles for multiplication/division facts. These first two pages of cards will be used in the following lesson.

◆ Math Boxes 11.6 (*Math Journal 2,* p. 288)

INDEPENDENT ACTIVITY

Mixed Review This journal page provides opportunities for cumulative review or assessment of concepts and skills.

◆ Home Link 11.6 (*Math Masters,* p. 395)

Home Connection Children show someone at home what they know about multiplication facts, explain why 0s and 1s facts are easy to solve, and make up their own problems.

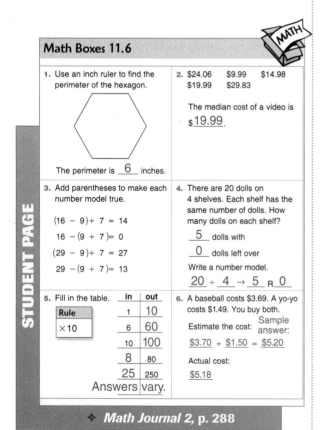

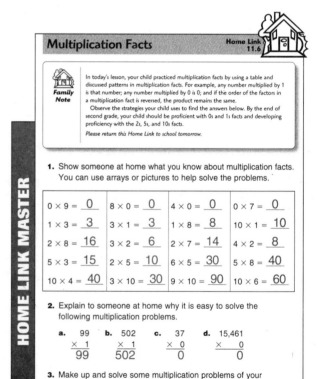

3 Options for Individualizing

◆ ENRICHMENT Investigating Square Numbers (*Math Masters*, pp. 86, 197, and 198)

SMALL-GROUP ACTIVITY   15–30 min

Children build square arrays for as many numbers as possible, beginning with 2. They record their arrays on centimeter grid paper. As children build arrays for larger products, they will need to tape sheets of grid paper together.

Children write a number model under each array diagram. Then they make a table of the factors and the products and try to discern number patterns.

◆ EXTRA PRACTICE Minute Math

SMALL-GROUP ACTIVITY  5–15 min

To offer children more experience with multiplication facts through 10s, see the following page in *Minute Math:*

Basic Routines: p. 15

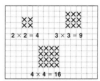

11.7 Multiplication/ Division Fact Families

OBJECTIVES To introduce multiplication and division fact families; and to practice multiplication and division facts.

summaries / materials

1 Teaching the Lesson

Children make up and solve division stories based on multiplication stories, using the same diagram to solve both kinds; children are introduced to multiplication/division fact families; children use Fact Triangles to practice multiplication and division facts. [Operations and Computation; Patterns, Functions, and Algebra]

- ☐ *Math Journal 2,* p. 289 and Activity Sheets 6 and 7
- ☐ Home Link 11.6
- ☐ Teaching Master transparencies (*Math Masters,* pp. 193 and 199; optional)
- ☐ scissors; paper clip

***See* Advance Preparation**

2 Ongoing Learning & Practice

Children practice multiplication and division facts with 2, 5, and 10. [Operations and Computation; Patterns, Functions, and Algebra]

Children practice and maintain skills through Math Boxes and Home Link activities.

- ☐ *Math Journal 2,* pp. 290 and 291
- ☐ Home Link Masters (*Math Masters,* pp. 396 and 397)

3 Options for Individualizing

Enrichment Children make up and solve multiplication and division number stories. [Operations and Computation]

Extra Practice Children write multiplication/division fact families using three given numbers. [Operations and Computation; Patterns, Functions, and Algebra]

- ☐ Teaching Master (*Math Masters,* p. 22)
- ☐ *Minute Math*®, p. 41

Additional Information

Advance Preparation Plan on spending two days on this lesson.

For the Day 1 activities in Part 1, decide how you will display a multiplication/division diagram and a Fact Triangle. You can make an overhead transparency of *Math Masters,* pages 193 and 199 or draw the diagram and triangle on the board, preferably with semipermanent chalk. For the *Introducing Fact Families for Multiplication and Division* activity, you may want to create an overhead transparency of *Math Masters,* page 199.

For the teaching activities in Part 1, children will need the Fact Triangles cut from Activity Sheets 6 and 7.

Vocabulary • multiplication/division diagram • fact family

Getting Started

Mental Math and Reflexes

Pose times-0, times-1, times-2, times-5, and times-10 facts like the following:

$4 \times 10 = ?$ 40 $3 \times 5 = ?$ 15 $9 \times 0 = ?$ 0 $8 \times 2 = ?$ 16 $4 \times 1 = ?$ 4

Math Message

Tennis balls are sold 3 per can.
Write and solve a multiplication number story about tennis balls.

**Home Link 11.6
Follow-Up**
Review answers.

1 Teaching the Lesson

DAY 1

◆ Math Message Follow-Up

WHOLE-CLASS DISCUSSION

Have children share a few multiplication stories and their solutions.

◆ Making Division Stories from Multiplication Stories (*Math Masters*, p. 193)

WHOLE-CLASS ACTIVITY

Choose two or three of children's multiplication stories. Help the class make up division stories related to the multiplication stories. For example, from the multiplication story below, one can make up two division stories in which the product is divided by one of the factors. Display **multiplication/division diagrams** for each.

Multiplication story

5 cans
3 tennis balls per can
How many tennis balls in all?

```
        3
      ● ● ●
      ● ● ●
   5  ● ● ●
      ● ● ●
      ● ● ●
    ? in all
```

cans	tennis balls per can	tennis balls in all
5	3	?

$5 \times 3 = 15$
Answer: 15 balls

NOTE: This diagram was called a *multiplication diagram* when it was first used in Lesson 11.3 because it was used to record information in multiplication number stories. The same diagram can also be used to record information in division number stories. It is, therefore, more accurate to refer to the diagram as a *multiplication/division diagram*.

Division story   ?

15 tennis balls in 5 cans
How many tennis balls in each can?   5
How many tennis balls left over?

                                                                    15 in all

cans	tennis balls per ___can___	tennis balls in all
5	?	15

$15 \div 5 \rightarrow 3$ R0
Answer: 3 tennis balls per can, 0 tennis balls left over

Division story   3

15 tennis balls in all
3 balls per can
How many cans?   ?
How many tennis balls left over?

                                                                    15 in all

cans	tennis balls per ___can___	tennis balls in all
?	3	15

$15 \div 3 \rightarrow 5$ R0
Answer: 5 cans, 0 tennis balls left over

As in previous lessons, draw pictures or arrays, make and
fill in diagrams (similar diagrams can be used for all three
related stories), and write number models.

◆ Introducing Fact Families for Multiplication and Division (*Math Masters*, p. 199)

WHOLE-CLASS DISCUSSION

Briefly review the concept of **fact families** for addition
and subtraction. Refer to the related multiplication and
division stories you have just discussed to illustrate that
there are also fact families for multiplication and
division. For each multiplication fact, there is a turn-around
multiplication fact and two related division facts (except
for certain 0 facts and doubles facts).

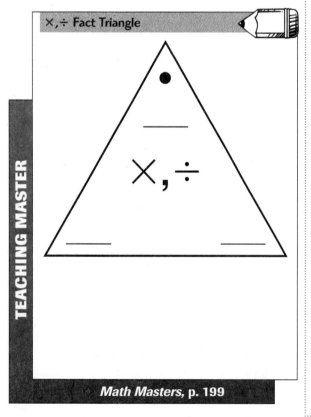

×, ÷ Fact Triangle

×, ÷

TEACHING MASTER

◆ *Math Masters*, p. 199

Example: $5 \times 3 = 15$

The turn-around multiplication fact is $3 \times 5 = 15$.

The two related division facts are $15 \div 5 = 3$ and $15 \div 3 = 5$.

Draw a large Fact Triangle on the board and write $\times, \div$ in the center and • in the top corner; or display an overhead transparency of *Math Masters,* page 199. Write 3, 5, and 15 in the corners (see below). Call children's attention to the symbols in the middle of the triangle, which distinguish multiplication/division Fact Triangles from addition/subtraction Fact Triangles.

Point to the number in each corner and ask how that number is related to the other two numbers. Write the fact family on the board.

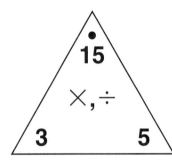

$$5 \times 3 = 15$$
$$3 \times 5 = 15$$
$$15 \div 5 = 3$$
$$15 \div 3 = 5$$

Each number triplet is used to name two multiplication and two division facts.

Give children several multiplication facts and ask them to complete each fact family as you model the facts on the board using Fact Triangles.

✦ Completing Fact Families for Fact Triangles
(*Math Journal 2,* p. 289)

INDEPENDENT ACTIVITY

As children complete fact families for different Fact Triangles, remind them that they need to use all three numbers in each of the four number models.

DAY 2

✦ Practicing with Multiplication/Division Fact Triangles (*Math Journal 2,* Activity Sheets 6–7)

PARTNER ACTIVITY

If children have not already cut out the multiplication/division Fact Triangles from Activity Sheets 6 and 7, have them do that now. Children can store these Fact Triangles in the same envelope as their

Multiplication/Division Fact Families

Write the fact family for each Fact Triangle.

1. 10 / 2 / 5 — $\times, \div$
$$\underline{5} \times \underline{2} = \underline{10}$$
$$\underline{2} \times \underline{5} = 10$$
$$\underline{10} \div \underline{2} = \underline{5}$$
$$10 \div \underline{5} = \underline{2}$$

2. 12 / 3 / 4 — $\times, \div$
$$\underline{4} \times \underline{3} = 12$$
$$\underline{3} \times \underline{4} = 12$$
$$12 \div \underline{4} = \underline{3}$$
$$12 \div \underline{3} = \underline{4}$$

3. 21 / 3 / 7 — $\times, \div$
$$\underline{3} \times \underline{7} = 21$$
$$\underline{7} \times \underline{3} = 21$$
$$21 \div \underline{7} = \underline{3}$$
$$21 \div \underline{3} = \underline{7}$$

4. 40 / 5 / 8 — $\times, \div$
$$\underline{5} \times \underline{8} = 40$$
$$\underline{8} \times \underline{5} = 40$$
$$40 \div \underline{8} = \underline{5}$$
$$40 \div \underline{5} = \underline{8}$$

5. 54 / 6 / 9 — $\times, \div$
$$\underline{6} \times \underline{9} = 54$$
$$\underline{9} \times \underline{6} = 54$$
$$54 \div \underline{9} = \underline{6}$$
$$54 \div \underline{6} = \underline{9}$$

6. 28 / 4 / 7 — $\times, \div$
$$\underline{4} \times \underline{7} = 28$$
$$\underline{7} \times \underline{4} = 28$$
$$28 \div \underline{4} = \underline{7}$$
$$28 \div \underline{7} = \underline{4}$$

✦ *Math Journal 2,* p. 289

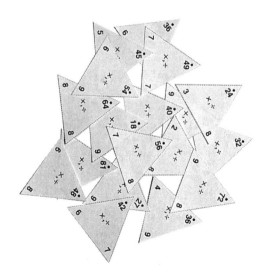

Activity Sheets 8 and 9 contain these Fact Triangles. Assign these if you think your children are ready to practice these harder facts.

Multiplication and Division with 2, 5, and 10

1. double 8 = __16__   __18__ = double 9
   $2 \times 4 =$ __8__   __2__ $= 2 \times 1$
   $7 \times 2 =$ __14__   __0__ $= 0 \times 2$

2. 40 cents = __8__ nickels $5 \div 1 =$ __5__
   $15 \div 5 =$ __3__   __5__ nickels = 25 cents

3. 40 cents = __4__ dimes   __60__ $\div 10 = 6$
   $20 \div 10 =$ __2__   __9__ dimes = 90 cents

4. For each multiplication fact, give two division facts in the same fact family.

   $2 \times 6 = 12$ __12__ $\div$ __2__ $=$ __6__   __12__ $\div$ __6__ $=$ __2__
   $5 \times 9 = 45$ __45__ $\div$ __5__ $=$ __9__   __45__ $\div$ __9__ $=$ __5__
   $10 \times 4 = 40$ __40__ $\div$ __10__ $=$ __4__   __40__ $\div$ __4__ $=$ __10__
   $3 \times 2 = 6$ __6__ $\div$ __3__ $=$ __2__   __6__ $\div$ __2__ $=$ __3__
   $8 \times 5 = 40$ __40__ $\div$ __8__ $=$ __5__   __40__ $\div$ __5__ $=$ __8__
   $5 \times 10 = 50$ __50__ $\div$ __5__ $=$ __10__   __50__ $\div$ __10__ $=$ __5__

Math Journal 2, p. 290

addition/subtraction Fact Triangles. Show them how to hold the cards together with a paper clip.

Review the procedure for practicing with Fact Triangles: While one partner covers one corner of the triangle with a thumb or finger, the other partner tells the related fact.

At first, children should limit their practice to finding products. That is, one partner covers the number below the dot and the other gives the product of the uncovered factors. When children are well on their way to memorizing products, they can cover one of the other two numbers at a time to practice finding missing factors.

ONGOING ASSESSMENT

As children work, ask them to sort their Fact Triangles into two piles—facts they know and facts they still need to practice. Have children record the facts that they need to practice on a sheet of paper and give it to you. The purpose of recording the facts is twofold. First, by writing those facts, children are doing additional practice. Second, you have a record of a child's progress.

Math Boxes 11.7

1. Mrs. Bell had 30 pennies. She gave $\frac{1}{3}$ of the pennies to Max and $\frac{1}{2}$ of the pennies to Julie.

   Max received __10__ pennies.

   Julie received __15__ pennies.

   How many pennies did Mrs. Bell have left? __5__ pennies

2. Write >, <, or =.

   $70 + 39$ _<_ $59 + 60$

   $98 - 70$ _>_ $62 - 40$

   $156 - 90$ _=_ $26 + 40$

3. Leah swam 10 meters. Andrea swam 6 times as far. How far did Andrea swim?

   __60__ meters

   Write the number model.
   __$10 \times 6 = 60$__

4. Use your calculator. Enter the problems. Write the answers in dollars and cents.

   64¢ + $1.73 = $ __2.37__

   85¢ + 53¢ = $ __1.38__

   $2.08 + $5.01 = $ __7.09__

   37¢ + 26¢ = $ __0.63__

5. Estimate, then solve.

   $\begin{array}{r} 262 \\ -\ 139 \\ \hline \end{array}$

   Estimate: Sample answer:

   __260__ − __140__ = __120__

   Answer: __123__

6. Multiply. If you need help, make arrays. | Unit |

   $4 \times 5 =$ __20__

   $6 \times 2 =$ __12__

   $1 \times 10 =$ __10__

Math Journal 2, p. 291

◆ Multiplying and Dividing with 2, 5, and 10 (*Math Journal 2*, p. 290)

INDEPENDENT ACTIVITY

Children practice facts by completing number models, finding equivalent amounts of money using nickels and dimes, and writing related division facts for a multiplication fact.

◆ Math Boxes 11.7 (*Math Journal 2*, p. 291)

INDEPENDENT ACTIVITY

Mixed Review This journal page provides opportunities for cumulative review or assessment of concepts and skills.

◆ Home Link 11.7 (*Math Masters,* pp. 396 and 397)

Home Connection Children show someone at home how to use Fact Triangles to practice multiplication and division facts. The Family Note explains what Fact Triangles are.

3 Options for Individualizing

◆ ENRICHMENT Making up and Solving Multiplication and Division Number Stories
(*Math Masters,* p. 22)

INDEPENDENT ACTIVITY   15–30 min

Children write multiplication and division number stories, draw pictures to illustrate them, and find the solutions. You may wish to compile children's number stories into books. Children may look these over in their free time or check them out to take home.

◆ EXTRA PRACTICE Minute Math

SMALL-GROUP ACTIVITY   5–15 min

To offer children more experience with multiplication/ division fact families, see the following page in *Minute Math:*

Operations: p. 41

 Family Note

Fact Triangles are tools for building mental arithmetic skills. You might think of them as the *Everyday Mathematics* version of the flash cards that you may remember from grade school. Fact Triangles, however, are more effective for helping children memorize facts because they emphasize fact families.

A **fact family** is a collection of related facts made from the same three numbers. For the numbers 4, 6, and 24, the multiplication/division fact family consists of 4 × 6 = 24, 6 × 4 = 24, 24 ÷ 6 = 4, and 24 ÷ 4 = 6.

Please help your child cut out the Fact Triangles attached to this letter.

To use Fact Triangles to practice multiplication with your child, cover the number next to the dot with your thumb. The number you have covered is the product.

Your child uses the numbers that are showing to tell you one or two multiplication facts: 3 × 5 = 15 or 5 × 3 = 15.

Multiplication

To practice division, use your thumb to cover a number without a dot.

Your child uses the numbers that are showing to tell you the division fact 15 ÷ 5 = 3.

Now cover the other number without a dot. Your child now tells you the other division fact 15 ÷ 3 = 5.

Division

If your child misses a fact, flash the other two fact problems on the card and then return to the fact that was missed.

Example: Sue can't answer 15 ÷ 3. Flash 3 × 5, then 15 ÷ 5, and finally 15 ÷ 3 a second time.

Make this activity brief and fun. Spend about 10 minutes each night for the next few weeks, or until your child masters all of the facts. The work you do at home will support the work your child is doing at school.

Division

◇ Math Masters, p. 396

Cut out the Fact Triangles. Show someone at home how you can use them to practice multiplication and division facts.

◇ Math Masters, p. 397

HOME LINK MASTER

11.8 Multiplication/ Division Fact Practice

OBJECTIVE To practice multiplication and division facts.

summaries	materials
1 Teaching the Lesson	
Children write division stories and practice multiplication facts by playing a multiplication version of *Beat the Calculator*. [Operations and Computation]	☐ *Math Journal 2*, pp. 292 and 293 ☐ Home Link 11.7 ☐ half-sheet of paper ☐ calculator
2 Ongoing Learning & Practice	
Children practice multiplication and division facts with Fact Triangles. [Operations and Computation; Patterns, Functions, and Algebra] Children practice and maintain skills through Math Boxes and Home Link activities.	☐ *Math Journal 2*, p. 296 ☐ Home Link Master (*Math Masters*, p. 398) ☐ Fact Triangles (cut from *Math Journal 2*, Activity Sheets 6–9)
3 Options for Individualizing	
Extra Practice Children write the corresponding fact families on the backs of their Fact Triangles. [Operations and Computation; Patterns, Functions, and Algebra]	☐ Fact Triangles (cut from *Math Journal 2*, Activity Sheets 6–9)

Getting Started

Mental Math and Reflexes

Write problems about addition with money on the board. Children record estimates on their slates. For each problem, discuss how children arrived at their estimates. *Suggestions:*

- $1.68 + $1.31 $3.00
- $0.19 + $0.68 $0.90
- $4.72 + $5.37 $10.10

Math Message

Write a division story on a half-sheet of paper.

Use the numbers on this Fact Triangle.

Home Link 11.7 Follow-Up

Poll the class to see how much time children spent practicing with the Fact Triangles. Ask, *How can you find the range of practice times?* The range is the difference between the maximum and minimum practice times.

1

Teaching the Lesson

✦ Math Message Follow-Up

WHOLE-CLASS DISCUSSION

Children share a few division stories. The Fact Triangle numbers can be used for two division facts: $10 \div 2 = 5$, and $10 \div 5 = 2$. Ensure that at least one story for each number model is discussed. Sample stories: If 2 persons share 10 cookies, each person gets 5 cookies. If 5 persons share 10 cookies, each person gets 2 cookies.

✦ Playing a Multiplication Version of *Beat the Calculator* (*Math Journal 2,* pp. 292 and 293)

SMALL-GROUP ACTIVITY

Children have played *Beat the Calculator* to practice addition facts. A similar version of the game may be used to practice multiplication facts. Select 3 children to demonstrate how to play the game. Designate one child as the Caller, a second as the Brain, and the third as the Calculator. Record their results.

Divide the class into groups of three to play *Beat the Calculator.*

Circulate as children play; offer guidance when needed.

Journal page 293 includes all the multiplication facts on the first two pages of Fact Triangles (Activity Sheets 6 and 7). Most of these facts are "easier" facts.

 Adjusting the Activity Suggest that children "think doubles" for times-2 facts and "think nickels" for times-5 facts. *For example:*

▷ $2 \times 6 = ?$ Think "double 6." The answer is 12.

▷ $3 \times 5 = ?$ Think "3 nickels is 15 cents." The answer is 15.

If one of the factors is 4, suggest that children "think doubles and then doubles again." *For example:*

▷ $4 \times 3 = ?$ Double 3 is 6. Double 6 is 12. The answer is 12.

Beat the Calculator

Materials	❏ calculator
Players	3 (Caller, Brain, and Calculator)

Directions

1. The Caller reads fact problems from the Brain's journal—in the order listed on the next page.

2. The Brain solves each problem and says the answer.

3. While the Brain is working on the answer, the Calculator solves each problem using a calculator and says the answer.

4. If the Brain beats the Calculator, the Caller makes a check mark next to the fact in the Brain's journal.

✦ *Math Journal 2,* p. 292

Beat the Calculator (cont.)

✓	✓	✓	Fact Problem	✓	✓	✓	Fact Problem
			$2 \times 4 =$ ___				$7 \times 3 =$ ___
			$3 \times 5 =$ ___				$5 \times 2 =$ ___
			$2 \times 2 =$ ___				$6 \times 4 =$ ___
			$4 \times 3 =$ ___				$2 \times 7 =$ ___
			$5 \times 5 =$ ___				$3 \times 2 =$ ___
			$6 \times 2 =$ ___				$4 \times 4 =$ ___
			$6 \times 5 =$ ___				$4 \times 1 =$ ___
			$3 \times 3 =$ ___				$4 \times 7 =$ ___
			$4 \times 5 =$ ___				$7 \times 5 =$ ___
			$3 \times 6 =$ ___				$0 \times 2 =$ ___

✦ *Math Journal 2,* p. 293

2 Ongoing Learning & Practice

✦ Practicing Multiplication with Fact Triangles
(*Math Journal 2,* Activity Sheets 6–9)

PARTNER ACTIVITY 👥

At first, children should limit their practice to finding products. One partner covers the number below the dot, and the other partner gives the product of the uncovered factors. When children are well on their way to memorizing products, they can cover one of the other two numbers at a time to practice finding missing factors.

Assign the last two pages of Fact Triangles (Activity Sheets 8 and 9) whenever you think your children are ready to practice the "harder" facts.

✦ Math Boxes 11.8 (*Math Journal 2,* p. 296)

INDEPENDENT ACTIVITY 👤

Mixed Review This journal page provides opportunities for cumulative review or assessment of concepts and skills.

STUDENT PAGE

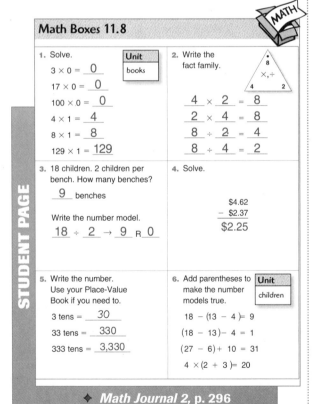

Math Boxes 11.8

1. Solve.

    Unit: books

    $3 \times 0 = $ __0__

    $17 \times 0 = $ __0__

    $100 \times 0 = $ __0__

    $4 \times 1 = $ __4__

    $8 \times 1 = $ __8__

    $129 \times 1 = $ __129__

2. Write the fact family.

    $4 \times 2 = $ __8__

    $2 \times 4 = $ __8__

    $8 \div 2 = $ __4__

    $8 \div 4 = $ __2__

3. 18 children. 2 children per bench. How many benches?

    __9__ benches

    Write the number model.

    $18 \div 2 \rightarrow 9$ R 0

4. Solve.

    $\begin{array}{r} \$4.62 \\ - \ \$2.37 \\ \hline \$2.25 \end{array}$

5. Write the number. Use your Place-Value Book if you need to.

    3 tens = __30__

    33 tens = __330__

    333 tens = __3,330__

6. Add parentheses to make the number models true.

    Unit: children

    $18 - (13 - 4) = 9$

    $(18 - 13) - 4 = 1$

    $(27 - 6) + 10 = 31$

    $4 \times (2 + 3) = 20$

✦ *Math Journal 2,* p. 296

◆ Home Link 11.8 (*Math Masters,* p. 398)

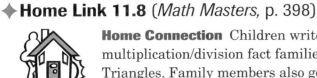

Home Connection Children write multiplication/division fact families for Fact Triangles. Family members also go over the Fact Triangles from Home Link 11.7 with children.

3 Options for Individualizing

◆ EXTRA PRACTICE Writing Fact Families

INDEPENDENT ACTIVITY 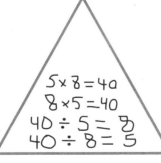 **5–15 min**

Children write the corresponding fact families on the backs of their Fact Triangles.

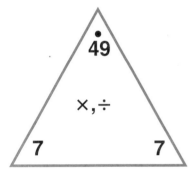

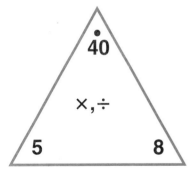

Fact Triangles and corresponding fact families

Fact Families

Home Link
11.8

 Today your child continued to practice multiplication and division facts by playing a game called *Beat the Calculator* and by using Fact Triangles. Observe as your child writes the fact family for each Fact Triangle below. Use the Fact Triangles that your child brought home yesterday. Spend about 10 minutes practicing facts with your child. Make the activity brief and fun. The work you do at home will support the work your child is doing at school.

Please return this Home Link to school tomorrow.

Family
Note

Write the fact family for each Fact Triangle.

1.
35
×, ÷
5   7

2.
18
×, ÷
3   6

3.
24
×, ÷
4   6

$5 \times 7 = 35$
$7 \times 5 = 35$
$35 \div 5 = 7$
$35 \div 7 = 5$

$3 \times 6 = 18$
$6 \times 3 = 18$
$18 \div 3 = 6$
$18 \div 6 = 3$

$4 \times 6 = 24$
$6 \times 4 = 24$
$24 \div 4 = 6$
$24 \div 6 = 4$

4.
30
×, ÷
5   6

$5 \times 6 = 30$ $30 \div 5 = 6$
$6 \times 5 = 30$ $30 \div 6 = 5$

◆ *Math Masters,* p. 398

11.9

Climate Comparisons

OBJECTIVES To read and record information from a map; to find the middle value and range of a set of data; and to make difference and ratio comparisons.

Lesson 11.9 (D.RE.02.02)
Part : "Comparing the Precipitation in Various Places on the Map", J 295: Use vocabulary "**maximum**" and "**minimum**" when discussing "**range**." Use the term "**median**" interchangeably with "middle value."

1 Teaching the Lesson

Children record, analyze, and compare annual precipitation data obtained from a map, including finding the middle value and the range. [Data and Chance; Operations and Computation]

materials

- ☐ *Math Journal 2*, pp. 294 and 295
- ☐ Home Link 11.8
- ☐ Teaching Master (*Math Masters*, p. 200)
- ***See* Advance Preparation**

2 Ongoing Learning & Practice

Children practice multiplication facts by playing *Beat the Calculator*. [Operations and Computation]

Children practice multiplication/division facts using Fact Triangles. [Operations and Computation]

Children practice and maintain skills through Math Boxes and Home Link activities.

- ☐ *Math Journal 2*, pp. 292, 293, and 297
- ☐ Home Link Master (*Math Masters*, p. 399)
- ☐ calculator
- ☐ Fact Triangles (cut from *Math Journal 2*, Activity Sheets 6–9)

3 Options for Individualizing

Language Diversity Children recognize key words in difference and ratio comparisons. [Operations and Computation]

Extra Practice Children practice doubling, tripling, and quadrupling 1-digit numbers. [Operations and Computation]

- ☐ *Minute Math*®, p. 48

Additional Information

Advance Preparation For the Math Message, make 1 copy of *Math Masters,* page 200 for every 4 children. Cut copies apart and place them near the Math Message problem.

Vocabulary • precipitation • middle value • range

Vocabulary (teacher) • difference comparison • ratio comparison

Getting Started

Mental Math and Reflexes

Pose division number stories. *Suggestions:*

- 14 dog biscuits. 4 dogs share them equally. How many biscuits per dog? 3 How many biscuits left over? 2

- 16 cookies. 3 cookies per child. How many children? 5 How many cookies left over? 1

Math Message

Work with a partner to solve the problem [given on Math Masters, *page 200].*

Home Link 11.8 Follow-Up

Review answers.

1 Teaching the Lesson

◆ Math Message Follow-Up
(*Math Masters,* p. 200)

WHOLE-CLASS DISCUSSION

Briefly go over the answers. You may want to have children act out the story.

Children have studied two ways of comparing quantities: by finding the difference between them (How much more? How much less?) and by finding a ratio of one to the other (How many times as many? What fraction of?).

Pose additional problems that ask children to compare quantities. Help children understand that the wording of a problem (more, less, times as many) can determine whether the problem involves a **difference comparison** or a **ratio comparison.** Select number stories that involve simple numbers, and consider having children act out the stories.

Use a routine like the following. Say:

1. I have 12 cubes. (Show children 12 centimeter cubes.)

2. I have *2 more* cubes than you. How many do you have? 10

3. I have *10 fewer* cubes than you. How many do you have? 22

Math Message

Name _____	Name _____
Lynn has a dime.	Lynn has a dime.
Joe has half as much money as Lynn.	Joe has half as much money as Lynn.
Duane has 15¢ more than Joe.	Duane has 15¢ more than Joe.
Kim has twice as much money as Duane.	Kim has twice as much money as Duane.
How much money does each person have?	How much money does each person have?
Lynn $ 0.10 Joe $ 0.05	Lynn $_____ Joe $_____
Duane $ 0.20 Kim $ 0.40	Duane $_____ Kim $_____
Name _____	Name _____
Lynn has a dime.	Lynn has a dime.
Joe has half as much money as Lynn.	Joe has half as much money as Lynn.
Duane has 15¢ more than Joe.	Duane has 15¢ more than Joe.
Kim has twice as much money as Duane.	Kim has twice as much money as Duane.
How much money does each person have?	How much money does each person have?
Lynn $_____ Joe $_____	Lynn $_____ Joe $_____
Duane $_____ Kim $_____	Duane $_____ Kim $_____

TEACHING MASTER

◆ *Math Masters,* p. 200

Days of Rain or Snow in 1 Year (12 Months)

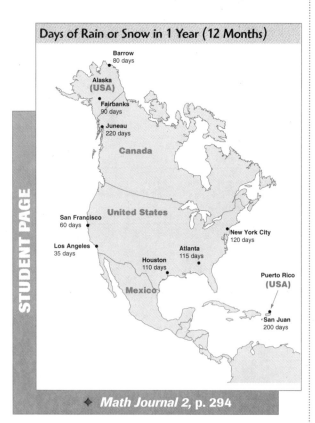

Barrow
80 days

Alaska
(USA)

Fairbanks
90 days

Juneau
220 days

Canada

United States

San Francisco
60 days

Los Angeles
35 days

Houston
110 days

Atlanta
115 days

New York City
120 days

Mexico

Puerto Rico
(USA)

San Juan
200 days

✦ Math Journal 2, p. 294

Days of Rain or Snow in 1 Year (cont.)

Rain and snow are called **precipitation**.

1. About how many days per year does it rain or snow in these cities?

City	Days of Precipitation	City	Days of Precipitation
Los Angeles	about 35	New York City	about 120
San Francisco	about 60	San Juan	about 200
Houston	about 110	Juneau	about 220
Atlanta	about 115		

2. Complete.

	Name of City	Number of Days
Most days of precipitation:	Juneau	about 220
Fewest days of precipitation:	Los Angeles	about 35

Middle value: about 115 days

Range: about 185 days

Complete.

Name of Place

3. Atlanta has about
55 more days of rain or snow than   San Francisco

4. New York City has about
80 fewer days of rain or snow than   San Juan

5. Juneau has about
twice as many days of rain or snow as   Houston

6. San Francisco has about
½ as many days of rain or snow as   New York City

✦ Math Journal 2, p. 295

4. I have *twice as many* cubes as you. How many do you have? 6

5. I have *half as many* cubes as you. How many do you have? 24

6. You have *3 times as many* cubes as I do. How many do you have? 36

✦ Discussing the Map of Rainy or Snowy Days
(*Math Journal 2*, p. 294)

WHOLE-CLASS DISCUSSION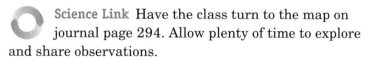

Science Link Have the class turn to the map on journal page 294. Allow plenty of time to explore and share observations.

For purposes of this lesson, "rough" averages are being used: the "exact" data have been rounded to numbers that end in 0 or 5. Discuss the map with the class. *Suggestions:*

• What countries are identified on the map? Canada, United States, Mexico Are all these countries in North America? yes

NOTE: At the time this book is being printed, Puerto Rico is a self-governing commonwealth associated politically and economically with the United States. Puerto Rico may eventually become a state in the Union or an independent nation.

• What do the numbers of days on the map represent? The approximate number of days of rain or snow in one year **Precipitation** is another word for rain or snow.

• How might the data on the map have been obtained? List any answer that is reasonable on the board. For example, the number of days was collected over many years for each place, and a middle value obtained.

• In which place did it rain or snow on about half the days? San Juan On about one-third of the days? Atlanta, Houston, and New York City On about one-tenth of the days? Los Angeles

✦ Comparing the Precipitation in Various Places on the Map
(*Math Journal 2*, pp. 294 and 295)

PARTNER ACTIVITY

Partners use the map to complete Problem 1 on journal page 295. Ask partners to fill in the number of days of precipitation for each of the places listed. Review the meanings of **middle value** and **range** before children complete Problem 2.

Before children go on to Problems 3–6, ask:

- About how many *more* days of precipitation does Juneau have than Houston? 110

- About how many *times as many* days of precipitation does Juneau have than Houston? About twice as many

Partners should need little help in completing the page. Bring the class together to go over answers.

2 Ongoing Learning & Practice

◆ Playing *Beat the Calculator*
(*Math Journal 2,* pp. 292 and 293)

SMALL-GROUP ACTIVITY

The multiplication version of this game was introduced in Lesson 11.8.

◆ Practicing Multiplication and Division with Fact Triangles
(*Math Journal 2,* Activity Sheets 6–9)

PARTNER ACTIVITY

To practice finding products, one partner covers the number below the dot and the other partner gives the product of the uncovered factors. To practice division facts, one partner covers a number without a dot and the other partner finds the quotient of the uncovered numbers.

◆ Math Boxes 11.9 (*Math Journal 2,* p. 297)

INDEPENDENT ACTIVITY

 Mixed Review This journal page provides opportunities for cumulative review or assessment of concepts and skills.

◆ Home Link 11.9 (*Math Masters,* p. 399)

 Home Connection Children make difference and ratio comparisons of age data and find the middle value and the range.

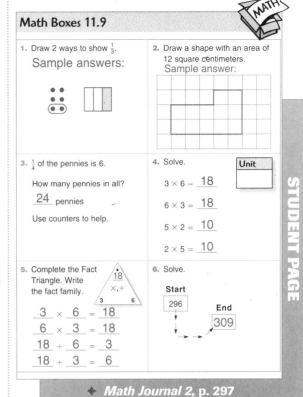

1. Draw 2 ways to show $\frac{1}{3}$.
   Sample answers:

2. Draw a shape with an area of 12 square centimeters.
   Sample answer:

3. $\frac{1}{4}$ of the pennies is 6.
   How many pennies in all?
   __24__ pennies
   Use counters to help.

4. Solve.
   $3 \times 6 =$ __18__
   $6 \times 3 =$ __18__
   $5 \times 2 =$ __10__
   $2 \times 5 =$ __10__

   Unit

5. Complete the Fact Triangle. Write the fact family.
   __3__ × __6__ = __18__
   __6__ × __3__ = __18__
   __18__ ÷ __6__ = __3__
   __18__ ÷ __3__ = __6__

6. Solve.
   Start
   296
   End
   309

STUDENT PAGE

Data Analysis   Home Link 11.9

Family Note In this lesson, your child used multiplication and division to compare data. The **range** of a set of data is the difference between the greatest and the least values. In the table below, the range of the age data is 40 − 8, or 32 years. The **middle value** of a set of data is the number in the middle when the data are arranged in ascending or descending order. In the table below, the middle value of the age data is 12 years.

Please return this Home Link to school tomorrow.

Lily collected information about the ages of people in her family.

Complete.

1. The oldest person is __Dave__.
   Age: __40__ years

2. The youngest person is __Lily__.
   Age: __8__ years

3. Range of the ages: __32__ years

4. Middle value of the ages: __12__ years

Fill in the blanks with the name of the correct person.

5. Jillian is about 4 years older than __Lily__.

6. Lara is about 26 years younger than __Diane__.

7. Diane is about 3 times as old as __Jillian__.

8. Lara is about $\frac{1}{4}$ as old as __Dave__.

Name	Age (Years)
Dave	40
Diane	36
Jillian	12
Lara	10
Lily	8

HOME LINK MASTER

◆ LANGUAGE DIVERSITY Recognizing Key Words in Difference and Ratio Comparisons

SMALL-GROUP ACTIVITY 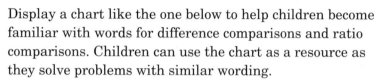   5–15 min

Display a chart like the one below to help children become familiar with words for difference comparisons and ratio comparisons. Children can use the chart as a resource as they solve problems with similar wording.

Allison has 6 cubes.	🎲🎲🎲 🎲🎲🎲 Allison
Janine has 3 cubes *more than* Allison.	🎲🎲🎲 🎲🎲🎲 Allison 🎲🎲🎲 🎲🎲🎲 Janine
Tom has 2 cubes *fewer than* Allison.	🎲🎲🎲 🎲🎲🎲 Allison 🎲 🎲🎲🎲 Tom
Hannah has *twice as many* cubes as Allison.	🎲🎲🎲 🎲🎲🎲 Allison 🎲🎲🎲 🎲🎲🎲 🎲🎲🎲 🎲🎲🎲 Hannah
Jeremy has *half as many* cubes as Allison.	🎲🎲🎲 🎲🎲🎲 Allison 🎲🎲🎲 Jeremy
Martin has *3 times as many* cubes as Allison.	🎲🎲🎲 🎲🎲🎲 Allison 🎲🎲🎲 🎲🎲🎲 🎲🎲🎲 🎲🎲🎲 🎲🎲🎲 🎲🎲🎲 Martin

◆ EXTRA PRACTICE Minute Math

SMALL-GROUP ACTIVITY   5–15 min

To offer children more experience with practicing multiplication facts, see the following page in *Minute Math:*

Operations: p. 48

11.10

Unit 11 Review and Assessment

OBJECTIVE To review and assess children's progress on the material covered in Unit 11.

---

1   Assess Progress

learning goals

11a   **Developing Goal** Estimate and solve addition and subtraction number stories with dollars and cents. **(Lessons 11.1 and 11.2)**

11b   **Developing Goal** Solve 1-digit multiplication stories (multiples of equal groups). **(Lessons 11.3 and 11.7)**

11c   **Developing Goal** Solve simple division stories (equal sharing and equal grouping). **(Lessons 11.4 and 11.7)**

11d   **Developing Goal** Multiply numbers with 2, 5, or 10 as a factor. **(Lessons 11.5–11.9)**

11e   **Developing Goal** Construct multiplication/division fact families. **(Lessons 11.7 and 11.8)**

11f   **Developing Goal** Make difference and ratio comparisons. **(Lessons 11.2 and 11.9)**

11g   **Secure Goal** Multiply numbers with 0 or 1 as a factor. **(Lesson 11.6)**

activities

- ❑ Oral Assessment, Problems 1 and 2
- ❑ Written Assessment, Problems 1–3

- ❑ Slate Assessment, Problem 2
- ❑ Written Assessment, Problems 4, 5, 6, and 8

- ❑ Slate Assessment, Problem 3
- ❑ Written Assessment, Problem 8

- ❑ Slate Assessment, Problem 1

- ❑ Written Assessment, Problem 7

- ❑ Slate Assessment, Problem 4

- ❑ Slate Assessment, Problem 1

materials

- ❑ *Math Journal 2,* pp. 292 and 293
- ❑ Home Link 11.9
- ❑ Assessment Master (*Math Masters,* p. 435)

- ❑ Teaching Master (*Math Masters,* p. 201)
- ❑ Fact Triangles (cut from *Math Journal 2,* Activity Sheets 6–9)
- ❑ slate; calculator

---

2   Build Background for Unit 12

summaries

Children practice and maintain skills through Math Boxes and Home Link activities.

materials

- ❑ *Math Journal 2,* p. 298
- ❑ Home Link Masters (*Math Masters,* pp. 400–403)

Each **learning goal** listed above indicates a level of performance that might be expected at this point in the *Everyday Mathematics* K–6 curriculum. For a variety of reasons, the levels indicated may not accurately portray your class's performance.

Getting Started

Math Message

Write the rule on your slate. Then copy the table and fill in the blanks.

Rule
?

in	out
3	15
2	10
1	5
5	25
6	30

Answers vary.

Home Link 11.9 Follow-Up
Review answers.

1 Assess Progress

◆ Math Message Follow-Up

WHOLE-GROUP DISCUSSION

Children give the rule and the "in" and "out" numbers that are missing from the table. Ask children to describe any strategies that they know for memorizing the times-5 facts. Sample answers: Use clock facts, nickels, or arrays

◆ Oral and Slate Assessments

SMALL-GROUP ACTIVITY

If the following list of suggested problems is not appropriate for your class's level of performance, adjust the numbers in the problems or adjust the problems themselves to better assess your children's abilities.

Oral Assessment Suggestions

1. I buy a bag of potato chips for 89 cents and a soda for 65 cents. Is the total cost more or less than $2.00? less How do you know? **Goal 11a**

2. I buy a notebook for $1.39. I pay with a $5 bill. Will I get back more or less than $3.00 in change? more How do you know? **Goal 11a**

1. Dictate problems like those in the following table.
   Goals 11d and 11g

Zeros	Ones	Doubles	Fives	Tens
0×5 0	4×1 4	2×1 2	5×3 15	10×3 30
9×0 0	1×8 8	2×3 6	5×4 20	4×10 40
0×0 0	1×9 9	5×2 10	6×5 30	10×6 60
10×0 0	1×10 10	2×7 14	8×5 40	7×10 70
0×75 0	1×27 27	100×2 200	5×100 500	10×100 1,000
287×0 0	890×1 890	2×400 800	$5 \times 1,000$ 5,000	$10 \times 1,000$ 10,000

2. Children solve number stories involving multiples of equal groups. **Goal 11b**

   • 2 birthday cakes. 7 candles on each cake. How many candles in all? 14 candles

   • 3 birthday presents. 4 bows on each present. How many bows in all? 12 bows

   • 10 birthday invitations. 1 stamp per invitation. How many stamps in all? 10 stamps

3. Children solve number stories involving equal sharing and equal grouping. **Goal 11c**

   • 10 children play *Pin the Tail on the Donkey*. 5 children on each team. How many teams? 2 teams

   • 6 children share 15 balloons equally. How many balloons per child? 2 balloons How many balloons left over? 3 balloons

   • 18 sodas. 2 sodas per child. How many children? 9 children

   • 4 clowns share 4 big red noses equally. How many noses per clown? 1 nose How many noses left over? 0

4. Children solve ratio comparison and difference comparison problems. **Goal 11f**

   • What number is 10 more than 14? 24

   • What number is 5 less than 12? 7

   • What number is three times as much as 25? 75

   • What number is half as much as 20? 10

Unit 11 Checking Progress

Add or subtract.

1. $1.30 − $0.64 **Answer** $0.66

2. $3.46 + $1.78 **Answer** $5.24

3. $5.82 − $2.47 **Answer** $3.35

Multiply. If you need help, make arrays with 0s or Xs.

4. $3 \times 6 = \underline{18}$

5. $5 \times 4 = \underline{20}$

6. $8 \times 3 = \underline{24}$

7. Write the fact family for the Fact Triangle.

$$\underline{3} \times \underline{9} = \underline{27}$$
$$\underline{9} \times \underline{3} = \underline{27}$$
$$\underline{27} \div \underline{3} = \underline{9}$$
$$\underline{27} \div \underline{9} = \underline{3}$$

27
×, ÷
3   9

8. Write a multiplication story and a division story on the back of this page. **Answers vary.**

• Draw a picture or diagram.
• Write the answer.
• Write a number model.

◆ *Math Masters*, p. 435

ASSESSMENT MASTER

TEACHING MASTER

Museum Store Poster

Elephant $0.72
Kite $1.86
Plane $0.27
Magnet $1.39
Pen $0.30
Ring $0.18
Shell $0.48
Dinosaur $0.59
Number Puzzle $0.75

◆ *Math Masters*, p. 201

◆ **Written Assessment** (*Math Masters*, p. 435)

INDEPENDENT ACTIVITY

Read the instructions aloud, repeating as needed. Children respond on the masters.

• Add or subtract. (Problems 1–3) **Goal 11a**

• Multiply. If you need help, make arrays with 0s or Xs. (Problems 4–6) **Goal 11b**

• Write the fact family for the Fact Triangle. (Problem 7) **Goal 11e**

• Write a multiplication story and a division story on the back of this page. **Goals 11b and 11c**

◆ **ALTERNATIVE ASSESSMENT OPTION**
Write about Mathematics

INDEPENDENT ACTIVITY

Children respond, in writing, to the following question:

Draw a diagram or picture to show how 3 + 3 + 3 + 3 + 3 + 3 + 3 is similar to 7 × 3.

Portfolio Ideas

◆ **ALTERNATIVE ASSESSMENT OPTION**
Make up and Solve Addition, Subtraction, Multiplication, and Division Number Stories
(*Math Masters*, p. 201)

PARTNER ACTIVITY

Working with a partner or in small groups, children make up an addition, a subtraction, and a multiplication number story using the Museum Store Poster. If appropriate, challenge children to write a division number story as well. *For example:*

• What is the cost of an elephant and a seashell?

• How much more than a seashell does an elephant cost?

Portfolio Ideas

• How much do 3 dinosaurs cost?

• If 3 children share the cost of a number puzzle, how much will each child need to pay?

Play *Beat the Calculator*
(*Math Journal 2*, pp. 292 and 293)

SMALL-GROUP ACTIVITY

Use *Beat the Calculator* as a way of assessing children's mastery of multiplication facts. Use journal pages 292 and 293 as the problem list and recording sheet. Children receive check marks each time they *Beat the Calculator*. Once they have received three check marks next to a fact, they can write in the product to indicate that fact has been mastered.

Practice Multiplication Facts with Fact Triangles

PARTNER ACTIVITY

As children work, ask them to sort their Fact Triangles into two piles—facts they know and facts they still need to practice. Have children record the facts that they need to practice on a sheet of paper and give to you. The purpose of recording the facts is twofold. First, by writing the facts, children are doing additional practice. Second, you have a record of children's progress.

2 Build Background for Unit 12

◆ Math Boxes 11.10 (*Math Journal 2*, p. 298)

INDEPENDENT ACTIVITY

Mixed Review This journal page provides opportunities for cumulative review or assessment of concepts and skills. The skills in Problem 5 are prerequisite for Unit 12.

◆ Home Link 11.10: Unit 12 Family Letter
(*Math Masters*, pp. 400–403)

Home Connection This Home Link is a four-page newsletter that introduces parents and guardians to Unit 12's topics and terms. The letter also offers ideas for home-based mathematics activities that are supportive of classroom work.

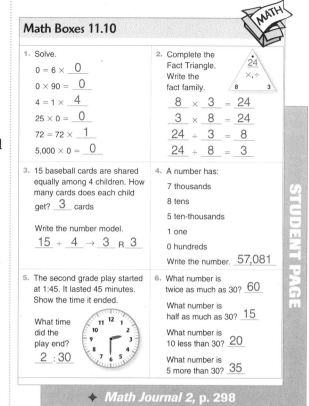

Math Boxes 11.10

1. Solve.

    $0 = 6 \times \underline{0}$

    $0 \times 90 = \underline{0}$

    $4 = 1 \times \underline{4}$

    $25 \times 0 = \underline{0}$

    $72 = 72 \times \underline{1}$

    $5{,}000 \times 0 = \underline{0}$

2. Complete the Fact Triangle. Write the fact family.

    $8 \times 3 = 24$

    $3 \times 8 = 24$

    $24 \div 3 = 8$

    $24 \div 8 = 3$

3. 15 baseball cards are shared equally among 4 children. How many cards does each child get? $\underline{3}$ cards

    Write the number model.

    $15 \div 4 \rightarrow 3$ R 3

4. A number has:

    7 thousands

    8 tens

    5 ten-thousands

    1 one

    0 hundreds

    Write the number. $57{,}081$

5. The second grade play started at 1:45. It lasted 45 minutes. Show the time it ended.

    What time did the play end?

    $\underline{2}$: $\underline{30}$

6. What number is twice as much as 30? 60

    What number is half as much as 30? 15

    What number is 10 less than 30? 20

    What number is 5 more than 30? 35

◆ Math Journal 2, p. 298

STUDENT PAGE

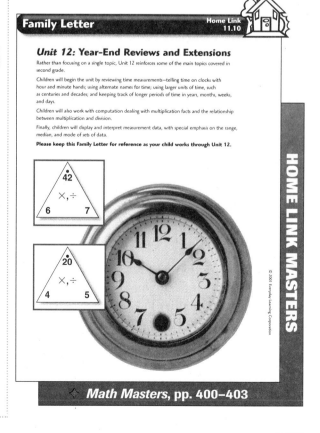

Unit 12: Year-End Reviews and Extensions

Rather than focusing on a single topic, Unit 12 reinforces some of the main topics covered in second grade.

Children will begin the unit by reviewing time measurements—telling time on clocks with hour and minute hands; using alternate names for time; using larger units of time, such as centuries and decades; and keeping track of longer periods of time in years, months, weeks, and days.

Children will also work with computation dealing with multiplication facts and the relationship between multiplication and division.

Finally, children will display and interpret measurement data, with special emphasis on the range, median, and mode of sets of data.

Please keep this Family Letter for reference as your child works through Unit 12.

◆ Math Masters, pp. 400–403

HOME LINK MASTERS

Unit 12
Year-End Reviews and Extensions

overview

Unit 12 reviews and extends three of the main topics covered in second grade: time measurement, mental and algorithmic computation, and data representation and interpretation. These topics will also be reviewed in the early part of third grade.

While this unit introduces little new material, many of the activities are open-ended enough to fill several days of relaxed review. You might want to skip around the unit, choosing topics that are of particular interest to you and your class or topics that your class particularly needs to review.

contents

UNIT
12

learning goals
in perspective

learning goals	links to the past	links to the future
12a **Beginning Goal** Use alternate names for times. **(Lesson 12.2)**	Children have been informally exposed to alternate names for times and have had numerous experiences with telling time throughout second grade. *(Related Grade 2 lessons: 1.3, 3.3, 3.4, 5.1)*	Time equivalencies will continue to be emphasized in *Third Grade Everyday Mathematics.*
12b **Beginning Goal** Know "harder" multiplication facts. **(Lesson 12.5)**	Children were introduced to multiplication as they explored geoboard arrays and recorded their data with multiplication models and on multiplication diagrams. Children learned the 0-facts, the 1-facts, and the turn-around rule for multiplication. *(Related Grade 2 lessons: 6.8–6.10, 11.3, 11.5–11.8)*	Throughout third grade, children will practice "harder" multiplication facts through games and in a variety of problem-solving situations.
12c **Beginning Goal** Determine the mode of a data set. **(Lesson 12.7)**	Children have previously explored other data landmarks, such as the median. *(Related Grade 2 lessons: 3.5, 6.3, 7.8–7.9, 11.9)*	In subsequent grades, children will represent the mode of a data set with pictographs, bar graphs, stem-and-leaf plots, and other representations.
12d **Developing Goal** Determine the median, maximum, minimum, and range of a data set. **(Lessons 12.6 and 12.7)**	In first grade, children were introduced to the concept of the middle value of a data set. Children found the median of a data set in Unit 7. *(Related Grade 2 lessons: 3.5, 6.3, 7.8, 7.9, 11.9)*	In subsequent grades, children will work with a variety of graphs and data landmarks to make conclusions in problem-solving situations.
12e **Developing/Secure Goal** Construct multiplication/division fact families. **(Lessons 12.1 and 12.5)**	Fact Triangles and multiplication/division diagrams are two of the tools children used to explore the relationship between multiplication and division. *(Related Grade 2 lessons: 5.3, 6.7–6.11, 7.1–7.3, 7.5, 8.2, 11.7, 11.8)*	Children will continue relating multiplication with division through the use of Fact Triangles and multiplication/division diagrams.
12f **Developing/Secure Goal** Multiply numbers with 2, 5, and 10 as a factor. **(Lesson 12.4)**	In Kindergarten and first grade, children skip counted and marked counting patterns on number lines and number grids to prepare them to learn these multiplication facts. *(Related Grade 2 lessons: 5.3, 6.7–6.11, 11.5–11.8)*	Children will extend their multiplication skills beyond the facts extending 2s, 5s, and 10s facts and by learning to use fact extensions and algorithms, such as the partial-products method and the lattice method.
12g **Secure Goal** Tell time to 5-minute intervals. **(Lessons 12.1 and 12.2)**	Children estimated time using the hour hand and the minute hand. They also matched analog and digital times. *(Related Grade 2 lessons: 1.3, 3.3, 3.4, 5.1)*	Children will continue to refine and practice their time-telling skills throughout the grades.
12h **Secure Goal** Demonstrate calendar concepts and skills. **(Lesson 12.1)**	Children worked with ordinal numbers as they created calendars. Children also reviewed such terms as *day, week,* and *month. (Related Grade 2 lesson: 1.3)*	Calendar concepts and skills will be reviewed in third grade.
12i **Secure Goal** Compare quantities from a bar graph. **(Lessons 12.6 and 12.7)**	Children gathered data, entered it into a table, and drew a bar graph. *(Related Grade 2 lessons: 3.5, 6.3, 7.7, 7.9)*	Children will work with horizontal and vertical bar graphs to analyze data. They will read and interpret, as well as create, bar graphs.

assessment
ongoing • product • periodic

✓ Informal Assessment

Math Boxes These *Math Journal* pages provide opportunities for cumulative review or assessment of concepts and skills.

Ongoing Assessment: Kid Watching Use the Ongoing Assessment suggestions in the following lesson to make quick, on-the-spot observations about children's understanding of:
• Operations and Computation **(Lesson 12.4)**

Portfolio Ideas Samples of children's work may be obtained from the following assignments:
• Creating a Timeline of a Person's Life **(Lesson 12.3)**
• Connecting Comparisons of Animal Speeds to Literature **(Lesson 12.6)**
• Collecting and Displaying Class Height Data **(Lesson 12.7)**

✓ Unit 12 Review and Assessment

Math Message Use the question in Lesson 12.8 to assess children's progress toward the following learning goal: **Goal 12c**

Oral and Slate Assessments Use oral or slate assessments during Lesson 12.8 to assess children's progress toward the following learning goals: **Goals 12a, 12b, 12c, 12d, 12e, and 12h**

Written Assessment Use a written review during Lesson 12.8 to assess children's progress toward the following learning goals: **Goals 12c, 12d, 12e, 12f, 12g, and 12i**

Performance/Group Assessment Use a small-group activity in Lesson 12.8 to assess children's progress toward the following learning goals: **Goals 12a, 12b, and 12f**

assessment handbook

For more information on how to use different types of assessment in Unit 12, see the Assessment Overview on pages 77–79 in the *Assessment Handbook*. The following Assessment Masters can be found in the *Math Masters* book:

• Unit 12 Checking Progress, pp. 436 and 437
• Unit 12 Class Checklist, p. 470
• Unit 12 Individual Profile of Progress, p. 471
• Class Progress Indicator, p. 488
• Math Logs, pp. 493–495
• Self-Assessment Forms, pp. 496 and 497
• Interest Inventories, pp. 491 and 492
• End-of-Year Assessment, pp. 441–447

problemsolving

A process of modeling everyday situations using tools from mathematics

Encourage children to use a variety of strategies when attacking a given problem—and to explain those strategies. *Strategies children might use in this unit:*

- Acting out the problem
- Using a picture
- Using a diagram
- Reading and making a bar graph
- Using and making a table
- Using computation
- Using estimation

Four Problem-Solving REPRESENTATIONS

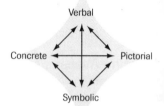

Lessons that teach *through* problem solving, not just *about* problem solving

Lesson	Activity	Lesson	Activity
12.1	How long is the school day?	**12.6**	What are distances traveled in 10 seconds?
12.2	Solving number stories involving time before or after a given time	**12.6**	What are the life spans of some living beings?
12.3	Calculating elapsed time between inventions	**12.7**	Finding the range, median, and mode of sets of button data and height data
12.5	Solving number stories involving multiplication and division facts		

For more information about problem solving in *Everyday Mathematics,* see the *Teacher's Reference Manual,* pp. 197–208.

cross-curricularlinks

social studies

- Children discuss ways in which people communicate with one another across distances. **(Lesson 12.3)**

science

- Children compare the speeds of various animals. **(Lesson 12.6)**

literature

- Read "The Tortoise and the Hare." Children connect comparisons of animal speeds to literature. **(Lesson 12.6)**

meeting INDIVIDUAL needs

UNIVERSAL ACCESS

✦ RETEACHING

The following features provide additional instructional support:

Adjusting the Activity

- **Lesson 12.1, Part 1**
- **Lesson 12.4, Part 1**
- **Lesson 12.5, Part 1**
- **Lesson 12.6, Parts 1, 2**
- **Lesson 12.7, Part 1**

✦ ENRICHMENT

The following features suggest enrichment and extension activities:

Adjusting the Activity

- **Lesson 12.1, Part 1**
- **Lesson 12.2, Part 1**

Options for Individualizing

- **Lesson 12.3** Creating a Timeline of a Person's Life
- **Lesson 12.4** Introducing the "9s Facts on Fingers" Shortcut
- **Lesson 12.6** Connecting Comparisons of Animal Speeds to Literature

✦ MULTIAGE CLASSROOM

The following chart lists related lessons from Grades 1 and 3 that can help you meet your instructional needs:

Grade 1	1.9 3.7 4.8	2.5 6.10 10.2	4.9			1.7 3.13 4.7	4.7 6.12 10.1
Grade 2	12.1	12.2	12.3	12.4	12.5	12.6	12.7
Grade 3	1.4	1.12	5.12 11.8	4.5– 4.8 7.2	4.4 4.6 7.6	1.5 5.12 10.10	3.1 10.7 10.10

materials

lesson	math masters pages	manipulative kit items	other items
12.1	Home Link Master, p. 404 Teaching Masters, pp. 202 and 203; and p. 204 (optional)	slate	class calendar Fact Triangle cards ***See* Advance Preparation, p. 836**
12.2	Home Link Master, p. 405 Teaching Masters, pp. 203 and 205	slate	demonstration clock tool-kit clock
12.3	Home Link Master, p. 406		ruler
12.4	Home Link Masters, pp. 407 and 408 Teaching Master, p. 206		demonstration clock Fact Triangles
12.5	Home Link Masters, pp. 409 and 410 Teaching Masters, pp. 207, 208, and 209 transparency of Teaching Master, p. 199 ***See* Advance Preparation, p. 853**	slate	Fact Triangles number cards 1–20 calculator
12.6	Home Link Masters, pp. 411 and 412 Teaching Master, p. 109	slate (optional)	"The Tortoise and the Hare" ***See* Advance Preparation, p. 858**
12.7	Home Link Master, p. 413	slate measuring tape	stick-on notes ruler ***See* Advance Preparation, p. 864**
12.8	Home Link Masters, pp. 414–417 Teaching Masters, pp. 77–79 Assessment Masters, pp. 436, 437, and 441–447	slate clock-face stamp stamp pad	Fact Triangles envelope

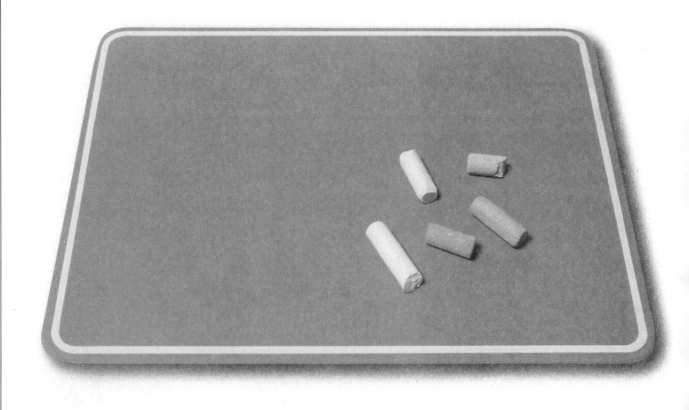

planning**tips**

Pacing

Pacing depends on a number of factors, such as children's individual needs and how long your school has been using *Everyday Mathematics*. At the beginning of Unit 12, review your Content by Strand Poster to help you set a monthly pace.

		◄—MOST CLASSROOMS—►	
A P R I L	M A Y		J U N E

Home Communication

Share Home Links 12.1–12.7 with families to help them understand the content and procedures in this unit. At the end of the unit, use Home Link 12.8. Supplemental information can be found in the *Home Connection Handbook*.

NCTM Standards

Standard	1	2	3	4	5	6	7	8	9	10
Unit 12 Lessons	1–7	1, 4–7	1, 3	1–3, 5, 6	6, 7	1–7	1–7	1–7	1–7	1–7

Content Standards
1 Number and Operation
2 Patterns, Functions, and Algebra
3 Geometry and Spatial Sense
4 Measurement
5 Data Analysis, Statistics, and Probability

Process Standards
6 Problem Solving
7 Reasoning and Proof
8 Communication
9 Connections
10 Representations

PRACTICE *through* Games

Everyday Mathematics uses games to help children develop good fact power and other math skills.

- Practice adding three numbers under 20 with *Addition Card Draw* **(Lesson 12.5)**

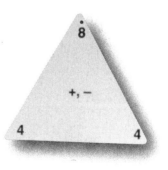

unit 12 content highlights

The notes below highlight the major content ideas presented in Unit 12. These notes may help you establish instructional priorities.

Time Measurement (Lessons 12.1–12.3)

These lessons deal with both calendar and clock skills.

In Lesson 12.1, children review equivalencies among larger units of time: centuries, decades, years, months, weeks, and days. As an optional activity, children make a calendar for the summer months and use it to determine the number of days of vacation they can look forward to. They may want to take their calendars home to use during their vacation.

Children also complete a written assessment of time-telling skills, which will help you determine how much of the review and practice (provided in Lesson 12.2) are needed. In addition to telling time to 5 minutes, children review alternate ways of naming time and calculate elapsed time. You might suggest, for the fun of it, some nonstandard names, such as those listed in the margin. The military and the transportation industry use a continuous hour count. For example, 1300 hours is used instead of 1:00 P.M. A continuous, 24-hour count has the advantage of avoiding the occasional confusion that may result from the use of A.M. and P.M., and it is much easier to use in elapsed-time computation.

Lesson 12.3 reviews ordering 4-digit numbers in the context of a timeline of inventions in communication. Don't expect children to be too precise about exact placement of the dots on the timeline; a few dates are very close together and labeling may be tricky.

> three-quarters past 10 for 10:45
>
> five-quarters past 12 for 1:15
>
> 7:90 for 8:30
>
> 13 o'clock for 1:00 P.M.
>
> Some nonstandard ways to name times

1870 1880 1890 1900 1910 1920 1930 1940 1950

Computation (Lessons 12.1, 12.2, and 12.4–12.6)

By Unit 12, the authors assume that children have mastered the addition and subtraction facts. Children who have not mastered these facts may practice them by playing some of the math games introduced in *Everyday Mathematics*. You might want to send a letter home suggesting that someone at home play these games with children during the summer vacation.

The game of *Addition Card Draw* is introduced in Lesson 12.5 to provide practice with addition of three small numbers. Formal procedures for adding three or more multidigit numbers will be introduced in third grade.

Lesson 12.2 provides practice with addition and subtraction of multidigit numbers. Encourage children to extend the mental arithmetic strategies emphasized up to this point by considering several reliable procedures for paper-and-pencil computation. This activity should be regarded as a checkpoint, not as a test of mastery. Since the emphasis is on consistency, not speed, avoid time pressures.

Lessons 12.1, 12.4, and 12.5 provide a number of opportunities for using Fact Triangles and fact families to practice the multiplication facts and to explore the relationship between multiplication and division. One of the primary goals of second grade is to make a good start toward memorizing the multiplication facts. Most children should be making good progress with the "easy" facts, found on the first set of Fact Triangles (*Math Journal 2,* Activity Sheets 6 and 7). If children haven't started to work with the "harder" facts, found on the second set of Fact Triangles, this is a good time to do so.

Data Representation and Interpretation
(Lessons 12.6 and 12.7)

These related lessons may take several days to complete. They focus on data collection and analysis related to measurement, using ...

- line plots and frequency tables to organize data.

- bar graphs to display data.

- the range, median, and mode to interpret data.

36 in.	39 in.
38 in.	40 in.
38 in.	40 in.
38 in.	42 in.

The mode (38 in. in this case) is the number that occurs most frequently in a set of data.

Review and Assessment (Lessons 12.1 and following)

If you are planning a quarterly assessment for Units 10–12, you may want to refer to the Grade 2 *Assessment Handbook.* The quarterly learning goals, Class Checklist, and Individual Profile of Progress (*Math Masters,* pages 481–483) are useful tools for keeping track of each child's progress.

For **additional information** on the following topics, see the *Teacher's Reference Manual:*

- basic facts
- data collection, organization, and analysis
- multiplication facts
- time

12.1

Review: The Calendar

OBJECTIVES To review time equivalencies and calendar facts; and to assess time-telling skills.

Lesson 12.1 (M.UN.02.05)
Part 1, "Administering a Time-Telling
Assessment": Extend to include students writing
___mins. after ___, ___ mins. before ___ for problems
6, 7, & 8.

summaries | materials

1 Teaching the Lesson

Using the Class Calendar, children review the relationships among various units of time; children review telling time to the nearest five minutes. [Measurement and Reference Frames]

☐ Teaching Masters (*Math Masters,* pp. 202 and 203)
☐ class calendar
See **Advance Preparation**

2 Ongoing Learning & Practice

Children use Fact Triangles to practice multiplication/division facts. [Operations and Computation; Patterns, Functions, and Algebra]

Children practice and maintain skills through Math Boxes and Home Link activities.

☐ *Math Journal 2,* p. 299
☐ Home Link Master (*Math Masters,* p. 404)
☐ Fact Triangles (cut from *Math Journal 2,* Activity Sheets 8 and 9)
☐ scissors

3 Options for Individualizing

Extra Practice Children calculate the exact number of days in their summer vacation. [Measurement and Reference Frames; Operations and Computation]

Extra Practice Children identify days, months, and dates. [Measurement and Reference Frames]

☐ Teaching Master (*Math Masters,* p. 204; optional)
☐ *Minute Math®,* p. 20
See **Advance Preparation**

Additional Information

Advance Preparation For the Math Message, make 1 copy of *Math Masters,* page 202 per 4 children. Cut the copies apart and place them near the Math Message directions.

Before working on the first optional Extra Practice activity in Part 3, look up the dates for the first day of summer vacation and the first day of the next school year.

Getting Started

Mental Math and Reflexes

Pose problems involving multiples of 10.
Suggestions:
• What number is twice as much as 200? 400
• What number is half as much as 1,000? 500
• What number is 200 less than 700? 500
• What number is 300 more than 900? 1,200

Math Message

Take a slip and complete the problems.

1

Teaching the Lesson

◆ Math Message Follow-Up
(*Math Masters,* p. 202)

WHOLE-CLASS DISCUSSION

Review the names and order of the months. Then review time equivalencies, proceeding from larger units of time to smaller ones. Ask such questions as the following:

* How many months are there in 1 year? 12 About what fractional part of 1 year is 1 month? About $\frac{1}{12}$ (Since the number of days in 1 month varies, one cannot say that one month is exactly $\frac{1}{12}$ of a year.)

* About how many weeks are there in 1 year? About 52 (52 weeks × 7 days per week = 364 days, but a year has 365 or 366 days) About what fractional part of 1 year is 1 week? About $\frac{1}{52}$

Ask similar questions about days in a week, hours in a day, minutes in an hour, and seconds in a minute. Review the names of the days of the week.

◆ Reviewing Calendar Facts

WHOLE-CLASS DISCUSSION

Display a calendar and ask:

* Do all months have the same number of days? no

* Which months have exactly 30 days? April, June, September, and November Exactly 31 days? January, March, May, July, August, October, December Exactly 28 or 29 days? February

 Adjusting the Activity Children who have trouble remembering the number of days in various months might memorize the following traditional rhyme:

Thirty days hath September
April, June, and November,
All the rest have thirty-one,
Excepting February alone,
Which hath but twenty-eight, in fine,
Till leap year gives it twenty-nine.

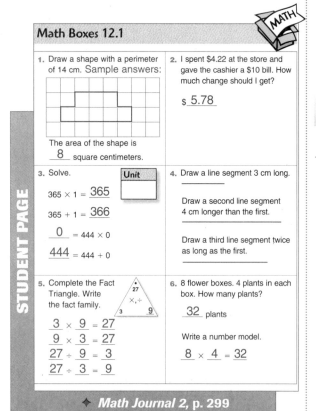

TEACHING MASTER

Review: Telling Time

1. How many hours do clock faces show? __12__ hours

2. How long does it take the hour hand to move from one number to the next? __60 minutes__

3. How long does it take the minute hand to move from one number to the next? __5 minutes__

4. How many times does the hour hand move around the clock face in one day? __2__ times

5. How many times does the minute hand move around the clock face in one day? __24__ times

Write the time shown by each clock.

6. __2__ : __25__
7. __5__ : __40__
8. __11__ : __55__

Draw the hour and minute hands to match the time.

9. 8:00
10. 6:45
11. 4:10

- How many days does a year usually have? 365 days Which years have 366 days? Leap years, when February has an additional (29th) day

- How often is a year a leap year? Leap years occur every 4 years.

Tell the class in what year the last leap year occurred.

- Is the current year a leap year?

- When will the next leap year be?

 Adjusting the Activity Two major events take place during leap years: the election of the President of the United States and the Summer Olympics. Challenge children to find the date of the last presidential election and to determine in which year the next presidential election will be held. 1996, 2000, 2004, 2008, ... are leap years and presidential election years.

◆ Administering a Time-Telling Assessment
(*Math Masters,* p. 203)

INDEPENDENT ACTIVITY

Read the questions on *Math Masters,* page 203 to the class as necessary. Use the master to help you determine how much time you need to spend reviewing time-telling skills. Be sure to correct children's papers before the next lesson.

STUDENT PAGE

Math Boxes 12.1

1. Draw a shape with a perimeter of 14 cm. Sample answers:

   The area of the shape is __8__ square centimeters.

2. I spent $4.22 at the store and gave the cashier a $10 bill. How much change should I get?

   $ __5.78__

3. Solve.

Unit

   $365 \times 1 =$ __365__

   $365 + 1 =$ __366__

   __0__ $= 444 \times 0$

   __444__ $= 444 + 0$

4. Draw a line segment 3 cm long.

   Draw a second line segment 4 cm longer than the first.

   Draw a third line segment twice as long as the first.

5. Complete the Fact Triangle. Write the fact family.

   $3 \times 9 = 27$
   $9 \times 3 = 27$
   $27 \div 9 = 3$
   $27 \div 3 = 9$

6. 8 flower boxes. 4 plants in each box. How many plants?

   __32__ plants

   Write a number model.

   $8 \times 4 = 32$

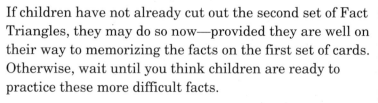

Ongoing Learning & Practice

◆ Practicing Multiplication and Division Facts Using Fact Triangles
(*Math Journal 2,* Activity Sheets 8 and 9)

PARTNER ACTIVITY

If children have not already cut out the second set of Fact Triangles, they may do so now—provided they are well on their way to memorizing the facts on the first set of cards. Otherwise, wait until you think children are ready to practice these more difficult facts.

✦ Math Boxes 12.1 (*Math Journal 2*, p. 299)

INDEPENDENT ACTIVITY

Mixed Review This journal page provides opportunities for cumulative review or assessment of concepts and skills.

✦ Home Link 12.1 (*Math Masters*, p. 404)

Home Connection Children fill in the missing numbers on multiplication/division Fact Triangles. Then, using the numbers on these Fact Triangles, children write the fact families.

3 Options for Individualizing

✦ EXTRA PRACTICE Finding the Number of Days of Summer Vacation
(*Math Masters*, p. 204)

SMALL-GROUP ACTIVITY   15–30 min

On the board, write the dates for the first day of summer vacation and the first day of school next fall. Circle these dates on the class calendar. Ask children to figure out the exact number of days of vacation they will have this summer.

You may prefer to have children work together in small groups to complete calendar pages for the months that include any vacation days. For example, if your vacation runs from May 27 to August 21, give each small group four copies of *Math Masters*, page 204—for the months of May, June, July, and August. As children complete the calendars, suggest that they record important events on them. Children use their completed calendars to find the number of days of vacation they will have this summer.

✦ EXTRA PRACTICE Minute Math

SMALL-GROUP ACTIVITY   5–15 min

To offer children more experience with reviewing dates, see the following page in *Minute Math:*

Basic Routines: p. 20

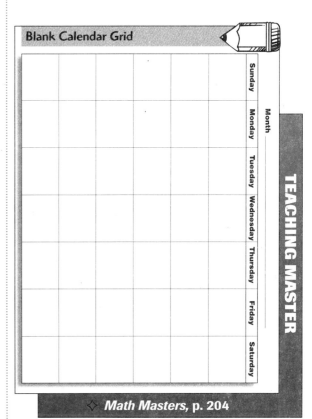

Blank Calendar Grid

Month _____

Sunday | Monday | Tuesday | Wednesday | Thursday | Friday | Saturday

◇ *Math Masters*, p. 204   TEACHING MASTER

12.2 Review: Clock Skills

OBJECTIVES To read times in different ways; to show time (to 5 minutes) on a clock face; and to calculate a time that is earlier or later than a given time.

Lesson 12.2 (M.UN.02.05)
Do Part 3: "Minute Math" pp. 71 & 73.

summaries · materials

1 Teaching the Lesson

Children review telling time, using a variety of ways of naming the time; children use tool-kit clocks to tell what time it will be in a given number of minutes or what time it was a given number of minutes ago. [Measurement and Reference Frames]

- ☐ *Math Journal 2*, pp. 300 and 301
- ☐ Home Link 12.1
- ☐ Teaching Master (*Math Masters*, p. 203)
- ☐ slate; demonstration clock; tool-kit clock

***See* Advance Preparation**

2 Ongoing Learning & Practice

Children practice solving multidigit addition and subtraction problems. [Operations and Computation]

Children practice and maintain skills through Math Boxes and Home Link activities.

- ☐ *Math Journal 2*, pp. 302–304
- ☐ Home Link Master (*Math Masters*, p. 405)

3 Options for Individualizing

Extra Practice Children practice telling time to 5 minutes. [Measurement and Reference Frames]

Extra Practice Children tell time to 5 minutes, give a time in different ways, and use a clock to tell what time it will be in a given number of minutes or what time it was a given number of minutes ago. [Measurement and Reference Frames]

- ☐ Teaching Master (*Math Masters*, p. 205)
- ☐ tool-kit clock
- ☐ *Minute Math*®, pp. 71 and 73

Additional Information

Advance Preparation Before starting the teaching activities in Part 1, correct the written assessments from Lesson 12.1 (*Math Masters*, page 203).

Getting Started

Mental Math and Reflexes

Pose 0, 1, 2, 5, and 10 multiplication facts. *For example:*

10 × 4 40   5 × 3 15   0 × 9 0
2 × 8 16   4 × 1 4

Math Message

School starts at
____ : ____ *A.M.*
School is out at ____ : ____ *P.M.*
How long does the school day last?
____ *hours*

Home Link 12.1 Follow-Up

Briefly go over the answers.

Teaching the Lesson

◆ Math Message Follow-Up

WHOLE-GROUP DISCUSSION

As children share their answers, ask someone to act out the school day using a tool-kit clock. Check that children know the meanings of *A.M.* and *P.M.*

◆ Reviewing Clock Skills (*Math Masters*, p. 203)

WHOLE-CLASS ACTIVITY

Before you begin your review, be sure to check children's responses on *Math Masters*, page 203 so that you will know how much review your class actually needs. Practice telling time to 5 minutes and to the nearest minute if children are ready to do so.

▷ Show a time on the demonstration clock. Children write the time on their slates.

▷ Write a time on the board. Children show the time on their tool-kit clocks.

◆ Discussing Alternate Names for Times

WHOLE-CLASS ACTIVITY

Because clocks with clock faces were used for centuries before the invention of digital clocks, people often name the time by describing the positions of the hour and minute hands. You can review these alternate names with such activities as the following:

▷ Show 8:30 on the demonstration clock and ask children to name the time in several different ways. Eight thirty; 30 minutes after 8; half-past 8 Ask: *Why is "half-past 8" a good name for 8:30?* The minute hand has moved around half of the clock face since 8:00.

▷ Repeat with 3:15. Three fifteen; a quarter-past or a quarter-after 3; 15 minutes after 3 Ask: *Why is "a quarter-past 3" a good name for 3:15?* The minute hand has moved around one quarter of the clock face since 3:00.

Half past

A quarter past

A quarter to

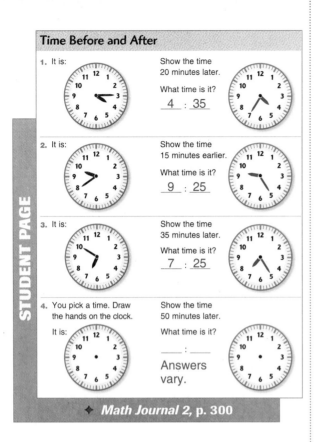

Time Before and After

1. It is: | Show the time 20 minutes later. What time is it? <u>4</u> : <u>35</u>

2. It is: | Show the time 15 minutes earlier. What time is it? <u>9</u> : <u>25</u>

3. It is: | Show the time 35 minutes later. What time is it? <u>7</u> : <u>25</u>

4. You pick a time. Draw the hands on the clock. It is: ___ : ___ | Show the time 50 minutes later. What time is it? ___ : ___ Answers vary.

◆ *Math Journal 2,* p. 300

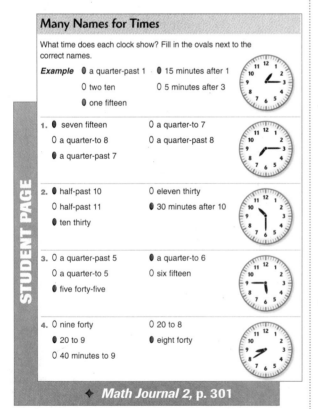

Many Names for Times

What time does each clock show? Fill in the ovals next to the correct names.

Example ● a quarter-past 1 ● 15 minutes after 1
    ○ two ten ○ 5 minutes after 3
    ● one fifteen

1. ● seven fifteen ○ a quarter-to 7
    ○ a quarter-to 8 ○ a quarter-past 8
    ● a quarter-past 7

2. ● half-past 10 ○ eleven thirty
    ○ half-past 11 ● 30 minutes after 10
    ● ten thirty

3. ○ a quarter-past 5 ● a quarter-to 6
    ○ a quarter-to 5 ○ six fifteen
    ● five forty-five

4. ○ nine forty ○ 20 to 8
    ● 20 to 9 ● eight forty
    ○ 40 minutes to 9

◆ *Math Journal 2,* p. 301

▷ Repeat with 5:10. Five ten; 10 minutes after 5; 10 past 5

▷ Show 7:35 on the demonstration clock. Move the minute hand to 8:00 while children count by 5s. Ask: *How many minutes are there from 7:35 to 8:00?* 25 Discuss the fact that "25 minutes before 8" and "25 to 8" are other names for 7:35.

▷ Repeat with 1:45. One forty-five; a quarter-to 2; 15 minutes to 2 Ask: *Why is "a quarter-to 2" a good name for 1:45?* The minute hand has moved around $\frac{3}{4}$ of the clock face since 1:00, and it must move around the remaining $\frac{1}{4}$ clock face to reach 2:00.

Adjusting the Activity Repeat the activity with other times as needed. You might include nonstandard ways of naming the time. For example: *What is another name for 70 minutes after 10?* 11:10; 10 past 11 *For 13 o'clock?* 1 o'clock

You might want to include military time. For example, *What is fifteen hundred hours?* 3 o'clock P.M. *Twenty-one hundred hours?* 9 o'clock P.M.

◆ **Finding the Time before and after a Given Time** (*Math Journal 2,* p. 300)

WHOLE-CLASS ACTIVITY

Tell the following number story:

Bob started working on a Home Link at 6:10. It took him 25 minutes to finish it. At what time did he finish it? 6:35

Encourage children to share and demonstrate their strategies on their tool-kit clocks. For example, they can show 6:10 on their clocks, then move the minute hand forward 25 minutes while counting by 5s, and then adjust the hour hand. Ask children to name the time in more than one way. Six thirty-five; 35 minutes after 6; 35 past 6; 25 minutes before 7; 25 to 7

Try another story:

Carmen finished getting dressed at 7:45. She got up 35 minutes earlier. At what time did she get up? 7:10

After the class finishes discussing the solution to the story, children complete the journal page.

◆ **Practicing Using Alternate Names for Times** (*Math Journal 2,* p. 301)

INDEPENDENT ACTIVITY 🏃

Children choose alternate ways of naming the times shown on clock faces.

Ongoing Learning & Practice

◆ Solving Multidigit Addition and Subtraction Problems (*Math Journal 2,* pp. 302 and 303)

INDEPENDENT ACTIVITY

Children use their favorite algorithms to solve addition and subtraction problems.

◆ Math Boxes 12.2 (*Math Journal 2,* p. 304)

INDEPENDENT ACTIVITY

Mixed Review This journal page provides opportunities for cumulative review or assessment of concepts and skills.

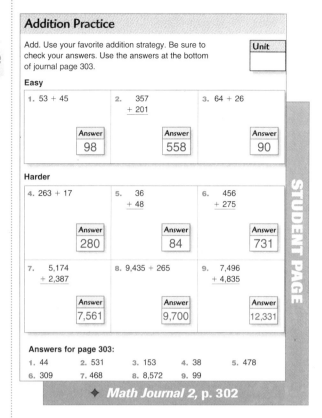

Addition Practice

Add. Use your favorite addition strategy. Be sure to check your answers. Use the answers at the bottom of journal page 303.

Unit

Easy

1. 53 + 45
Answer 98

2. 357 + 201
Answer 558

3. 64 + 26
Answer 90

Harder

4. 263 + 17
Answer 280

5. 36 + 48
Answer 84

6. 456 + 275
Answer 731

7. 5,174 + 2,387
Answer 7,561

8. 9,435 + 265
Answer 9,700

9. 7,496 + 4,835
Answer 12,331

Answers for page 303:
1. 44   2. 531   3. 153   4. 38   5. 478
6. 309   7. 468   8. 8,572   9. 99

◆ *Math Journal 2, p. 302*

STUDENT PAGE

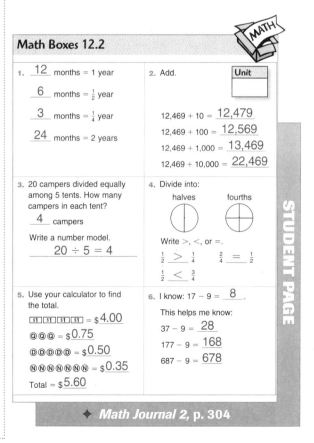

Subtraction Practice

Subtract. Use your favorite subtraction strategy. Be sure to check your answers. Use the answers at the bottom of journal page 302.

Unit

Easy

1. 68 − 24
Answer 44

2. 563 − 32
Answer 531

3. 486 − 333
Answer 153

Harder

4. 65 − 27
Answer 38

5. 784 − 306
Answer 478

6. 555 − 246
Answer 309

7. 506 − 38
Answer 468

8. 9,006 − 434
Answer 8,572

9. 233 − 134
Answer 99

Answers for page 302:
1. 98   2. 558   3. 90   4. 280   5. 84
6. 731   7. 7,561   8. 9,700   9. 12,331

◆ *Math Journal 2, p. 303*

STUDENT PAGE

Math Boxes 12.2

1. <u>12</u> months = 1 year
<u>6</u> months = $\frac{1}{2}$ year
<u>3</u> months = $\frac{1}{4}$ year
<u>24</u> months = 2 years

2. Add.
Unit

$12,469 + 10 = \underline{12,479}$
$12,469 + 100 = \underline{12,569}$
$12,469 + 1,000 = \underline{13,469}$
$12,469 + 10,000 = \underline{22,469}$

3. 20 campers divided equally among 5 tents. How many campers in each tent?
<u>4</u> campers
Write a number model.
$20 \div 5 = 4$

4. Divide into:
halves   fourths

Write >, <, or =.
$\frac{1}{2} > \frac{1}{4}$ $\frac{2}{4} = \frac{1}{2}$
$\frac{1}{2} < \frac{3}{4}$

5. Use your calculator to find the total.
[$1][$1][$1][$1] = $4.00
Q Q Q = $0.75
D D D D D = $0.50
N N N N N N N = $0.35
Total = $5.60

6. I know: 17 − 9 = <u>8</u>.
This helps me know:
$37 − 9 = \underline{28}$
$177 − 9 = \underline{168}$
$687 − 9 = \underline{678}$

◆ *Math Journal 2, p. 304*

STUDENT PAGE

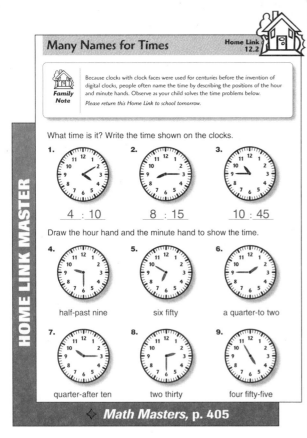

◆ **Math Masters, p. 405**

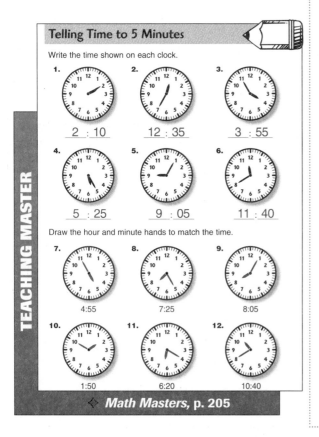

◆ **Math Masters, p. 205**

◆ Home Link 12.2 (*Math Masters*, p. 405)

Home Connection Children name the times shown on clock faces. They draw the hands on clock faces to show times.

3 Options for Individualizing

◆ EXTRA PRACTICE Telling Time to 5 Minutes (*Math Masters*, p. 205)

SMALL-GROUP ACTIVITY 👥👥   **5–15 min**

Assign the problems on this master to children who still have difficulty telling time to 5 minutes. Circulate with your demonstration clock and assist as necessary. Make sure that children are using their tool-kit clocks correctly.

◆ EXTRA PRACTICE Minute Math

SMALL-GROUP ACTIVITY 👥👥   **5–15 min**

To offer children more experience with telling time, see the following pages in *Minute Math*:

Measurement: pp. 71 and 73

PLANNING AHEAD

In preparation for Lesson 12.3, draw a timeline on the board showing 10-year intervals from 1830 to 2010.

1830   1890   1900   1910   1920   1930   1940   1950   2010

12.3 Timelines

summaries / materials

1 Teaching the Lesson

Children discuss timelines and various ways people exchange information; children plot the dates for the inventions of some communications devices on a timeline. [Measurement and Reference Frames]

☐ *Math Journal 2*, p. 306
☐ Home Link 12.2
See Advance Preparation

2 Ongoing Learning & Practice

Children calculate the elapsed time between inventions displayed on a timeline. [Measurement and Reference Frames; Operations and Computation]

Children practice and maintain skills through Math Boxes and Home Link activities.

☐ *Math Journal 2*, pp. 305 and 307
☐ Home Link Master (*Math Masters,* p. 406)

3 Options for Individualizing

Enrichment Children create a timeline showing important events in a person's life. [Measurement and Reference Frames]

☐ ruler

Additional Information

Advance Preparation For the teaching activities in Part 1, draw a timeline on the board, showing 10-year intervals from 1830 to 2010.

1830 1890 1900 1910 1920 1930 1940 1950 2010

Vocabulary • communicate • timeline • decade • century

Getting Started

Mental Math and Reflexes

Suggestions

What number is:

• three times as much as 9? 27

• half as much as 20? 10

• 10 more than 73? 83

• 20 less than 34? 14

Math Message

On what date were you born? In what year will you become 10 years old?

Home Link 12.2 Follow-Up

Briefly go over the answers. Ask children to name the time as it appears on the classroom clock in as many different ways as they can.

Teaching the Lesson

◆ Math Message Follow-Up

WHOLE-CLASS DISCUSSION

Ask several volunteers to share their answers with the class.

◆ Discussing Ways in Which People Communicate with One Another across Distances

WHOLE-CLASS DISCUSSION

Social Studies Link On the board, list the years in which the telephone, radio, and television were invented. (See the margin.)

- What do these three inventions have in common? They are devices with which people can talk to others from a distance.

Talk about the meaning of the word **communicate**—to exchange information.

- What are some ways in which people can communicate with one another? By talking, writing, drawing pictures, singing, using sign language, using Morse code

- Can you name other means of communication besides the telephone, radio, and television? Newspapers, magazines, photographs, paintings, telegrams, audiotapes, videos, movies, computers

◆ Examining a Timeline as a Way of Displaying Events in Sequential Order

WHOLE-CLASS DISCUSSION

Children experienced **timelines** when they made a timeline of school days in first grade, so they should be familiar with timelines as devices for showing when certain events took place.

Point to the timeline on the board and remind the class that the numbers stand for years.

- This timeline is divided into 10-year intervals. What is the name for a period of 10 years? **decade**

- (Underline the years 1900 and 2000.) How many decades are between 1900 and 2000? 10 How many years? 100 What is the name for a period of 100 years? **century**

Inventions

1876	telephone
1906	radio
1926	television

Note that timelines may be divided into other time intervals—centuries, years, months, days, hours, and so on.

On the timeline, draw a dot to represent the year the telephone was invented (1876) and label the dot (see below). Then ask volunteers to draw and label dots to show the years the radio (1906) and the television (1926) were invented.

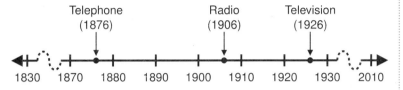

Telephone (1876) Radio (1906) Television (1926)

1830 1870 1880 1890 1900 1910 1920 1930 2010

Ask such questions as:

- About how many decades have there been since the invention of the telephone? About how many years is that? There are 124 years between 1876 and 2000, or about $12\frac{1}{2}$ decades. Adjust this by adding on elapsed years since 2000.

- About how many decades have elapsed between the invention of the telephone and the radio? About how many years is that? 3 decades, or 30 years

✦ Showing Dates for Inventions on a Timeline
(*Math Journal 2*, p. 306)

INDEPENDENT ACTIVITY

Assign journal page 306. Use the invention of the telephone to illustrate how to plot the dates for different inventions on the timeline. For each invention listed, children make a dot in the appropriate place on the timeline and write the corresponding letter above it. Circulate and offer help as needed.

2 Ongoing Learning & Practice

✦ Calculating Elapsed Time for Events on the Timeline (*Math Journal 2*, p. 307)

INDEPENDENT ACTIVITY

Children complete the journal page.

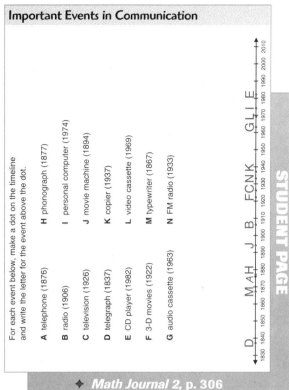

Important Events in Communication

For each event below, make a dot on the timeline and write the letter for the event above the dot.

A telephone (1876)
B radio (1906)
C television (1926)
D telegraph (1837)
E CD player (1982)
F 3-D movies (1922)
G audio cassette (1963)
H phonograph (1877)
I personal computer (1974)
J movie machine (1894)
K copier (1937)
L video cassette (1969)
M typewriter (1867)
N FM radio (1933)

D M A H J B FCNK G L I E

1800 1810 1820 1830 1840 1850 1860 1870 1880 1890 1900 1910 1920 1930 1940 1950 1960 1970 1980 1990 2000 2010

STUDENT PAGE

✦ *Math Journal 2*, p. 306

Interpreting a Timeline

1. What is the earliest invention on the timeline on journal page 306? __telegraph__
   What is the most recent invention? __CD player__

For each pair of inventions:

- tell about how many decades there were between inventions.

- tell about how many years there were between inventions.

Reminder: 1 decade is 10 years. 1 century is 100 years. 1 century is 10 decades.

2. typewriter and movie machine
   about __3__ decades   about __30__ years

3. phonograph and video cassette
   about __9__ decades   about __90__ years

4. telegraph and CD player (14 and 140 are also correct)
   about __15__ decades   about __150__ years

About how many years ago were these things invented? Answers vary.

5. CD player: about _____ years ago

6. FM radio: about _____ years ago

7. 3-D movies: about _____ years ago

8. typewriter: about _____ years ago

STUDENT PAGE

✦ *Math Journal 2*, p. 307

Student Page

1.

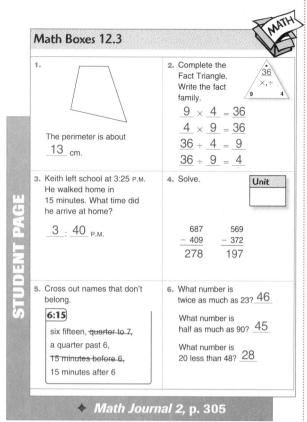

The perimeter is about ___13___ cm.

2. Complete the Fact Triangle. Write the fact family.

36
×,÷
9   4

$9 \times 4 = 36$

$4 \times 9 = 36$

$36 \div 4 = 9$

$36 \div 9 = 4$

3. Keith left school at 3:25 P.M. He walked home in 15 minutes. What time did he arrive at home?

___3___ : ___40___ P.M.

4. Solve.

Unit

$$\begin{array}{r} 687 \\ - 409 \\ \hline 278 \end{array} \qquad \begin{array}{r} 569 \\ - 372 \\ \hline 197 \end{array}$$

5. Cross out names that don't belong.

6:15

six fifteen, ~~quarter to 7,~~
a quarter past 6,
~~15 minutes before 6,~~
15 minutes after 6

6. What number is twice as much as 23? ___46___

What number is half as much as 90? ___45___

What number is 20 less than 48? ___28___

Math Journal 2, p. 305

◆ Math Boxes 12.3 (*Math Journal 2,* p. 305)

INDEPENDENT ACTIVITY 👤

Mixed Review This journal page provides opportunities for cumulative review or assessment of concepts and skills.

◆ Home Link 12.3 (*Math Masters,* p. 406)

Home Connection Children fill in a timeline for Emily's day at the beach and answer questions involving elapsed time between activities.

3 Options for Individualizing

◆ ENRICHMENT Creating a Timeline of a Person's Life

INDEPENDENT ACTIVITY 👤   **15–30 min**

Children choose a family member or famous person and create a timeline to display the important events of that person's life in sequential order. Children share their timelines with the class.

Portfolio Ideas

Home Link Master

Timelines   Home Link 12.3

Family Note A timeline is a way to display events in sequential order. Timelines may be divided into intervals, such as centuries, years, months, days, and hours. Observe your child as he or she fills in the timeline at the right.

Please return this Home Link to school tomorrow.

Emily's Day at the Beach

1. For each event below, make a dot on the timeline and write the letter for the event above the dot.

A Ate lunch (12:30 P.M.)

B Went fishing in a boat (10:00 A.M.)

C Arrived at the beach (9:00 A.M.)

D Returned from fishing trip (11:30 A.M.)

E Played volleyball (1:30 P.M.)

F Went swimming (2:00 P.M.)

G Drove home (4:00 P.M.)

H Built sandcastles (3:00 P.M.)

2. How long did Emily spend at the beach before she went on the fishing trip? ___1___ hour(s)

3. How long was the fishing trip? ___$1\frac{1}{2}$___ hour(s)

4. How long was Emily's day at the beach? ___7___ hour(s)

5. Did Emily spend more time playing volleyball or swimming? ___swimming___

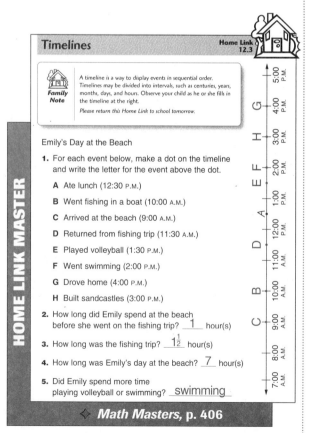

Math Masters, p. 406

12.4 Practice Multiplication Facts

OBJECTIVES To review and extend shortcuts and strategies for learning multiplication facts; and to practice multiplication facts.

summaries | materials

1 Teaching the Lesson

Children use the Products Table to illustrate the turn-around rule and the 0 and 1 shortcuts for multiplication and to review strategies for learning the times-2, times-5, and times-10 facts; children use Fact Triangles to practice multiplication facts. [Operations and Computation]

☐ *Math Journal 2,* p. 286
☐ Home Link 12.3
☐ class demonstration clock
☐ Fact Triangles (cut from *Math Journal 2,* Activity Sheets 8 and 9)

2 Ongoing Learning & Practice

Children complete an individual assessment of the "easier" multiplication facts, in which one factor is 2, 3, 4, or 5. [Operations and Computation]

Children practice and maintain skills through Math Boxes and Home Link activities.

☐ *Math Journal 2,* p. 308
☐ Home Link Masters (*Math Masters,* pp. 407 and 408)
☐ Teaching Master (*Math Masters,* p. 206)
***See* Advance Preparation**

3 Options for Individualizing

Enrichment Children learn the "9s Facts on Fingers" shortcut. [Operations and Computation]

Additional Information

Advance Preparation For the assessment activity in Part 2, make 1 copy of *Math Masters,* page 206 for every 2 children. Cut the copies in half.

Vocabulary • **factor** • **product** • **turn-around rule**

Getting Started

Mental Math and Reflexes

Pose number stories involving multiplication and division facts. *Suggestions:*

- 9 cookies per pack. 2 packs. How many cookies? 18
- 20 sticks of gum. 5 children. How many sticks of gum per child? 4

Math Message

Look at the Products Table on page 286 in your journal. What can you say about the third row and the third column?

Home Link 12.3 Follow-Up

Ask volunteers to demonstrate on the class demonstration clock how they calculated the answers to Problems 2–5.

Products Table

0×0 =0	0×1 =0	0×2 =0	0×3 =0	0×4 =0	0×5 =0	0×6 =0	0×7 =0	0×8 =0	0×9 =0	0×10 =0
1×0 =0	1×1 =1	1×2 =2	1×3 =3	1×4 =4	1×5 =5	1×6 =6	1×7 =7	1×8 =8	1×9 =9	1×10 =10
2×0 =0	2×1 =2	2×2 =4	2×3 =6	2×4 =8	2×5 =10	2×6 =12	2×7 =14	2×8 =16	2×9 =18	2×10 =20
3×0 =0	3×1 =3	3×2 =6	3×3 =9	3×4 =12	3×5 =15	3×6 =18	3×7 =21	3×8 =24	3×9 =27	3×10 =30
4×0 =0	4×1 =4	4×2 =8	4×3 =12	4×4 =16	4×5 =20	4×6 =24	4×7 =28	4×8 =32	4×9 =36	4×10 =40
5×0 =0	5×1 =5	5×2 =10	5×3 =15	5×4 =20	5×5 =25	5×6 =30	5×7 =35	5×8 =40	5×9 =45	5×10 =50
6×0 =0	6×1 =6	6×2 =12	6×3 =18	6×4 =24	6×5 =30	6×6 =36	6×7 =42	6×8 =48	6×9 =54	6×10 =60
7×0 =0	7×1 =7	7×2 =14	7×3 =21	7×4 =28	7×5 =35	7×6 =42	7×7 =49	7×8 =56	7×9 =63	7×10 =70
8×0 =0	8×1 =8	8×2 =16	8×3 =24	8×4 =32	8×5 =40	8×6 =48	8×7 =56	8×8 =64	8×9 =72	8×10 =80
9×0 =0	9×1 =9	9×2 =18	9×3 =27	9×4 =36	9×5 =45	9×6 =54	9×7 =63	9×8 =72	9×9 =81	9×10 =90
10×0 =0	10×1 =10	10×2 =20	10×3 =30	10×4 =40	10×5 =50	10×6 =60	10×7 =70	10×8 =80	10×9 =90	10×10 =100

✦ *Math Journal 2,* p. 286

Teaching the Lesson

✦ **Math Message Follow-Up** (*Math Journal 2,* p. 286)

WHOLE-CLASS DISCUSSION

Remind children of the phrases and vocabulary used to talk about multiplication. *For example:*

▷ 4 × 2 is read "4 times 2" or "4 multiplied by 2."

▷ In the number model 4 × 2 = 8, 4 and 2 are called **factors,** and 8 is called the **product.**

Ask children to share their observations. These might include the following:

▷ The facts in the third column and third row are all "times-2 facts": 2 is one of the factors.

▷ The facts in the third column and third row are "doubles facts." For example, both 2 × 6 and 6 × 2 have "double 6" as the product.

▷ The facts in the third column are the same as the facts in the third row. The only difference is that the order of the factors is reversed.

Remind children that if the order of the factors is reversed, the product remains the same. This is called the **turn-around rule** for multiplication.

✦ **Reviewing Multiplication Shortcuts and Strategies** (*Math Journal 2,* p. 286)

WHOLE-CLASS DISCUSSION

Remind children about shortcuts and strategies they have already used:

Turn-around rule

Have children verify the turn-around rule for multiplication by selecting examples from the Products Table. For example, 3 × 5 = 15 and 5 × 3 = 15; 7 × 4 = 28 and 4 × 7 = 28.

0-shortcut

The product of 0 and any number is 0. Have children verify by using examples from the first row and the first column of the Products Table.

1-shortcut

The product of 1 and any number is that number. Have children verify by using examples from the second row and the second column of the Products Table.

A times-2 strategy

To multiply a number by 2, think "double the number." Use examples like the following: $2 \times 9 = ?$ Think "double 9." Answer: 18

A times-5 strategy

To multiply a number by 5, think "nickels." Use examples like the following: $3 \times 5 = ?$ Think "3 nickels is 15 cents." Answer: 15

A times-10 strategy

To multiply a number by 10, think "dimes." Use examples like the following: $7 \times 10 = ?$ Think "7 dimes is 70 cents." Answer: 70

 Adjusting the Activity If children have difficulty with the times-10 facts, mention another strategy: To multiply a number by 10, write the number and write 0 as the final digit. Verify by using examples from the final row and column of the Products Table.

You may want to introduce a times-4 strategy: If one of the factors is 4, think "double, then double again." For example, to solve $4 \times 3 = ?$, double 3 6 and then double 6. 12

◆ Practicing Multiplication Facts with Fact Triangles
(*Math Journal 2,* Activity Sheets 8 and 9)

PARTNER ACTIVITY

There are four pages of Fact Triangles in children's journals; each page consists of a set of 9 cards. Children have previously cut apart the first two pages of cards and used these to practice the "easier" multiplication facts. If your class is ready to practice "harder" multiplication facts on the second two pages and children have not already cut them apart, they should do so now.

If necessary, remind children how to use the cards: One partner covers the number by the dot (the product) with a thumb or finger; the other partner gives the product of the two uncovered numbers (the factors).

 ONGOING ASSESSMENT
By the end of second grade, you should expect near mastery of the multiplication facts on the first set of 18 Fact Triangle cards. Progress on the remaining facts will vary.

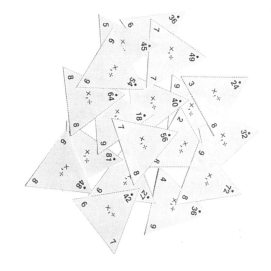

▼ This *Math Masters* page accompanies the first activity on the following page.

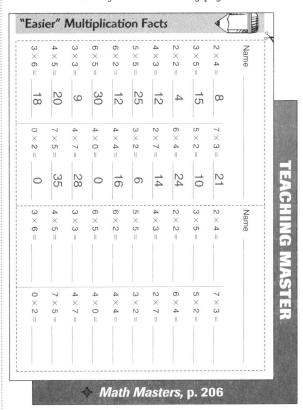

"Easier" Multiplication Facts

$3 \times 6 =$ 18	$0 \times 2 =$ 0	
$4 \times 5 =$ 20	$7 \times 5 =$ 35	
$3 \times 3 =$ 9	$4 \times 7 =$ 28	
$6 \times 5 =$ 30	$4 \times 0 =$ 0	
$6 \times 2 =$ 12	$4 \times 4 =$ 16	
$5 \times 5 =$ 25	$3 \times 2 =$ 6	
$4 \times 3 =$ 12	$2 \times 7 =$ 14	
$2 \times 2 =$ 4	$6 \times 4 =$ 24	
$3 \times 5 =$ 15	$5 \times 2 =$ 10	
$2 \times 4 =$ 8	$7 \times 3 =$ 21	

Math Masters, p. 206

TEACHING MASTER

Math Boxes 12.4

STUDENT PAGE

1. Put parentheses to make each number model true.

$21 = (39 - 10) - 8$

$4 \times (3 + 7) = 40$

$(3 \times 5) + 2 = 17$

2. Put the numbers in order.

35, 64, 27, 86, 71

<u>27</u>, <u>35</u>, <u>64</u>, <u>71</u>, <u>86</u>

The median is <u>64</u>.

The difference between the highest and lowest number (range) is <u>59</u>.

3. Fill in the frames.

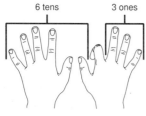

×10   −10

2   20   10

900   90   100

4. In 43,692, the value of

4 is <u>40,000</u>.

3 is <u>3,000</u>.

6 is <u>600</u>.

9 is <u>90</u>.

2 is <u>2</u>.

5. Solve.

Unit

$4 \times 0 = $ <u>0</u>

<u>63</u> $= 63 \times 1$

$7 \times 10 = $ <u>70</u>

<u>300</u> $= 100 \times 3$

6. Julia has 9 teddy bears. Natalie has $\frac{1}{3}$ as many. How many does Natalie have?

<u>3</u> teddy bears

Draw a picture to help.

J • • • | • • | • • •

N • • •

✦ *Math Journal 2, p. 308*

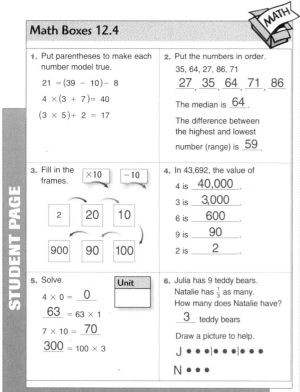

6 tens   3 ones

$7 \times 9 = 63$

HOME LINK MASTER

×, ÷ Fact Triangles

Home Link 12.4

Family Note Your child has been practicing multiplication facts. Today children reviewed shortcuts for solving multiplication problems with the numbers 2, 5, and 10. Encourage your child to practice with the Fact Triangles over the summer in preparation for third grade.

Cut out the Fact Triangles on these pages. Show someone at home how you can use them to practice multiplication facts.

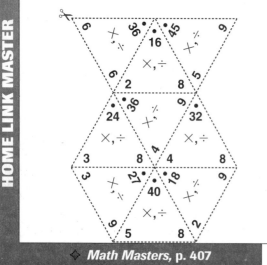

✦ *Math Masters, p. 407*

2 Ongoing Learning & Practice

✦ Administering a Written Assessment for the "Easier" Multiplication Facts
(*Math Masters*, p. 206)

INDEPENDENT ACTIVITY

Read the 20 fact problems listed on the half-sheet of paper and ask children to record their answers. Collect and correct their work. This problem set includes nearly the same multiplication facts that appear on the first two pages of Fact Triangles (the "easier" multiplication facts).

NOTE: If you have been working with the second set of Fact Triangles for some time, you might choose to skip this activity.

✦ Math Boxes 12.4 (*Math Journal 2*, p. 308)

INDEPENDENT ACTIVITY

Mixed Review This journal page provides opportunities for cumulative review or assessment of concepts and skills.

✦ Home Link 12.4 (*Math Masters*, pp. 407 and 408)

Home Connection Children practice multiplication facts with the second set of Fact Triangles.

3 Options for Individualizing

✦ ENRICHMENT Introducing the "9s Facts on Fingers" Shortcut

INDEPENDENT ACTIVITY   5–15 min

Hold both hands open, palms down. (See the margin.) To multiply any number less than 10 by 9 (such as 7×9), count fingers, starting with the little finger of the left hand. If the factor is greater than 5, continue counting with the thumb of the right hand. Put down the last finger in your count. (For 7×9, the "down" finger is the index finger of the right hand.) The number of fingers to the left of the "down" finger represents the tens digit in the product. The number of fingers to the right represents the ones digit.

12.5 Division from Multiplication

OBJECTIVES To review multiplication/division fact families; and to investigate the relationship between multiplication and division.

summaries	materials
1 Teaching the Lesson	
Children review the turn-around rule for multiplication and learn that there is no turn-around rule for division; children use Fact Triangles to generate multiplication and division facts; children write and solve related division facts for given multiplication facts. [Operations and Computation; Patterns, Functions, and Algebra]	☐ *Math Journal 2,* pp. 286, 309, and 310 ☐ Home Link 12.4 ☐ Teaching Master transparency (*Math Masters,* p. 199; optional) ☐ 2 sheets of paper for demonstration ☐ Fact Triangles (*Math Journal 2,* Activity Sheets 8 and 9) ***See* Advance Preparation**
2 Ongoing Learning & Practice	
Children practice adding three numbers by playing *Addition Card Draw.* [Operations and Computation] Children practice and maintain skills through Math Boxes and Home Link activities.	☐ *Math Journal 2,* p. 311 ☐ Teaching Masters (*Math Masters,* pp. 207 and 208) ☐ Home Link Masters (*Math Masters,* pp. 409 and 410) ☐ number cards 1–20 (from Everything Math Deck, if available) ☐ slate or scratch paper
3 Options for Individualizing	
Extra Practice Children complete "What's My Rule?" tables involving multiplication and division facts. [Operations and Computation; Patterns, Functions, and Algebra] **Extra Practice** Children write multiplication/division fact families using three given numbers. [Operations and Computation; Patterns, Functions, and Algebra]	☐ Teaching Master (*Math Masters,* p. 209) ☐ calculator ☐ *Minute Math®,* p. 41

Additional Information

Advance Preparation For the *Using Fact Triangles for Division* activity in Part 1, you might want to make an overhead transparency of *Math Masters,* page 199.

Getting Started

Mental Math and Reflexes

Pose multiplication facts appropriate to children's progress.

Math Message

Write the fact family for the Fact Triangle.

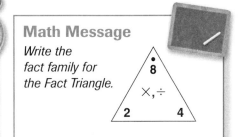

Home Link 12.4 Follow-Up

If time permits, poll the class to see how much time children spent practicing with the Fact Triangles. What is the median practice time?

Fact Family

$2 \times 4 = 8$
$4 \times 2 = 8$
$8 \div 2 = 4$
$8 \div 4 = 2$

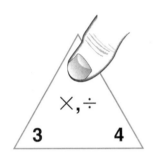

The multiplication problem $3 \times 4 = ?$

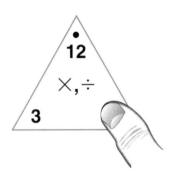

The division problem $12 \div 3 = ?$

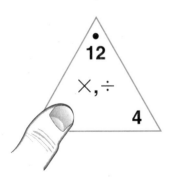

The division problem $12 \div 4 = ?$

1 Teaching the Lesson

◆ Math Message Follow-Up

WHOLE-CLASS DISCUSSION

List the facts in the fact family on the board as children name them (see the margin). Some children may forget to name the division facts because they have used Fact Triangles mainly to practice multiplication facts.

Review the turn-around shortcut for multiplication. To illustrate that there is no turn-around rule for division, pose the following problems:

Four granola bars are shared equally by 2 children. How many bars does each child get? 2 bars

Summarize with a number model: $4 \div 2 = 2$.

Two granola bars are shared equally by 4 children. How many bars does each child get?

To act out the problem, represent the two bars with two identical rectangular pieces of paper. Ask a volunteer to show how to share the bars equally among 4 children. Tear each piece of paper in half. Each child gets $\frac{1}{2}$ of a granola bar.

Summarize with a number model: $2 \div 4 = \frac{1}{2}$.

Therefore, $4 \div 2$ is not equal to $2 \div 4$.

◆ Using Fact Triangles for Division
(*Math Journal 2,* Activity Sheets 8 and 9; *Math Masters,* p. 199)

PARTNER ACTIVITY

Remind children that one partner can cover any of the three numbers on a Fact Triangle before showing it to the other partner.

▷ To generate a multiplication problem, cover the top number (by the dot).

▷ To generate a division problem, cover either of the bottom numbers.

Draw a large Fact Triangle on the board or use an overhead transparency of *Math Masters,* page 199. Fill it in to show a division problem. For example, write 20 at the top, 5 and ? at the bottom, and $20 \div 5 = ?$ under the Fact Triangle. Remind children that a good way to solve a division problem is to think multiplication. For example, to solve $20 \div 5 = ?$, think: *5 times what number equals 20?*

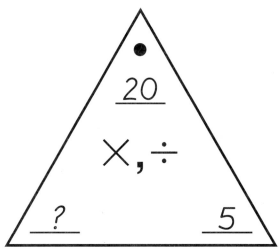

This shows $20 \div 5 = ?$
Since $5 \times 4 = 20$, then $20 \div 5 = 4$.

Repeat this routine. For each division problem, write a related multiplication number model.

Examples: $14 \div 2 = ?$ Think: $2 \times ? = 14$
$15 \div 3 = ?$ Think: $3 \times ? = 15$
$80 \div 10 = ?$ Think: $10 \times ? = 80$

One of the advantages of Fact Triangles is that they remind children to do division by asking: *By what number do I **multiply**?* For each division problem, the child receives two visual messages—a division message and a related multiplication message.

◆ Solving Related Multiplication/Division Fact Problems (*Math Journal 2,* pp. 286, 309, and 310)

PARTNER ACTIVITY

Go over the example on journal page 309 before asking partners to do the other problems. Note that some of the harder multiplication facts have been selected.

Adjusting the Activity Since children are not expected to have memorized all of these facts, they can use their Product Tables (journal page 286) to complete the problems.

Addition Card Draw

Materials	☐ score sheet from *Math Masters*, p. 208
	☐ 1 each of the number cards 0–20
	☐ slate or scratch paper
Players	2

Directions

Shuffle the cards and place the deck with the numbers facing down. Take turns.

1. Draw the top 3 cards from the deck.

2. Record the numbers on the score sheet. Put the 3 cards in a separate pile.

3. Find the sum. Use your slate or paper to do the computation.

After 3 turns:

4. Check your partner's work. Use a calculator.

5. Find the total of the 3 answers. Write the total on the score sheet. The player with the higher total wins.

◇ *Math Masters*, p. 207

 Ongoing Learning & Practice

◆ Playing *Addition Card Draw*
(*Math Masters*, pp. 207 and 208)

PARTNER ACTIVITY

This game provides practice with adding three numbers. You may want to explain the rules of the game, as given on *Math Masters*, page 207.

◆ Math Boxes 12.5 (*Math Journal 2*, p. 311)

INDEPENDENT ACTIVITY

Mixed Review This journal page provides opportunities for cumulative review or assessment of concepts and skills.

◆ Home Link 12.5 (*Math Masters*, pp. 409 and 410)

Home Connection Children solve pairs of related division and multiplication problems. Pictures of Fact Triangles are shown to help children solve the problems.

Addition Card Draw Score Sheet

Game 1

1st turn:

___ + ___ + ___ = ___

2nd turn:

___ + ___ + ___ = ___

3rd turn:

___ + ___ + ___ = ___

Total: _____

Game 2

1st turn:

___ + ___ + ___ = ___

2nd turn:

___ + ___ + ___ = ___

3rd turn:

___ + ___ + ___ = ___

Total: _____

Game 3

1st turn:

___ + ___ + ___ = ___

2nd turn:

___ + ___ + ___ = ___

3rd turn:

___ + ___ + ___ = ___

Total: _____

Game 4

1st turn:

___ + ___ + ___ = ___

2nd turn:

___ + ___ + ___ = ___

3rd turn:

___ + ___ + ___ = ___

Total: _____

◇ *Math Masters*, p. 208

Math Boxes 12.5

1.

Rule ×4	in	out
	4	16
	9	36
	7	28
	5	20
	10	40

Answers vary.

2. Write the time in hours and minutes.

half-past six	6 : 30
quarter-past 4	4 : 15
quarter-to 12	11 : 45
twenty minutes to 2	1 : 40

3. Jon's piano lesson started at a quarter-past four. It lasted 30 minutes. Show and write the time when he was finished.

4 : 45

4. Solve.

5. Write turnarounds and solve.

8 × 5 $\underline{5} \times \underline{8} = \underline{40}$

3 × 7 $\underline{7} \times \underline{3} = \underline{21}$

2 × 8 $\underline{8} \times \underline{2} = \underline{16}$

6 × 6 $\underline{6} \times \underline{6} = \underline{36}$

6. I want to buy a kite for $3.59 and string for $2.50. How many dollar bills do I need?

__7__ dollar bills

◆ *Math Journal 2*, p. 311

3 Options for Individualizing

◆ EXTRA PRACTICE Completing "What's My Rule?" Tables (*Math Masters*, p. 209)

INDEPENDENT ACTIVITY   5–15 min

Children complete "What's My Rule?" tables in which some input and some output numbers are missing. These problems provide children with another way to look at the relationship between multiplication and division facts.

◆ EXTRA PRACTICE Minute Math

SMALL-GROUP ACTIVITY   5–15 min

To offer children more experience with multiplication/division fact families, see the following page in *Minute Math:*

Operations: p. 41

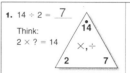

Family Note In this lesson, your child has connected multiplication and division facts by using Fact Triangles and completing fact families. A good way to solve division problems is to think in terms of multiplication. For example, to divide 20 by 5, ask yourself: *5 times what number equals 20?* Since 5 × 4 = 20, 20 ÷ 5 = 4.
Please return this Home Link to school tomorrow.

Solve these division facts. Think multiplication.
Use the Fact Triangles to help you.

1. 14 ÷ 2 = __7__
Think:
2 × ? = 14
(Triangle: 14, 2, 7)

2. 24 ÷ 4 = __6__
Think:
4 × ? = 24
(Triangle: 24, 4, 6)

3. 21 ÷ 3 = __7__
Think:
3 × ? = 21
(Triangle: 21, 3, 7)

4. 18 ÷ 6 = __3__
Think:
6 × ? = 18
(Triangle: 18, 6, 3)

5. 28 ÷ 7 = __4__
Think:
7 × ? = 28
(Triangle: 28, 7, 4)

6. 16 ÷ 4 = __4__
Think:
4 × ? = 16
(Triangle: 16, 4, 4)

◆ *Math Masters*, p. 409

HOME LINK MASTER

"What's My Rule?"

Complete the tables in Problems 1–3.

1. Rule ×2

in	out
3	6
5	10
7	14
8	16
6	12

2. Rule ×10

in	out
2	20
4	40
1.5	15
7	70
2.5	25

3. Rule ×5

in	out
0	0
3	15
10	50
8	40
20	100

Complete the table and write the rule.

4. Rule ×2

in	out
1	2
2	4
3	6
5	10
8	16

Complete the table and write the rule.

5. Rule ×4

in	out
3	12
5	20
2	8
6	24
10	40

Write a rule of your own. Fill in the table. Answers vary.

6. Rule

in	out

TEACHING MASTER

◆ *Math Masters*, p. 209

×, ÷ Facts Practice (cont.)   Home Link 12.5

7. 20 ÷ 5 = __4__
Think:
5 × ? = 20
(Triangle: 20, 5, 4)

8. 30 ÷ 6 = __5__
Think:
6 × ? = 30
(Triangle: 30, 6, 5)

9. 35 ÷ 5 = __7__
Think:
5 × ? = 35
(Triangle: 35, 5, 7)

10. 32 ÷ 4 = __8__
Think:
4 × ? = 32
(Triangle: 32, 4, 8)

11. 42 ÷ 6 = __7__
Think:
6 × ? = 42
(Triangle: 42, 6, 7)

12. 63 ÷ 7 = __9__
Think:
7 × ? = 63
(Triangle: 63, 7, 9)

13. 54 ÷ 9 = __6__
Think:
9 × ? = 54
(Triangle: 54, 6, 9)

14. 81 ÷ 9 = __9__
Think:
9 × ? = 81
(Triangle: 81, 9, 9)

HOME LINK MASTER

◆ *Math Masters*, p. 410

12.6 Graphs: Comparing Speeds of Animals and People

OBJECTIVES To read, draw, and interpret bar graphs; and to find the range and middle value (median) for a set of data.

summaries	materials

1 Teaching the Lesson

Children interpret a bar graph that compares the running speeds of various animals; children make and interpret a bar graph that compares speeds for various modes of travel by adults. [Data and Chance]

- ☐ *Math Journal 2*, pp. 312–315
- ☐ Home Link 12.5

2 Ongoing Learning & Practice

Children practice division facts using Fact Triangles. [Operations and Computation]

Children practice and maintain skills through Math Boxes and Home Link activities.

- ☐ *Math Journal 2*, p. 316
- ☐ Home Link Masters (*Math Masters*, pp. 411 and 412)
- ☐ Fact Triangles (cut from *Math Journal 2*, Activity Sheets 8 and 9)
- ☐ slate (optional)

3 Options for Individualizing

Enrichment Children read or are told Aesop's fable about the tortoise and the hare; children research the speeds of the two animals and write number stories. [Operations and Computation]

- ☐ Teaching Master (*Math Masters*, p. 109)
- ☐ "The Tortoise and the Hare"

See **Advance Preparation**

Additional Information

Advance Preparation For the optional Enrichment activity in Part 3, you may want to obtain a copy of Aesop's fable "The Tortoise and the Hare" or use the version of the fable by Jean de La Fontaine.

Vocabulary • median • range

Getting Started

Mental Math and Reflexes

The following problems provide preparation for reading the values of the bars in a bar graph when the values fall between two horizontal or vertical grid lines.

Name the number halfway between:

- 100 and 200 150
- 50 and 100 75
- 250 and 300 275
- 100 and 150 125
- 600 and 700 650
- 150 and 200 175
- 0 and 50 25
- 200 and 250 225

1 Teaching the Lesson

◆ Math Message Follow-Up
(*Math Journal 2,* p. 312)

WHOLE-CLASS ACTIVITY

Science Link Ask children to describe the
information shown on the graph. Mention that it is
difficult to measure how fast animals can run and that the
distances on the graph are estimates. You also might want
to point out that some animals are built to run fast over
short distances, while others are able to run very long
distances.

Ask children to cover the numbers at the left side of the
graph with the edge of a sheet of paper. Then pose
questions like the following and ask children to try to
answer the questions without looking at the numbers:

• Which animal can cover the longest distance in
  10 seconds? cheetah

• Which animal covers the shortest distance in
  10 seconds? Mamba snake

• Which animal can run about twice as far as the ostrich
  in 10 seconds? cheetah

• Which animal can run about the same distance as the
  wild horse in 10 seconds? Red fox

• Name the animals in order of distance covered in
  10 seconds, from greatest distance to least distance.
  Cheetah, jack rabbit, ostrich, wild horse, red fox,
  human, mamba snake List the animals on the board as
  children name them.

Point out that graphs are useful when one wants to make
rough comparisons quickly and easily.

NOTE: You might mention that the cheetah is
the fastest running mammal on Earth,
reaching speeds that are greater than the
speed limit on most highways. But the cheetah
is not the fastest animal; the frigate bird can
fly more than twice as fast as the cheetah can
run, and the peregrine falcon can dive almost
three times as fast.

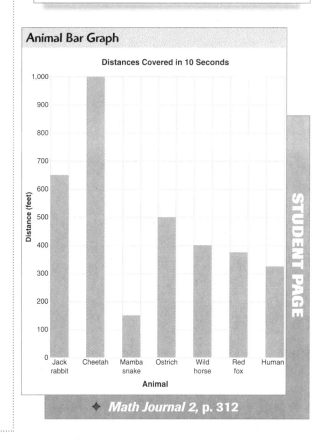

Animal Bar Graph

Distances Covered in 10 Seconds

✦ *Math Journal 2,* p. 312

STUDENT PAGE

Interpreting an Animal Bar Graph

1. In the table, list the animals in order of distance covered in 10 seconds. List the animals from the greatest distance to the least distance.

Distances Covered in 10 Seconds	
Animal	**Distance**
largest: cheetah	1,000 ft
jack rabbit	650 ft
ostrich	500 ft
wild horse	400 ft
red fox	375 ft
human	325 ft
least: mamba snake	150 ft

2. Find the middle value of the distances. The middle value is also called the **median**.

   The median is __400__ feet.

3. The longest distance is __1,000__ feet.

   The shortest distance is __150__ feet.

4. Fill in the comparison diagram with the longest distance and the shortest distance.

Quantity	
1,000 ft	

Quantity	Difference
150 ft	?

5. Find the difference between the longest and shortest distances. The difference between the largest and smallest numbers in a data set is called the **range**.

   The range is __850__ feet.

✦ *Math Journal 2*, p. 313

✦ Finding the Middle Value (Median) and Range of the Distances
(*Math Journal 2*, pp. 312 and 313)

WHOLE-CLASS ACTIVITY

Work together to fill in the table in Problem 1 on journal page 313. First, ask children to copy the list of animals (in order of distance covered) that you have written on the board.

Then ask volunteers to find the approximate distance covered by each animal in 10 seconds. Remind children to use the distances marked along the side of the graph. On journal page 313, children record the distance run by each animal next to the name of the animal.

It may be difficult for children to approximate some of the distances, and you may have to help them for bars that fall in between the horizontal grid lines. *For example:*

▷ The bar for the jack rabbit ends halfway between the lines marked as distances of 600 and 700 feet. A good estimate for the jack rabbit distance is 650 feet.

▷ The bar for the red fox ends between the lines marked as distances of 300 and 400 feet, but it ends closer to the line marked 400 feet. Any estimate in the 360–390 foot range is fine.

Continue working together to complete the problems on journal page 313. The data table for Problem 1 lists the distances in order from greatest to least.

▷ Children should have little difficulty identifying the middle (**median**) distance in this list. 400 feet, the distance covered by a wild horse

▷ The longest distance (1,000 feet, cheetah) and the shortest distance (150 feet, mamba snake) are the items at the top and bottom of the list in the data table. Ask children to use the comparison diagram to find the difference between the longest and shortest distances. 850 feet, since $1,000 - 150 = 850$

The difference between the greatest and the least numbers in a data set is called the **range.** Use this term, but do not insist that children use it.

If children have difficulty naming the middle (median) distance, use the following demonstration: Start with the list of animals and their distances in the table for Problem 1. (These data are sorted from longest to shortest distance.) Draw lines through the first and last rows (cheetah and mamba snake). Then draw lines through the first and last remaining items (jack rabbit and human). Again, draw lines through the first and last remaining items (ostrich and red fox). The single item remaining shows the middle distance (wild horse, 400 feet). The middle, or median, distance is 400 feet.

Children may be interested in the fact that the giant tortoise is one of the slowest animals on Earth; its speed is about $\frac{1}{100}$ that of the wild horse. Ask: *About what distance can a tortoise cover in 10 seconds?* About 4 feet. The tortoise travels about 1 foot for every 100 feet that the wild horse travels, and the wild horse travels about 400 feet in 10 seconds.

A snail can cover barely half a foot in 10 seconds. *About how far will it go in 1 minute?* It covers about 1 foot in 20 seconds; about 2 feet in 40 seconds; and about 3 feet in 60 seconds, or 1 minute.

◆ Comparing Distances an Adult Can Cover by Various Modes of Travel
(*Math Journal 2,* pp. 314 and 315)

PARTNER ACTIVITY

Introduce the journal pages to help children understand what they are expected to do. The data are given on the pages as poster data.

Briefly discuss the information on the two axes of the graph. Then demonstrate how to draw the bar for the distance covered walking for 10 seconds. Partners then complete the graph to answer the follow-up questions.

Distances

Distances athletic adults can travel in 10 seconds:

Walking 125 feet

Cross-country skiing 200 feet

Ice skating 450 feet

Swimming 75 feet

Running hurdles 275 feet

Running 325 feet

◆ *Math Journal 2,* p. 314

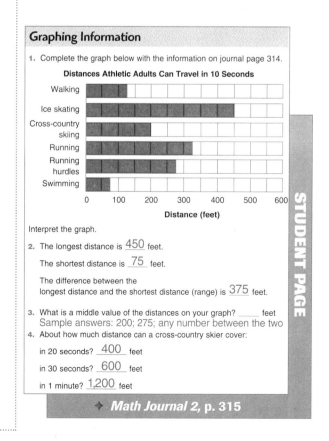

Graphing Information

1. Complete the graph below with the information on journal page 314.

Distances Athletic Adults Can Travel in 10 Seconds

(bar graph with categories: Walking, Ice skating, Cross-country skiing, Running, Running hurdles, Swimming; Distance (feet) axis 0 to 600)

Interpret the graph.

2. The longest distance is 450 feet.

   The shortest distance is 75 feet.

   The difference between the longest distance and the shortest distance (range) is 375 feet.

3. What is a middle value of the distances on your graph? _____ feet
   Sample answers: 200; 275; any number between the two

4. About how much distance can a cross-country skier cover:

   in 20 seconds? 400 feet

   in 30 seconds? 600 feet

   in 1 minute? 1,200 feet

◆ *Math Journal 2,* p. 315

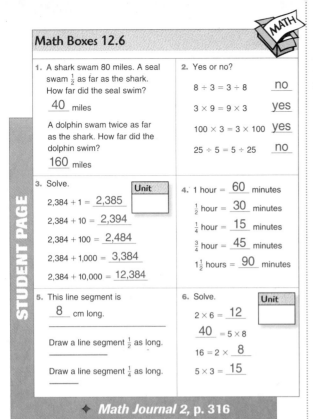

Math Boxes 12.6

1. A shark swam 80 miles. A seal swam $\frac{1}{2}$ as far as the shark. How far did the seal swim?

__40__ miles

A dolphin swam twice as far as the shark. How far did the dolphin swim?

__160__ miles

2. Yes or no?

$8 \div 3 = 3 \div 8$ __no__

$3 \times 9 = 9 \times 3$ __yes__

$100 \times 3 = 3 \times 100$ __yes__

$25 \div 5 = 5 \div 25$ __no__

3. Solve.

Unit

$2,384 + 1 =$ __2,385__

$2,384 + 10 =$ __2,394__

$2,384 + 100 =$ __2,484__

$2,384 + 1,000 =$ __3,384__

$2,384 + 10,000 =$ __12,384__

4. 1 hour = __60__ minutes

$\frac{1}{2}$ hour = __30__ minutes

$\frac{1}{4}$ hour = __15__ minutes

$\frac{3}{4}$ hour = __45__ minutes

$1\frac{1}{2}$ hours = __90__ minutes

5. This line segment is __8__ cm long.

Draw a line segment $\frac{1}{2}$ as long.

Draw a line segment $\frac{1}{4}$ as long.

6. Solve.

Unit

$2 \times 6 =$ __12__

__40__ $= 5 \times 8$

$16 = 2 \times$ __8__

$5 \times 3 =$ __15__

STUDENT PAGE

✦ *Math Journal 2, p. 316*

---

2 Ongoing Learning & Practice

✦ Practicing Division Facts with Fact Triangles
(*Math Journal 2,* Activity Sheets 8 and 9)

PARTNER ACTIVITY

Partners say, or write on their slates, the answers to division facts that are flashed by their partners. Remind children that each card shows two division facts; partners should flash both of these for each card used.

When a child misses a division fact, the partner should cover the top number and flash the related multiplication fact; then he or she should return to the fact that was missed.

 Adjusting the Activity For children who are struggling, limit division practice to the simpler facts. Ask children to use only the Fact Triangles that have a 2 or a 5 as one of the bottom numbers (factors).

✦ Math Boxes 12.6 (*Math Journal 2,* p. 316)

INDEPENDENT ACTIVITY

Mixed Review This journal page provides opportunities for cumulative review or assessment of concepts and skills.

✦ Home Link 12.6 (*Math Masters,* pp. 411 and 412)

Home Connection Children interpret a bar graph displaying the typical life spans of various animals.

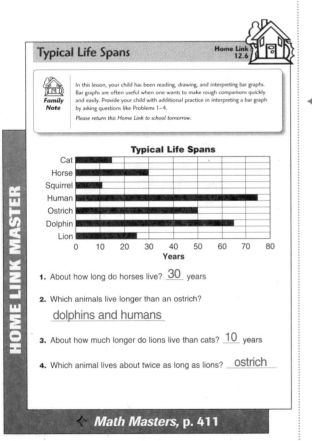

Typical Life Spans

Home Link 12.6

Family Note

In this lesson, your child has been reading, drawing, and interpreting bar graphs. Bar graphs are often useful when one wants to make rough comparisons quickly and easily. Provide your child with additional practice in interpreting a bar graph by asking questions like Problems 1–4.

Please return this Home Link to school tomorrow.

Typical Life Spans

Cat
Horse
Squirrel
Human
Ostrich
Dolphin
Lion

0   10   20   30   40   50   60   70   80
Years

1. About how long do horses live? __30__ years

2. Which animals live longer than an ostrich?

__dolphins and humans__

3. About how much longer do lions live than cats? __10__ years

4. Which animal lives about twice as long as lions? __ostrich__

HOME LINK MASTER

✦ *Math Masters, p. 411*

3 Options for Individualizing

◆ ENRICHMENT Connecting Comparisons of Animal Speeds to Literature
(*Math Masters,* p. 109)

SMALL-GROUP ACTIVITY ●●●●● 15–30 min

Literature Link Tell Aesop's fable "The Tortoise and the Hare" to the class, or have children read the story on their own. In the fable, the tortoise wins a race against the hare because the hare ambles along out of overconfidence.

You may want to have children do research to find out the actual speeds of these two animals. Ask children to write a number story about the animals' speeds.

Portfolio Ideas

---

5. List the animals in order from the shortest life span to the longest life span.

Life Spans

Animal	Years
shortest: squirrel	11
cat	15
lion	25
horse	30
ostrich	50
dolphin	65
longest: human	75

6. What is the middle value? __30__ years
This is the **median**.

◆ *Math Masters,* p. 412

HOME LINK MASTER

A Number Story

_____

_____

_____

_____

_____

_____

_____

_____

_____

Answer to my number story: _____

Number model: _____

◆ *Math Masters,* p. 109

TEACHING MASTER

12.7

The Mode of a Set of Data

OBJECTIVES To organize a set of data with a line plot and frequency table; to display a set of data with a bar graph; and to identify the range, median, and mode.

Lesson 12.7 (D.RE.02.01, D.RE.02.02, D.RE.02.03)
Getting Started, Homelink Follow-up (using Homelink from L. 12.6): Use *The Graph Club* software to create a pictograph using one animal symbol to represent 10 yrs. of life span. Discuss, interpret, & analyze data (using questions at bottom of homelink 12.6).

materials

1 Teaching the Lesson

Children make a line plot and find the median and mode for the number of buttons that children in the class have on their clothes. [Data and Chance]

Children make a line plot, a frequency table, and a graph of data for the height changes of a hypothetical class of second graders; children identify key values in the data, such as the maximum, minimum, median, and mode. [Data and Chance]

- ☐ *Math Journal 2*, pp. 318–320
- ☐ Home Link 12.6
- ☐ slate
- ☐ 2 stick-on notes

***See* Advance Preparation**

2 Ongoing Learning & Practice

Children practice and maintain skills through Math Boxes and Home Link activities.

- ☐ *Math Journal 2*, p. 317
- ☐ Home Link Master (*Math Masters*, p. 413)

3 Options for Individualizing

Extra Practice Children measure each other's heights; make a line plot of the data; determine the range, median, and mode of the data; and compare the data of their heights to the data provided for 8-year-olds. [Data and Chance; Measurement and Reference Frames]

- ☐ centimeter ruler or measuring tape per partnership
- ☐ stick-on note

Additional Information

Advance Preparation For the Math Message, draw a number line on the board and mark it 0, 1, 2, ..., 9, 10. Put a pad of stick-on notes near the directions.

Vocabulary • mode

Getting Started

Mental Math and Reflexes

Pose "harder" multiplication facts.
Suggestions:

6 × 8 48	5 × 9 45	8 × 4 32
6 × 9 54	7 × 7 49	8 × 9 72

Math Message

Take 2 stick-on notes. Count the buttons on the clothes you are wearing. Write the number on a stick-on note and put it in the right place above the number line. Save the other stick-on note.

Home Link 12.6 Follow-Up

Go over the answers. Ask children to calculate the range of the data. About 64 years If time permits, pose additional problems similar to Problems 1–4.

1 Teaching the Lesson

◆ Math Message Follow-Up

WHOLE-CLASS ACTIVITY

The stick-on notes should form neat columns above the tick marks and numbers on the number line on the board. Straighten the stick-on notes if necessary.

The stick-on notes form a line plot. The number of notes above a number on the number line indicates how many children have that number of buttons. Ask such questions as the following:

- How many children have 2 buttons? 5 buttons? 0 buttons?
- What is the smallest number of buttons mentioned?
- What is the largest number of buttons mentioned?
- Which number of buttons is the most frequently mentioned?

Tell the class that the number of buttons reported most often is called the **mode.** The mode is the value or category that occurs most often in a set of data.

Ask children to find the median number of buttons reported. Use the line plot of stick-on notes to find the median, as follows:

1. Remove the last stick-on note at each end of the line plot and reattach it below the number line. (If there are several stick-on notes forming a column at one end of the line plot, remove the top one.)

2. Repeat this task over and over. Every time the stick-on notes at each end are moved below the line, the number of notes above the line is reduced by two.

3. Eventually, there will be only one or two notes left above the line. If one note remains, the number on that note is the middle value (the median). If two notes remain, the numbers on those notes are the middle values, and the median is either of these middle values or any value between the two.

Ask children if the median and the mode for the number of buttons are the same. If they are the same, do children think that the median and mode are always the same? No; they depend on the data.

NOTE: If your school requires a uniform, modify the number of buttons activity to include the number of pencils, pens, or other objects children can tally.

Height Changes

The data in the table show the height of 30 children at ages 7 and 8.
Your teacher will show you how to make a line plot for the data.

Student	Height		Student	Height	
	7 Years	8 Years		7 Years	8 Years
#1	120 cm	123 cm	#16	118 cm	122 cm
#2	132 cm	141 cm	#17	120 cm	126 cm
#3	112 cm	115 cm	#18	141 cm	148 cm
#4	122 cm	126 cm	#19	122 cm	127 cm
#5	118 cm	122 cm	#20	120 cm	126 cm
#6	136 cm	144 cm	#21	120 cm	124 cm
#7	123 cm	127 cm	#22	136 cm	142 cm
#8	127 cm	133 cm	#23	115 cm	118 cm
#9	115 cm	120 cm	#24	122 cm	130 cm
#10	119 cm	125 cm	#25	124 cm	129 cm
#11	122 cm	126 cm	#26	123 cm	127 cm
#12	103 cm	107 cm	#27	131 cm	138 cm
#13	129 cm	136 cm	#28	126 cm	132 cm
#14	124 cm	129 cm	#29	121 cm	123 cm
#15	109 cm	110 cm	#30	118 cm	123 cm

◆ Math Journal 2, p. 318

Height Changes (cont.)

Use the line plot your class made to make a frequency table
for the data.

Frequency Table

Change in Height	Number of Children
0 cm	
1 cm	/
2 cm	/
3 cm	///
4 cm	//// ///
5 cm	////
6 cm	//// /
7 cm	///
8 cm	//
9 cm	/
10 cm	

◆ Math Journal 2, p. 319

◆ Making a Line Plot, Frequency Table, and Bar Graph of Height Changes
(*Math Journal 2*, pp. 318–320)

WHOLE-CLASS ACTIVITY

1. Discuss the data set shown on journal page 318. Heights are given for a group of boys and girls. Two heights are reported, because children were measured when they were 7 years old and then again when they were 8 years old. All measurements were made to the nearest centimeter.

2. Assign one student number from the data set to each child in your class. For example, if you have 24 children, assign student numbers 1 through 24. Ask children to calculate the change in height over one year for the student number they have been assigned. For example, suppose that a child was assigned student number 11. According to the data in the table, student number 11 was 122 centimeters tall at age 7 and 126 centimeters tall at age 8. The change in height for student number 11 is 4 centimeters.

Adjusting the Activity If children are having difficulty, assign pairs of children to work together to calculate the height changes for the assigned student numbers from the data set.

3. Draw a number line on the board. Make tick marks along the line, about every 6 inches, and label these marks 0, 1, 2, ..., 10. As children calculate the height change for their assigned student number, they write the height change on a stick-on note and attach it in the appropriate place above the number line on the board. If necessary, straighten the stick-on notes so that they form neat columns above the tick marks and numbers along the number line.

4. Draw a frequency table on the board. Working together, use the line plot of stick-on notes to complete the table. Children complete the table on journal page 319. For example, if there are 2 stick-on notes above 7 cm on the number line, then two children's heights increased by 7 centimeters.

5. Make a bar graph. If the stick-on notes have been carefully placed to form neat columns along the number line, the line plot can also serve as a bar graph. Help children start the bar graph on journal page 320. What numbers should they write below the horizontal axis? The same numbers listed beneath the line plot: 0 cm, 1 cm, 2 cm, ..., 9 cm, 10 cm. Children should be able to check their own work because their completed graphs should resemble the line plot of stick-on notes.

6. Identify key values in the data: minimum, maximum, mode, median. Children work with partners, or independently, to complete journal page 320. They can use the line plot, the frequency table, or the bar graph to identify the smallest height change, the largest height change, and the mode. If they have difficulty finding the median, use the line plot of stick-on notes and follow the procedure described above.

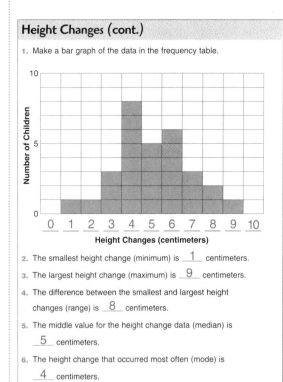

Height Changes (cont.)

1. Make a bar graph of the data in the frequency table.

Number of Children (vertical axis, 0 to 10)
Height Changes (centimeters) (horizontal axis, 0 to 10)

2. The smallest height change (minimum) is __1__ centimeters.

3. The largest height change (maximum) is __9__ centimeters.

4. The difference between the smallest and largest height changes (range) is __8__ centimeters.

5. The middle value for the height change data (median) is __5__ centimeters.

6. The height change that occurred most often (mode) is __4__ centimeters.

✦ *Math Journal 2*, p. 320

STUDENT PAGE

---

2 Ongoing Learning & Practice

✦ **Math Boxes 12.7** (*Math Journal 2*, p. 317)

INDEPENDENT ACTIVITY

Mixed Review This journal page provides opportunities for cumulative review or assessment of concepts and skills.

Math Boxes 12.7

1. Rule: ×3

in	out
0	0
1	3
2	6
3	9
4	12
10	30

2. A brachiosaurus is 72 ft long, a diplodocus is 90 ft long, and a stegosaurus is 23 ft long. If they get in line behind one another, how long is the line?

The line is __185__ feet long.

Number model:
$72 + 90 + 23 = 185$

3. Gary ran 800 meters. Kristen ran 628 meters. How much farther did Gary run?

He ran __172__ meters farther.

Number model:
$800 - 628 = 172$
or $628 + 172 = 800$

4. I bought a beach ball for $1.49 and a sand toy for $3.96. How much change will I get from a $10 bill?

$__4.55__

5. Write 3 ways to say 8:45.
Sample answers:
__eight forty-five__

__quarter-to nine__

__fifteen minutes to nine__

6. Complete the Fact Triangle. Write the fact family.

(triangle: 16, 2, 8, ×,÷)

$2 × 8 = 16$
$8 × 2 = 16$
$16 ÷ 8 = 2$
$16 ÷ 2 = 8$

✦ *Math Journal 2*, p. 317

STUDENT PAGE

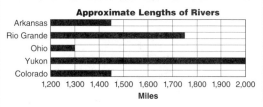

HOME LINK MASTER

Interpret a Bar Graph
Home Link 12.7

Family Note In class today, your child interpreted graphs and identified the greatest value, the least value, the range, the middle value or the median, and the mode. The mode is the value or category that occurs most often in a set of data. For example, in the bar graph below, the river length of 1,450 miles is the mode.

Please return this Home Link to school tomorrow.

Approximate Lengths of Rivers

Arkansas
Rio Grande
Ohio
Yukon
Colorado

1,200 1,300 1,400 1,500 1,600 1,700 1,800 1,900 2,000
Miles

1. a. What is the length of the Colorado River? About __1,450__ miles
   b. Of the Rio Grande? About __1,750__ miles

2. a. What is the length of the longest river? About __2,000__ miles
   b. What is the length of the shortest river? About __1,300__ miles
   c. What is the difference in length between the longest and the shortest rivers? About __700__ miles. This is the **range**.

3. Which river length occurs most often? About __1,450__ miles This is the **mode**.

4. What is the middle length of the rivers? About __1,450__ miles This is the **median**.

✦ *Math Masters*, p. 413

✦ Home Link 12.7 (*Math Masters*, p. 413)

Home Connection Children identify the minimum, maximum, range, median, and mode of a set of data displayed on a bar graph.

---

3 Options for Individualizing

✦ EXTRA PRACTICE Collecting and Displaying Class Height Data

PARTNER ACTIVITY   15–30 min

Children measure each other to determine their heights to the nearest centimeter. They use stick-on notes to make a line plot of the data. Children then determine the maximum, minimum, range, median, and mode of the data and compare these landmarks to the data provided for 8-year-olds.

Portfolio Ideas

12.8 Unit 12 Review and Assessment

OBJECTIVE To review and assess children's progress on the material covered in Unit 12.

---

1 Assess Progress

learning goals

12a **Beginning Goal** Use alternate names for times. **(Lesson 12.2)**

12b **Beginning Goal** Know "harder" multiplication facts. **(Lesson 12.5)**

12c **Beginning Goal** Determine the mode of a data set. **(Lesson 12.7)**

12d **Developing Goal** Determine the median, maximum, minimum, and range of a data set. **(Lessons 12.6 and 12.7)**

12e **Developing/Secure Goal** Construct multiplication/division fact families. **(Lessons 12.1 and 12.5)**

12f **Developing/Secure Goal** Multiply numbers with 2, 5, and 10 as a factor. **(Lesson 12.4)**

12g **Secure Goal** Tell time to 5-minute intervals. **(Lessons 12.1 and 12.2)**

12h **Secure Goal** Demonstrate calendar concepts and skills. **(Lesson 12.1)**

12i **Secure Goal** Compare quantities from a bar graph. **(Lessons 12.6 and 12.7)**

activities

- ❑ Oral Assessment, Problem 1

- ❑ Slate Assessment, Problem 1

- ❑ Slate Assessment, Problem 4
- ❑ Written Assessment, Problem 21

- ❑ Slate Assessment, Problem 4
- ❑ Written Assessment, Problems 17–19

- ❑ Slate Assessment, Problem 3
- ❑ Written Assessment, Problem 7

- ❑ Written Assessment, Problems 8–16

- ❑ Written Assessment, Problems 1–6

- ❑ Oral Assessment, Problems 2 and 3
- ❑ Slate Assessment, Problem 2

- ❑ Written Assessment, Problem 20

materials

- ☐ Home Link 12.7
- ☐ Assessment Masters (*Math Masters,* pp. 436, 437, and 441–447)

- ☐ Teaching Masters (*Math Masters,* pp. 77–79)
- ☐ slate
- ☐ Fact Triangles (cut from *Math Journal 2,* Activity Sheets 6–9)
- ☐ per group: clockface stamp; stamp pad; envelope; scissors

---

2 Build Background for Grade 3

summaries

Children practice and maintain skills through Math Boxes and Home Link activities.

materials

- ☐ *Math Journal 2,* p. 321
- ☐ Home Link Masters (*Math Masters,* pp. 414–417)

Each **learning goal** listed above indicates a level of performance that might be expected at this point in the *Everyday Mathematics* K–6 curriculum. For a variety of reasons, the levels indicated may not accurately portray your class's performance.

Getting Started

Math Message

4, 7, 9, 5, 5
What is the median of these numbers? 5
What is the mode? 5

Home Link 12.7 Follow-Up

Review answers.

1 Assess Progress

◆ Math Message Follow-Up

WHOLE-GROUP DISCUSSION

Ask children if the median and the mode are always the same. No; they depend on the data. Can children make up a set of data whose median and mode are not the same? Sample answer: 4, 5, 7, 9, 9

◆ Oral and Slate Assessments

SMALL-GROUP ACTIVITY

If the list of suggested problems below is not appropriate for your class's level of performance, adjust the numbers in the problems or adjust the problems themselves to better assess your children's abilities.

Oral Assessment Suggestions

1. Display the following times on a demonstration clock. Ask children to use alternate ways to name the time. **Goal 12a**

   • 6:30 Half-past 6; 30 minutes past 6; six thirty

   • 10:45 15 minutes till 11; a quarter till 11; ten forty-five

   • 2:15 A quarter-past 2; two fifteen; 15 minutes past 2

   • 7:50 10 till 8; seven fifty

2. Name the days of the week. **Goal 12h**

3. Name the months of the year. **Goal 12h**

Slate Assessment Suggestions

1. Children solve multiples-of-equal-groups number stories with "harder" multiplication facts. **Goal 12b**

- 9 boxes of cards. 4 packages per box. How many packages in all? 36
- 3 children. 8 pencils per child. How many pencils in all? 24
- 7 journal pages. 7 problems per page. How many problems in all? 49
- 6 shelves. 9 books per shelf. How many books in all? 54

2. Pose time equivalency problems, such as the following: **Goal 12h**

- How many months in a year? 12
- How many days in a week? 7
- How many hours in a day? 24
- How many minutes in an hour? 60
- How many seconds in 1 minute? 60

3. Write the fact family for 8, 7, and 56.

$8 \times 7 = 56$ $56 \div 8 = 7$
$7 \times 8 = 56$ $56 \div 7 = 8$

Write the fact family for 6, 8, and 48.

$6 \times 8 = 48$ $48 \div 6 = 8$
$8 \times 6 = 48$ $48 \div 8 = 6$

Goal 12e

4. Write the following numbers on the board:
4, 8, 9, 2, 7, 8, 5

Ask children to determine the minimum 2, the maximum 9, the range 7, the median 7, and the mode. 8 **Goals 12c and 12d**

✦ Written Assessment
(*Math Masters*, pp. 436 and 437)

INDEPENDENT ACTIVITY

Read the instructions aloud, repeating as needed. Children respond on the masters.

- Record the time shown on the clock. (Problems 1–3) **Goal 12g**
- Draw the hour and minute hands to match the time. (Problems 4–6) **Goal 12g**
- Write the fact family for the Fact Triangle. (Problem 7) **Goal 12e**
- Solve. (Problems 8–16) **Goal 12f**

Unit 12 Checking Progress ✓

Record the time shown on the clock.

1.   **2.**   **3.**

   3 : 55   6 : 25   9 : 40

Draw the hour and minute hands to match the time.

4.   **5.**   **6.**

   4:10   10:50   2:05

7. Write the fact family for the Fact Triangle.

$6 \times 7 = 42$ $42 \div 7 = 6$
$7 \times 6 = 42$ $42 \div 6 = 7$

Solve.

8. $6 \times 10 = 60$ **9.** $2 \times 7 = 14$ **10.** $6 = 3 \times 2$

11. $20 = 4 \times 5$ **12.** $30 = 3 \times 10$ **13.** $3 \times 5 = 15$

14. $6 \times 2 = 12$ **15.** $5 \times 6 = 30$ **16.** $70 = 7 \times 10$

Math Masters, p. 436

ASSESSMENT MASTER

The bar graph shows the number of miles each member of the track team ran during practice.

- What was the fewest number of miles? What was the greatest number of miles? (Problem 17) **Goal 12d**

- What is the difference between the fewest and the greatest numbers of miles (range)? (Problem 18) **Goal 12d**

- What is the middle number of miles (median)? (Problem 19) **Goal 12d**

- Who ran fewer miles than Justin? Who ran more miles than Angela? (Problem 20) **Goal 12i**

- What is the number of miles that occurred most often (mode)? (Problem 21) **Goal 12c**

◆ **ALTERNATIVE ASSESSMENT OPTION**
Practice Multiplication Facts with Fact Triangles
(*Math Journal 2,* Activity Sheets 6–9)

PARTNER ACTIVITY

As children work, ask them to sort their Fact Triangles into two piles—facts they know and facts they still need to practice. Have children record the facts that they need to practice on a sheet of paper and give it to you. The purpose of recording the facts is twofold. First, by writing those facts, children are doing additional practice. Second, you have a record of children's progress.

◆ **ALTERNATIVE ASSESSMENT OPTION**
Play *Clock Concentration*
(*Math Masters,* pp. 77–79)

SMALL-GROUP ACTIVITY

In Lesson 5.1, children played *Clock Concentration* to practice using equivalent times: analog and digital. To create an advanced version of this game, children use the cards on *Math Masters,* page 79. On one half of the card, they stamp a clockface and draw an hour hand and a minute hand to show a time. On the other half of the card, children write an alternate name for the time shown, such as "quarter-past 6" or "fifteen after six." Children follow the rules on *Math Masters,* page 78. Instructions for preparing the cards for the regular version are on *Math Masters,* page 77. Circulate and assess as children construct the cards and play the game.

✦ End-of-Year Assessment
(*Math Masters,* pp. 441–447)

The Midyear and End-of-Year Assessment Masters (*Math Masters,* pages 438–447) provide additional assessment opportunities that you may want to use as part of your balanced assessment plan. These tests cover only some of the important concepts and skills in *Second Grade Everyday Mathematics.* They should be used along with ongoing, product, and periodic assessment opportunities within the lessons and at the ends of the units. Please see pages 93–96 of the *Assessment Handbook* for answers to the End-of-Year Assessment.

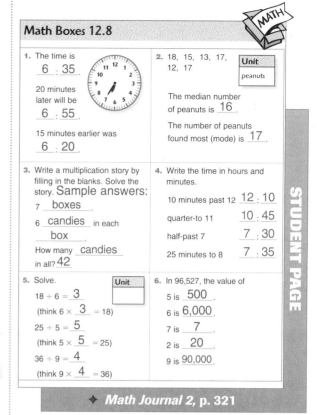

Math Boxes 12.8

1. The time is
   6 : 35
   20 minutes later will be
   6 : 55
   15 minutes earlier was
   6 : 20

2. 18, 15, 13, 17, 12, 17   **Unit** peanuts
   The median number of peanuts is 16.
   The number of peanuts found most (mode) is 17.

3. Write a multiplication story by filling in the blanks. Solve the story. Sample answers:
   7 boxes.
   6 candies in each box.
   How many candies in all? 42

4. Write the time in hours and minutes.
   10 minutes past 12   12 : 10
   quarter-to 11   10 : 45
   half-past 7   7 : 30
   25 minutes to 8   7 : 35

5. Solve.   **Unit**
   18 ÷ 6 = 3
   (think 6 × 3 = 18)
   25 ÷ 5 = 5
   (think 5 × 5 = 25)
   36 ÷ 9 = 4
   (think 9 × 4 = 36)

6. In 96,527, the value of
   5 is 500.
   6 is 6,000.
   7 is 7.
   2 is 20.
   9 is 90,000.

Math Journal 2, p. 321

② Build Background for Grade 3

✦ Math Boxes 12.8 (*Math Journal 2,* p. 321)

INDEPENDENT ACTIVITY

Mixed Review The problems on this page review important concepts and skills.

✦ Home Link 12.8: Unit 12 Family Letter
(*Math Masters,* pp. 414–417)

Home Connection This Home Link thanks family members for their participation in *Second Grade Everyday Mathematics,* suggests home-based activities for the long vacation, and provides a "sneak preview" of *Third Grade Everyday Mathematics.*

Math Masters, pp. 414–417

Appendices

contents

Boxes, Boxes, Beautiful Boxes

OBJECTIVES To name fractional parts; to practice following directions; and to use paper-folding techniques to make useful, open paper boxes.

background information

Recommended Use: During Unit 2 or Unit 7

See the discussion of Projects in the Management Guide section of the *Teacher's Reference Manual.*

materials

☐ several sheets of any rectangular and square pieces of paper (shiny magazine covers, pages from store catalogs, construction paper, and so on) per child

☐ large rectangular piece of paper for demonstration

☐ *Fun with Easy Origami: 32 Projects and 24 Sheets of Origami Paper*

☐ *Complete Origami: An A–Z of Facts and Folds, with Step-by-Step Instructions for Over 100 Projects*

***See* Advance Preparation**

Project Information

Advance Preparation You may want to obtain the following books for the Extension Suggestions in Part 2:

▷ *Fun with Easy Origami: 32 Projects and 24 Sheets of Origami Paper* by John Montroll (Dover, 1993)

▷ *Complete Origami: An A–Z of Facts and Folds, with Step-by-Step Instructions for Over 100 Projects* by Eric Kenneway (St. Martin's, 1987)

---

1 Doing the Project

✦ Making Boxes

Mary Lewis of Carnegie School shared these directions for making an open paper box. She used them successfully many times with her students.

Model each step with a large rectangular piece of paper. After you complete a step, have children do that step with their papers.

1. Fold the paper in half lengthwise. Make sure that all corners are even. Unfold the paper.

   Ask, *How many parts are there?* 2 *Each part is what fraction of the whole paper?* Half, or one-half

2. Fold each long side so that the outside edge comes exactly to the middle line, as shown below.

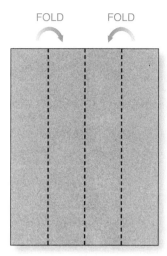

Unfold the paper. Ask, *How many parts are there now?* 4 *Each part is what fraction of the whole paper?* One-fourth, or one quarter

3. Fold the paper in half across the width. Unfold it.

Ask, *How many parts are there now?* 8 *Each part is what fraction of the whole paper?* one-eighth

4. Fold the short edges of the paper exactly to the middle width line, as shown below.

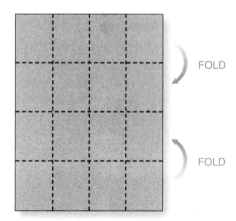

Unfold the paper. Ask, *How many parts are there now?* 16 *Each part is what fraction of the whole paper?* one-sixteenth

5. Fold the short edges back to the middle again. Crease the folds hard.

6. Fold a triangle at a corner. One side of the triangle should match up to the fold nearest the corner. Fold a triangle at the other corners. Crease the folds hard.

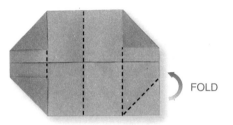

FOLD

7. Fold back the long edges at the center, over the corner folds, to form two cuffs, as shown below. Crease hard.

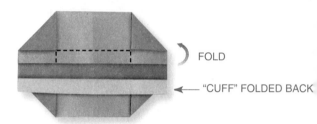

FOLD

←— "CUFF" FOLDED BACK

8. Gently open the box by pulling apart the center of the cuffs. Recrease the four corners of the box.

A completed box

Extending the Project

◆ Extension Suggestions

1. Have children make a second box, slightly larger than the first, to use as a cover.

2. Have children make boxes from different-size rectangles or squares. They can use almost any kind of sturdy paper.

3. **Literature Link** Obtain a book on origami, such as *Fun with Easy Origami: 32 Projects and 24 Sheets of Origami Paper* by John Montroll (Dover, 1993) or *Complete Origami: An A–Z of Facts and Folds, with Step-by-Step Instructions for Over 100 Projects* by Eric Kenneway (St. Martin's, 1987), and have children make some of the figures.

◆ Home Link Suggestions

Children tell the box-making steps in order to a family member. Then they list the steps in order for making (or doing) something else with which they are familiar, such as making a sandwich, getting dressed, or using a computer program.

PROJECT 2

Weather Station

OBJECTIVES To read thermometers using both the Fahrenheit and Celsius scales; and to observe and collect data on outdoor weather conditions and temperatures.

background information

Recommended Use: During Unit 2 or Unit 8

See the discussion of Projects in the Management Guide section of the *Teacher's Reference Manual*.

materials

□ Project Masters (*Math Masters*, pp. 211 and 212)

□ class outdoor thermometer; scissors; tape or glue

□ red crayon or marker

□ clear, self-adhesive vinyl sheets (optional)

□ weather reports from different parts of the country

□ encyclopedia

□ literature selections

□ barometer (optional)

See **Advance Preparation**

Project Information

Advance Preparation You may want to obtain the following books for the Extension Suggestions in Part 2:

▷ *Weather* by Tom Kierein (National Geographic, 1995)
▷ *The Magic School Bus Wet All Over: A Book about the Water Cycle* (Scholastic, 1996)
▷ *Weather Forecasting* by Gail Gibbons (Aladdin, 1993)
▷ *Weather,* edited by Lee Bennett Hopkins (HarperCollins, 1994)

1 Doing the Project

◆ Assembling Paper Thermometers
(*Math Masters,* p. 211)

Science Link Guide children through the following steps to assemble their paper thermometers from *Math Masters,* page 211:

1. Color the bulb at the bottom of the thermometer red.

2. Color the strip marked "Color this red."

3. Cut out both strips and the thermometer.

4. Tape or glue the strips together on the space marked to make a single indicator strip.

   Optional: At this point, laminate the thermometers or cover them with clear, self-adhesive vinyl sheets to make them more durable.

5. Cut slits along the dashed lines at the top and bottom of the thermometer.

6. Insert the indicator strip (with the red part at the bottom) through the slits so that it slides down the face of the thermometer, as shown in the margin below.

◆ Reviewing Thermometers and Temperature Readings

Have available both the class outdoor thermometer and children's paper thermometers. The scales on the class outdoor thermometer and the paper thermometers may not be exactly alike. If they differ somewhat, focus on the paper thermometers.

Ask, *Which unit are temperatures reported in?* degrees

Point out the two scales: °F and °C. Ask, *What are the names of the two scales? What do F and C stand for?* Fahrenheit and Celsius *What does the small raised circle mean?* degrees

Ask a volunteer to explain why many thermometers have two different scales. The Celsius scale is used in most of the world; the Fahrenheit and Celsius scales are used in the United States. Ask such questions as the following:

- Are the two scales the same? No. On the Fahrenheit scale, water freezes at 32°. On the Celsius scale, water freezes at 0°.

- On each scale there are three different size marks. How many degrees are shown between a long mark and the next long mark? 10 degrees How many degrees are shown between a shortest mark and the next shortest mark? 2 degrees How many degrees are shown between a mark and the next mark? 1 degree

- What are temperatures below zero called? negative

- Which scale is more likely to record negative temperatures? Celsius, because all temperatures below freezing are negative Which scale is more likely to record 3-digit temperatures? Fahrenheit, because 3-digit Fahrenheit temperatures begin a little below 38 degrees Celsius

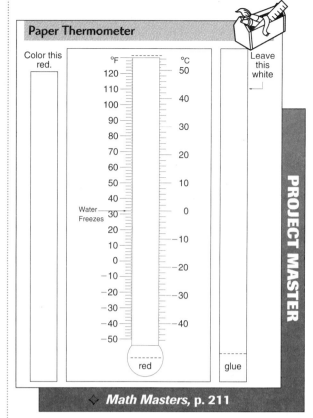

Paper Thermometer

Color this red.

Leave this white

°F
120
110
100
90
80
70
60
50
40
Water Freezes 30
20
10
0
−10
−20
−30
−40
−50

°C
50
40
30
20
10
0
−10
−20
−30
−40

red

glue

◇ *Math Masters,* p. 211

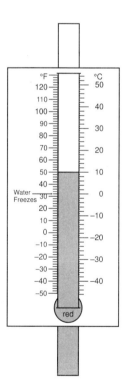

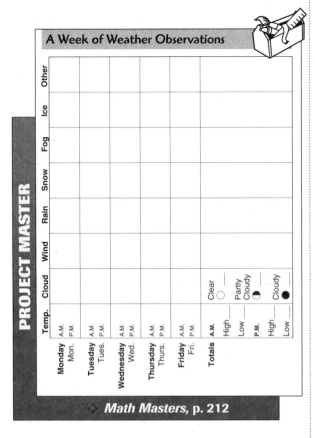

Math Masters, p. 212

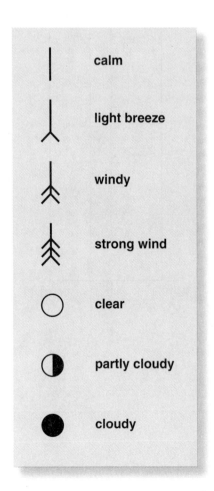

	calm
	light breeze
	windy
	strong wind
	clear
	partly cloudy
	cloudy

Say several temperatures. Have children display these temperatures on their paper thermometers as you circulate and check. Include some negative temperatures. Compare pairs of temperatures: Which is warmer, colder? Repeat this activity often over the next few days.

Give children two different temperatures in the same scale to compare. For example, *How much warmer is 50 degrees Fahrenheit than 30 degrees Fahrenheit?* 20 degrees Fahrenheit *How much colder is 5 degrees Celsius than 15 degrees Celsius?* 10 degrees Celsius Encourage children to share their solution strategies; record them on the board. Repeat this activity often as a review, especially during the week of this Project.

◆ Collecting Weather Data
(*Math Masters,* p. 212)

Examine the Project Master with the class. Point out the following:

▷ The rows are labeled at the left with the five days of the school week.

▷ The columns are labeled at the top with various weather conditions.

▷ The large row at the bottom is used to record information or summaries for the week.

Discuss how to fill in the chart for the current day. Help the class reach a consensus about how to describe the day—sunny, cloudy, windy, or something else. Design and record symbols as needed, such as those for wind and cloud cover shown in the margin.

Have a volunteer read and report the current outside temperature. Note that the temperature column has spaces for A.M. and P.M. readings. Recording morning and afternoon temperatures shows how the temperature changes during the day and provides real data for temperature-difference problems.

Each day for a week, allow a few minutes for children to fill in their weather observation chart for the day. Assign a pair of students to create a report for the class.

At the end of the week, children fill in the bottom row with the week's high and low morning and afternoon temperatures; the number of clear, partly cloudy, and cloudy days; and other comments or data.

2 Extending the Project

✦ Extension Suggestions

1. Repeat this activity during different seasons of the year.

2. Find out the temperatures in other parts of the country and compare them to the class readings.

3. Literature Link Read about weather and weather forecasting in an encyclopedia or in such books as *Weather* by Tom Kierein (National Geographic, 1995), *The Magic School Bus Wet All Over: A Book about the Water Cycle* (Scholastic, 1996), or *Weather Forecasting* by Gail Gibbons (Aladdin, 1993). *Weather,* edited by Lee Bennett Hopkins (HarperCollins, 1994), is a collection of poems about weather.

4. Have children read, watch, or listen to weather reports to find out amounts of rain or snow, wind speeds, and so on for the previous day. They then incorporate this information into their charts.

5. Have children read, watch, or listen to weather forecasts and compare them to the actual weather.

6. Introduce the barometer and its role in weather forecasting. Barometric pressure readings are part of many weather reports.

✦ Home Link Suggestions

Children and family members take turns making up and solving temperature-comparison number stories. These stories can be generated while the family watches a televised weather report for your local area or for the entire country.

PROJECT

Chinese Calendar

OBJECTIVES To count up and back by 12s using 4-digit numbers; and to become familiar with the Chinese 12-year animal cycle.

background information

Recommended Use: During Unit 2 or Unit 7

See the discussion of Projects in the Management Guide section of the *Teacher's Reference Manual*.

materials

☐ Project Masters (*Math Masters,* pp. 213 and 214)

☐ crayons or markers

☐ *The Greenwich Guide to Time and the Millennium*

***See* Advance Preparation**

Project Information

Advance Preparation You may want to obtain the following book for the Extension Suggestions in Part 2:

▷ *The Greenwich Guide to Time and the Millennium* by Graham Dolan (Heinemann Library, 1999)

1 Doing the Project

◆ Discussing the Chinese Calendar's 12-Year Animal Cycle (*Math Masters,* p. 213)

The ancient Chinese developed an accurate calendar based on the motion of the Sun and Moon. Beginning in the Zhou dynasty (1045 B.C.), the Chinese numbered years in a 12-year cycle. (*Source:* E. G. Richards, *Mapping Time: The Calendar and Its History* (Oxford University, 1998))

Social Studies Link In the Chinese calendar, each year of the 12-year cycle is represented by a different animal (6 wild and 6 domesticated), as shown below:

Number	Name	Animal
1	Zi	Rat
2	Chou	Ox
3	Yin	Tiger
4	Mao	Rabbit
5	Chen	Dragon
6	Si	Snake
7	Wu	Horse
8	Wei	Sheep
9	Shen	Monkey
10	You	Rooster
11	Xu	Dog
12	Hai	Pig

The animals repeat in this order every 12 years. (According to legend, Buddha called all the animals to him before he left Earth. Only twelve came. He named a year after each in the order in which they arrived.) In addition to the 12-year cycle, there is a 60-year cycle (five 12-year cycles). The 79th cycle began in 1996.

The first circle on *Math Masters,* page 213 shows the cycle going back 12 years from 2000; the second circle shows it going forward 12 years from 2000.

Ask questions about the master.

Suggestions

- On our calendar, this is 2001 (use the actual current year.) Which Chinese year is it? snake

- When will the year of the snake come again? 2013 Besides using the Project Master, is there another way to figure out the next year of the snake? Add 12 to the current year

- When was the last year of the snake? 1989 How can you figure this out mathematically? Subtract 12 from the current year

Have children share their strategies for mentally adding and subtracting 12. For example, count up or back by 1s; count up or back by 10s and then add or subtract 2; count up or back by 6s; and so on. The years in the cycle can also be determined by counting up or back by 12s on the calculator.

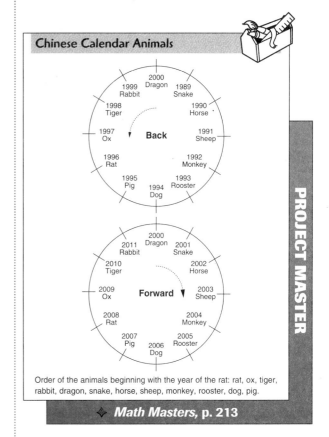

Chinese Calendar Animals

Order of the animals beginning with the year of the rat: rat, ox, tiger, rabbit, dragon, snake, horse, sheep, monkey, rooster, dog, pig.

◆ *Math Masters,* p. 213

PROJECT MASTER

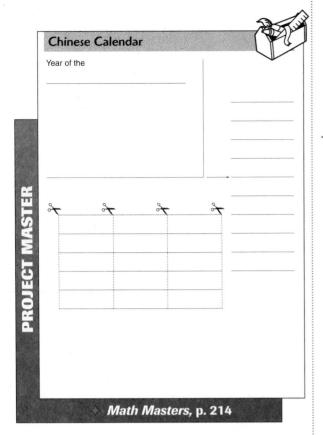

Chinese Calendar

Year of the

_____

◆ *Math Masters,* **p. 214**

Determine the birth years of different members of the class. Then have children find the animals that represent the years of those births. When will the years of those particular animals come again?

◆ Listing Past and Future Animal Years
(*Math Masters,* pp. 213 and 214)

If possible, assign two children to each of the animals represented in the cycle. Have them fill in the name of their animal and draw a picture of it in the blank space on *Math Masters,* page 214.

Children find their animal on one of the circles on *Math Masters,* page 213 and write the corresponding year on the line next to the arrow on *Math Masters,* page 214. Then they fill in the four years before (above) and four years after (below) their initial year by adding and subtracting 12 years from that line. That is, they are to count by 12 forward and back, using whichever method they wish. Encourage them to use scratch paper if they need to.

As you circulate, check the mathematics and talk about the methods children are using to determine the years into the future and the past.

If children are interested in making a scroll by extending their counts in either direction, have them cut out the columns on *Math Masters,* page 214 and glue or tape them to the bottom and/or top of their initial columns.

You can post the completed scrolls or lists on a bulletin board so that the entire animal cycle can be seen.

GONG XI FA CAI!

("Happy and Prosperous New Year")

Extending the Project

◆ Extension Suggestions

1. The date of the Chinese New Year varies from late January to the middle of February—February 5 in 2000, January 24 in 2001, February 12 in 2002, and so on. Children can investigate the Chinese New Year and how it is celebrated on the following Web sites:

   http://homex.s-one.net.sg/member/crescent/index.htm

   http://dir.yahoo.com/Society_and_Culture/Cultures_and_Groups/Cultures/Chinese/Holidays_and_Observances/Chinese_New_Year/

2. Help children read about calendars and timekeeping in such books as *The Greenwich Guide to Time and the Millennium* by Graham Dolan (Heinemann Library, 1999).

◆ Home Link Suggestions

Children take home copies of *Math Masters,* page 213. With the help of family members, they find the animal that represents their birth year. They then list the next three years represented by that particular animal.

Dates on Pennies

OBJECTIVES To gain experience working with 4-digit numbers within familiar yearly notation (1998, 1999, and so on); and to use tallies and graphs to compare data.

background information

Recommended Use: During or after Unit 3

See the discussion of Projects in the Management Guide section of the *Teacher's Reference Manual.*

materials

☐ small magnifying lenses (optional); about 1,000 pennies

☐ Class Data Pad (optional); coin collector's catalog

☐ literature selections

***See* Advance Preparation**

Project Information

Advance Preparation You may want to obtain the following books for the Extension Suggestions in Part 2:

▷ *Let's Find Out about Money* by Kathy Barabas (Scholastic, 1997)

▷ *Money* by Joe Cubb (Knopf, 1990)

1 Doing the Project

✦ Observing Dates on Pennies

Each child examines a few pennies to find the years the pennies were made (minted). Some dates have a "D" under the year, indicating that those pennies were minted in the Denver Mint. Make sure most children can find the dates easily. Small magnifying lenses may help.

Have children call out some of their pennies' years as you record them on the board in a systematic way. Continue until you have a range of years. Use a tally mark to record each reoccurrence. Ask, *In which year were the oldest pennies minted? The newest pennies?*

✦ Tallying Dates for a Large (Diverse) Collection of Pennies

In roughly equal batches, distribute the collection of pennies among pairs of children. Have partners record the year and make a tally mark for each penny in their collection. They can use the method you modeled on the board or devise their own recording scheme.

After all or most of the pennies have been recorded, bring the class together and record on the board or the Class Data Pad the total number for each year found. Compare the range of years and the various totals by asking questions about the data. *Suggestions:*

- What is the range of years?
- In which year were the fewest pennies minted? How many pennies were minted in that year? What is the difference between the fewest number of pennies minted and the most?
- Why are there fewer older pennies?
- Are there pennies older than class members? How much older?
- How much older is the oldest penny than the newest?

◆ Graphing the Data

Work with children to construct a bar graph showing the years in the class penny collection. After the class starts building the graph, assign each partnership one or two years to add to the graph by using the information on the board or the Class Data Pad. (See the margin.)

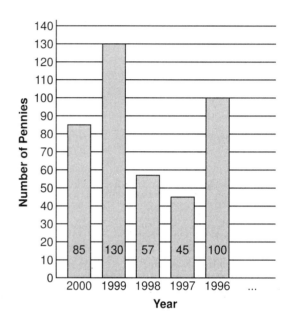

Extending the Project

◆ Extension Suggestions

1. Obtain a catalog of U.S. coins that features illustrations of pennies and other coins over the years and gives prices for them.

2. **Literature Link** Suggest that children read about money in such books as *Let's Find Out about Money* by Kathy Barabas (Scholastic, 1997) and *Money* by Joe Cubb (Knopf, 1990).

◆ Home Link Suggestions

Children tally the dates found on pennies at home. They explain to family members how to compare the data represented by these pennies. Children may also tally the dates found on nickels, dimes, and quarters found at home.

PROJECT 5

Snowflakes

OBJECTIVES To experiment with paper folding; and to create paper snowflakes that represent real 6-sided water crystals.

background information

Recommended Use: During Unit 4, Unit 6, or Unit 8

Children use lightweight paper in this Project because it is easy to fold and cut; 8" × 11" is a good size to begin with.

See the discussion of Projects in the Management Guide section of the *Teacher's Reference Manual*.

materials

☐ lightweight, white pieces of paper of various sizes

☐ scissors

☐ literature selections

See **Advance Preparation**

Project Information

Advance Preparation If possible, ask at least two adults to help children with the initial paper folding. Or, if your school has a program in which your class is paired with an older class for certain activities, this is a good activity to incorporate older children. It's helpful if helpers know the folding routine in advance!

The paper needs to be square. You may want to cut square pieces yourself, or you can have children cut square pieces as the first step (see the second activity).

You may want to obtain the following books for the Extension Suggestions in Part 2:

▷ *Snow Crystals* by W. A. Bentley and W. J. Humphreys (Dover, 1931)
▷ *Snowflake Bentley* by Jacqueline Briggs Martin (Houghton Mifflin, 1998)
▷ *Snow* by Uri Shulevitz (Farrar Straus & Giroux, 1998)
▷ *The Snowy Day* by Ezra Jack Keats (Viking, 1962)

1 Doing the Project

◆ Talking about Snowflakes

Snowflakes are hexagonal (6-sided) crystals of water that form in clouds. Snowflakes come in many forms, from 6-sided clumps to lace-like, 6-pointed stars. The type that forms depends on the temperature and on the amount of moisture in the air.

It was once thought that no two snowflakes are alike, but identical snowflakes have been found. However, these are rare. Like the paper snowflakes children will make, most real snowflakes are unique.

✦ Making Paper Snowflakes

Follow these directions, or use other directions with which you are familiar.

1. If the paper is not already square, make it square by first folding it and then cutting it.

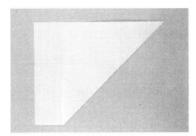

2. Fold a square sheet of paper in half along a diagonal to make a triangle. Place the fold at the bottom.

3. Fold the triangle into thirds. *Hint:* To fold into thirds, first find the center of the bottom edge. This will be the point of the triangular-shape folded paper. Put the tip of an index finger here while folding.

   Be careful to fold exactly into thirds. The edge of one side must match the fold on the other side.

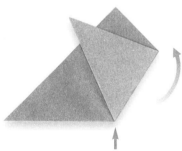

CENTER OF THE BOTTOM EDGE

4. Fold in half again. *Hint:* Fold back so that an "ear" is on the outside top of the folded paper.

5. Cut off the "ears" along the straight edges on top. This makes each "arm" of the snowflake identical.

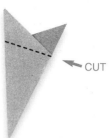

6. Draw a curved or jagged line to indicate the shape you would like the snowflake to be. Begin near the bottom point of the double-folded edge; end near the top of the single-folded edge. *Hint:* Do not draw too close to the bottom point or the snowflake will fall apart when it is cut out.

7. Cut along the line drawn.

8. Carefully unfold the snowflake. The darkened part of the snowflake in the picture is the part originally drawn.

Children cut out additional snowflakes as time permits. The beauty of making snowflakes is that it gets easier each time children do it! Encourage them to experiment with different shapes and to make small cutouts along the single fold or the spine of the points of the snowflake.

Extending the Project

✦ Extension Suggestions

1. Discuss features of children's snowflakes. For example, each snowflake is *symmetric*—it can be folded in half so that the two halves match. Ask, *In how many ways can a snowflake be folded so that the two halves match?* 3 The six "arms" are *congruent*—they all are the same shape and size.

Children go outside to observe actual snowflakes with a magnifying lens, weather permitting.

2. **Science Link** Read about snow in such books as *Snow Crystals* by W. A. Bentley and W. J. Humphreys (Dover, 1931), which contains over 2,000 illustrations of snowflakes. W. A. Bentley, who devoted his life to studying snow, is the subject of the biography *Snowflake Bentley,* written for children by Jacqueline Briggs Martin (Houghton Mifflin, 1998). The book includes sidebars describing Bentley's experiments and techniques for photographing snowflakes.

3. **Literature Link** Read stories about snow, such as *Snow* by Uri Shulevitz (Farrar Straus & Giroux, 1998). *The Snowy Day* by Ezra Jack Keats (Viking, 1962) is a beautifully illustrated, classic book for younger children.

✦ Home Link Suggestion

Children take one of their snowflakes home. They explain the process of making a paper snowflake to family members. With the assistance of an older child or adult, children make another snowflake or a different item (such as a boat or a hat) out of paper.

PROJECT

Time Capsule

OBJECTIVES To agree on, collect, and display information to be included in a time capsule; and to make predictions about life four years from now.

---

background information

Recommended Use: During or after Unit 7; possibly at the end of the year

Children gather information about themselves and make predictions which are then sealed in a "time capsule." The time capsule is left with the principal to be opened in sixth grade (or another appropriate grade) when children are about to leave the school.

See the discussion of Projects in the Management Guide section of the *Teacher's Reference Manual.*

materials

☐ shoe box or other "time capsule" container

☐ calculator

***See* Advance Preparation**

Project Information

Advance Preparation Arrange ahead of time with the principal for delivery of the capsule to his or her care (preferably in front of the whole class).

---

1 Doing the Project

◆ Explaining the Purpose of the Time Capsule

Discuss the idea of a time capsule with the class. Explain that a time capsule is a container holding items that represent a group, such as the residents of a town, at a particular moment in history. The items might be handicrafts, commercial products, newspapers, books, photographs, audiotapes, videotapes, and so on. The time capsule is buried or otherwise preserved for the future. Time capsules are often placed in the cornerstones of new buildings to be opened after a certain time or when the buildings are remodeled or torn down.

The object shown in the margin was sent as a time capsule on two Voyager space probes that have left the solar system. It is a 12-inch gold-plated copper disk containing sounds and images selected to portray the diversity of life and culture on Earth. There are images, recorded sounds, musical selections from different cultures and eras, spoken greetings in 55 languages, and printed messages. The contents were chosen in order to represent civilization on Earth in a way that might be understood by a distant civilization.

The idea of a second grade time capsule is to have children seal information about themselves in a box and, instead of leaving it for a far distant age, leave it with the principal of the school until they are in sixth grade. When they open the time capsule, they will find instructions to help them determine what things have changed about the class and how accurate (or inaccurate) some of their predictions were.

✦ Deciding upon the Contents of the Time Capsule

Have children suggest items to include in the time capsule. List their suggestions on the board. *For example:*

▷ a class photograph with each person identified

▷ the median height and weight of the class

▷ surveys of favorite activities, sports teams, food, television shows, musical groups, school subjects, topics in mathematics, and so on

▷ the distance some of us can run in 10 seconds (see Project 8); the distance some of us can throw a ball

▷ a list of important world, national, and local events

Have the class choose about six topics about which to gather data for the time capsule. Each child might write a brief description of herself or himself—likes, dislikes, height, weight, and so on and seal it in an envelope to be put into the time capsule. Encourage children to include pictures and recordings that they think might be interesting additions to the time capsule.

✦ Preparing Information for the Time Capsule

Divide the class into small groups. Assign one or more data-gathering tasks to each group. Within the groups, let children decide how they are going to collect and display the information assigned to them.

Bring the class together and have each group present its plan. Work with the class as a whole to fine-tune the plans; children from other groups might have suggestions for improving or adding to some of the plans. Ask children what to tell the sixth grade class (themselves!) about comparing the data from second grade to the data from sixth grade.

Develop a schedule for carrying out each group's plans over the next few days. For example, if a survey of favorite foods is needed, the group takes a poll and carries out its plan for displaying that information. If predictions are made, these are written up with space allowed for the future sixth graders to compare predictions to reality in order to see how accurate those predictions were.

Encourage children to look ahead four years and make predictions to include in the time capsule. *For example:*

- How many members of the current class will be in the same classroom or at the same school in sixth grade?
- About how much will class members have grown—that is, what will be median number of inches grown or pounds gained?
- Will their favorite television shows still be on the air? Will their favorite musical groups still be together?
- What will computers and the Internet be like?
- Will the United States have the same president?

✦ Preparing the Time Capsule

After all of the information has been gathered, each group takes a few minutes to share its data with the rest of the class. Then seal all the information and other items in a shoe box or other appropriate container. Be sure to label the time capsule with instructions for opening at the appropriate time. Deliver the time capsule to the principal.

✦ Asking Time Capsule Questions

Ask the class the following questions: If the time capsule is opened the same day of the year in *sixth* grade …

- How many years will have gone by since second grade?
- Will the date fall on a school day?
- How old will you be?
- How many months until then? (Use a calculator to help.)
- Will there be a leap year between now and then?

You and children will have more ideas. Discuss and share responses.

Extending the Project

◆ Extension Suggestions

1. Have children research the time capsule shown on page 895 at:

   http.//vraptor.jpl.nasa.gov/voyager/gold.gif.

2. Suggest that children investigate time capsules that have been placed in cornerstones of buildings in your community.

◆ Home Link Suggestion

Children plan and create a time capsule with members of their family. They devise a plan, gather information, and prepare the time capsule. Encourage children to write a short paragraph describing their family time capsules.

Collections

OBJECTIVE To describe a collection in terms of number, size, age, and other attributes.

---

background information

Recommended Use: During Unit 7 or Unit 11

Children prepare an information sheet about a collection of their own, of someone in their family, or of someone they know well. They bring a selection from the collection to display. If the collection is too fragile or too valuable for classroom display, children represent it in some other way.

See the discussion of Projects in the Management Guide section of the *Teacher's Reference Manual.*

materials

☐ writing paper

☐ *A Kid's Guide to the Smithsonian*

***See* Advance Preparation**

Project Information

Advance Preparation You may want to explore the feasibility of this project in advance by surveying the class to find out if children have a collection of any particular objects or know someone who has.

Send a note home explaining the Project. If possible, children bring in a collection or a selection from a collection; alternatively, they bring in a representation of the collection (photos, drawings, lists, catalog pictures, and so on).

You may want to obtain the following book for the Extension Suggestions in Part 2:

▷ *A Kid's Guide to the Smithsonian* by Ann Phillips Bay (Smithsonian Institution, 1996)

---

1 Doing the Project

◆ Talking about Collections

Many children have collections of different types of toys, rocks, hats, tropical fish, seashells, stamps, books, sports cards, and so on. Encourage them to talk about their collections as you list the different kinds on the board. Some children may feel they have no collections. Ask if they have several of one kind of toy (such as cars, dolls, or stuffed animals). They may have collections and not realize it!

The start of a collection

Children who have no collections can talk about a collection they know about—maybe a friend's or a family member's. Or they can work with a classroom partner who has a collection.

◆ Collecting Data about the Collections

Discuss what kinds of data or information about the collections might be of interest to other people. List responses on the board. *For example:*

▷ the size of the collection

▷ categories or organization within the collection, such as stamps by country, year, intended use, or denomination

▷ the approximate length of time since the collection began

▷ the smallest or largest item in the collection

▷ the source(s) of items in the collection

▷ items most prized (and why)

▷ reasons the collection was begun

◆ Preparing Information Sheets

Using the list on the board, children decide which data are appropriate for their collections. Then they prepare an information sheet to remind them of the data on which they wish to report.

Children take the information sheets home to complete. You may want to send them as Home Links. (See the next page). Children bring the information sheets back to school in 2–3 days. They also bring to class a few representative items from the collections they described, or a representation of several items—photos, drawings, lists, videotapes, catalog pictures, and so on.

◆ Reporting on the Collections

Over the course of the next few days, allow time for children to report on and display selections from their collections.

Extending the Project

◆ Extension Suggestions

1. Invite a parent, friend, or local expert (for example, a baseball card collector) to class to display and describe a collection.

2. Go on a field trip to a museum or art gallery featuring a particular collection.

3. Have children read about collections of diverse things, from dinosaurs to Dorothy's red shoes to the Apollo 11 command module that returned from the Moon in *A Kid's Guide to the Smithsonian* by Ann Phillips Bay (Smithsonian Institution, 1996).

✦ Home Link Suggestion

Children complete their information sheets. They discuss with family members which items, if any, they will take to school. Children take photos, draw pictures, or make a list of items in their collections.

How Far Can I Run in 10 Seconds?

OBJECTIVE To measure the distances children can run in 10 seconds.

background information

Recommended Use: During Units 10, 11, or 12

See the discussion of Projects in the Management Guide section of the *Teacher's Reference Manual.*

materials

☐ Project Master (*Math Masters,* p. 215)

Per group of 3:

☐ string or yarn

☐ masking tape, chalk, colored blocks, or another marker

☐ stopwatch or watch with second hand (optional)

☐ slip of paper or stick-on note

See Advance Preparation

Project Information

Advance Preparation You may want to enlist the help of the physical education teacher in collecting the data.

Each group of three children will need a 10-foot piece of string or yarn marked off at 1-foot intervals. You may want to have several children help you prepare these. In addition, children will need some way of timing 10-second intervals. While this can be done by counting aloud using a clock, a watch, or a stopwatch that shows seconds will give more accurate results.

1 Doing the Project

✦ Finding out How Far Children Can Run in 10 Seconds (*Math Masters,* p. 215)

Plan for the actual data collection to take place outside, on the playground or other large, open space.

Children are to collect the data in groups of 3; they will take turns being "runner," "timer," and "spotter." Before you leave the classroom, explain the steps for collecting the data:

Data-Collecting Steps

1. The timer gives the runner the signal to start and begins timing.

2. The spotter follows the runner.

3. When 10 seconds are up, the timer says "Stop!" and drops a raised arm or gives some other prearranged signal.

4. The spotter marks the spot reached by the runner with masking tape, chalk, a colored block, or some other marker.

5. The group cooperatively uses a 10-foot string to measure the distance covered.

6. The runner records the distance run in 10 seconds on a slip of paper or stick-on note.

Once the class gets to the running location, have each group mark a starting line with chalk, masking tape, or some other marker. Be sure there is enough room between starting lines so that groups will not get in one another's way.

Before groups start running, have several volunteers demonstrate how to measure a distance greater than 10 feet by laying a 10-foot length of string end-to-end.

Also demonstrate how to time the runners. If children count to time the runners, remind them to do it aloud: 1,001, 1,002, 1,003, ...

2 Extending the Project

◆ Extension Suggestions

1. If children record their distances on stick-on notes, collect the notes and make a bar graph of the data on the wall. (See margin.)

2. Have children find the range of 10-second distances, as well as a middle 10-second distance.

◆ Home Link Suggestion

Children discuss with family members what they have learned about the speed at which children run. They investigate the speed at which adults run by conducting an activity similar to the one in the Project with adult volunteers.

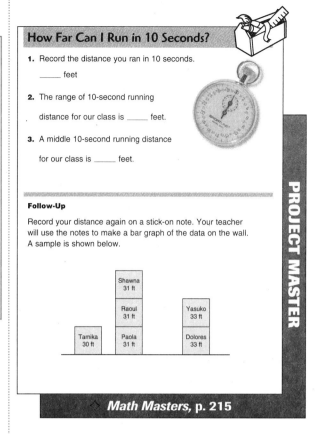

How Far Can I Run in 10 Seconds?

1. Record the distance you ran in 10 seconds.

   _____ feet

2. The range of 10-second running distance for our class is _____ feet.

3. A middle 10-second running distance for our class is _____ feet.

Follow-Up

Record your distance again on a stick-on note. Your teacher will use the notes to make a bar graph of the data on the wall. A sample is shown below.

Math Masters, p. 215

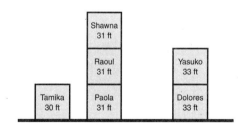

Second Grade Key Vocabulary

For a more extensive glossary that includes additional illustrations and references, please refer to the *Teacher's Reference Manual*.

addend   One of two or more numbers that are added.

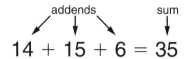

$$14 + 15 + 6 = 35$$

addition   A mathematical operation based on putting together two or more quantities.

addition fact   Two 1-digit numbers and their sum, such as $9 + 7 = 16$.

algorithm   A set of step-by-step instructions for doing something, such as carrying out a computation or solving a problem.

A.M.   The abbreviation for *ante meridiem,* which means "before the middle of the day"; from midnight to noon.

analog clock   A clock that shows the time by the positions of the hour and minute hands.

angle   A figure that is formed by two rays or two line segments with a common endpoint.

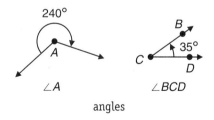

angles

area   The measure of a bounded surface.

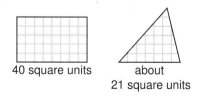

arm span   The distance from fingertip to fingertip of a person's outstretched arms.

array   A rectangular arrangement of objects in rows and columns.

arrow path   In *Everyday Mathematics,* a route to follow on a number grid.

arrow rule   In *Everyday Mathematics,* the operation that determines the number that goes in the next frame in a Frames-and-Arrows diagram. See *Frames and Arrows.*

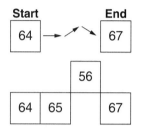

arrows   In *Everyday Mathematics,* the links representing the rule that determines which numbers go in the frames of a Frames-and-Arrows diagram. See *arrow rule.*

associative property   A property of addition and multiplication (but not of subtraction or division) that says that changing the grouping of the elements being added or multiplied will not change the sum or product. *For example:*

$$(4 + 3) + 7 = 4 + (3 + 7)$$

attribute   A feature of an object or a common feature of a set of objects. Examples of attributes include size, shape, color, and number of sides. See *property*.

ballpark estimate   A rough estimate used as a check on the reasonableness of an answer or when an exact figure is not necessary.

bank draft   A written order for the exchange of money. $1,000 bills are no longer in existence, so $1,000 bank drafts are issued. People can exchange $1,000 bank drafts for smaller bills (for example, 10 bills of $100 each).

bar graph   A graph that shows the relationships among variables by the use of bars to represent quantities.

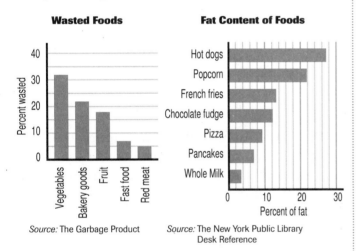

bar graphs

base   1. Any side of a polygon, usually used, along with the altitude perpendicular to it, for computing area.

Bases are shown in blue.

2. The flat face or faces that define the shape when classifying polyhedrons.

base-10 shorthand   In *Everyday Mathematics,* a system to represent base-10 blocks.

Name	Base-10 block	Base-10 shorthand
cube	▱	▪
long			
flat		□
big cube		

big cube   In *Everyday Mathematics,* the term for the 10 cm by 10 cm by 10 cm base-10 block. A big cube is worth 1,000 cm cubes.

capacity   A measure of how much a container can hold, usually in units such as quarts, gallons, cups, or liters.

Celsius   The temperature scale on which 0° is the temperature at which pure water at sea level freezes and 100° is the temperature at which it boils. The Celsius scale is used in the metric system.

centimeter (cm)   In the metric system, a unit of length equivalent to 10 millimeters, $\frac{1}{10}$ of a decimeter, and $\frac{1}{100}$ of a meter.

centimeter cube   In *Everyday Mathematics,* the term for the smallest of the base-10 blocks, measuring 1 cm on each edge.

change diagram   In *Everyday Mathematics,* a diagram used to represent situations in which quantities are either increased or decreased.

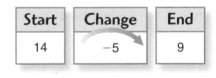

$14 - 5 = 9$

circle The set of all points in a plane that are equally distant from a given point in the plane called the *center* of the circle.

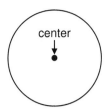

center

Class Data Pad In *Everyday Mathematics,* a large pad of paper where data collected by the class can be stored for use (and reuse) throughout the year.

column A vertical arrangement of objects or numbers in an array or table.

commutative property A property of addition and multiplication (but not of subtraction or division) that says that changing the order of the elements being added or multiplied will not change the sum or product. For example, $5 \times 8 = 40$ and $8 \times 5 = 40$.

comparison diagram In *Everyday Mathematics,* a diagram used to represent situations in which two quantities are compared.

Quantity
12

Quantity	Difference
9	?

$12 = 9 + ?$

cone A 3-dimensional shape having a circular base, a curved surface, and one vertex, called the apex.

consecutive Following one another in an uninterrupted order, such as A, B, C, D or 6, 7, 8, 9.

corner See *vertex.*

counting numbers The numbers used to count things. The set of counting numbers is {1, 2, 3, 4, ...}. Sometimes 0 is included with the counting numbers.

cube A polyhedron with six square faces. One of the five regular polyhedra. See *regular polyhedron.*

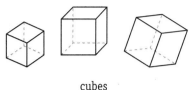

cubes

cubit An ancient unit of length, measured from the point of the elbow to the end of the middle finger.

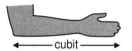

cubit

cup In the U.S. customary system, a unit of capacity equal to 8 fluid ounces; $\frac{1}{2}$ pint.

curved surface or face A surface which does not lie in a plane; for example, a sphere or cylindrical surface. Also, a nonbase face of a cone or cylinder.

customary system The measuring system used most often in the United States, in contrast to the metric system used nearly everywhere else. See *U.S. customary system.*

cylinder A 3-dimensional shape having a curved surface and parallel circular or elliptical bases that are the same size. A can is an object shaped like a cylinder.

data Information gathered by observing, counting, or measuring. *Data* is the plural of *datum.*

deci- Prefix meaning one-tenth.

decimal point The mark that separates the whole number from the fraction in decimal notation; in expressing money, it separates the dollars from the cents.

decimeter (dm) In the metric system, a unit of length equivalent to $\frac{1}{10}$ of a meter or 10 centimeters.

degree (°) A unit for measuring temperature. Also a unit of measure for angles based on dividing one complete circle (rotation) into 360 equal parts. The small raised symbol (°) is called the *degree symbol*.

denominator The number written below the line in a fraction. In a part-whole fraction, the number of equal parts into which the whole (ONE) is divided. Compare to *numerator*.

diagonal (of a table) A line of objects or numbers from upper left to lower right, or from lower left to upper right in an array or a table.

+, −	0	1	2	3	4	5	6	7	8	9
0	0	1	2	3	4	5	6	7	8	9
1	1	2	3	4	5	6	7	8	9	10
2	2	3	4	5	6	7	8	9	10	11
3	3	4	5	6	7	8	9	10	11	12
4	4	5	6	7	8	9	10	11	12	13
5	5	6	7	8	9	10	11	12	13	14
6	6	7	8	9	10	11	12	13	14	15
7	7	8	9	10	11	12	13	14	15	16
8	8	9	10	11	12	13	14	15	16	17
9	9	10	11	12	13	14	15	16	17	18

The diagonal is shown in blue.

difference The amount by which one number is greater or less than another number.

digit In the base-ten numeration system, one of the symbols 0, 1, 2, 3, 4, 5, 6, 7, 8, and 9 which can be used to write any number.

digital clock A clock that uses numbers to show the time in hours and minutes, with a colon used to separate them.

division The operation used to solve equal-sharing problems. It is used to find how a total amount can be separated into an equal number of groups, or into groups of equal size.

$$24 \div 4 = 6$$

doubles fact The addition and multiplication facts without turn-around partners. A doubles fact names the sum or product of a 1-digit number and itself, such as $4 + 4 = 8$ or $3 \times 3 = 9$.

edge A line segment where two faces of a polyhedron meet.

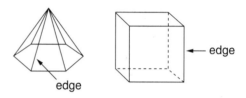

edge

edge

endpoint A point at the end of a line segment or a ray. A line segment is named by its two endpoints. "Segment *LT*" or "segment *TL*" is the line segment between points *L* and *T*.

endpoints

T   *L*

equal-grouping story A number story that involves separating something into equal groups. In such a problem, the total and the number in each group are known. Division can often be used to solve equal-grouping stories.

equal groups Sets with the same number of elements.

equal-sharing story A number story that involves sharing something equally. In such a problem, the total and the number of groups are known. Division can often be used to solve equal-sharing stories.

equivalent names   Different ways of naming the same number. For example, $2 + 6$, $4 + 4$, $12 - 4$, $18 - 10$, $100 - 92$, $5 + 1 + 2$, eight, VIII, and ̶H̶H̶ /// are all equivalent names for 8. See *name-collection box.*

estimate   1. *n*. A close, rather than exact, answer. A number close to another number. 2. *v*. To make an estimate.

even number   A whole number that can be evenly divided by 2. It has 0, 2, 4, 6, or 8 in the ones place. Compare to *odd number.*

Exploration   In *Everyday Mathematics,* an independent or small-group activity that may involve concept development, manipulatives, data collection, problem solving, games, and skill reviews.

extended fact   A variation of a basic arithmetic fact involving multiples of 10, 100, and so on. For example, $30 + 70 = 100$, $40 \times 5 = 200$, and $560 \div 7 = 80$ are extended facts.

face   A surface that bounds a 3-dimensional shape. It may be curved (as on a cylinder or a cone) or flat (as on a prism).

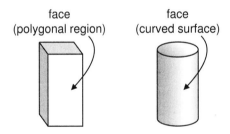

face
(polygonal region)

face
(curved surface)

fact extensions   Calculations with larger numbers using knowledge of basic facts. For example, knowing the basic fact $5 + 8 = 13$ makes it easy to solve problems such as $50 + 80 = ?$ and $65 + ? = 73$. Fact extensions can also be applied to basic subtraction, multiplication, and division facts.

fact family   A collection of related addition and subtraction facts, or multiplication and division facts, made from the same numbers. For 5, 6, and 11, the addition/subtraction family consists of $5 + 6 = 11$, $6 + 5 = 11$, $11 - 5 = 6$, and $11 - 6 = 5$. For 5, 7, and 35, the multiplication/division family consists of $5 \times 7 = 35$, $7 \times 5 = 35$, $35 \div 7 = 5$, and $35 \div 5 = 7$.

fact power   In *Everyday Mathematics,* a term that refers to the ability to recall basic number facts automatically without having to figure them out.

Fact Triangle   A triangular flash card labeled with the numbers of a fact family for practice with addition/subtraction and multiplication/division facts.

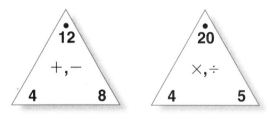

factors   The numbers being multiplied in a multiplication number model. In the number model $4 \times 3 = 12$, 4 and 3 are factors.

Facts Table   A chart of rows and columns, also known as an Addition/Subtraction Facts Table or a Multiplication/Division Facts Table, for use in finding addition and subtraction or multiplication and division facts.

Fahrenheit   The temperature scale on which pure water at sea level freezes at $32°$ and boils at $212°$. The Fahrenheit scale is used in the U.S. customary system.

flat   In *Everyday Mathematics,* the term for the base-10 block consisting of 100 cm cubes.

foot (ft)   In the U.S. customary system, a unit of length equivalent to 12 inches, or $\frac{1}{3}$ of a yard.

fraction   A number in the form of $\frac{a}{b}$ or a/b that names part of an object or collection of objects, compares two quantities, or represents division. A fraction names equal parts of a whole.

Frames and Arrows   In *Everyday Mathematics,* diagrams used to represent number sequences— sets of numbers ordered according to a rule. The diagrams consist of *frames* in which numbers are written and *arrows* that represent rules for moving from one frame to another.

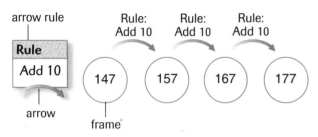

Frames-and-Arrows diagram

frequency   The number of times a value occurs in a set of data.

frequency graph   A graph showing how often each value in a data set occurs.

frequency table   A chart on which data is tallied to find the frequency of given events or values.

function machine   In *Everyday Mathematics,* a diagram of an imaginary machine programmed to process numbers according to a certain rule. A number (input) is put into the machine and is transformed into a second number (output) through the application of a rule.

in	out
1	2
2	4
3	6
5	10
10	20
20	40

function machine with input/output table

gallon (gal)   In the U.S. customary system, a unit of capacity equal to 4 quarts.

geometric solid   A 3-dimensional shape bounded by surfaces. Common geometric solids include the rectangular prism, square-based pyramid, cylinder, cone, and sphere.

geometry   The study of spatial objects and their properties and relationships. The word *geometry* is derived from the Greek words for "earth" and "measure."

gram (g)   In the metric system, a unit of mass equal to $\frac{1}{1,000}$ of a kilogram.

height   A measure of how tall something is.

heptagon   A 7-sided polygon.

hexagon   A 6-sided polygon.

Home Link   In *Everyday Mathematics,* a suggested follow-up or enrichment activity to be done at home.

inch (in.)   In the U.S. customary system, a unit of length equal to $\frac{1}{12}$ of a foot and equivalent to 2.54 centimeters.

input   A number inserted into an imaginary function machine, which processes numbers according to a designated rule. See *function machine.*

kilogram (kg)   In the metric system, the fundamental unit of mass; it is equal to 1,000 grams. 1 kilogram equals about 2.2 pounds.

kilometer (km)   In the metric system, a unit of length equal to 1,000 meters. One kilometer equals about 0.62 miles.

kite   A quadrilateral with two pairs of adjacent sides that are the same length. (A rhombus is not a kite.)

kite

label Descriptive word or phrase used to put numbers in context. Using a label reinforces the idea that numbers refer to something. Flags, snowballs, and scary monsters are examples of labels.

length Usually, but not necessarily, the longer dimension of a rectangle or a rectangular object.

line A straight path that extends infinitely in opposite directions.

line of symmetry A line that divides a figure into two halves that are mirror images.

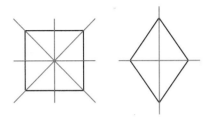

Lines of symmetry are shown in blue.

line plot A sketch of data in which checkmarks, Xs, or stick-on notes above a number line show the frequency of each value.

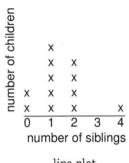

line plot

line segment A straight path joining two points.

liter (L) In the metric system, a unit of capacity equal to 1,000 milliliters. A liter is a little larger than a quart.

long In *Everyday Mathematics,* the term for the base-10 block consisting of 10 cm cubes.

Math Boxes In *Everyday Mathematics,* a format to provide review problems and to practice skills. A set of Math Boxes for each lesson are found in the student *Math Journals.*

Math Journal In *Everyday Mathematics,* a student record of mathematical discoveries and experiences. It provides visual models for conceptual understanding and problems, and includes activities for individuals and small groups.

Math Masters Pages ready for duplicating. Most of these are used by children in carrying out suggested activities. Some will be used more than once during the school year.

Math Messages In *Everyday Mathematics,* activities for children to complete at the start of each lesson. Math Messages may be problems that introduce the day's lesson, directions to follow, sentences to complete or correct, or reading assignments.

mathematics A study of relationships among numbers, shapes, systems, and patterns. It is used to count and measure things, to discover similarities and differences between them, to solve problems, and to learn about and organize the world.

measurement unit The reference unit used when measuring length, weight, capacity, time, or temperature. Ounces, degrees, and centimeters are examples of measurement units.

median The middle value in a set of data when the data are listed in order from least to greatest (or greatest to least). See *middle value.*

memory Mechanical or electronic storage of information for later recall, as in computers or calculators.

memory keys Keys to manage a calculator's memory. The memory keys are commonly labeled (M+), (M−), and (MRC). The (M+) key is used to add a number to the number stored in the calculator's memory; the (M−) key is used to subtract a number from the number in memory. The (MRC) key, pressed once, displays the number currently stored in memory; when the key is pressed twice, the calculator's memory is cleared.

mental arithmetic   Computations done by people "in their heads," either in whole or in part.

Mental Math and Reflexes   In *Everyday Mathematics,* exercises (usually oral) suggested at the start of most lessons. They are designed to strengthen children's number sense and to review and advance essential basic skills.

meter (m)   In the metric system, the fundamental unit of length, equal to 10 decimeters, 100 centimeters, or 1,000 millimeters.

metric system   A measurement system based on the base-ten numeration system and used in most countries in the world. Units for linear measure (length, distance) include millimeter, centimeter, meter, and kilometer; units for mass include gram and kilogram; units for capacity include milliliter and liter; and the unit for temperature change is degrees Celsius.

middle value   The number in the middle when a set of data is organized in sequential order. Also called the *median.*

mile (mi)   In the U.S. customary system, a unit of length equivalent to 5,280 feet, 1,760 yards, or about 1,609 meters.

milliliter (mL)   In the metric system, a unit of capacity equal to $\frac{1}{1,000}$ of a liter; 1 cubic centimeter.

millimeter (mm)   In the metric system, a unit of length equivalent to $\frac{1}{10}$ of a centimeter or $\frac{1}{1,000}$ of a meter.

mode   The value or values that occur most often in a set of data. For example, in the data set 3, 4, 4, 4, 5, 5, 6, 4 is the mode.

multiples   Repeated groups of the same amount. Multiples of a number are the products of that number and whole numbers.

multiplication   The operation used with whole numbers, fractions, or decimals to find the total number of things in several equal groups.

multiplication/division diagram   Used to represent numbers in which several equal groups are being considered together. The diagram has three parts: a number of groups, a number in each group, and a total number.

boxes	candies per box	candies in all
3	6	18

$3 \times 6 = 18$

multiplication fact   The product of two 1-digit numbers, such as $6 \times 7 = 42$.

name-collection box   In *Everyday Mathematics,* a boxlike diagram tagged with a given number and used for collecting equivalent names for that number.

25 37 − 12   20 + 5

~~HHT~~ ~~HHT~~ ~~HHT~~ ~~HHT~~ ~~HHT~~

twenty-five   X X X X X
X X X X X
veinticinco   X X X X X
X X X X X
X X X X X

name-collection box

number family   A triplet of numbers consisting of two addends and their sum or two factors and their product.

number grid   A table in which consecutive numbers are arranged in rows of ten. A move from one number to the next number within a row is a change of one; a move from one number to the next number within a column is a change of ten.

number-grid puzzle   In *Everyday Mathematics,* a piece of a number grid in which some, but not all, of the numbers are missing. Number-grid puzzles are used for practice with place-value concepts.

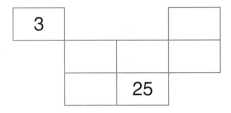

number-grid puzzle

number line   A line on which equidistant points correspond to numbers in order. Used as a frame of reference for counting and numeration activities.

number model   A number sentence that models or fits a situation. For example, the situation *Sally had $5 and then she earned $8,* can be modeled as $5 + 8 = 13$.

number scroll   In *Everyday Mathematics,* number-grid pages taped together. See *number grid.*

number sequence   A list of numbers often generated by some rule. See *Frames and Arrows,* which generate number sequences.

number story   A story that contains a problem that can be solved using one or more of the four basic arithmetic operations or by sorting out relations such as equals, is less than, or is greater than.

numerator   The number written above the line in a fraction. In a part-whole fraction, it names the number of equal parts of the whole being considered.

octagon   An 8-sided polygon.

odd number   A number that cannot be evenly divided by 2. It has 1, 3, 5, 7, or 9 in the ones place. Compare to *even number.*

ONE   In *Everyday Mathematics,* a way of denoting the unit whole in part-whole fractions and other similar situations.

1-facts   The sum of two 1-digit numbers where one of the numbers is one, such as $6 + 1 = 7$. If one is added to any number, or vice versa, the result is the next higher number. Also, the product of two numbers where one of the numbers is 1, such as $1 \times 3 = 3$. The product of 1 and any number is equal to that number.

operation   An action performed on one or two numbers producing a single number result.

ordinal number   A number used to express position or order in a series, such as first, third, and tenth.

ounce (oz)   In the U.S. customary system, a unit of weight equal to $\frac{1}{16}$ of a pound. One ounce is 31.103 grams.

outcome   A possible result of a random process. Heads and tails are the two outcomes of tossing a coin.

output   The number resulting from the application of a rule used by an imaginary function machine to process numbers.

pan balance   A device used to weigh objects or to compare their weights.

parallel   Lines, rays, line segments, or planes that are equidistant at all points, no matter how far extended; never meeting.

parallelogram   A quadrilateral that has two pairs of parallel sides and opposite sides that are congruent.

partial-sums algorithm   An addition procedure in which sums are computed for each place separately and then added to yield the final sum.

	268
	+ 483
1. Add 100s.	600
2. Adds 10s.	140
3. Add 1s.	+ 11
4. Add partial sums.	751

parts-and-total diagram In *Everyday Mathematics,* a diagram used to represent problems in which two or more quantities are combined to form a total quantity. It is often used when the parts are known and the total is unknown. It can also be used when the total and one or more parts are known, but one part is unknown.

Total	
13	
Part	Part
8	?

parts-and-total diagram

pattern A model or plan by which objects or numbers can be arranged so that what comes next can be predicted.

Pattern-Block Template In *Everyday Mathematics,* a sheet of plastic with geometric shapes cut out, used to draw patterns and designs.

pentagon A 5-sided polygon.

per *In each* or *for each,* as in ten chairs per row or six tickets per family.

percent (%) Per hundred, or out of a hundred. Times $\frac{1}{100}$; times 0.01; 1 one-hundredth. 15% means $\frac{15}{100}$, or 0.15 of a number.

perimeter The distance around a closed plane figure or region. *Peri-* comes from the Greek word for "around" and *meter* comes from the Greek word *metron* that means "measure"; perimeter means "around measure."

pictograph A graph constructed with pictures or symbols. A pictograph makes it possible to compare at a glance the relative amounts of two or more counts or measures.

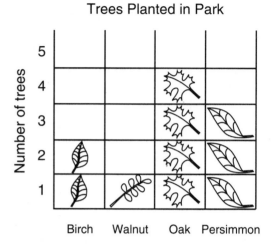

Trees Planted in Park

pint In the U.S. customary system, a unit of capacity equal to 2 cups or 16 fluid ounces.

place value The relative worth of each digit in a number, which is determined by its position. Each place has a value ten times that of the place to its right and one-tenth of the value of the place to its left.

point An exact location in space. Points are usually labeled with capital letters.

polygon A closed plane figure formed by three or more line segments that meet only at their endpoints. The word comes from Greek: *poly* means "many" and *gon* (from *gonia*) means "angle."

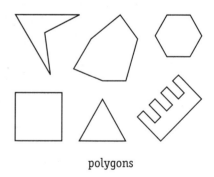

polygons

polyhedron   A closed 3-dimensional shape, all of whose surfaces (faces) are flat. Each face consists of a polygon and the interior of the polygon.

poster   In *Everyday Mathematics,* a page displaying a collection of numerical data. The poster may be referred to as a source of data for developing number stories.

pound (lb)   In the U.S. customary system, a unit of weight equal to 16 ounces and defined as 0.45359237 kilograms.

prism   A polyhedron with two parallel flat faces (bases) with the same size and shape. The other faces are bounded by parallelograms. Prisms are classified according to the shape of the two parallel bases.

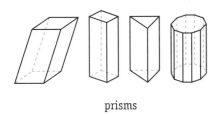

prisms

probability   A number from 0 to 1 that indicates the likelihood that an event will happen. The closer a probability is to 1, the more likely it is that the event will happen. The closer a probability is to 0, the less likely it is that the event will happen. For example, the probability that a fair coin will show heads is 1/2.

product   The result of doing multiplication. In the number model *4 × 3 = 12,* 12 is the product.

Project   In *Everyday Mathematics,* a thematic activity to be completed in one or more days by small groups or by the whole class. Projects often involve collecting and analyzing data and are usually cross-curricular in nature.

property   A feature of an object. For example, size, shape, color, and number of parts are all properties. Same as *attribute.*

pyramid   A polyhedron (3-dimensional shape) in which one face (the base) is a polygon and the other faces are triangles with a common vertex called the apex. A pyramid is classified according to the shape of its base.

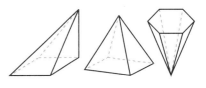

pyramids

quadrangle   A 4-sided polygon. Same as *quadrilateral.*

quadrilateral   A 4-sided polygon. Same as *quadrangle.*

quart   In the U.S. customary system, a unit of capacity equal to 32 fluid ounces, 2 pints, or 4 cups.

quotient   The result of dividing one number by another number; the number of equal shares. In the division number model *15 ÷ 5 = 3,* 3 is the quotient.

range   The difference between the greatest and least numbers in a set of data.

rectangle   A parallelogram whose angles are all right angles. See *parallelogram.*

rectangular prism   A prism whose bases are rectangles.

rectangular pyramid   A pyramid whose base is a rectangle.

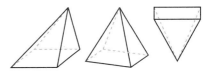

rectangular pyramids

regular polygon   A polygon whose sides are all the same length and whose angles are all equal.

regular polyhedron   A polyhedron whose faces are all congruent regular polygons and with the same number of faces meeting at every vertex, all at the same angle.

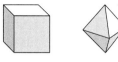

cube   octahedron

relation symbol   A symbol used to express a relationship between two quantities. Some relation symbols used in number sentences are = (is equal to), < (is less than), and > (is greater than).

remainder   The amount left over when things are divided into equal shares. In the division number model *16 ÷ 3 → 5 R1*, the remainder is 1.

rhombus   A parallelogram with sides that are all the same length. The angles may be right angles, in which case the rhombus is a square.

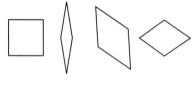

rhombuses

right angle   A square corner; a 90° angle. See *angle*.

round   1. *v.* To express a number in a simplified way. Examples of rounding include expressing a measure of weight to the nearest pound and expressing an amount of money to the nearest dollar. 2. *adj.* Circular in shape.

rule table   In *Everyday Mathematics,* a table for displaying the input, output, and rule of a function in the "What's My Rule?" routine.

scale   The ratio of the distance on a map, globe, or drawing to the actual distance. On a thermometer, a vertical number line used for measuring temperature.

set   A collection or group of objects, numbers, or other items.

side   Any one of the line segments that make up a polygon. Sometimes a face of a 3-dimensional figure is called a side.

slate   Lap-size (about 8" × 11") chalkboard or whiteboard that children use in *Everyday Mathematics* for a variety of purposes, including recording responses during group exercises and informal group assessments.

sphere   A 3-dimensional shape whose curved surface is, at all points, a given distance from its center point. A ball is shaped like a sphere. A sphere is hollow; it does not include the points in its interior.

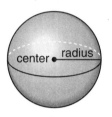

sphere

square   A rectangle whose sides are all the same length.

square number   A number that is the product of a whole number and itself. A square number can be represented by a square array.

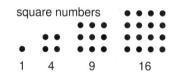

square of a number   The product of number and itself.

square pyramid   A pyramid with a square base.

square pyramid

square units   The units used to measure area. A square unit represents a square with the measure of each side being one of that unit. For example, a square inch represents a square that measures one inch on each side.

straightedge   A tool, such as a ruler, used to draw line segments. A straightedge does not need to have measure marks on it.

subtraction   A mathematical operation based on taking away one quantity from another or decreasing a quantity.

sum   The result of adding two or more numbers. For example, in *5 + 3 = 8,* 8 is the sum. See *addition.*

survey   A study that collects data. In *Everyday Mathematics,* surveys are used to generate data for graphing and analysis.

symmetry   The property of exact balance in a figure; having the same size and shape across a dividing line or around a point.

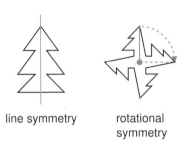

line symmetry   rotational
                       symmetry

symmetry

tally marks   Marks (𝈐 ////) used to keep track of a count.

tens   The place-value position equal to ten times the unit value.

tetrahedron   A polyhedron with four faces.

3-dimensional (3-D)   Objects that are not completely within a single flat surface; objects with thickness as well as length and width.

tiling   An arrangement of closed shapes that covers a surface completely without overlaps or gaps.

time line   A device for showing in sequence when events took place. A time line is a number line with the numbers naming years, days, and so on.

tool kit   In *Everyday Mathematics,* a bag or a box containing a calculator, measuring tools, and manipulatives often used in the program.

trade-first subtraction   A subtraction procedure in which all necessary trades are done before any subtractions are carried out. This simplifies the algorithm since the user can concentrate on one thing at a time.

trapezoid   A quadrilateral that has one pair of parallel sides. No two sides need be the same length.

trapezoid

triangle   A 3-sided polygon.

triangular prism   A prism whose bases are triangles.

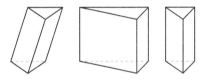

triangular prisms

triangular pyramid   A pyramid in which all faces are triangles, any one of which can be called the base.

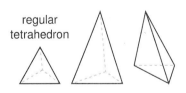

regular
tetrahedron

triangular pyramids

turn-around facts   A pair of addition or multiplication (but not subtraction or division) facts in which the order of the addends or the factors is reversed. For example, 3 + 5 = 8 and 5 + 3 = 8 or 3 × 9 = 27 and 9 × 3 = 27. If a fact is known, its turnaround is also known.

2-dimensional (2-D)   Objects completely within a plane; objects with length and width, but no thickness.

unit   A label, descriptive word, or unit of measure used to put a number in context. Using a unit with a number reinforces the idea that numbers refer to something. Fingers, snowballs, miles, and cents are examples of units. Same as *label*.

unit box   In *Everyday Mathematics*, a rectangular box displayed alongside a set of numbers or problems. It contains the unit or label for the numbers in use.

unit box

U.S. customary system   The measuring system most frequently used in the United States. Units for linear measure (length, distance) include inch, foot, yard, and mile; units for weight include ounce and pound; units for capacity include cup, pint, quart, and gallon; for temperature change, degrees Fahrenheit.

vertex (vertices)   The point at which the rays or line segments of an angle, sides of a polygon, or the edges of a polyhedron meet. Same as *corner*.

weight   A measure of how heavy something is.

"What's My Rule?"   In *Everyday Mathematics*, a routine that involves a set of number pairs in which the numbers in each pair are related to each other according to the same rule. The problems are usually displayed in table format in which two of the three parts (input, output, rule) are known and the goal is to find the unknown part.

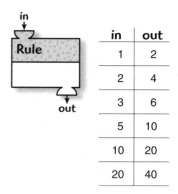

in	out
1	2
2	4
3	6
5	10
10	20
20	40

"What's My Rule?" problem

width of a rectangle   Length of one side of a rectangle or rectangular object; often the shorter side.

x-by-y array   An arrangement having x rows of y per row, representing x sets of y objects in each set.

Array of Dots   Array of Squares

2-by-6 arrays: 2 rows, 6 per row

yard (yd)   Historically, the distance from the tip of the nose to the tip of the longest finger.

In the U.S. customary system, a unit of length equivalent to 3 feet or 36 inches.

zero facts   The sum of two 1-digit numbers where one of the addends is zero, such as $0 + 5 = 5$. If zero is added to any number, or vice versa, there is no change in the number. Also, the product of two 1-digit numbers where one of the factors is zero, such as $4 \times 0 = 0$. The product of a number and 0 is always 0.

Scope and Sequence Chart

Throughout *Everyday Mathematics,* children repeatedly experience concepts and skills in each of the mathematical strands. Each exposure builds on and extends children's understanding. They study important concepts over consecutive years through a variety of formats. The Scope and Sequence Chart shows the units in which exposures occur and the developmental level of the skill or concept. The three levels of skill and concept development used in the chart are Beginning, Developing, and Secure. These levels refer here to unit content within the *K–6 Everyday Mathematics* curriculum rather than performance expectations for children.

The skills and concepts are divided according to the mathematical strands below.

Mathematical Strands	Pages
Numeration	920–923
Operations and Computation	924–926
Patterns, Functions, and Algebra	927–928
Geometry	929–931
Measurement and Reference Frames: Measurement	932–935
Measurement and Reference Frames: Reference Frames	936–937
Data and Chance	938–939

How to Read the Scope and Sequence Chart

Each section of the chart includes a mathematical strand title, three grade level columns divided by units, and a list of specific skills and concepts grouped by major concepts.

Numeration

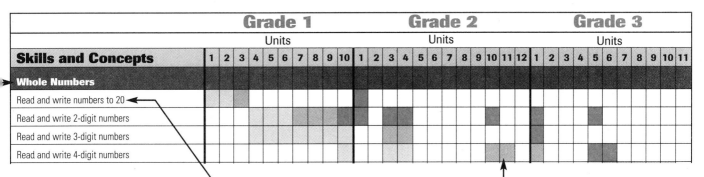

–Major mathematical concepts within each strand. A list of related skills and concepts appear below this head.

Find specific skills and concepts in this list and then follow across the row for units in which they appear at each grade level.

The shading in the cells indicates the skill and concept development level for a particular exposure. The lightest shading shows beginning exposures, the medium shading designates developing exposures, and the darkest shading indicates secure exposures.

Numeration

Skills and Concepts	Grade 1 — Units										Grade 2 — Units												Grade 3 — Units										
	1	2	3	4	5	6	7	8	9	10	1	2	3	4	5	6	7	8	9	10	11	12	1	2	3	4	5	6	7	8	9	10	11
Whole Numbers																																	
Read and write numbers to 20																																	
Read and write 2-digit numbers																																	
Read and write 3-digit numbers																																	
Read and write 4-digit numbers																																	
Read and write larger numbers																																	
Read and write ordinal numbers																																	
Order numbers to 20																																	
Order 2-digit numbers																																	
Order 3-digit numbers																																	
Order 4-digit numbers																																	
Order larger numbers																																	
Compare numbers to 20																																	
Compare 2-digit numbers																																	
Compare 3-digit numbers																																	
Compare 4-digit numbers																																	
Compare larger numbers																																	
Compare numbers using <, >, and = symbols																																	
Perform rote counting																																	
Perform rational counting																																	
Skip count by 2s, 5s, and 10s																																	
Count by 25s																																	
Count by 100s, 1,000s and 10,000s																																	
Count using a calculator																																	

Whole Numbers (cont.)

- Use Roman numerals
- Identify even and odd numbers
- Find equivalent names for numbers
- Make and solve number-grid puzzles
- Explore place value using a number grid
- Identify place value in 2-digit numbers
- Identify place value in 3-digit numbers
- Identify place value in 4-digit numbers
- Identify place value in larger numbers
- Make exchanges among place values
- Find complements of 10
- Find complements for multiples of 10
- Make least and greatest numbers with randomly selected digits
- Write numbers in expanded notation
- Display and read numbers on a calculator
- Explore magnitude of numbers
- Identify square numbers

Money and Decimals

- Use cents notation
- Use dollars-and-cents notation
- Display money amounts on a calculator
- Identify equivalencies and make coin exchanges
- Identify equivalencies and make coin/bill exchanges
- Show money amounts with coins
- Show money amounts with coins/bills

Beginning **Developing** **Secure**

Scope and Sequence Chart 921

Numeration (cont.)

	Grade 1 — Units										Grade 2 — Units												Grade 3 — Units										
Skills and Concepts	1	2	3	4	5	6	7	8	9	10	1	2	3	4	5	6	7	8	9	10	11	12	1	2	3	4	5	6	7	8	9	10	11
Money and Decimals (cont.)																																	
Compare money amounts using <, >, and = symbols																																	
Identify pennies and dimes as fractional parts of a dollar.																																	
Calculate the value of coin combinations																																	
Calculate the value of coin/bill combinations																																	
Explore uses for decimals																																	
Identify and name decimal numbers																																	
Identify place value in decimals through thousandths																																	
Model decimals with base-10 materials																																	
Compare and order decimals																																	
Read and write 1- and 2-digit decimals																																	
Read and write 3-digit decimals																																	
Count by tenths																																	
Relate decimals to metric measurement																																	
Count by thousandths																																	
Read and write decimals beyond thousandths																																	
Write decimals with expanded notation																																	
Fractions																																	
Understand the meaning of fractions																																	
Identify numerator and denominator																																	
Identify fractional parts of a region																																	
Identify fractional parts of a set																																	
Find equivalent fractions																																	

Fractions (cont.)

Compare and order fractions

Explore uses of fractions

Use fractions in number stories

Write fraction words

Identify fractions on a number line

Identify and name mixed numbers

Convert between mixed numbers and fractions

Positive and Negative Numbers (Integers)

Count back past zero

Explore uses for positive and negative numbers (integers)

Explore reference points for zero

Use positive and negative numbers (integers) in number stories

Beginning **Developing** **Secure**

Notes on Scope and Sequence

Operations and Computation

Skills and Concepts	Grade 1 Units	Grade 2 Units	Grade 3 Units
	1 2 3 4 5 6 7 8 9 10	1 2 3 4 5 6 7 8 9 10 11 12	1 2 3 4 5 6 7 8 9 10 11

Addition and Subtraction

- Understand meaning of addition/subtraction
- Solve addition/subtraction number stories
- Make up addition/subtraction number stories
- Solve addition number stories with 3 or more addends
- Solve multi-step addition/subtraction number stories
- Find/use complements of 10
- Find/use complements of 100
- Solve change-to-more and change-to-less number stories/diagrams
- Solve parts-and-total number stories/diagrams
- Solve comparison number stories
- Find patterns in addition/subtraction facts
- Add/subtract using a number line
- Add/subtract using a number grid
- Add/subtract using a calculator
- Find sums of even and odd numbers
- Practice basic facts
- Practice extensions of basic facts
- Use mental arithmetic to add/subtract
- Investigate relationships between addition and subtraction
- Add/subtract multiples of 10
- Add/subtract multiples of 100

Addition and Subtraction (cont.)

- Add/subtract money amounts/decimals
- Add 3 or more 1-digit numbers
- Add/subtract 2-digit numbers
- Add/subtract 2-digit numbers in number sentences containing parentheses
- Add 3 or more 2-digit numbers
- Add/subtract 3- and 4-digit numbers
- Investigate properties of addition/subtraction
- Use an Addition/Subtraction Facts Table
- Make change
- Use estimation to add/subtract
- Use addition/subtraction algorithms
- Estimate to check reasonableness of an answer
- Add/subtract positive and negative numbers
- Explore calculator functions

Multiplication and Division

- Understand meaning of multiplication/division
- Solve multiplication/division number stories
- Make up multiplication/division number stories
- Interpret a remainder in division number stories
- Solve multi-step multiplication/division number stories
- Solve problems involving ratios
- Investigate properties of multiplication/division
- Practice multiplication/division facts
- Explore square numbers
- Use arrays to model multiples of equal groups
- Use manipulatives to model multiplication

Beginning **Developing** **Secure**

Operations and Computation (cont.)

Skills and Concepts	Grade 1 Units 1–10	Grade 2 Units 1–12	Grade 3 Units 1–11
Multiplication and Division (cont.)			
Investigate relationships between multiplication and division			Grade 3: Units 4, 11
Multiply/divide using a number line		Grade 2: Unit 6	Grade 3: Units 4, 10
Find patterns in multiplication/division facts			Grade 3: Units 4, 7, 10, 11
Find patterns in multiples of 10, 100, and 1,000		Grade 2: Units 10, 11	Grade 3: Units 5, 10, 11
Multiply/divide with 2-digit numbers			Grade 3: Units 5, 8
Use estimation to multiply/divide			Grade 3: Units 4, 8
Multiply/divide with large numbers			Grade 3: Unit 7
Use a calculator to multiply or divide			
Use a Multiplication/Division Facts Table		Grade 2: Units 10, 11	Grade 3: Units 7, 9
Multiply/divide 1- and 2-digit numbers in number sentences with parentheses			
Use mental arithmetic to multiply/divide		Grade 2: Unit 11	Grade 3: Unit 9
Multiply/divide multiples of 10, 100, and 1,000 by 1-digit numbers			
Multiply/divide money amounts			Grade 3: Unit 10
Use multiplication/division algorithms			
Identify factors of a number			Grade 3: Units 9, 10
Use a multiplication algorithm to multiply 3-digit numbers by 2-digit numbers			
Solve missing factor number models			Grade 3: Unit 11

Patterns, Functions, and Algebra

Skills and Concepts	Grade 1 Units										Grade 2 Units												Grade 3 Units										
	1	2	3	4	5	6	7	8	9	10	1	2	3	4	5	6	7	8	9	10	11	12	1	2	3	4	5	6	7	8	9	10	11
Visual Patterns																																	
Create patterns with 2-dimensional shapes																																	
Sort and identify shapes/objects by attributes																																	
Explore and extend visual patterns																																	
Find patterns in the real world																																	
Find common attributes in objects and people																																	
Create patterns with 3-dimensional shapes																																	
Number Patterns																																	
Count up and back on a number grid																																	
Investigate even and odd number patterns																																	
Identify and use patterns on a number grid																																	
Add and subtract using a number grid																																	
Find patterns in addition and subtraction facts																																	
Find patterns in multiplication and division facts																																	
Find equivalent names for numbers																																	
Investigate square numbers																																	
Find number patterns that describe the relationship between similar figures																																	
Explore patterns in doubling numbers																																	
Plot points on a coordinate grid																																	
Find locations on a map																																	

Legend: Beginning · Developing · Secure

Patterns, Functions, and Algebra (cont.)

Skills and Concepts	Grade 1 Units										Grade 2 Units												Grade 3 Units										
	1	2	3	4	5	6	7	8	9	10	1	2	3	4	5	6	7	8	9	10	11	12	1	2	3	4	5	6	7	8	9	10	11
Number Patterns (cont.)																																	
Find number patterns in data																										■							
Sequences																																	
Count up and back on a number line		■										■				■								■		■	■						
Make/complete a number line					■																												
Count by 2s, 5s, and 10s		■						■				■				■		■		■				■									
Count by numbers greater than 10																																	
Complete number sequences				■								■					■							■					■				
Solve Frames-and-Arrows problems with one rule									■				■																				
Solve Frames-and-Arrows problems with two rules																■		■						■									
Explore counting patterns using a calculator																																	
Functions																																	
Solve "What's My Rule?" (function machine) problems					■				■			■							■														
Number Sentences																																	
Use symbols +, −, =								■								■		■			■												
Write/solve addition and subtraction number sentences																		■						■	■								
Write/solve number sentences with missing addends																■		■															
Explore number properties (commutative, zero, identity)																				■		■											
Use symbols ×, ÷, =																														■			
Write and solve multiplication number sentences																										■				■			
Write/solve number sentences with missing factors																																	
Write and solve division number sentences																																	
Make up/solve number sentences with parentheses																															■		
Inequalities																																	
Compare numbers using <, > symbols																																	

Geometry

Skills and Concepts	Grade 1 Units										Grade 2 Units												Grade 3 Units										
	1	2	3	4	5	6	7	8	9	10	1	2	3	4	5	6	7	8	9	10	11	12	1	2	3	4	5	6	7	8	9	10	11
2-Dimensional Shapes (Polygons)																																	
Identify 2-dimensional shapes																																	
Create/extend designs with 2-dimensional shapes																																	
Make 2-dimensional shapes on a geoboard																																	
Record geoboard shapes on dot paper																																	
Draw triangles and quadrilaterals																																	
Explore shape relationships																																	
Explore the relationship between diameter and circumference																																	
Identify characteristics of 2-dimensional shapes																																	
Compare 2-dimensional shapes																																	
Construct 2-dimensional shapes																																	
Solve 2-dimensional-shapes problems																																	
Record designs with 2-dimensional shapes																																	
Compare polygons and non-polygons																																	
Complete shape patterns																																	
Sort shapes by attributes																																	
Explore similarities and differences among quadrilaterals																																	
Form shapes by combining polygons																																	
Model polygons with rope																																	
Classify and name polygons																																	
Construct models of polygons with straws																																	

Legend: Beginning · Developing · Secure

Geometry (cont.)

Skills and Concepts	Grade 1 Units										Grade 2 Units												Grade 3 Units										
	1	2	3	4	5	6	7	8	9	10	1	2	3	4	5	6	7	8	9	10	11	12	1	2	3	4	5	6	7	8	9	10	11
3-Dimensional Shapes																																	
Identify 3-dimensional shapes							▓							▓	▓													▓			▓	▓	
Identify characteristics of 3-dimensional shapes															▓													▓					
Construct 3-dimensional shapes																												▓					
Explore similarities and differences among 3-dimensional shapes															▓																		
Explore the relationship among the number of faces, edges, and vertices of pyramids															▓																		
Identify faces, edges, vertices, and bases of prisms and pyramids															▓													▓					
Identify the shapes of faces																▓											▓	▓					
Explore slanted 3-dimensional shapes																											▓	▓					
Symmetry																																	
Fold and cut symmetrical shapes																▓											▓	▓	▓				
Create/complete a symmetrical design									▓							▓											▓	▓	▓				
Identify symmetrical figures									▓	▓																	▓	▓	▓				
Identify lines of symmetry																											▓	▓	▓				
Make symmetrical shapes on a geoboard																											▓	▓	▓				
Congruence																																	
Identify congruent figures																												▓					
Identify similar figures								▓							▓														▓				
Points, Lines, and Angles																																	
Draw line segments with a straightedge								▓																				▓					
Draw line segments to a specified length																															▓		
Identify parallel and nonparallel line segments																																	

Points, Lines, and Angles (cont.)

Identify and name points				
Identify and name line segments				
Identify and name lines				
Identify and name intersecting lines				
Identify and name rays				
Draw lines and rays				
Model parallel lines on a geoboard				
Draw parallel lines with a straightedge				
Draw designs with line segments				
Model line segments, rays, and angles				
Model intersecting lines on a geoboard				
Identify and name angles				
Model clockwise and counterclockwise turns/rotations				
Draw angles to record rotations				
Measure angles with nonstandard units				
Measure angles with degree units				
Solve degree problems				

■ **Beginning**   ■ **Developing**   ■ **Secure**

Notes on Scope and Sequence

Measurement and Reference Frames: Measurement

Skills and Concepts	Grade 1 Units										Grade 2 Units												Grade 3 Units										
	1	2	3	4	5	6	7	8	9	10	1	2	3	4	5	6	7	8	9	10	11	12	1	2	3	4	5	6	7	8	9	10	11
Length																																	
Estimate and compare distances																										■					■		
Estimate and compare lengths/heights of objects		■																							■								
Measure lengths with nonstandard units				■																					■								
Measure to the nearest foot				■					■								■								■					■	■		
Measure to the nearest inch										■									■				■		■						■		
Investigate the yard																	■								■						■		
Measure to the nearest centimeter							■	■											■											■			
Investigate the meter								■								■							■						■	■			
Solve length/height number stories											■							■															
Name tools used to measure length																		■							■						■		
Measure to the nearest ½ inch																										■				■			
Measure to the nearest ½ centimeter																									■								
Measure to the nearest yard																			■				■								■		
Identify equivalent customary units of length																															■	■	
Identify equivalent metric units of length																									■		■					■	
Choose the appropriate unit of measure															■										■								
Measure to the nearest decimeter																																■	
Investigate the mile																								■									
Investigate the kilometer																						■											
Solve distance number stories		■																															
Measure to the nearest meter																										■							
Use a map scale																																■	

Length (cont.)

- Use a mileage map
- Use a scale drawing
- Measure to the nearest $\frac{1}{4}$ inch
- Measure to the nearest $\frac{1}{8}$ inch
- Read measurement to the nearest mile
- Measure to the nearest millimeter
- Measure diameter and circumference

Capacity and Volume

- Compare capacities of containers
- Name tools used to measure capacity
- Identify customary units of capacity
- Identify equivalent customary units of capacity
- Identify metric units of capacity
- Identify equivalent metric units of capacity
- Measure capacities of irregular containers
- Name tools used to measure volume
- Find volume
- Estimate volume
- Order objects by volume
- Investigate the relationship between volume and weight
- Choose the appropriate unit of measure
- Solve capacity number stories

Weight

- Use a pan balance
- Solve weight number stories

Beginning Developing Secure

Measurement and Reference Frames: Measurement (cont.)

Skills and Concepts	Grade 1 — Units										Grade 2 — Units												Grade 3 — Units										
	1	2	3	4	5	6	7	8	9	10	1	2	3	4	5	6	7	8	9	10	11	12	1	2	3	4	5	6	7	8	9	10	11
Weight (cont.)																																	
Identify customary units of weight												▓							▓					▓							▓		
Identify metric units of weight												▓							▓												▓		
Use a spring scale																			▓														
Name tools used to measure weight																			▓														
Choose the appropriate unit of measure																			▓														
Estimate and compare weights					▓									▓			▓		▓					▓					▓	▓			
Use a bath scale																			▓														
Identify equivalent customary units of weight																			▓														
Identify equivalent metric units of weight																			▓														
Choose the appropriate scale																			▓														
Order objects by weight																																	
Perimeter and Area																																	
Investigate area						▓													▓					▓						▓			
Estimate area																																	
Name tools used to measure area																																	
Find the perimeter of irregular shapes																			▓							▓				▓			
Find the perimeter of regular shapes												▓							▓						▓	▓				▓			
Find the area of regular shapes																			▓												▓		
Estimate perimeter																																	
Compare perimeter and area																																	
Find the area of irregular shapes																					▓												

Money

- Recognize pennies and nickels
- Use cents notation
- Calculate the value of coin combinations
- Recognize dimes
- Use dollars-and-cents notation
- Compare values of sets of coins
- Recognize quarters
- Show money amounts with coins
- Show money amounts with coins/bills
- Recognize dollars
- Solve money number stories
- Make change
- Calculate the value of coin/bill combinations
- Calculate the value of bill combinations
- Identify equivalencies and make coin exchanges
- Identify equivalencies and make bill exchanges
- Add money amounts
- Subtract money amounts
- Estimate costs
- Identify pennies and dimes as fractional parts of a dollar
- Divide money amounts

Beginning **Developing** **Secure**

Measurement and Reference Frames: Reference Frames

	Grade 1 — Units										Grade 2 — Units												Grade 3 — Units										
Skills and Concepts	1	2	3	4	5	6	7	8	9	10	1	2	3	4	5	6	7	8	9	10	11	12	1	2	3	4	5	6	7	8	9	10	11
Time																																	
Use the calendar																																	
Compare the hour and minute hands																																	
Tell time on the hour																																	
Investigate A.M. and P.M.																																	
Estimate the duration of a minute																																	
Investigate the duration of an hour																																	
Tell time on the half-hour																																	
Tell time on the quarter-hour																																	
Use digital notation																																	
Tell time to the nearest 5 minutes																																	
Investigate the second hand																																	
Solve time number stories																																	
Investigate 1-minute intervals																																	
Calculate elapsed time																																	
Show days/events on a timeline																																	
Number and name the months in a year																																	
Write today's date																																	
Tell time to the nearest minute																																	
Name tools used to measure time																																	
Identify time equivalencies																																	

Time (cont.)

Skill										
Read time in different ways										
Choose the appropriate unit of measure										

Temperature

Skill										
Use the Fahrenheit temperature scale										
Use a thermometer										
Solve temperature number stories										
Use a weather map										
Use the Celsius temperature scale										

■ **Beginning**　■ **Developing**　■ **Secure**

Notes on Scope and Sequence

Grade 1										Grade 2												Grade 3										

Skills and Concepts — Units

Grade 1 Units: 1 2 3 4 5 6 7 8 9 10	Grade 2 Units: 1 2 3 4 5 6 7 8 9 10 11 12	Grade 3 Units: 1 2 3 4 5 6 7 8 9 10 11

Collecting Data
- Collect data by counting
- Collect data by interviewing
- Collect data from print sources
- Collect data from posters
- Collect data from a map
- Make predictions about data
- Explore random sampling
- Conduct a survey

Recording/Displaying Data
- Make a tally chart
- Make a bar graph
- Record data in a table/chart
- Record data on a map
- Make a frequency table
- Make a line plot

Evaluating Data
- Find the range
- Find the mode
- Find the median
- Find the mean
- Compare two sets of data

Evaluating Data (cont.)

- Compare the median and mean
- Find the minimum/maximum
- Read tables, graphs, and maps
- Use data in problem solving
- Summarize and interpret data

Probability and Chance

- Explore equal-chance events
- Predict outcomes
- Find combinations
- Classify events
- Use fraction notation to express probability
- Conduct experiments
- Explore *fair* and *unfair* games
- Solve problems involving chance outcomes
- Use an area model of probability

Beginning **Developing** **Secure**

Notes on Scope and Sequence

Index

H

Half-pictures of Pattern-Block Template shapes, completing, 334
Halving
  numbers, 534–536
  patterns in, 533–538
  visual images, 538
Heavier, 119
Height, 866–868
Height changes, 866–867, 868
Hepta-, 302
Heptagon, 302
Hexa-, 302
Hexagon, 302
History link, 160
Hit the Target game, 505, 524–525, 526, 536, 543, 566, 765, 773, 781
Home Link, 14, 68,
Hour hand, 30, 180, 181

I

In balance, 119
Inch (in.), 638
  grid, 664
  measuring to nearest, 637–638, 639
  measuring to nearest half, 645, 646
  scales, 258–259, 262
In each, 784
Inequalities, 69
Input, 139–140
Inverse relationship, 123–127
Is equal to, 14, 65–69, 250
Is greater than, 14, 65–69, 250
  mnemonic devices for, 251
Is less than, 14, 65–69, 250
  mnemonic devices for, 251

K

Kilogram (kg), 680
  and pound collection, 682
Kilometer (km), 653
Kite, 316

L

Label, 93
Language arts link, 6, 29, 84, 180, 185, 284, 302, 306, 346, 376, 572, 609, 620, 649, 653, 692, 704, 751, 762, 784
Language link, 84, 129, 692
Learning goals, 4, 82, 158, 214, 282, 344, 500, 570, 618, 690, 760, 828
Length, 122
  Exploration, 259
  exploring, 257–262
  fish, 370, 686–687
  fractional units of, 626, 642–647
  measuring to nearest centimeter, 545–549
  measuring to nearest inch, 545–549

measuring with a nonstandard unit, 631–632
  measuring with a ruler, 520
Lighter, 119
Line, 306
Linear measures, 626, 636–641, 657, 659
  units of metric, 647
Line plot
  of arm spans, 558–559
  of height changes, 866–867
Line segments, 288, 305–309
  counting, 323
  drawing, 307, 309, 312, 323
  naming, 306–307
  parallel, 310–313
Lines of symmetry, 333
  finding, 333–334
Line symmetry, 289, 332–336
  with geoboards, 336
Liter (L), 675
Literature and art link, 284, 303, 323, 335
Literature and history link, 160
Literature link, 6, 20, 84, 97, 104, 132, 160, 177, 216, 238, 260, 284, 302, 318, 346, 399, 404, 414, 502, 538, 543, 572, 582–583, 593, 620, 635, 641, 673, 692, 701, 726, 762, 786, 793, 802, 830, 863, 879, 883, 889, 893
Long, 15, 169, 733
Lost-and-Found Box, 23

M

Magic squares, completing, 171
Making Change game, 163, 205, 210–211
Maps, 654, 818–819
Materials, 8, 86, 162, 218, 286, 348, 504, 574, 622, 694, 764, 832
Math Boxes, 13, 44–47
Mathematic modeling, 748, 751, 788–794
Mathematics
  All Around bulletin board, 20
  sharing ideas about, 19
  writing about, 824
Math Journal, 18
Math Masters, 8, 86, 162, 218, 286, 348, 504, 574, 622, 694, 764, 832
Math Message, 11–12, 16–21
Measurement, 616–687
  need for accurate, 643–644
  systems, 633, 638, 674, 680
  time, 834
  unit, 633, 638, 674, 680
Measures
  of capacity, 629, 657
  linear, 626, 636–641, 657, 659
  of volume, 657
  of weight, 629, 657

Measure sense, 625
Measures All Around, 627–628, 656–660
  Museum, 625
Measuring
  in centimeters, 639
  in decimeters, 639
  distances, 902–903
  distances around shapes, 649
  in feet, 639
  in inches, 639
  longer distances, 627, 652–655
  with meters, 626, 630–635
  to nearest centimeter, 637–638
  to nearest half-centimeter, 645, 646
  to nearest half-inch, 645, 646
  to nearest inch, 637–638
  objects, 554
  perimeter in paces, 651
  tools booklet, 660
  with yards, 626, 630–635
Median, 190, 550–555, 557
  of distances, 860–861
  length of arm spans, 560
Mental arithmetic, 220–221, 291, 296, 528–532, 713
Meter (m), 633, 638, 645
Meters, measuring with, 626, 630–635
Metric linear measure, units of, 647
Metric system, 633, 638
Middle number
  of pockets, 189–190
Middle value, 552, 818. *See also* Median
Mile (mi), 653
milli-, 645
Milliliter (ml), 645
Millimeter (mm), 645
Minuend, 124, 379
Minute hand, 30, 180, 181
Missing measurements story, 686
Mnemonic devices, 251
Mode, 191
  of a set of data, 864–868
Money, 164–165, 698–756
  amounts with a calculator, 708–713
  calculating sums of, 779
  comparing place value with, 734
  counting, 41
  decimal notation for, 702–707
  equivalent amounts, 701
  Exploration, 541–542
  exploring, 235–240
  Frames-and-Arrows problems, 181
  number stories, 276, 303, 606, 611, 716, 776–781
  from other countries, 700
  using a calculator to solve problems, 714–717
Money Exchange Game, 9, 42, 59, 695, 735, 745
  with bank drafts, 43
  with base-10 blocks, 43
  with coins and $1 bills, 43

horizontal, 517–518
making by coloring grids, 514–515
number, 506–507
number-grid, 34, 53, 516–521
two-block, 542–543
vertical, 517–518
Pennies
dates on, 436–437, 888–889
as fractional parts of a dollar, 704
fractions of collections of, 591–592
how many weigh 1 ounce, 680
relationship with other money, 706–707
Penny, 174
Penny Cup game, 9, 46
Penny Grab game, 349, 365
Penta-, 302
Pentagon, 302
Per, 784
Perimeter, 627, 648–651, 655
measuring in paces, 651
of polygons, 650
of rectangles, 649–650
relationship to area, 669–670
Personal measures
arm spans, 545, 546, 548
height changes, 866–867, 868
Pick-a-Coin game, 695, 710–712, 713, 717, 730, 756
Pictograph, 882
Pictures, 129
Pint, 673
Pin the Number on the Number Grid game, 9, 63
Place value, 44–47, 164, 168–172, 268, 688, 732–735
comparing with base-10 blocks and money, 734
notation for ten-thousands, 742–746
relationships among, 744
skills, 696–697
tools, 736–741
Place-Value Book, 737
Place-value problems
4- and 5-digit, 744
Play money bills, 56, 173, 198, 202, 207, 252, 257, 275, 295, 590, 698, 702, 722, 732, 752
P.M., 180
Pockets data, 188–192
bar graph, 191
comparing, 192
tallying, 191
Pockets Data Table, 166–167
Point, 306
Points, 288, 305–309
naming, 306
Poly-, 302
Polygons, 288
Exploration, 302–303
exploring, 300–304, 727–731
fractions of, 605, 612, 613
naming by number of sides or angles, 302

perimeter of, 650
regular, 291, 316
Polyhedron. *See* Prisms *and* Pyramids
Portfolio ideas, 39, 51, 78, 95, 108, 185, 238, 274, 298, 303, 313, 317, 336, 340, 371, 376, 389, 392, 420, 515, 521, 549, 566, 593, 609, 613, 614, 654, 655, 660, 671, 755, 756, 774, 780, 811, 824, 848, 863, 868
Poster, 64, 71, 222, 237, 370, 583, 676–677, 715
Pound (lb), 119, 680
and kilogram collection, 682
Precipitation, 818
Predict outcomes, 189
Prices, comparing, 717
Prisms, rectangular, 309, 320
compared to cubes, 322
compared to cylinders, 322
compared to pyramids, 322
Prize Time game, 163, 182
Probability, 189
Problem solving, 6, 84, 160, 216, 284, 346, 502, 572, 620, 692, 762, 830
Product, 784, 801, 850
using arrays to find, 798
Products table, 800–805
Projects
Boxes, Boxes, Beautiful Boxes, 424–427, 876–879
Chinese Calendar, 432–435, 884–887
Collections, 446–449, 898–901
Dates on Pennies, 436–437, 888–889
How Far Can I Run in 10 Seconds?, 902–903
Snowflakes, 438–441, 890–893
Time Capsule, 442–445, 894–897
Weather Station, 428–431, 880–883
Property, 106, 747–751
Puzzles
arrow-path, 519–520, 521
coin, 201
frames-and-arrows, 167
number-grid, 53, 55, 78, 94–95, 517–518, 519–520
parentheses, 749, 750
Pyramids, 309, 320, 325–331
compared to cones, 321
compared to rectangular prisms, 322
construction, 329
hexagonal, 328
pentagonal, 328
rectangular, 328
out of straws, 327, 328
square, 327
triangular, 328, 329

Quad-, 302

Quadrangles, 302, 314–318
Quadrilaterals, 302
exploring similarities and differences, 315–316
Quart, 673
Quarter, 174, 709
"Quick graph" for future data displays, 561
Quotient, 790

R

Range, 818
of distances, 860–861
Rate multiplication stories, 785
Ratios
comparisons with, 768
Rectangles, 315
making shapes from, 317
perimeter of, 649–650
Region
fractional parts of a, 613
models, 602–605
Regions, estimating, 605
Regular polygons, 291, 316
Relation symbols, 14, 65–69, 250
Remainder, 411, 790
Reminders and review activities, 11
Review and assessment, 15, 75–79, 91, 152–155, 167, 207–211, 223, 275–279, 289, 337–341, 352–353, 416–421, 562–567, 610–615, 683–687, 752–756, 821–825, 869–873
Rhombus, 301, 315
Riddles, creating and solving, 108–109
Road-map stories, 654
Roman numerals, 21, 129
Routines
and devices, 10
frames-and-arrows, 133–137
numbers and, 2–79
partner study, 13, 31–35
slate, 13, 36–39
"What's My Rule?," 138–142
Row, 101
Ruler, 306,
measuring with a, 520
Rules
exploring, 290–294
Rule table, 675

S

Scale, 679
bath, 679–680
centimeter (cm), 258–259, 262
inch (in.), 258–259, 262
exploring, 90, 118–122
spring, 679–680
Science link, 6, 71, 216, 221–222, 346, 371, 620, 644, 818, 830, 859, 893

notes

notes

notes

notes

notes

notes